MACHINERY Classic Tractor PRICE GUIDE

1st Edition

by Greg Peterson

Edited by Margy Eckelkamp
Designed by Lori Hays

Also from the publishers of
Classic Tractor Price Guide:
Annual Auction Price Guide

For more information about
used farm equipment values, visit
www.machinerypete.com
(800) 381-0423

ISBN 978-0-578-14520-4
Printed in the U.S.

Letter From Greg Peterson

When I look back on the past 25 years of compiling auction prices, one word comes to mind: thankful.

I started with the goal to give the market a trusted resource for current and accurate hard cash values. When folks ask, "What's it worth?" why guess? My goal was to provide five, 10 or 20 machines that recently sold to see what folks paid. My hope remains the same today.

This book compiles the past four-plus years of auction prices from my database of more than 500,000 items. The Classic Tractor Price Guide highlights farm equipment made in 1978 and prior—even back to the early 1900s.

In addition to tractors, it includes sale prices on trucks, drills, plows, hay balers and more. We actually had to trim quite a bit of data to keep this book under 800 pages. We certainly don't want to break any toes in case it falls off your coffee table.

Sprinkled throughout the book are some of my favorite stories and tales from the auction trail—what we call "Pete's Picks."

One trend the data highlights is the rapidly growing market for "the new collector tractors," which are original condition or restored models from the mid-1960s to mid-1970s. Check out those prices. Wow!

It's time for more gratitude and thank-yous. Thanks goes to my dad, Jerry Peterson, a third-generation implement dealer in Benson, Minn., for the sound and wise advise he gave to me back in 1989. He said: "This auction data is really good information. I'm not sure what you can make it into, but you're young, might be good time to give it a shot."

The auction industry is filled with amazing people. Thanks goes to the nearly 1,000 auction firms I've connected with during the past two and a half decades. I'm happy to count so many of them as friends.

I appreciate those of you who follow Machinery Pete. Thank you for reading my magazine columns all these years, for following along as I've pushed forward on YouTube and Facebook, for watching our new Machinery Pete show on RFD-TV and for buying our new book. I've been looking forward to publishing The Classic Tractor Price Guide for some time. Enjoy!

Machinery Pete

Machinery Pete

www.MachineryPete.com
facebook.com/machinerypete
@MachineryPete
youtube.com/machinerypete

TRACTORS
IMPLEMENTS
COMBINES
TRUCKS

Abbreviations

adj. = adjustable

air = air conditioning

auto = automatic transmission

aux. = auxiliary

bu. = bushel

cu. in. = cubic inch(es)

cyl. = engine cylinders

diff. lock = differential lock

EROPS = enclosed rollover protection structure

F/A = fore and aft

gal. = gallon(s)

GP = general purpose

gpm = gallons per minute

GPS = global positioning system

Hi/Lo = high/low speed transmission

HD = heavy-duty

HFWD = hydrostatic front-wheel drive

HID = high-intensity discharge lights

hp = horsepower

hyd. = hydraulics

hydro = hydrostatic drive

L = liter(s)

lb. = pound(s)

LP = liquefied petroleum gas

MFWD = mechanical front-wheel drive

ML = manual locks

MW = manual windows

NF = narrow front

NR = narrow row

OD = overdrive

OH = overhaul

OROPS = open rollover protection structure

Power adj. = power adjustable rear wheels

PS = powershift transmission

PT = pull-type

PTO = power take-off

QR = Quad Range transmission

R = row(s)

ROPS = roll-over protective structure

rpm = revolutions per minute

RWA = rear-wheel assist

RWD = rear-wheel drive

sep. = separator

SF = single front

SN = serial number

SP = self-propelled

SS = stainless steel

TA = torque amplifier

tach. = tachometer

V = volts

VIN = vehicle identification number

WF = wide front

WR = wide row

yd. = yard(s)

1 hyd. = one hydraulic outlet

2 hyd. = two hydraulic outlets

3 hyd. = three hydraulic outlet

4 hyd. = four hydraulic outlets

1 pt. = one-point hitch

2 pt. = two-point hitch

3 pt. = three-point hitch

2WD = two-wheel drive

4WD = four-wheel drive

Area

The abbreviation under this column represents the region of a state in which the machinery is sold. Examples: **NEIA** = northeast Iowa; **SCCA** = south-central California; **NWMB** = northwest Manitoba (Canada).

Condition

The following indicates the overall condition of the machinery as it sold at auction.

P = poor

F = fair

G = good

E = excellent

Advance-Rumely

Model	Year	Hours	Condition	Price	Date	Area	Comments
K12/20	1919		G	$22,000	11/16/2013	SCVA	Oil Pull, 7.4L, 2 cyl. kerosene, manufactured in La Porte, Ind., neighbor says he has heard it run, was in parades approx. 4 years back, shed kept

Allis-Chalmers

Model	Year	Hours	Condition	Price	Date	Area	Comments
15-25			G	$62,500	9/21/2013	WCNY	Runs, restored, SN 21199
15-30	1918		G	$17,600	11/3/2011	Online	*PurpleWave.com,* item in Kansas, SN 5572
20-35	1928		G	$2,750	7/25/2013	WCSK	2WD, 30 hp gas, steel wheels, spade lugs, running
20-35	1929		F	$1,400	5/26/2010	ECSD	Complete, not running
20-35	1929		P	$2,200	5/26/2010	ECSD	On steel, not running
20-35			G	$4,000	9/9/2010	NWWI	
160			G	$2,530	7/25/2012	Online	*PurpleWave.com,* item in Missouri, Perkins 3 cyl. diesel, 40 hp, manual, differential lock, spring seat, power steering, aux. foot throttle, toolbox
160		3,825	F	$2,050	11/22/2011	WCIL	13.x28 rear tires, 540 PTO
160		5,102	G	$3,100	12/2/2010	NEMI	Diesel, 3 pt., PTO, 14.9x28 tires, 1 hyd., rare, only 4,110 made
160			F	$3,600	4/9/2010	WCNE	Hydro, PS, Du-Al loader, good rubber
170	1968		G	$7,400	11/27/2013	ECSD	Hours unknown but low, one owner, 3 hyd., Case 31 backhoe mounted

---

A 1982 Allis-Chalmers 4W-305 with 1,675 original one-owner hours sold for $71,000 at an April 12, 2014 farm auction in Kemptville, Ontario. You won't find that sale in this book because a 1982 model is a little too new for farm equipment from the 1970s and prior, but I chose to highlight it here as an insightful look ahead at what's coming. That is a new record high auction price by a mile. The previous high price was $34,000 for a 1982 model with 4,598 hours at a Nov. 22, 2010 farm sale in west-central Illinois.

At the April 2014 sale, the winning bidder was a young farmer named Kevin Wilson from Ontario who will use the tractor on his 5,200 acre farm. "We have been looking for a 300 hp tractor for a long time. We had a local dealer come out and show us a new one for $450,000, but I'd like to pay off the tractor in my lifetime," said Wilson. The runner-up bidder was from Colorado, and he wanted it for his tractor museum.

PETE'S PICK

"In my 43 years in the auction business, we've never had as much interest in an item," said auctioneer Stewart James.

Allis-Chalmers

Model	Year	Hours	Condition	Price	Date	Area	Comments
170	1971		G	$5,600	1/28/2012	ECMO	One owner
170	1973		G	$3,600	12/18/2013	SEIA	2 hyd., 3 pt., 540 PTO, 16.9x28 tires, SN 1709005
170	1974	3,785	G	$2,930	12/10/2013	Online	*IQBID.com,* 3 pt., 540 PTO
170		2,930	G	$5,060	2/26/2014	Online	*PurpleWave.com,* item in Missouri, 4 cyl. diesel, 8 speed, spring suspension seat
170			G	$7,750	12/27/2013	ECIL	Gas, WF, 2 hyd., Great Bend 440 loader with quick attach 6' bucket
170			G	$3,650	7/27/2012	SWKY	
170		4,901	G	$5,700	1/28/2012	ECMO	Allis-Chalmers 500 series loader, 3 pt., 2 hyd.
170		3,165	G	$5,200	12/17/2011	NETX	Gas, loader, 2 hyd., 3 pt., PTO, loader bucket
170			G	$4,300	7/30/2011	ECMO	2400 quick attach loader, gas, 3 pt., dual hyd.
170		5,293	G	$3,900	12/17/2010	WCIL	Utility tractor, Work Master 880 loader, bucket, 2 hyd., 540 PTO, 18.4x28 tires
170		4,101	G	$4,500	11/6/2010	SEMN	Gas, open station, fenders, duals, hyd. loader, 3 pt., 16.9x28 rubber 75%, clean
175	1970		G	$6,500	7/31/2013	ECND	WF, 55 hp, gas, cab, heater, 2 hyd., 3 pt., live PTO, 1998 Allied 595 loader, quick attach loader bucket, 700 hours on engine OH
175	1977	2,401	G	$5,000	2/1/2011	NEIN	
175	1978	2,402	G	$5,000	2/1/2011	NEIN	Diesel, cab, dual hyd.
180	1967	3,618	G	$6,900	11/27/2012	WCIN	Diesel, WF, 3 pt., 540 PTO, 2 hyd., 18.4x28 tires on adj. rims, 4 speed, Hi-Lo, nice original tractor, SN 2650
180	1968	7,266	G	$4,015	4/24/2013	Online	*BigIron.com,* item in Nebraska, 8F/2R
180	1968	4,923	G	$3,500	8/13/2011	WCIL	Diesel, land handler, 18.4x28 rear tires, 2 hyd., 540 PTO
180	1969	5,597	G	$1,500	7/30/2011	ECMO	Diesel, category II hitch, 3 pt., 540 PTO, dual hyd., Bush Hog loader
180	1971	5,445	G	$5,000	12/7/2011	NCIA	Diesel, 18.4x34 tires
180	1973		G	$5,600	4/11/2011	Online	*AuctionTime.com,* loader
180			F	$2,200	12/4/2013	ECND	3 pt., PTO, Farmhand F21 loader
180			G	$3,500	6/1/2013	SEMN	Diesel, 18.4x28 rubber, 3 pt., 2 hyd., dual PTO, hyd. clutch
180		5,868	G	$4,610	5/1/2013	Online	*BigIron.com,* item in Nebraska, 8 speed, 6 cyl. diesel
180			G	$2,700	4/2/2013	ECIA	Full vision cab, 4 speed, Hi/Lo, 4 hyd., 3 pt., quick attach, 540 PTO, head gasket and oil changed
180			G	$3,400	3/2/2013	NETN	Diesel, PS
180		4,620	G	$5,000	3/2/2013	ECMN	3 pt., rock box
180			G	$4,100	6/7/2012	NEIN	
180			G	$3,850	8/13/2011	WCIL	18.4x28 tires, diesel, 2 hyd., 540 PTO, New Idea loader
180			G	$1,900	8/9/2010	WCMO	Tires 50%
180			F	$3,200	3/20/2010	WCOH	Bad paint job
185	1970	2,741	G	$5,500	3/20/2010	SEIA	New paint, 2 hyd.

Allis-Chalmers

Model	Year	Hours	Condition	Price	Date	Area	Comments
185	1971		G	$4,600	12/26/2013	Online	*BigIron.com,* item in Nebraska, crop hustler, 8F/2R, 6 cyl. diesel, 18.4x28 rear tires, 9.5Lx15 front tires, 75 PTO hp, 64 drawbar hp
185	1971	5,217	G	$5,350	1/9/2013	Online	*BigIron.com,* item in Kansas, row crop, 4.9L, 6 cyl. diesel, 75 PTO hp, 2 hyd., 18.4x28 rear tires, 7.5x16 front tires, adj. front axle
185	1973	4,200	G	$3,000	6/5/2010	NWIA	Hinker cab
185	1976	2,241	G	$5,300	12/10/2010	NWMO	2WD, new 18.4x30 tires, new paint, 2 hyd.
185	1976	2,497	G	$6,500	1/2/2010	NWOH	Clean, open station, T-rail duals, 6 front duals
185	1977	6,044	G	$3,600	2/22/2014	NEIN	Dual hyd., dual PTO, 3 pt. Farmhand loader, OH at 5,500 hours
185	1977	3,477	G	$4,850	2/1/2011	NEIN	
190	1969		G	$4,600	7/13/2011	Online	*BigIron.com,* item in Kansas, series 3, diesel, 2 hyd., 540 PTO, rebuilt rear end, lights work
190		2,550	G	$2,300	3/22/2014	NWMO	Gas, WF, front weights, 3 pt., dual hyd., console control, 18.4x34 spin out rubber
190		7,281	G	$6,200	9/12/2013	SEIA	
190			P	$800	7/27/2013	WCIL	Lots of great parts
190		8,198	G	$3,500	6/22/2013	SEMN	18.4x34, 3 pt., dual hyd., PTO
190		2,116	F	$2,860	9/26/2012	Online	*PurpleWave.com,* item in Oklahoma, Allis-Chalmers 2800, 6 cyl., 3 pt.
190			G	$2,200	8/21/2012	WCIL	Loader
190		1,800	G	$4,300	8/16/2012	Online	*IQBID.com,* item in Minnesota, 2WD, gas, cab, heat, 2 hyd., 3 pt., PTO, top link, 18.4x34 tires
190			F	$3,500	6/8/2012	ECND	Farmhand F228 loader, cracked frame on loader, undiagnosed throttle issues
190			F	$3,000	3/10/2012	NWIL	Gas, WF, IHC 2350 loader
190			F	$2,000	7/27/2011	ECND	
190			G	$1,500	3/25/2011	WCIL	Dual hyd., gas, loader, front boom attachment
190		3,951	F	$4,800	12/2/2010	ECWY	Diesel, 2 hyd., 8 speed Hi/Lo, 18.4x34 tires, 3 pt., PTO, Ezee-On loader and 7' bucket
190XT	1965		G	$4,000	2/12/2013	WCIL	
190XT	1965	6,810	G	$2,000	3/31/2012	SWSK	2WD, 80 hp, Power Director transmission, 8F/2R, cab, 2 hyd., dual PTO
190XT	1965	8,113	G	$2,750	4/27/2011	Online	*BigIron.com,* item in Nebraska, 4 speed Hi/Lo neutral transmission, 6 cyl. diesel, 540 PTO, 3 pt., dual valves, WF axle, power steering, fenders, American Classic loader, 3 hyd., 5' bucket, 3 TINE grapple fork
190XT	1967	4,691	G	$3,300	4/25/2012	Online	*PurpleWave.com,* item in Missouri, Allis-Chalmers 2900 6 cyl. diesel, 100 hp, manual, 8F/2R, power adj. wheels in rear, Excel Industries cab, spring ride seat, AM/FM, 3 pt.
190XT	1967	3,000	G	$5,500	12/1/2011	WCMN	WF, cab, loader, 3 pt., PTO

Allis-Chalmers

Model	Year	Hours	Condition	Price	Date	Area	Comments
190XT	1969		F	$2,000	3/10/2010	ECND	Series 3, open station, 2 hyd., 540 PTO
190XT	1970		G	$4,500	12/4/2013	ECND	Open station, 3 pt., PTO, Koyker 500 loader, quick attach 8' bucket
190XT	1970	6,600	G	$4,425	10/11/2011	Online	*BidNow.com,* series 3, 93 hp, OH at 4,100 hours, Year-A-Round cab heat, new paint
190XT	1971		F	$2,600	2/12/2013	WCIL	18.4xR34, 2 hyd., dual PTO, engine weak
190XT	1971		G	$5,000	11/17/2010	SCMT	Series 3, diesel, 75 hp, 3 pt., PTO, cab, dual hyd.
190XT		3,670	G	$7,000	2/12/2014	ECWI	2WD, diesel, WF, OS, 3 pt., PTO, 2 hyd., 18.4xR38 tires 80%, clamp duals
190XT			G	$4,600	12/30/2013	SEMN	Gas
190XT			G	$3,630	12/17/2013	ECWI	Diesel, WF, 3 pt., dual hyd., new injection pump and injectors
190XT		4,479	G	$4,500	1/28/2012	ECMO	1,000 PTO, 3 pt., 2 hyd.
190XT			P	$2,500	12/7/2011	NCIA	Rough, cab, diesel
190XT		2,600	G	$2,600	9/14/2011	Online	*BigIron.com,* item in Nebraska, 6 cyl. diesel, 540 PTO, control console inside, rear wheel weights, 2 hyd., hyd. with splitter, 3 pt., missing top link, 5' bucket, manual hyd. controls, four tine grapple, 1 tine missing, 3 bucket teeth damaged
190XT			G	$7,200	8/2/2011	ECNE	Series 3, Westendorf loader, grapple
190XT		2,539	G	$4,000	7/30/2011	ECMO	
190XT		2,204	G	$925	6/22/2011	Online	*BigIron.com,* item in Nebraska, 8 speed Hi/Lo, 6 cyl. diesel, 2 hyd., 540 PTO, does not run, 3 pt., swing drawbar
190XT			G	$1,100	4/27/2011	Online	*BigIron.com,* item in Oklahoma, manual 4 speed, 6 cyl. 2900 diesel, 2 hyd., single axle 540 PTO, attached push blade
190XT			G	$3,200	4/2/2011	ECMN	
190XT			F	$1,950	1/29/2011	ECMO	Loader, gas, jumps out of gear
190XT			G	$3,750	9/4/2010	NEIN	Series 2, diesel, high crop
190XT		5,713	G	$3,500	3/6/2010	SEMN	
200	1972		G	$5,050	4/2/2011	ECMN	Year-A-Round cab
200	1973		G	$5,000	10/1/2010	WCWI	Diesel, factory turbo, factory cab, factory rock box, 110 hp, starts and runs
200	1974	2,599	E	$6,750	11/23/2013	WCIL	2 hyd., Year-A-Round cab, diesel, one owner
200	1974	7,523	G	$2,600	2/7/2013	NEIN	18.4x38 tires at 80%, 2 hyd.
200	1975	4,100	G	$5,300	6/2/2012	SEIA	4 speed Power Director, 18.4Rx38 rear tires, front weights
200			G	$4,000	3/13/2014	SCID	Diesel, hours unknown, 8 speed, 2 hyd., 540 PTO, 3 pt.
200		2,269	G	$4,200	3/13/2014	SCID	Diesel, 8 speed, 2 hyd., 540 PTO, 3 pt., 15.5x38 rubber
200		3,476	G	$6,100	2/22/2014	NEIN	Dual hyd., 3 pt., PTO
200		2,900	G	$5,000	3/30/2013	SCMN	Minneapolis Moline all hyd. loader, 3 pt., dual hyd., factory cab, 18.4x38 rear

Allis-Chalmers

Model	Year	Hours	Condition	Price	Date	Area	Comments
200		8,000	G	$4,000	2/9/2013	SWOH	WF
200		7,523	G	$2,600	2/7/2013	NEIN	
200		5,996	G	$2,255	9/12/2012	Online	*PurpleWave.com,* item in Kansas, Allis-Chalmers 2900 4.9L, 6 cyl. turbo diesel, manual
200		2,400	G	$4,100	1/28/2012	ECMO	540 PTO, cab, 2 hyd.
200			P	$2,100	3/25/2011	WCIL	Diesel, cab, salvage
200			G	$2,750	3/25/2011	WCIL	Diesel, cab, salvage
200		4,500	G	$4,700	5/26/2010	ECSD	Fenders, 3 pt.
200			P	$3,000	1/30/2010	WCIL	Cab, duals, rough
210	1972		G	$26,500	8/7/2010	WCMN	Diesel, engine rebuilt
210			G	$7,500	8/19/2011	NWIL	No cab, good paint and tires
210			G	$7,000	9/4/2010	NEIN	Two sets rear weights, dual hyd.
220	1969		G	$18,000	8/7/2010	WCMN	Diesel, cab, engine rebuilt
220	1971	5,100	G	$6,500	11/22/2010	WCIL	Factory cab, 18.4x38 and 11x16 tires, 2 hyd., 1,000 PTO, 3 pt., rear weights, SN 2528
220	1972	2,824	G	$6,350	12/8/2010	NECO	WF, diesel, 3 pt., cab
5020	1978	2,381	G	$1,600	3/15/2014	WCIL	Utility, 540 PTO, 3 pt.
5040	1976		G	$1,815	5/30/2012	Online	*PurpleWave.com,* item in Kansas
5050	1977		F	$3,900	1/21/2012	SEIL	Loader, good rubber
7000	1976	7,530	G	$3,300	10/14/2013	WCSK	2WD, 106 PTO hp, 3 speed PS, cab, air, dual hyd., 18.4x38 rubber, OH at 5,000 hours
7000	1976		F	$3,700	9/28/2013	NEIA	18.4x38 tires, clamp-on duals, OH 1,500 hours ago, AC did not work
7000	1976	2,795	G	$6,000	9/12/2013	SEIA	Cab, 3 pt., 540 PTO, 2 hyd.
7000	1976	5,342	F	$3,250	4/14/2012	NEIA	Diesel, factory cab, WF, 3 pt., 18.4x34 rear, pops out of second gear under heavy load
7000	1976	4,001	G	$4,600	11/3/2011	ECIL	SN 2833, cab, 18.4x38 tires, 2 hyd.
7000	1977	4,000	G	$7,000	3/1/2014	SEPA	Open station, heavy front axle, dual hyd., dual PTO, 3 pt., 4 speed with 3 range shift on the go, 18.4x38 tires 10%
7000	1977	5,600	G	$2,800	1/29/2011	ECMO	Cab, air, heat, 540 PTO, 3 pt., dual hyd., power steering
7000	1978		G	$3,630	10/10/2012	Online	*PurpleWave.com,* item in Kansas, Allis-Chalmers 2900 diesel, partial PS
7000		625	G	$3,800	4/3/2014	NEIN	2WD, 18.4x34, 2 hyd., quick hitch, 540 PTO
7000			G	$1,237	10/10/2013	Online	*HansenAndYoung.com,* item in Wisconsin, cab, 3 pt., WF, motor needs work, not running, new front tires, clamp on duals
7000		7,700	G	$7,000	2/23/2013	NCIN	No duals, maroon belly
7000			G	$3,050	2/7/2013	NEIN	2WD, cab, 18.4x38, 2 hyd.
7000			G	$3,050	2/7/2013	NEIN	Cab, air, heat
7000		2,782	G	$4,400	12/12/2012	SESD	
7000			G	$4,900	10/24/2012	WCWI	18.4x38 tires, PS
7000			G	$4,200	8/4/2012	SWKY	
7000		5,506	F	$2,600	1/21/2012	SEIL	Cab, OH at 2,890 hours

Allis-Chalmers

Model	Year	Hours	Condition	Price	Date	Area	Comments
7000			F	$1,800	10/29/2011	ECMN	
7000			F	$2,200	6/29/2011	Online	*PurpleWave.com,* item in Kansas, Allis-Chalmers 2900 6 cyl. diesel, 12F/3R PS, low range is noisy in PS, 3 pt., drawbar
7000			G	$5,300	4/2/2011	ECMN	Maroon, cab, heat, air, 12 speed
7020	1978	6,300	G	$7,750	3/21/2012	ECMN	Hub duals, 2 hyd., dual PTO, 3 pt.
7030	1973	1,101	G	$6,110	5/9/2012	Online	*BigIron.com,* item in Oklahoma, loader, 5 speed Hi/Lo with traction booster, turbo diesel, 3 hyd., 540 PTO, AC/heat, 3 pt., 3 wheel weights each side
7030	1974	5,327	G	$6,700	12/7/2011	NCIA	Cab, air, heat, 18.4x38 tires
7030	1974	889	G	$3,100	11/9/2011	Online	*BigIron.com,* item in Missouri, 2WD, 5 speed Hi/Lo, diesel, 130 hp, 2 hyd., 1,000 PTO, 3 pt.
7030	1974		G	$4,300	2/1/2011	NEIN	Cab
7030		2,982	G	$4,400	10/16/2013	Online	*PurpleWave.com,* item in Kansas, Allis-Chalmers 3500 6 cyl. diesel, Power Director transmission
7030		11,334	G	$2,600	8/14/2013	WCMN	540 PTO, 3 pt., 2 hyd., 18.4x38 tires, new clutch February 2012
7030		11,334	G	$2,500	3/20/2013	WCMN	540 PTO, 3 pt., 2 hyd., new clutch February 2013
7030		2,786	F	$2,700	11/23/2011	Online	*BigIron.com,* item in Nebraska, 6 cyl. diesel, 3 hyd., 540 PTO, does not start, no batteries, 3 pt.
7030			P	$3,900	3/25/2011	WCIL	Diesel, open station, salvage
7040	1974	543	G	$3,000	6/22/2011	NECO	Diesel, WF, duals, front weights
7040	1975		G	$4,500	3/15/2014	WCIL	PS, 2 hyd., 540 PTO, 3 pt., 20.8xR38 rear tires, front weights
7040	1975		G	$3,000	10/14/2013	WCSK	2WD, 136 PTO hp, Power Director transmission, cab, 20.8x38 rear, 4 RIB front, 10,000 hours estimated
7040	1975		G	$4,350	8/20/2013	WCIL	Cab, 2 hyd., 1,000 PTO, 18.4x38 tires
7040	1975		F	$5,500	7/19/2010	NCIA	Cab, air, 2 hyd., front weights, rock box, OH, band duals separate
7040	1976	6,663	G	$5,000	10/17/2013	SWSK	2WD, 135 PTO hp, 20F/4R standard, PTO, 2 hyd., 20.8x38 singles, 3 rib front
7040	1976		G	$7,000	7/27/2013	WCIL	Diesel, cab, PS, 2 hyd., full set of suitcase weights (15), 18.4x38 rear tires, SN 7040S5657
7040	1976	6,275	G	$4,000	3/27/2013	Online	*BigIron.com,* item in Nebraska, 2WD
7040	1976	6,275	G	$3,900	2/6/2013	SESD	Red belly, Power Director, cab, air, heat, WF, 3 pt., 18.4x38 tires, Ride-N-Drive, replaced AC compressor in 2012
7040	1976		P	$975	11/9/2011	Online	*BigIron.com,* item in Missouri, 2WD, 5 speed Hi/Lo, diesel, 140 hp, 2 hyd., dual PTO, selling for parts
7040	1976	5,000	G	$3,600	12/8/2010	NECO	WF, diesel, power shift
7040	1978		F	$5,000	2/18/2012	ECIL	Clamp on duals, front weights, less than 1,000 hours on OH
7040			F	$3,600	12/27/2013	ECIL	Cab, PS, 2 hyd., 20.8x38 tires, weights
7040		2,640	G	$7,000	12/27/2013	NCOH	Diesel, rear duals

TRACTORS

Allis-Chalmers

Model	Year	Hours	Condition	Price	Date	Area	Comments
7040			G	$5,000	12/12/2013	NCIA	
7040		4,184	G	$5,830	11/28/2012	Online	*PurpleWave.com,* item in Missouri, 6 cyl. diesel, Power Director transmission, AC cab, AC/heat, spring seat, 3 pt., drawbar, 540 PTO
7040			G	$5,800	8/30/2012	SEMN	
7040			G	$3,630	4/25/2012	Online	*PurpleWave.com,* item in Kansas
7040			F	$3,350	2/18/2012	ECIL	Diesel, cab, air, heat
7040		7,705	G	$3,400	1/28/2012	ECMO	1,000 PTO, 3 pt., hyd., cab, air, heat
7040		4,723	G	$5,100	4/13/2011	Online	*BigIron.com,* item in Nebraska, PS, 6 cyl. diesel, 2 hyd., dual PTO, 3 pt., front weight bracket, seat suspension needs repair, 18.4x38 axle-mounted duals and hubs
7040		4,517	E	$14,500	3/26/2011	SEMN	Diesel, Power Director, 18.4x38 duals, 3 pt., 2 hyd.
7040		3,464	G	$5,200	2/28/2011	SCMI	Cab, 3 pt., hyd., PTO, WF
7040			G	$6,000	3/6/2010	SEMN	PS, 20.8x38 tires, one owner
7045	1978	10,600	G	$6,700	12/14/2011	WCMN	2WD, 145 hp, radial dual tires, new cab interior, air, heat, 3 hyd., PTO, 3 pt.
7045	1978	4,318	G	$6,000	9/22/2010	ECND	Cab, air, heat, PS, 6 speed Hi/Lo, 2 hyd., 540 PTO, 20.8x38 band duals, front weights
7050	1973	222	G	$11,752	7/27/2011	Online	*BigIron.com,* item in Iowa, loader bucket and forks, 20 speed, 6 cyl. diesel, 155 hp, 2 hyd., 1,000 PTO, 3 pt. hitch, Allied 795 loader
7050		5,323	G	$3,650	11/23/2011	Online	*BigIron.com,* item in Nebraska, 6 cyl. diesel, 2 hyd., 540 PTO, 3 pt., duals, no batteries
7050		6,119	G	$4,050	4/27/2011	Online	*BigIron.com,* item in Kansas, 5 and 2 transmission, diesel, 3 hyd., small 1,000 PTO, clamp on duals, 15 suit case weights, 3 pt. with third member, hood bent
7050			G	$5,100	12/8/2010	NECO	WF, diesel, duals
7060	1975		G	$7,000	4/23/2010	NENE	Cab, WF, 3 pt., duals
7060	1976	9,400	G	$3,000	7/25/2013	WCSK	2WD, 162 PTO hp, 24.5x32 rear, 2 hyd., 540 PTO, 10 speed, suitcase weights, 11x16 front
7060	1976	9,388	G	$3,500	6/20/2013	ECSK	2WD, 162 PTO hp, 540/1,000 dual PTO, 24.5x32 rear
7060	1976	4,700	G	$6,100	3/28/2013	SCMN	2WD, 20 speed Power Director transmission, cab, air, heat, rock box, 3 hyd., 3 pt., dual PTO
7060	1976		G	$7,590	11/30/2011	Online	*PurpleWave.com,* item in Kansas, 2802 hours on aftermarket meter, 7.0L, diesel, 192 hp, PS, hydro steering, extra temperatue gauge, extra lights, 7' loader bucket, dual PTO
7060	1977	3,815	F	$3,100	11/9/2011	Online	*BigIron.com,* item in Missouri, 2WD, 5 speed Hi/Lo transmission, diesel, 160 hp, 2 hyd., 3 pt. hitch, dual PTO, swivel drawbar, air not working

Allis-Chalmers

Model	Year	Hours	Condition	Price	Date	Area	Comments
7060	1977	5,836	G	$8,500	11/22/2010	WCIL	Cab, PS, 20.8x38 and 11x16 tires, 2 hyd., dual PTO, 3 pt., front weights, SN 4674
7060	1978	2,540	E	$12,000	11/23/2013	WCIL	2WD, Power Director transmission, excellent tires, 1,820 hours shows on tach., replaced at 720 hours, one owner
7580	1977	5,355	F	$5,500	12/27/2012	NCIA	4WD, 18.4xR38 tires, duals, 3 pt., three years on new motor, 1,000 PTO, 3 hyd.,
7580	1978	6,193	G	$7,000	11/22/2010	WCIL	4WD, cab, Power Director trans., 20.8x38 tires, clamp-on duals, 3 hyd., 3 pt., big 1,000 PTO, SN 2133
A			G	$13,000	3/23/2013	NEIN	Restored, new tires, runs
A			G	$11,550	11/3/2011	Online	*PurpleWave.com,* item in Kansas
A			G	$6,200	4/16/2010	NEKS	Industrial, oil field unit
A			G	$12,500	4/16/2010	NEKS	
A			G	$14,100	4/16/2010	NEKS	
A			G	$25,000	4/16/2010	NEKS	
B	1938		G	$2,255	8/14/2012	Online	*PurpleWave.com,* item in Kansas, 4 cyl. gas, 3 speed, 4x15 front tires, 9.5x24 rear tires, 7-year-old restoration
B	1938		G	$2,000	3/26/2011	SEWI	
B	1938		G	$1,200	4/9/2010	NWMN	Electric start, WF, 60" Woods belly mower
B	1939		G	$1,900	4/12/2014	SEND	Woods 5' belly mower, new rubber, PTO, good runner
B	1939		G	$950	6/15/2013	WCMI	WF, 11x24 tires, SN 46156
B	1939		G	$1,000	6/15/2013	WCMI	WF, 9x24" tires, 2R mounted cultivators, SN 28106
B	1939		G	$1,000	5/19/2012	SWMI	WF, 10x24 tires, fenders, belt pulley, hyd. pump
B	1939		G	$1,200	7/10/2010	SEIA	Restored, WF
B	1940		E	$2,800	10/15/2011	ECIA	WF, parade ready, new Armstrong 9.5/9x24 rear tires
B	1940		G	$7,500	10/1/2010	WCWI	Orchard, 1 of 5 known to exist, prototype only, good rubber, starts and runs
B	1944		G	$2,700	8/24/2011	ECMN	Electric start, PTO, belt pulley, factory EZ ride seat, new 11.2x24 rubber
B	1952		G	$2,950	4/11/2011	Online	*AuctionTime.com,* 2WD
B	1953		F	$900	12/5/2013	SEMN	Woods belly mower
B			G	$3,600	12/28/2013	SEIA	Professionally restored, extra sharp, new 8.3x24 rear tires, new 4x15 3 rib front tires
B			G	$862	12/17/2013	ECWI	Restored, new paint
B			G	$800	10/3/2013	NCIN	
B			G	$1,200	9/12/2013	SEIA	WF, PTO, new 11.2-24 rear tires, Woods L59 mid-mount mower
B			G	$1,100	3/22/2013	WCIL	Woods belly mower, nice restoration
B			G	$1,400	10/24/2012	WCWI	Belly mower
B			G	$1,550	9/22/2012	NEOR	WF

TRACTORS

Allis-Chalmers

Model	Year	Hours	Condition	Price	Date	Area	Comments
B			G	$2,100	8/16/2012	Online	*IQBID.com,* item in Minnesota, WF, restored
B			F	$900	6/30/2012	ECIA	Belly mower, original
B			F	$1,150	6/8/2012	ECND	Woods L59 Mower, overall not in the best of condition but fully functionable
B			G	$1,200	11/30/2011	ECND	Electric start, 5' Woods L559 belly mower, good rear rubber, new battery
B			G	$1,550	10/15/2011	Online	*IQBID.com,* factory WF, gas, near new 9.5x24/9x24 rear, 5' Woods L59 belly mower
B			F	$800	12/17/2010	WCIL	Belly mower, does not run
B			G	$1,050	11/27/2010	SEMN	NF, 6' belly mower, 9.5x24 tires
B			F	$850	10/2/2010	ECMN	WF
B			F	$1,000	10/2/2010	ECMN	WF
B			G	$1,500	10/2/2010	ECMN	WF
B			F	$900	9/11/2010	SEIA	Belly mower
B			G	$1,200	6/5/2010	WCMO	
B			F	$1,500	4/17/2010	NEIA	WF, Woods L306 72" mower deck, good paint, runs
B			G	$1,250	4/16/2010	NEKS	
B			G	$1,500	4/16/2010	NEKS	High crop
B			G	$3,800	4/16/2010	NEKS	High crop Thompson
B			F	$1,000	3/13/2010	SEIA	WF, belly mower
B			F	$900	1/30/2010	NETX	
B1	1939		G	$1,350	6/15/2013	WCMI	WF, without frame, 9.5x24 turf tires, rear belt pulley, SN BI32502
C	1940		G	$2,100	12/1/2011	SEMN	B engine, WC frame
C	1945		G	$1,500	7/31/2013	ECND	NF, Woods L59 mower, mounted Fimco 30-gal. sprayer
C	1946		G	$1,705	10/22/2013	Online	*HansenAndYoung.com,* NF, side mount sickle mower
C	1946		G	$1,100	8/25/2011	ECND	NF, PTO, belt pulley, loose, 9x24 rear, 6' sickle mower, runs
C	1949		G	$1,018	8/14/2012	Online	*PurpleWave.com,* item in Kansas, 4 cyl. gas, 3 speed, 540 PTO, Woods 6' mower, 5x15 fronts, 11.2x24 rear
C	1949		G	$1,300	9/28/2011	Online	*BigIron.com,* item in Nebraska, mower, 3F/1R, 125 cu. in., 4 cyl. gas, 18 drawbar hp, 23 PTO hp, 540 PTO, 12V electrical system
C	1949		G	$875	2/20/2010	NCIL	NF, runs, Woods belly mower, gas
C	1951		G	$1,450	6/5/2010	ECMN	NF, Woods 60" belly mower
C			G	$5,750	3/22/2014	SWMI	
C			G	$1,300	12/4/2013	ECIN	NF
C			G	$1,175	6/28/2013	NEMO	11x24 rubber, 60" belly mower, SN C21438
C			G	$950	6/1/2013	SEMN	5' Woods belly mower, new blades, fenders, 1 hyd.
C			G	$7,250	6/1/2013	SEMN	Gas, WF
C			G	$2,225	4/24/2013	Online	*BigIron.com,* item in Colorado, 3F/1R, 4 cyl. gas

TRACTORS

Allis-Chalmers

Model	Year	Hours	Condition	Price	Date	Area	Comments
C			G	$1,900	3/23/2013	NEIN	Repainted, new tires, belt pulley, PTO, runs
C			G	$725	1/19/2013	NEMS	
C			G	$900	11/24/2012	SEMN	Belly mower, 11.2x24 tires
C			G	$925	11/3/2012	SWMO	Starts, runs, repainted, tractor club tractor
C			F	$1,600	8/1/2012	NCIA	6' Woods belly mower
C			F	$900	6/20/2012	SESD	
C			G	$1,100	6/2/2012	SEMN	60" Art's Way belly mower, new battery and caster wheels, NF, good rubber
C			F	$850	5/19/2012	SWMI	NF, 10x24 tires, cultivators, front blade
C			G	$1,400	4/10/2012	ECND	NF, Sears 5' belly mower
C			G	$1,100	3/14/2012	ECND	Belly mower
C			F	$850	1/28/2012	ECMO	Restored
C			G	$900	8/11/2011	WCMN	Sunmaster 5' belly mower, hyd. lift mower
C			G	$1,150	7/30/2011	ECMO	Restored, runs great
C			G	$900	7/26/2011	ECND	NF, Woods rotary belly mower
C			G	$1,500	3/10/2011	WCMN	12V system, 72" mid-mount belly mower
C			G	$1,000	11/13/2010	NCIA	72" Woods deck
C			G	$800	10/2/2010	SWWI	
C			F	$850	10/2/2010	ECMN	NF, loader
C			G	$1,000	7/31/2010	NWIL	Gas, restored, NF, on rubber
C			F	$800	6/5/2010	SEMN	Woods 60" mower
C			G	$2,600	4/16/2010	NEKS	
C			G	$1,100	4/1/2010	NCIN	59" belly mower
C			G	$950	2/26/2010	SEMN	Saw rig
C			G	$950	1/30/2010	NETX	
CA	1949		G	$1,050	3/22/2014	WCWA	4 cyl. gas, WF, hyd., PTO, Woods 80" mower, new 11.2x24 rear tires
CA	1951		G	$850	6/15/2013	WCMI	NF, rear belt pulley, remote hyd., 11x24 tires, SN 4176
CA	1951		G	$1,250	6/15/2013	WCMI	NF, 11.2x24 tires, snow plow, two bottom plow, SN 720
CA	1952		G	$2,200	9/21/2013	SEMN	Live power, WF
CA	1952		G	$1,500	6/15/2013	WCMI	WF, 3 pt., 12.4x24 tires, SN 21520
CA	1952		G	$1,900	10/1/2010	WCWI	Factory WF, all tuned up
CA	1953		G	$2,200	9/21/2013	WCMI	Gas, PTO, electric start, NF, 13.6x24 rear tires, restored
CA	1956		G	$850	6/15/2013	WCMI	WF, rear belt pulley, remote hyd., 11.2x24 tires, SN 38102
CA	1956		G	$1,200	6/15/2013	WCMI	WF, 3 pt., California high crop wheels, cultivator frame, 11.2x36 tires, SN 38129
CA			G	$1,600	9/12/2013	SEIA	WF, sickle bar, mower
CA			G	$1,950	9/12/2013	SEIA	Woods 5' mower, 540 PTO, 11.2x24
CA			G	$900	8/24/2013	SEMN	WF, Woods L59 60" belly mower
CA			G	$1,870	6/10/2013	NWWI	Runs, drives, cultivator, loader, WF, 2 pt.
CA			G	$1,550	5/11/2013	NCOH	Repainted, runs

Allis-Chalmers

Model	Year	Hours	Condition	Price	Date	Area	Comments
CA			F	$900	3/22/2013	WCMI	4 cyl. gas, WF, mounted back blade, 3 pt., PTO, 12.4x24 rear
CA			G	$1,550	4/7/2012	NWMI	WF, gas
CA			G	$975	9/4/2010	SEVA	4 cyl. gas
CA			G	$4,100	6/19/2010	SWIL	High crop, old restoration, repaint, fenders, PTO, lights, belt pulley
CA			F	$1,150	5/26/2010	ECSD	Not running
CA			G	$800	4/16/2010	NEKS	
CA			G	$925	4/16/2010	NEKS	
D10	1960		G	$7,100	4/2/2012	WCIL	Restored, 3 pt. hitch
D10	1964		G	$9,700	6/15/2013	WCMI	Series 3 high crop, WF 3 pt., 11.2x28 tires, SN 7683
D10			G	$3,200	3/30/2013	NWIL	Woods L306 belly mower, new spare front tire
D10			G	$2,000	3/23/2013	NEIN	Original, side dresser, runs
D10			G	$4,500	3/23/2013	NEIN	3 pt., repainted, runs
D10			G	$4,100	2/7/2013	NEIN	
D10			G	$4,100	2/7/2013	NEIN	
D10			F	$2,900	4/7/2012	SWIN	Average condition
D10			G	$4,300	3/24/2012	NEIN	Original, runs
D10			G	$5,100	2/2/2012	NEIN	
D10			G	$3,100	4/1/2011	ECND	
D10			G	$2,550	9/4/2010	NEIN	Snap coulter hitch, 3 pt.
D10			G	$5,500	9/4/2010	NEIN	Series 2, spin out rims
D10			G	$9,500	9/4/2010	NEIN	High crop, snap coulter hitch
D10			G	$1,800	4/16/2010	NEKS	
D12			G	$3,500	3/24/2012	NEIN	Factory 3 pt., original, runs
D12			G	$3,600	4/1/2011	ECND	
D12			G	$2,900	4/16/2010	NEKS	Street brush
D14	1951		G	$1,660	9/28/2011	Online	*BigIron.com,* item in Nebraska, WF, 4 speed Hi/Lo, 4 cyl. gas, 2 hyd., 540 PTO, steel fenders, original tin straight, power steering
D14	1957		G	$3,250	10/23/2010	SCPA	
D14	1959		E	$2,900	4/27/2011	NECO	WF, 3 pt., new paint, gas
D14	1959		F	$2,275	10/1/2010	WCWI	Factory WF, nearly new rubber, starts and runs like new
D14	1959	4,069	F	$1,801	6/23/2010	Online	*BigIron.com,* item in Nebraska, 4 speed, 4 cyl. gas, 13x26 rear tires, 6.5x16 front tires, 540 PTO
D14	1960		F	$1,000	1/26/2013	WCIL	1 owner, WF, gas, converted to alternator, new water pump
D14	1960		F	$2,000	5/26/2010	ECSD	High crop, motor OH
D14			G	$1,700	3/13/2014	SCID	Gas, 8 speed, 540 PTO, 13.6x28 power adjust rubber, 3 pt.
D14			G	$1,000	6/15/2013	WCMI	WF, Allis-Chalmers loader
D14			G	$1,600	3/24/2012	SWMI	Gas, 3 pt., PTO, WF, 13.6x26 tires
D14			F	$1,200	3/20/2012	WCIL	Blade
D14			G	$2,900	7/30/2011	WCWI	Gas, open station, loader, trip bucket

Allis-Chalmers

Model	Year	Hours	Condition	Price	Date	Area	Comments
D14			G	$1,925	6/29/2011	Online	*PurpleWave.com,* item in Kansas, 4 cyl. gas, 4F/1R transmission, 3 pt., 540 PTO, lights
D14			G	$3,900	5/7/2011	SESK	2WD, gas, PTO, 3 pt., 12V system, alternator, 50 hours since rebuilt
D14			G	$2,700	4/1/2011	ECND	Loader
D14			G	$2,700	3/25/2011	WCIL	Gas, WF, 3 pt., power steering, rear wheel weights
D14			G	$2,000	1/29/2011	ECMO	WF, gas, no drawbar
D14			G	$2,350	12/4/2010	SEMN	WF, gas, quick hitch
D14			G	$2,350	11/27/2010	SEMN	WF, gas, snap coulter hitch, 13.6x28 tires, new paint
D14			F	$1,850	5/26/2010	ECSD	Runs
D14			G	$1,200	4/16/2010	NEKS	
D14			G	$1,300	1/30/2010	NETX	
D15	1960		G	$1,400	3/24/2012	SETN	40 hp
D15	1966		G	$5,000	4/14/2014	Online	Series 2, 1 owner tractor, purchased new in 1967
D15			G	$850	9/12/2013	SEIA	Snap coulter hitch, 540 PTO, 2 hyd., NF, loader, PS
D15			G	$2,300	3/23/2013	NEIN	Gas, original, new tires, WF, runs
D15			G	$3,900	3/23/2013	NEIN	Repainted, 3 pt., WF, runs
D15			G	$3,700	8/21/2012	SENE	3 pt., good rubber, runs great
D15			G	$3,100	12/1/2011	NEIN	13.6x25 rear tires, spin out rims, WF, gas, hood guard
D15			G	$1,850	4/2/2011	SEMN	NF, steel weights
D15			G	$3,400	4/2/2011	SEMN	Series 2, NF, 3 pt.
D15			G	$2,000	11/20/2010	SCKY	Series 2
D15			G	$5,400	9/4/2010	SEVA	Series 2, all original
D15			G	$1,350	6/5/2010	ECMN	Gas, NF
D17	1958		G	$1,550	6/15/2013	WCMI	NF, 3 pt., 16.9x28 tires, rebuilt engine, hyd. lift snow plow, SN 7975
D17	1958		F	$1,100	8/22/2012	ECMN	Loader, 2 hyd., 2 pt., PTO, WF
D17	1958		G	$1,600	8/4/2012	ECMN	3 pt., 540 PTO, 1 hyd., 14.9x28 rubber
D17	1958		G	$2,700	1/30/2012	NEIA	Gas
D17	1959		G	$2,400	4/10/2012	ECND	WF, Hi/Lo, PTO, fenders, rear weights, Du-Al 325 loader, grapple, PTO pump, one owner
D17	1959		G	$1,595	7/28/2010	Online	*PurpleWave.com,* item in Kansas, 4 cyl. LP, 4 speed Hi/Lo, snap coulter hitch, 540 PTO
D17	1960		G	$2,200	11/30/2010	SWMN	Gas, WF
D17	1963		G	$5,100	4/18/2013	ECIL	Series 3, gas, 3 pt., snap coupler, Allis-Chalmers trip bucket loader
D17	1963		G	$1,100	8/22/2012	ECMN	Fair rubber
D17	1963		G	$2,350	10/1/2010	WCWI	Gas, factory WF, extra hyd., very good tires, 12V electrical outlets, starts, runs
D17	1963		G	$3,600	2/6/2010	ECIA	Series 3, gas, WF, SN 85939
D17	1964		G	$1,150	7/10/2010	SEIA	Series 3, original

Allis-Chalmers

Model	Year	Hours	Condition	Price	Date	Area	Comments
D17	1966	916	G	$2,425	6/8/2011	Online	*BigIron.com,* item in Kansas, 4 speed Hi/Lo, 4 cyl. gas, 1 hyd., tandem axle, 540 PTO
D17			G	$2,100	2/12/2014	ECWI	2WD, gas, NF, snap coulter hitch, 2 hyd., rusty paint
D17		7,512	G	$4,100	1/11/2014	ECIA	Series 4, snap coulter hitch
D17			G	$2,650	12/26/2013	Online	*BigIron.com,* item in Iowa, 4F/2R, shuttle clutch shifter, Allis-Chalmers 3.7L, 4 cyl., 63 hp, single hyd., 3 pt., 540 PTO
D17			F	$1,900	12/18/2013	SEIA	Series 1, 1 hyd., 3 pt., 540 PTO, SN 264118
D17			G	$1,815	10/28/2013	NWWI	WF, gas, 3 pt., 540 PTO
D17			G	$3,250	10/3/2013	NCIN	
D17			G	$1,200	9/28/2013	SWMN	WF, 16.9x23 tire, 3 pt.
D17			G	$2,500	9/28/2013	SWMN	WF, 16.9x23 tires, weights, Allis-Chalmers 500 loader
D17			G	$1,750	8/29/2013	NWIA	WF, 540 PTO, motor OH
D17			F	$1,540	8/28/2013	Online	*PurpleWave.com,* item in Kansas, 6 cyl. diesel, manual, 3 pt., drawbar, aux. outlet, 540 PTO, loader, 2 lever control
D17		5,108	G	$4,250	8/22/2013	SEMN	Farmhand F225 loader, bale spear, bucket, chains
D17			F	$900	7/27/2013	WCIL	WF, needs front seal, oil leaks
D17			F	$1,600	7/27/2013	WCIL	NF, starts and runs
D17			G	$1,306	7/17/2013	Online	*BigIron.com,* item in Nebraska, 4 speed, power steering
D17			G	$2,600	3/23/2013	NEIN	Series 3, repainted, runs
D17			G	$2,800	3/23/2013	NEIN	Repainted, WF, weights, runs
D17			G	$5,500	3/23/2013	NEIN	Series 4, factory LP, WF, original, dual hyd., runs
D17			G	$1,650	3/7/2013	SEIA	Gas, open station, power steering
D17			G	$1,900	3/7/2013	SEIA	Series 3, gas, open station, power steering, Du-Al loader
D17			G	$4,750	11/24/2012	SEMN	Schwartz loader, 3 pt., hyd., PTO, 16.9x28 tires, chains
D17			G	$1,150	11/13/2012	NCIA	Gas, NF
D17			G	$2,800	9/29/2012	WCNE	Diesel, Kosch double 7' attached mowers
D17		2,249	G	$1,000	9/13/2012	Online	*IQBID.com,* item in Iowa, 18.4x26 tires, 1 hyd., new brakes, new battery, new clutch
D17		3,317	G	$2,695	8/22/2012	Online	*PurpleWave.com,* item in Kansas, 4 cyl. gas, 63 hp, manual, 3 pt., drawbar
D17		6,187	G	$1,750	6/20/2012	SWMB	Loader, bucket, 3 pt.
D17			F	$1,225	6/7/2012	NEIN	
D17			G	$6,500	3/24/2012	NEIN	Diesel, series 4, PTO, 3 pt., power steering, runs
D17			G	$2,600	3/14/2012	ECND	WF, PTO
D17			G	$2,000	1/28/2012	ECMO	3 pt.
D17			G	$2,250	1/28/2012	ECMO	NF
D17			G	$2,950	1/28/2012	ECMO	Loader, 3 pt.

Allis-Chalmers

Model	Year	Hours	Condition	Price	Date	Area	Comments
D17			G	$3,400	1/28/2012	ECMO	Bush Hog 2400 QT loader, snap coulter hitch
D17		5,547	G	$4,800	12/28/2011	NEMO	Series 4, snap coulter hitch, rear weights, 2 hyd., Paulson hyd. loader, no 3 pt.
D17			G	$3,100	11/29/2011	WCMN	Series 3, gas, WF, 2, 489 hours showing, fenders, PTO, 1 hyd., 16.9x28 tires, rock box
D17		5,239	G	$3,700	11/29/2011	WCMN	Series 3, gas, WF, fenders, PTO, 1 hyd., 18.4x28 tires
D17			F	$2,300	11/3/2011	ECIL	WF, snap coupler, good 16.9x38 tires, Allis-Chalmers loader w/ trip bucket
D17			F	$1,750	10/29/2011	ECMN	
D17			F	$2,100	8/27/2011	SWIL	Series 3, WF, snap coulter hitch, like-new rear 16.9x28 Firestone tires
D17			F	$2,100	8/27/2011	SWIL	WF
D17			G	$4,000	8/26/2011	SWOH	Series 4, WF
D17		1,647	G	$1,800	8/10/2011	Online	*BigIron.com,* item in Nebraska, 4 speed, 4 cyl. gas, 1 hyd., 540 PTO, 3 pt.
D17			G	$1,800	7/30/2011	ECMO	Series 3
D17			G	$4,750	7/30/2011	ECMO	Series 3, new paint, rebuilt motor 100 hours ago, 3 pt., blade, post hold digger
D17			G	$2,100	4/2/2011	ECMN	Series 3
D17			G	$3,700	4/2/2011	SEMN	Series 3, 3 pt., rock box, WF
D17			G	$1,300	3/25/2011	WCIL	Diesel, WF, power steering, runs
D17			G	$1,450	3/25/2011	WCIL	Gas, WF, snap coulter hitch
D17			G	$2,000	3/25/2011	WCIL	Gas, WF, factory dual hyd., snap coulter hitch
D17			P	$1,350	3/5/2011	SEMN	Gas, WF, dual hyd., loader, 540 PTO, not running
D17		4,034	F	$1,900	11/20/2010	SEIA	Loader
D17			G	$1,800	9/25/2010	SEIA	
D17			G	$3,250	9/11/2010	ECIA	Series 4, snap coulter hitch, Allis-Chalmers loader, snow bucket
D17			G	$2,000	8/14/2010	WCMN	2 pt., snap coulter hitch, OH, good tin, PTO, new seat
D17			F	$2,250	5/26/2010	ECSD	WF, runs
D17			G	$3,050	5/26/2010	ECSD	Series 4, runs
D17			G	$4,000	5/26/2010	ECSD	
D17			G	$2,600	5/25/2010	SEIA	
D17			G	$2,600	5/8/2010	SEIA	WF
D17			G	$3,500	4/7/2010	NEMO	Gas, 18.4x34 tires, series 4, 3 pt., straight and very nice
D17			F	$2,200	3/6/2010	SEIN	Series 3, NI loader
D19	1962		G	$4,400	1/29/2014	Online	*BigIron.com,* item in Nebraska, 4 speed Hi/Lo, 321 cu. in. turbo diesel, 15.5x38R1 rear, LT11x15 front, 2 hyd. hyd. S, 2 pt., drawbar, new injection pump, new brakes in housing, 19 hours on new tach.
D19	1962		G	$3,800	10/1/2010	WCWI	Gas, factory WF, 3 pt., good rubber, starts and runs

Allis-Chalmers

Model	Year	Hours	Condition	Price	Date	Area	Comments
D19	1963	3,292	G	$5,250	8/22/2012	Online	*BigIron.com,* item in Colorado, manual 4F/2R, gas, 2 hyd., 540 PTO, handclutch hat runs in oil, WF, 3 pt., drawbar, spring ride seat, lights work, Du-Al 75 loader
D19	1963	5,059	G	$4,290	8/14/2012	Online	*PurpleWave.com,* item in Kansas, 6 cyl. gas, 75 hp, 4 speed, 540 PTO, snap coulter hitch, drawbar, 6.5x16 front tires, 16.9x34 rear tires
D19	1963		G	$3,300	1/31/2012	NEIN	3 pt., nice original
D19	1963		G	$2,500	10/7/2011	NWSD	Diesel, PTO, hyd., 3 pt., power steering, runs good, front sheet metal needs some work, WF
D19	1963		G	$2,600	10/7/2011	NWSD	Diesel, PTO, hyd., 3 pt., power steering, unrestored but straight, runs good
D19			G	$3,750	10/3/2013	NCIN	
D19			G	$2,400	8/24/2013	NEMD	
D19			F	$2,000	7/27/2013	WCIL	Gas
D19			F	$2,600	7/27/2013	WCIL	Gas, runs
D19			G	$3,100	3/24/2012	NEIN	Diesel, 3 pt., dual hyd., runs
D19			G	$1,500	1/31/2012	NEIN	Gas, original, dual hyd., PTO, snap coulter hitch
D19			G	$2,850	12/15/2011	Online	*IQBID.com,* WF, gas, 2 pt., PTO, dual hyd., loader, new rear tires
D19		3,077	G	$5,500	12/3/2011	NCOH	Rebuilt head/injectors, new front tires
D19		7,000	G	$2,100	8/27/2011	NEIA	Gas, WF, nice
D19			F	$1,750	11/18/2010	SEOK	
D19			G	$3,000	9/4/2010	NEIN	LP
D19			G	$3,100	9/4/2010	NEIN	Diesel
D19		3,008	G	$4,600	9/4/2010	SEVA	6 cyl. gas, Du-Al loader
D19			F	$1,500	6/5/2010	SEMN	WF, hyd. loader, snap coulter hitch, PTO, hyd.
D19			F	$2,400	5/26/2010	ECSD	LP gas, 3 pt., runs
D19			F	$2,650	5/26/2010	ECSD	
D19			G	$3,050	5/26/2010	ECSD	Runs
D19			G	$4,900	4/16/2010	NEKS	High crop
D19			G	$900	4/6/2010	NWKS	2 hyd., PTO, 2 pt., duals
D21	1967	4,200	E	$9,250	11/13/2010	NCIA	Bareback, 24.5x32 tires
D21			E	$30,000	8/10/2013	NCIA	Restored
D21			G	$16,000	3/23/2013	NEIN	Series 2, original, 3 pt., PTO, dual hyd., big rubber, runs
D21		6,588	G	$8,100	10/18/2012	WCNE	Wheatland, no 3 pt., Farmhand 228 loader, no welds on loader
D21			G	$4,200	10/22/2011	NECO	3 pt., PTO
D21			G	$4,700	10/22/2011	NECO	3 pt., PTO
D21			E	$8,250	11/13/2010	NCIA	
D21			G	$8,000	9/4/2010	NEIN	Series 2, 3 sets rear weights, dual hyd.
D21			G	$10,000	6/19/2010	SWIL	Running, restored, original, runs great, good transmission, 3 hyd.
G	1948		G	$2,900	2/22/2014	NEIN	Cultivators
G	1948		E	$4,100	2/22/2014	NEIN	Plow, cultivator, front weights
G	1948		G	$2,600	8/10/2013	NCIA	

Allis-Chalmers

Model	Year	Hours	Condition	Price	Date	Area	Comments
G	1948		G	$1,750	6/15/2013	WCMI	High crop WF, rear pulley, 5.5x44 tires, SN G266
G	1948		G	$1,800	6/15/2013	WCMI	High crop WF, 7x40 tires, remote hyd., SN G6661
G	1948		G	$1,800	6/15/2013	WCMI	WF, side pulley, hyd. rear cultivator, rear hyd. pump, SN G6214
G	1948		P	$4,070	8/14/2012	Online	*PurpleWave.com,* item in Kansas, sickle mower, cultivator, plow, 4x12 front tires, 7.2x30 rear tires, non-operational, engine is free
G	1949		G	$1,400	6/15/2013	WCMI	WF, converted to battery operation, 6x30 tires, SN G11012
G	1949		G	$2,300	6/15/2013	WCMI	WF, 7.2x20, hyd. rear cultivator
G	1949		G	$2,500	6/15/2013	WCMI	WF, hand lift, 1 bottom plow, FW, 6x30 tires, SN G17086
G	1949		G	$4,000	10/23/2010	SCPA	
G	1950		G	$1,850	6/15/2013	WCMI	WF, 7x30 tires, rear cultivator, front and rear hyd., SN G23651
G	1953		G	$1,975	6/15/2013	WCMI	WF, 6x30 tires, hyd., SN G27171
G			G	$5,600	3/22/2014	WCMO	Sickle mower, 1 bottom plow, cultivator
G			G	$3,000	6/22/2013	SEWA	4 cyl. gas, direct start, hyd., belly mounted Planet Jr. implements
G			G	$4,300	6/15/2013	WCMI	WF
G			G	$2,500	5/25/2013	NWMO	Restored, 6.2x30 rear on 5" rim
G			G	$2,000	5/11/2013	NCOH	Older repaint, runs
G			G	$3,400	5/11/2013	NCOH	Plow, new tires, belt pulley, original, runs
G			G	$3,700	3/23/2013	NEIN	Repainted, runs
G			G	$3,000	3/24/2012	NEIN	Repainted, runs
G			G	$1,525	1/10/2012	Online	*BidNow.com,* rear engine, rare, engine is not frozen
G			G	$1,600	12/1/2011	SEMN	Blade
G			G	$2,800	12/1/2011	SEMN	
G			G	$3,190	11/3/2011	Online	*PurpleWave.com,* item in Kansas
G			G	$3,100	3/26/2011	SEWI	
G			G	$2,550	10/2/2010	ECMN	
G			F	$2,300	9/4/2010	SEVA	4 cyl. gas, needs tune up
G			G	$2,500	6/5/2010	WCMO	Belly mower, belt pulley
G			G	$3,000	6/5/2010	WCMO	Belly mower, belt pulley
G			G	$3,800	6/5/2010	WCMO	Belt pulley, hyd.
G			G	$2,900	5/22/2010	SEMN	Cultivator parts and other extra parts, stuck valve in tractor
G			G	$3,300	4/16/2010	NEKS	
I600	1966	1,146	G	$2,300	10/24/2012	NECO	Gas, WF, 3 pt., loader
IB	1949		G	$2,050	6/15/2013	WCMI	WF, frame, 9.5x25 new tractor tread tires, SN IB3540
IB	1951		G	$2,100	10/1/2010	WCWI	1 of 2,550 made, installed by Drott Tractor Co., street broom, starts and runs
IB	1954		G	$4,500	10/23/2010	SCPA	
IB	1955		G	$3,400	10/2/2010	SWWI	Last factory built IB
RC	1939		G	$1,200	8/25/2011	ECND	NF, loose, belt pulley, PTO, new 13x26 rear

Allis-Chalmers

Model	Year	Hours	Condition	Price	Date	Area	Comments
RC	1939		F	$1,775	10/1/2010	WCWI	1 OF 5,500 made, starts and runs
RC			F	$1,980	11/3/2011	Online	*PurpleWave.com,* item in Kansas
RC			G	$1,500	10/2/2010	ECMN	
RC			P	$1,600	9/9/2010	NWWI	For parts
RC			G	$1,100	5/1/2010	SENE	
RC			G	$1,150	4/16/2010	NEKS	
RC			G	$3,000	4/16/2010	NEKS	
U	1935		G	$3,400	10/1/2010	WCWI	4 factory round spoked wheels, nearly new diamond tread turf tires, runs like new
U			G	$2,365	11/3/2011	Online	*PurpleWave.com,* item in Kansas
U			G	$1,000	4/16/2010	NEKS	
U			G	$2,500	4/16/2010	NEKS	
UC	1930		G	$2,800	6/15/2013	WCMI	High crop H 28 H (Thompson kit)
UC			F	$900	12/1/2011	SEMN	Continental engine, rubber over steel
UC			G	$1,155	11/3/2011	Online	*PurpleWave.com,* item in Kansas, UC 1350
UC			P	$1,500	9/3/2010	NEIN	High crop, dead row, needs work, may not run or drive, as is
UC			G	$1,600	4/16/2010	NEKS	High crop
UC			G	$3,300	4/16/2010	NEKS	High crop
WC	1934		P	$798	8/7/2013	Online	*PurpleWave.com,* item in Kansas, 4 cyl. gas, 4 speed manual, 5.5x16 front tires, 11.2x28 rear tires, non-operational
WC	1935		G	$4,800	6/30/2012	NEIA	Round spoke wheels, cultivator
WC	1937		F	$800	5/19/2012	SWMI	13x24 tires, fenders, round spoke front wheels
WC	1938		G	$850	8/7/2013	Online	*IQBID.com,* NF, PTO, fenders, rear spokes
WC	1938		F	$850	8/25/2011	ECND	NF, PTO, fenders, 13x24 rear, loose
WC	1939		F	$775	5/19/2012	SWMI	NF, 11x28 tires
WC	1939		F	$1,250	10/1/2010	WCWI	Unstyled, rare cast factory WF, rear steel
WC			G	$2,150	3/5/2014	Online	*BigIron.com,* item in Kansas, road patrol tractor, Ottawa loader, 4F/1R, no PTO, 10' blade on grader blade, hyd. pump for loader, 4' trip bucket
WC			G	$1,250	9/28/2013	SWMN	11.2x24, Allis-Chalmers mounted sickle mower, Allis-Chalmers 2R cultivator
WC			G	$1,300	9/12/2013	SEIA	NF
WC			G	$1,500	8/24/2013	SEMI	NF, gas
WC			G	$1,500	8/24/2013	SEMI	Pulling tractor, WF, eagle claw hitch, wheel weights
WC			G	$1,350	6/15/2013	WCMI	Reverse drive, orchard fork lift, NF, 12.4x28 tires
WC			F	$800	3/22/2013	WCMI	4 cyl. gas, hand crank, NF, drawbar, 13x24 rear, PTO, set of rear steel wheels
WC			G	$1,000	8/16/2012	NCIA	Crank start
WC			F	$907	11/3/2011	Online	*PurpleWave.com,* item in Kansas
WC			G	$1,072	11/3/2011	Online	*PurpleWave.com,* item in Kansas, rear steel wheels
WC			F	$1,375	11/3/2011	Online	*PurpleWave.com,* item in Kansas, cast iron oil pan

Allis-Chalmers

Model	Year	Hours	Condition	Price	Date	Area	Comments
WC			G	$1,000	1/29/2011	ECMO	On steel, unstyled
WC			F	$950	10/2/2010	ECMN	NF
WC			G	$1,600	10/2/2010	ECMN	NF
WC			G	$1,150	4/16/2010	NEKS	Roller front
WC			G	$1,350	4/16/2010	NEKS	
WC			G	$2,700	4/16/2010	NEKS	High crop Thompson
WC			G	$2,900	4/16/2010	NEKS	
WD	1947		F	$1,000	6/20/2012	SESD	NF, repainted, fenders, runs good
WD	1948		F	$1,300	12/7/2011	NCIA	Power steering, 3 pt.
WD	1949		G	$1,300	4/10/2012	ECND	WF, PTO
WD	1949		G	$1,400	4/10/2012	ECND	WF, fenders, PTO
WD	1949		G	$1,150	12/14/2011	WCMN	3 pt., trip bucket loader, 12V system, runs
WD	1949		G	$1,000	4/11/2011	Online	*AuctionTime.com*
WD	1950		G	$3,750	1/11/2013	NWIN	Rear forklift
WD	1950		G	$2,090	8/14/2012	Online	*PurpleWave.com,* item in Illinois, tractor-mounted 2R corn picker, 4 cyl. gas, manual, drawbar, 19 hp, 540 PTO, 26 hp, 15 gal. fuel cap, single rear hyd. remote
WD	1951		F	$900	7/17/2013	NEND	NF, new rear tires, recent engine OH, loader
WD	1951		F	$975	12/7/2011	NCIA	3 pt.
WD	1951		F	$900	11/12/2011	SEIA	New 13.6x28 tires
WD	1952		G	$1,800	1/11/2013	NWIN	NF
WD	1953		F	$775	4/25/2012	Online	*BigIron.com,* item in Missouri, 3 speed, 4 cyl. gas, 35 hp, 1 hyd., 540 PTO, snap coulter hitch, NF, power adj. rear wheels
WD	1953		F	$1,000	11/12/2010	ECIL	Power steering
WD	1953		G	$1,400	7/10/2010	SEIA	Restored, synchro transmission
WD	1953		G	$2,150	2/20/2010	NCIL	Woods L306 finishing deck, gas
WD			F	$975	3/22/2014	ECSD	
WD			G	$825	12/17/2013	ECWI	Loader, starts, runs
WD			P	$797	10/28/2013	NWWI	Like-new rear tires, 3 pt., gas
WD			F	$990	8/26/2013	NWWI	WF, runs, good sheet metal
WD			G	$775	7/10/2013	Online	*BigIron.com,* item in Nebraska, 4 cyl. gas, 540 PTO, electric start/hand crank Magneto
WD			G	$800	6/22/2013	SEMN	NF, MNT CULT
WD			G	$1,100	6/1/2013	SEMN	Gas, NF, fenders, 12.4x28 tires
WD			G	$900	5/11/2013	NCOH	Older repaint, PS, belt pulley, runs
WD			F	$900	12/12/2012	NCIL	NF, snap coupler
WD			G	$1,595	10/31/2012	Online	*PurpleWave.com,* item in Oklahoma, Allis 4 cyl. gas, manual, loader 41" bucket, 2-lever control, 3 pt., drawbar, 540 PTO, 1 rear hyd.
WD			G	$1,000	8/30/2012	SEMN	
WD			G	$1,810	8/22/2012	Online	*BigIron.com,* item in Nebraska, gas, 16.9x26 rear tires, 4x12 front tires, recent OH, set up for competitive pulling

Allis-Chalmers

Model	Year	Hours	Condition	Price	Date	Area	Comments
WD			G	$900	8/21/2012	WCIL	
WD			G	$1,900	3/24/2012	NEIN	Repainted, PTO, runs
WD			G	$850	12/15/2011	Online	IQBID.com, gas, NF, PTO, 13.6-38 rear
WD			G	$2,500	9/15/2011	ECIA	
WD			G	$1,100	8/24/2011	WCMN	Loader, reverse
WD			G	$1,700	8/20/2011	NEMN	WF, aftermarket 3 pt.
WD			G	$1,100	7/27/2011	Online	*BigIron.com,* item in Iowa, 4 speed, 4 cyl. gas, 35 hp, 1 hyd., 540 PTO, runs, snap coulter hitch, muffler needs replacing, live drive handclutch
WD			G	$775	4/13/2011	Online	*BigIron.com,* item in Nebraska, 4 speed, 4 cyl. gas, WF, 2 pt., drawbar, missing battery
WD			G	$900	4/2/2011	ECMN	
WD			G	$850	2/28/2011	SCMI	
WD			F	$850	2/5/2011	SEMI	
WD			G	$2,500	10/2/2010	ECMN	V8 engine
WD			G	$1,100	9/11/2010	SEIA	45 engine
WD			G	$1,500	9/9/2010	NWWI	NF, diesel
WD			F	$1,050	8/14/2010	SEMN	
WD			G	$1,700	8/7/2010	SCMN	WF, PTO, new 12.4x28 tires, SN WD73595
WD			G	$1,200	6/23/2010	Online	*BigIron.com,* item in Nebraska, power adjust wheels, Char Lynn power steering, 12V with alternator, tractor runs, 1 rear tire has vulcanized spot
WD			F	$1,750	6/5/2010	SEMN	WF, 3 pt., newer rear rubber
WD			G	$1,700	4/16/2010	NEKS	
WD45	1949		G	$2,100	7/10/2010	SEIA	Restored in 2007, new tires
WD45	1950		F	$853	9/24/2013	Online	*PurpleWave.com,* item in Wisconsin, 4 cyl. gas, 4 speed manual, spring susp seat, drawbar, 3 pt., emergency light
WD45	1952		G	$1,750	7/10/2010	SEIA	WD45 engine, WF, 3 pt., new tires
WD45	1953		G	$908	10/17/2012	Online	P*urpleWave.com,* item in Kansas, 4 cyl. gas, 4 speed, 540 PTO
WD45	1953		G	$1,600	8/4/2012	ECMN	Gas, WF, 22.5 rubber, good sheet metal
WD45	1953		F	$900	2/18/2012	ECIL	3 pt. arms, stock power steering, belt pulley
WD45	1953		G	$908	9/22/2010	Online	*PurpleWave.com,* item in Kansas, 4 cyl. gas, 4 speed, 540 PTO, drawbar, quick hitch
WD45	1953		G	$1,600	5/29/2010	NCIL	New back rubber
WD45	1954		G	$1,250	6/15/2013	WCMI	WF, PS, 14.9x28 tires, SN 176015
WD45	1954		G	$2,200	6/15/2013	WCMI	WF, 3 pt., remote hyd., PS, 14.9x28 tires, Kelley loader, SN 171418
WD45	1954		G	$4,600	3/2/2010	ECIL	WF
WD45	1955		G	$1,350	6/15/2013	WCMI	WF, 14.9x28 tires, back blade, SN 198800
WD45	1955		F	$1,000	11/29/2012	ECIL	14.9x28 tires, 1 set rear weights, SN 208663

Allis-Chalmers

Model	Year	Hours	Condition	Price	Date	Area	Comments
WD45	1955		G	$850	5/19/2012	WCIL	Gas, good paint
WD45	1955		F	$800	11/22/2011	NCMN	Diesel, factory WF, steel Rice tire
WD45	1955		G	$1,100	3/19/2011	SEIA	WF
WD45	1955		G	$1,300	7/10/2010	SEIA	Power steering, traction booster
WD45	1956		G	$2,400	9/21/2013	WCMI	Gas, PTO, electric start, NF, snap coulter hitch, 14.9x28 rear tires, restored
WD45	1956		G	$1,375	3/27/2013	Online	*PurpleWave.com,* item in Kansas, 3.7L, 4 cyl. gas, 43 hp, manual, 15 gal. fuel cap
WD45	1956		E	$4,900	10/7/2011	NWSD	Restored, PTO, power steering, gas, WF
WD45	1956		G	$1,350	10/1/2010	WCWI	LP, loader, starts and runs like new
WD45	1956		G	$7,000	10/1/2010	WCWI	Diesel, starts and runs
WD45	1957		G	$4,500	4/1/2014	WCMN	WF, PTO, fenders
WD45	1957		F	$1,200	2/21/2011	WCIL	Gas, WF
WD45	1964		F	$1,200	7/27/2011	ECND	Runs, paint and tires good
WD45			G	$1,000	2/5/2014	SESD	
WD45			G	$1,600	12/30/2013	SEMN	One owner
WD45			G	$800	12/5/2013	SCIA	
WD45			G	$900	12/5/2013	SCIA	3 pt., WF
WD45			G	$1,347	10/28/2013	NWWI	Gas, WF, spin out rear rims, 2 pt.
WD45			F	$908	9/25/2013	Online	*PurpleWave.com,* item in Kansas, inline 4 cyl. gas, 4 speed manual, 3 pt., drawbar, PTO, inoperable, battery dead
WD45			G	$800	8/24/2013	NWMO	3 pt., 540 PTO, aux. hyd., 14.9x28 rear tires in poor condition
WD45			G	$2,400	8/20/2013	WCIL	WF, snap coulter hitch
WD45			G	$900	6/15/2013	WCMI	Mid-1950s, WF, 3 pt., 14.9x28 tires, wheel weights
WD45			G	$900	6/15/2013	WCMI	NF, SN 24173
WD45			G	$1,750	6/15/2013	WCMI	Reverse drive orchard fork lift, NF
WD45			G	$1,900	5/18/2013	WCIA	Recent paint job, brand new rear tires
WD45			G	$1,200	4/10/2013	Online	*BigIron.com,* item in Nebraska, 2WD, 13.8x28 rear tires, 8x16 front tires, motor is free
WD45			G	$7,000	3/23/2013	NEIN	Diesel, WF, runs
WD45			G	$1,400	3/2/2013	ECMN	Loader
WD45			G	$1,126	2/1/2013	Online	*IQBID.com*, WF, 5 speed, hyd., 2 pt., PTO stub shaft, Allis-Chalmers hyd. loader
WD45			G	$2,200	10/25/2012	SCWI	NF
WD45			F	$800	9/22/2012	NEOR	
WD45			F	$1,500	6/7/2012	NEIN	Loader
WD45			G	$4,500	6/2/2012	SEMN	WF, 14.9x28 tires, rear original tires, 1980 repaint
WD45			G	$825	5/2/2012	Online	*PurpleWave.com,* item in Kansas, 4 cyl. gas, 4 speed, NF, 540 PTO, quick hitch, 1 hyd., 6' blade
WD45			F	$1,400	3/10/2012	NWIL	WF, factory power steering
WD45			G	$1,650	1/28/2012	ECMO	WF, belly mower
WD45			G	$2,200	1/28/2012	ECMO	WF, new front tires, new batteries

Allis-Chalmers

Model	Year	Hours	Condition	Price	Date	Area	Comments
WD45			F	$1,400	12/1/2011	SEMN	NF, alternator, change over kit
WD45			G	$1,350	8/13/2011	WCIL	13.6x28 tires, PTO, single remote, WF, runs well
WD45			G	$950	7/26/2011	ECND	WF, 2 pt., PTO, hyd., may need transmission work
WD45			G	$2,420	6/29/2011	Online	*PurpleWave.com,* item in Kansas, 4 cyl. gas, 4 speed, 3 pt., 540 PTO, drawbar, LTS, hand crank and lever start
WD45			G	$2,400	4/2/2011	SEMN	WF, wheel weights
WD45			G	$1,000	2/14/2011	NEMO	NF, fenders, 13x28 tires
WD45			G	$1,050	1/29/2011	ECMO	Snap coulter hitch, gas
WD45			G	$1,600	1/29/2011	ECMO	
WD45			G	$1,500	10/2/2010	ECMN	WF, loader
WD45			G	$2,800	9/9/2010	NWWI	WF, diesel
WD45			P	$2,100	9/3/2010	NEIN	Diesel, spin out rims, dead row, needs work and may not run or drive as is
WD45			F	$800	8/31/2010	WCIL	WF, fenders, 14.9x28 tires, has knock in engine
WD45			F	$950	7/10/2010	SEIA	
WD45			G	$1,400	7/10/2010	SEIA	New rubber, redone by Nevada, Iowa FFA club
WD45			G	$1,250	6/5/2010	WCMO	Loader
WD45			G	$3,100	6/5/2010	WCMO	Diesel, loader, WF, running
WD45			G	$4,200	6/5/2010	WCMO	Diesel, spin out rims, factory power steering, running
WD45			G	$2,850	5/26/2010	ECSD	WF, original, one owner
WD45			G	$5,150	5/26/2010	ECSD	WF
WD45			F	$950	5/22/2010	SEMN	NF
WD45			G	$3,000	5/8/2010	SEIA	Loader, wheel weights, power steering
WD45			G	$1,100	5/1/2010	NCOH	Older restoration, runs good, snap coulter hitch
WD45			G	$1,550	4/16/2010	NEKS	
WD45			G	$1,750	4/16/2010	NEKS	
WD45			G	$1,900	4/16/2010	NEKS	Diesel
WD45			F	$1,050	4/1/2010	NCIN	Snap coulter hitch, 540 PTO
WF	1947		G	$1,825	10/1/2010	WCWI	WF, starts and runs
WF	1948		G	$2,100	10/2/2010	SWWI	WF
WF	1949		G	$1,100	6/15/2013	WCMI	WF, 12.4x28 tires, SN 7099
WF	1950		G	$1,400	4/26/2011	ECSK	PTO, belt pulley, 11.2x28 rear tires, 3 rib front
WF			F	$4,840	11/3/2011	Online	*PurpleWave.com,* item in Kansas
WF			G	$1,175	12/1/2010	SCNE	Standard, very rare
WF			G	$2,000	10/2/2010	ECMN	WF
WF			G	$2,000	10/2/2010	ECMN	WF
WF			G	$4,250	6/19/2010	SWIL	Running, restored, fenders, PTO, belt pulley, professionally repainted
WF			G	$2,700	4/16/2010	NEKS	
WF			G	$3,000	4/16/2010	NEKS	
WF			G	$3,375	4/16/2010	NEKS	

Avery

Model	Year	Hours	Condition	Price	Date	Area	Comments
8-16			G	$40,000	9/21/2013	WCNY	Loose, repainted
8-16			G	$50,000	9/21/2013	WCNY	Loose, older repaint, original decals on inner fenders, contractor lugs, new rings in toolbox
14-28			G	$45,000	9/21/2013	WCNY	
20-35				$75,000	9/21/2013	WCNY	First Avery gas tractor, SN 471, older restoration, running, very rare, 2 cyl. opposed
20-35			G	$67,500	9/9/2010	NWWI	Open governor
45-65			G	$110,000	9/21/2013	WCNY	Imposing tractor, runs nice, older repaint, SN 27470
A	1943		G	$2,000	3/20/2013	WCMN	SF, hand brakes, runs great, completely restored
A			G	$900	10/2/2010	SWWI	
A			G	$1,450	6/5/2010	WCMO	
A			G	$1,500	5/1/2010	SENE	
BF	1946		E	$2,600	9/14/2011	NWIL	Gas, restored, good tires
BF	1946		G	$2,400	4/10/2010	NCTN	
BF	1950		G	$4,900	8/24/2011	ECMN	NF, tricycle front, hyd., PTO, belt pulley, power lift, new 12.4x24 rubber, low original hours
BF	1953		F	$2,075	5/1/2010	NCOH	NF, 1 of 358 made, older restoration, 3 pt.
BF			G	$1,300	5/11/2013	NCOH	Older repaint, new tires, SF, belt pulley, runs
BF			G	$1,500	6/5/2010	WCMO	Cultivators
V	1947		G	$4,000	8/7/2010	SEWI	Complete mechanical and cosmetic restoration
V	1951		G	$3,100	4/12/2014	SEND	WF, PTO, good runner, sharp
V			F	$800	6/9/2012	ECNE	Run, older repaint
N/A			G	$3,000	3/26/2011	SEWI	Complete restoration

Aumann Auctions, Inc. out of Nokomis, Ill., is one of the most prominent auction firms specializing in antique tractors. They had a memorable sale on Sept. 21, 2013 in west-central New York for well-known collector Jim Erdle. This sale included many very rare older tractors, including an Avery 20-35 (pictured). According to the serial number (SN 471), this was the first gas tractor Avery made. The older restoration in running condition sold for $75,000.

Also at this same auction, an Avery 45-65 sold for $110,000.

PETE'S PICK

TRACTORS

Case

Model	Year	Hours	Condition	Price	Date	Area	Comments
10-20			G	$70,000	9/21/2013	WCNY	Older, nice, SN 18236
10-20			G	$13,750	9/9/2010	NWWI	Single wheel engine
22-40			G	$14,000	9/21/2013	WCNY	Hard rubber on rear, SN 46328
200	1958		G	$3,410	11/3/2011	Online	*PurpleWave.com,* item in Kansas
300	1956		F	$1,100	8/8/2012	SEND	NF, diesel, 4 speed Hi/Lo, 1 hyd., 3 pt., PTO, 12x28 rear tires, does not run
300	1958		G	$6,000	10/7/2011	NWSD	PTO, 3 pt., NF, 12 speed
300		3,272	G	$800	1/4/2014	ECOH	Triple range drive
300			F	$775	6/17/2011	SWMN	
300			G	$2,400	4/21/2011	WCMI	Hyd. loader, 4 cyl. gas, Eagle hitch, good tires
300			F	$1,050	4/2/2011	SEMN	Gas, NF, Eagle 3 pt.
300			G	$2,300	10/6/2010	WCSD	Round nose, runs
300			G	$3,400	5/1/2010	SENE	
310	1958		F	$2,900	8/30/2013	NCIA	Utility tractor, loader, dual range
311			G	$1,300	5/15/2013	Online	*BigIron.com,* item in Missouri, 4 speed Hi/Lo, LP, 1 hyd., drawbar
311			G	$1,750	10/16/2010	SEMN	Gas, NF, 3 pt., 2 hyd., 540 PTO
312	1957		G	$2,650	6/15/2013	WCMI	NF, Eagle hitch, 11x36 tires with slotted rims, belt pulley, SN 6077742
320	1958		F	$1,900	2/27/2014	NWNE	Gas, WF, Eagle hitch, industrial front loader
350	1957		G	$2,700	6/15/2013	WCMI	WF, 12.4x36 tires, Eagle hitch, WF, SN 6081948
400	1955		G	$2,550	10/7/2011	NWSD	PTO, hyd., WF
400	1955		G	$3,100	10/7/2011	NWSD	PTO, hyd., WF, restored
400	1955		G	$1,700	6/23/2010	Online	*BigIron.com,* item in Iowa, 6 speed, gas engine, 50 hp, 1 hyd., live PTO, new Firestone tires, no power steering, fenders missing, after market WF
400	1956		G	$1,900	12/15/2012	WCMI	Diesel, WF, Eagle claw hitch, poor 15.5x38 tires, SN 80680

The trend I refer to as "the new collector tractor" describes models in either good original or good restored condition from the mid 1960s to mid 1970s.

This trend knows no color bounds. A great example can be found from an April 26, 2014 Case collector estate auction for Vernon Althoff in Manchester, Iowa.

PETE'S PICK

The unique 1966 Case 930 Western Special pictured here sold for $18,000, exactly doubling the previous record high auction sale price I'd seen on a Case 930. The previous record, which was $9,000, was from a March 23, 2013 Polk Auction antique consignment sale in northeast Indiana.

Case

Model	Year	Hours	Condition	Price	Date	Area	Comments
400	1956		G	$4,250	7/22/2011	SEMN	Diesel, WF, 1 hyd., PTO, power steering, Eagle hitch
400	1957		F	$1,000	12/4/2010	SEWY	SF, gas, 3 pt., Farmhand 5-11
400			F	$3,700	11/19/2013	WCMI	Loader, gas, 3 pt., live PTO, WF, power steering, bale spear mounted to bucket, 14.9x28 rear tires
400			G	$2,860	8/26/2013	NWWI	Gas, live power, hyd., fair tires, Schwartz loader
400			G	$3,100	3/23/2013	NEIN	Diesel, weights, runs, standard
430	1965		G	$5,500	4/26/2014	NEIA	
430			G	$2,500	12/17/2011	SEFL	No title
430			G	$3,700	9/23/2010	SWWI	Diesel
430			G	$1,600	4/10/2010	ECON	Loader
440	1964		G	$1,600	7/25/2013	WCSK	2WD, front-end loader, 33 PTO hp, running, 1 hyd., 540 PTO, 13x24 rear
470	1970	567	G	$14,750	6/29/2011	NEND	Low profile utility tractor, PTO, 2 hyd., new 14.9x28 rear tires
530	1962	2,458	G	$1,600	9/22/2010	NECO	WF, 3 pt.
530	1964	1,213	F	$1,700	11/12/2010	ECIL	Utility, hyd. loader
530	1966	6,726	G	$4,300	6/13/2012	Online	*BigIron.com,* item in Nebraska, 6' loader, 4 speed manual, 4 cyl. gas, 540 PTO, Construction King, torque converter, live power, 6' box scraper, ripper teeth
530			G	$3,000	2/22/2014	ECMI	Construction King Tractor, loader, backhoe, gas
530			G	$900	1/4/2014	WCNY	Fender tractor, loader frame, no bucket
530		3,709	G	$4,500	8/27/2013	NCWI	Construction King, WF, 3 pt., counterweight, Case #32 all hyd. loader, rear weights, like new 14.9x28 rears, repaint, 1,000 hours on rebuilt engine and clutch, SN 8264121
530			F	$5,500	3/9/2013	SWMN	Backhoe loader, shuttle transmission, needs work, gas
530			F	$2,500	2/6/2013	Online	Item in Illinois, Construction King, 3 pt., loader
530			G	$2,300	11/24/2012	WCIL	Gas
530		2,839	G	$950	3/30/2012	SEND	Gas, 3 pt., Case 41 hyd. level Construction King loader, forks
530			G	$3,500	3/1/2012	NWTX	
530			F	$1,100	6/22/2011	Online	*BigIron.com,* item in Nebraska, 4 speed, 4 cyl. gas, does not run, Case 32 loader, 6' bucket
530			G	$1,350	5/1/2010	SENE	Loader
530			G	$3,250	2/6/2010	ECIA	Gas, WF
600			F	$1,025	7/9/2013	Online	*IQBID.com,* gas, 1 hyd., 3 pt., 540 PTO, power steering, Case-O-Matic drive
600			G	$900	3/24/2012	SWMI	Case-O-Matic, NF, gas, 13.9x36 rear tires
600			G	$3,001	6/23/2010	Online	*BigIron.com,* item in Colorado, runs, diesel, power steering, PTO, hyd., 6 speed
600			G	$1,350	6/11/2010	SEAB	Diesel, dual hyd., live 540 PTO, power steering, Allied loader

TRACTORS

Case

Model	Year	Hours	Condition	Price	Date	Area	Comments
630			E	$3,700	6/13/2012	SWOH	WF, gas
630			G	$1,200	8/11/2010	ECMN	2WD, WF
700			G	$12,500	6/9/2012	ECNE	Diesel, high crop, power steering, original, runs, Eagle hitch, 1 of 13
730	1963		P	$900	5/18/2011	SEWY	WF, dual 345 loader, gas
730	1963		G	$4,250	3/20/2010	NWIA	Case-O-Matic reverse tractor, Westendorf 30 loader, one owner
730	1964		G	$1,850	3/23/2011	ECMN	Comfort King, Draft-O-Matic, WF, 3 pt., 2 hyd.
730	1965	2,702	G	$1,850	5/23/2012	Online	*BigIron.com,* item in Wyoming, Comfort King, 4 cyl. gas, 2 hyd., 540 PTO, Great Bend 800 loader, wheel weights, seat cushion missing, 3 pt. does not work
730	1967		G	$4,500	3/14/2012	WCNE	Gas, Comfort King, 16.9x34 rubber, with fluid and weights, 56 hp, 3 pt., live PTO, complete OH
730			G	$2,050	3/22/2014	ECSD	Diesel, low tin, good rubber
730			G	$1,950	8/8/2013	WCMN	Gas, WF, dual range drive, 1 hyd., PTO, second owner
730		5,136	G	$2,850	4/17/2013	Online	*BigIron.com,* item in Nebraska, Hi/Lo 8F/2R transmission, 4 cyl. gas
730			G	$4,600	3/9/2013	WCPA	Diesel, WF, fender tractor
730		4,550	G	$3,200	3/8/2013	SWMN	2WD, gas, 2 hyd., 3 pt., PTO, Du-Al 325 loader, 16.9x4 tires
730			G	$2,800	8/21/2012	WCIL	
730			G	$3,900	12/1/2011	WCMN	3 pt., 2 hyd., 540 PTO, low hour, estate tractor
730			G	$2,900	3/19/2011	NCPA	
730			F	$2,000	5/26/2010	ECSD	Comfort King, 3 pt., runs
730			G	$2,300	5/26/2010	ECSD	CK
730			G	$1,600	5/1/2010	NCOH	Orchard, excellent tires, full dress
741	1961		G	$1,155	7/28/2010	Online	*PurpleWave.com,* item in Kansas, 4 cyl. 58 hp gas, 8 speed, 540 PTO, 1 hyd.
770		4,493	G	$4,200	1/9/2013	Online	*BigIron.com,* item in Nebraska, 257 cu. in. diesel, 540 PTO, no cab, 3 pt., 2 hyd., started and ran
770			F	$3,500	4/8/2011	NEKS	Loader
800	1959		G	$2,100	4/1/2011	NCMN	Diesel, Case-O-Matic, new rubber
800	1959		G	$2,000	3/1/2011	SCNE	15.5x38 rear tires, 9.5Lx15 front tires, 1 hyd., 3 pt., 4 sets of rear weights, Du-Al loader, bucket, grapple fork, SN 8144650
800			G	$1,450	2/6/2013	SESD	
800			F	$900	12/13/2012	WCIA	One-way hyd., trip bucket, replaced hyd. pump, lights don't work, hyd. problem, Allis-Chalmers loader, SN 8122236
800			G	$2,000	8/11/2010	ECMN	NF, Case-O-Matic, PTO
800			G	$1,000	5/26/2010	ECSD	Standard
830	1963	2,140	G	$2,750	2/12/2013	WCIL	

Case

Model	Year	Hours	Condition	Price	Date	Area	Comments
830	1964		G	$1,500	5/5/2012	SWSK	2WD, New Idea 503 front-end loader, 64 PTO hp, standard
830	1964	5,323	G	$5,250	9/1/2011	WCMN	High crop, diesel, 3 pt., PTO, 1 hyd., fenders, original unrestored
830	1965	6,000	F	$5,000	6/10/2013	WCSK	Open station, 2WD, diesel, 70 series front-end loader, 65 PTO hp, standard, 2 hyd.
830	1966		G	$1,175	5/5/2011	ECNE	Case-O-Matic, gas, 8F/2R speed, newer hyd. pump, newer radiator, newer alternator, rebuilt engine
830	1966		G	$4,500	4/1/2011	NCMN	Diesel, 3 pt., 2 hyd.
830	1966		G	$5,600	4/17/2010	ECNE	Comfort King, Case-O-Matic, 2 hyd., 3 pt., WF, Koyker K5 loader
830	1967		G	$4,700	6/17/2011	WCSK	Comfort King, 2WD, 64 PTO, PS, 2 hyd., belt pulley, 3 rib front, new battery
830	1968		G	$4,250	10/14/2013	WCSK	2WD, Leach front-end loader, 64 PTO hp diesel, add on 3 pt., 18.4x34 rubber, 6' bucket
830	1969		G	$2,250	3/22/2013	WCMI	Comfort King, 4 cyl. gas, WF, 3 pt., PTO, power steering, dual hyd., 2 front weights, 18.4x24 rear tires
830			G	$1,700	12/20/2013	SCSD	Comfort King
830		1,204	G	$1,200	8/15/2013	ECMN	Comfort King, WF, Schwartz 1400 loader, trip manure bucket, not running, loader
830			G	$3,000	3/22/2013	NWMN	Gas, original, WF, weights, 3 pt., fenders, runs
830			P	$800	8/21/2012	SENE	WF, diesel
830			G	$3,600	6/9/2012	ECNE	Diesel, Comfort King, Case-O-Matic, 3 pt., PTO, hyd.
830			G	$3,250	3/24/2012	SWMI	Comfort King, 4 cyl. gas, 540 PTO, 3 pt., 2 hyd., WF, 18.4x34 rear tires
830			G	$3,200	12/22/2011	Online	*IQBID.com,* NF, 3 pt., PTO, belt pulley
830			G	$3,000	8/16/2011	Online	*BidNow.com,* Case-O-Matic, WF, hyd., PTO, 3 pt., 7.5Lx15 tires
830			G	$1,500	7/27/2011	ECND	Standard
830			G	$2,500	5/7/2011	SWMB	Loader
830		3,252	G	$3,000	12/17/2010	WCIL	Comfort King, gas, 18.4x34 tires, 2 hyd., 540 PTO
830			G	$4,250	12/8/2010	ECND	3 pt., PTO, 2 hyd.
830			G	$2,300	10/6/2010	WCSD	Row crop
830			F	$1,000	5/26/2010	ECSD	Comfort King, 3 pt., engine stuck
831	1963		G	$1,710	5/23/2012	Online	*BigIron.com,* item in South Dakota, 4 speed Case-O-Matic, 4 cyl. diesel, 1 hyd., 540 PTO, Eagle hitch, runs, shedded
841	1964	2,742	G	$1,900	8/22/2012	Online	*BigIron.com,* item in Nebraska, 8 speed manual, 284 cu. in. gas, 63 PTO hp, 540 PTO, 1 dual hyd., Eagle claw 3 pt., power steering, WF axle
870	1973		G	$5,250	11/19/2011	SEIA	Cab

Case

Model	Year	Hours	Condition	Price	Date	Area	Comments
870	1974		G	$5,550	4/12/2014	SEKS	4 cyl. diesel, PS, tilt wheel, power steering, WF, 3 pt., dual hyd., console control, 540/1,000 PTO, 70 PTO hp, 18.4x34 tires like-new, 490 hours on complete engine OH
870			G	$3,750	12/28/2013	NEWI	No cab
870		108	G	$2,500	8/15/2013	ECMN	Agri King, cab, WF, needs work
870		2,874	G	$3,025	11/19/2011	SEIA	Diesel, PS, 16.9x38 tires, 2 hyd.
870			G	$2,500	3/19/2011	SEIA	Diesel
870			G	$5,000	1/29/2011	ECMO	Top link loader
900	1957		G	$2,300	7/22/2011	SEMN	Diesel, power steering, 2 hyd., belt pulley, Rice tires, rear weights, 23.1x26 rear tires
900	1958		G	$2,200	10/7/2011	NWSD	PTO, hyd., WF
900	1959	6,023	G	$1,600	12/4/2013	ECND	WF, 2 hyd., fenders, not running
900			G	$1,000	9/12/2013	SEIA	Case 70 loader, 540 PTO, LP, does not run, 23.1x26 rear tires, 7.50x18 fronts
900B		1,059	G	$1,155	7/25/2012	Online	*PurpleWave.com,* item in Kansas, 6 cyl. diesel, manual, hand clutch, spring ride seat, 540 PTO, drawbar, rear weights
900B		5,861	G	$1,485	12/7/2011	Online	*PurpleWave.com,* item in Kansas, 6 cyl. diesel, hand clutch, spring ride seat, F11B loader, 540 PTO
900B		2,144	P	$1,100	6/22/2011	Online	*BigIron.com,* item in Nebraska, Wheatland, 6 speed, 6 cyl. diesel, does not run, wheel weights, engine bad
930	1961	636	G	$1,265	10/30/2013	Online	*PurpleWave.com,* item in Kansas, Case 6 cyl. diesel, 80 hp, 6 speed, drawbar
930	1961		G	$4,200	10/7/2011	NWSD	Diesel, PTO, hyd., WF, never restored
930	1962	6,134	G	$2,400	5/9/2012	Online	*BigIron.com,* item in Colorado, 6 speed, 6 cyl. diesel, 90 hp, 1 hyd., 540 PTO, hand clutch, water cooler, tinted front window
930	1963		G	$4,000	9/28/2013	NCKS	Diesel, 3 pt., 540 PTO
930	1963		F	$3,800	5/31/2013	SWSK	2WD, Case front-end loader, 81 PTO hp diesel, dual hyd., newer 18.4x34 tires, rear weights
930	1964		G	$2,200	12/1/2012	NWIL	2,300 hours showing, diesel, WF, good tires
930	1964		G	$2,200	11/17/2010	WCKS	3 pt., PTO, Great Bend 900 scoop, non-running
930	1965	6,378	G	$1,800	1/16/2013	SENE	*AuctionTime.com,* item in Indiana, 80 hp, 2WD, SN 8265067
930	1965		G	$4,450	12/3/2011	NWIL	Comfort King, open station, Draft-O-Matic., WF, fenders, 3 pt., 540 PTO, new batteries
930	1965		G	$1,650	5/26/2010	Online	*PurpleWave.com,* item in Kansas, 6 cyl. diesel, 6F/1R, hand clutch, 2 hyd.
930	1966	5,438	G	$1,100	3/31/2012	SWSK	2WD, 80 hp diesel, standard, cab, 2 hyd., 540 PTO, 18.4x34 rubber
930	1966	2,235	G	$4,600	3/5/2011	WCIL	Diesel, WF, no cab, 3 pt., 2 hyd., 540 PTO

Case

Model	Year	Hours	Condition	Price	Date	Area	Comments
930	1966		G	$2,400	11/17/2010	WCKS	3 pt., PTO
930	1966		P	$600	10/2/2010	SESK	2WD, square fenders, 18.4x34 tires, not running, SN 8304036
930	1967	3,063	G	$3,600	5/29/2013	Online	*BigIron.com,* item in Kansas, 4 speed plus Hi/Lo, 6 cyl.
930	1967		G	$3,000	3/28/2012	ECND	Row crop, 3 pt., PTO, 2 hyd., dual 325 loader, grapple
930	1968		F	$1,100	2/12/2013	WCIL	Diesel, no brakes
930	1968		F	$3,300	11/6/2012	ECOK	Du-Al 340 loader, bale spike, bucket
930			G	$2,600	9/28/2013	SWMN	Diesel, cab, 18.4x34, 3 pt. hitch, Du-Al 320 loader
930			P	$950	5/22/2013	WCMN	Parts of project
930			G	$826	5/15/2013	Online	*BigIron.com,* item in Nebraska, Comfort King, unreadable hours, 6 speed
930			G	$2,200	5/8/2013	Online	*BigIron.com,* item in Nebraska, Comfort King Wheatland, 6 cyl., 540 PTO, 2WD
930			G	$2,000	3/23/2013	NEIN	LP, belt pulley, PTO, runs
930			G	$9,000	3/23/2013	NEIN	Diesel, STD, Comfort King, nice original, dual hyd., 23.1x30 tires, runs, PTO
930		6,559	G	$2,650	8/22/2012	ECMN	Good rubber, straight tin all around, new battery, circulating water heater pump
930		4,992	G	$1,705	8/15/2012	Online	*PurpleWave.com,* item in Kansas, Comfort King, 6 cyl. LP, manual, front-end loader, 3 pt., drawbar, 540 PTO, 2 hyd., rear weights
930		7,191	G	$3,250	8/8/2012	Online	*BigIron.com,* item in Nebraska, 2WD, 4 speed Hi/Lo, diesel, 2 hyd., 540 PTO, 3 pt.
930			G	$2,000	8/1/2012	NEOK	Cab, loader, spear
930			G	$3,750	6/16/2012	WCSD	Comfort King, one owner
930		4,024	G	$1,375	5/9/2012	Online	*PurpleWave.com,* item in Oklahoma, Wheatland, 6 cyl. diesel, 50 gal. tank, manual, 2 rear hyd.
930		5,939	G	$4,100	3/24/2012	NEIN	Gas, WF, 3 pt., front/rear weights, cab, PTO, hyd., runs
930		5,025	G	$8,800	3/24/2012	NEIN	Comfort King, diesel, 3 pt., hyd., front/rear weights, front/rear fenders, cab, original
930			G	$2,500	2/20/2012	WCWI	No front weights, Comfort King
930			G	$3,650	2/20/2012	WCWI	Front weights, Comfort King
930			G	$4,400	8/24/2011	ECMN	4 speed, 3 ranges, 3 pt.
930			G	$3,400	7/30/2011	ECMO	
930			G	$3,700	3/5/2011	SEMN	Comfort King, 2 hyd., 540 PTO, 3 pt., unknown hours, new clutch, bearings and pressure plate
930		5,779	G	$2,600	12/2/2010	ECWY	Comfort King, WF, cab, 3 pt., diesel
930			F	$2,250	11/18/2010	SEOK	
930			G	$3,500	7/29/2010	WCMN	Comfort King, good rubber, 540 PTO, 3 pt., 2 hyd., quick attach
930			F	$900	6/5/2010	SEMN	Diesel, WF

Case

Model	Year	Hours	Condition	Price	Date	Area	Comments
930		3,759	F	$2,310	5/26/2010	Online	*PurpleWave.com,* item in Kansas, Case 6 cyl. diesel, 2 reverse gears, 540 PTO, missing third linkage, canopy
930			F	$1,900	3/6/2010	SEMN	Cracked glass in cab, 3 pt. 18.4x34 rear almost new
950	1964		G	$800	4/25/2012	Online	*BigIron.com,* item in Nebraska, 6 speed, 377 cu. in. LP, 71 hp gas, 2 hyd., Wheatland drawbar
970	1971	4,326	P	$4,700	11/13/2012	WCNE	Rough, SN 868480, PS, 18.4x34 tires 90%, good front tires, 3 pt., 2 hyd., PTO, rear weights
970	1971	7,635	G	$6,000	4/20/2011	WCSK	2WD, Leon front-end loader, 93 PTO hp, PS, dual hyd., 7' bucket
970	1972	1,051	G	$4,733	5/9/2012	Online	*BigIron.com,* item in Nebraska, diesel, 14.9x38 rear tires, 11Lx15SL front tires
970	1972	7,972	G	$5,000	4/13/2011	Online	*BigIron.com,* item in Nebraska, 6 cyl. 401 cu. in. diesel, 90 hp, 2 hyd., 540 PTO, 3 pt., WF, engine tank heater, started, ran, moved forward and reverse
970	1973	7,141	G	$6,500	6/21/2013	ECAB	2WD, Case front-end loader, 86 PTO hp, partial PS, dual PTO, 2 hyd., 18.4x38 rear, new 4 rib front rubber
970	1973		F	$2,950	6/13/2012	SWOH	Diesel, WF, 2 hyd.
970	1973	7,589	G	$9,000	6/14/2011	WCSK	2WD, Leon 707 front-end loader, 86 PTO hp, diesel, PS, dual PTO, 2 hyd., 4 rib front, 6' bucket
970	1974	8,761	F	$4,800	6/11/2013	SWSK	2WD, Allied 795 front-end loader, 93 PTO hp, PS, dual PTO, 2 hyd., 18.4x38 rear, 7' bucket
970	1974		F	$7,750	4/9/2013	SWSK	2WD, 86 PTO hp, standard, 2 hyd., 18.4x38 rear, 3 rib front
970	1976	5,875	G	$7,000	12/10/2010	NWMO	2WD, 18.4x34, 2 hyd., air not cold, #70 loader, bale spike
970	1976		G	$7,500	3/31/2010	ECND	Cab, air, heat, PS, 2 hyd., 3 pt., PTO, Du-Al 340 loader, 84" bucket
970	1978	6,833	G	$4,750	10/17/2013	SWSK	2WD, 85 PTO hp, 12F/4R partial PS, dual PTO, 2 hyd., 18.4x38 singles, 3 rib front
970		4,735	G	$6,500	3/15/2014	WCIL	Diesel, open station, 2 hyd., 540 PTO, 3 pt., 18.4x38 rear tires
970			G	$2,900	12/20/2013	SCSD	Cab, PS
970			G	$3,700	12/20/2013	SCSD	Cab, air, PS, Du-Al 3100 loader
970		6,686	G	$10,000	11/20/2013	NWNE	8' Koyker K5 loader, 4 tine grapple, 3 pt., 16.9x38 duals
970			G	$3,300	10/18/2012	WCMI	Cab, PS, 2 hyd.
970			G	$2,900	9/13/2012	Online	*IQBID.com,* item in Iowa, 18.4x38, 540 PTO, 2 hyd., new batteries and starter, motor is good
970		5,224	G	$4,600	8/13/2012	ECIL	Diesel, cab, air, quick hitch, 2 hyd., one owner
970		1,950	G	$4,600	5/23/2012	Online	*BigIron.com,* item in Kansas, PS, 6 cyl. diesel, 90 hp, 2 hyd., PTO, loader

Case

Model	Year	Hours	Condition	Price	Date	Area	Comments
970			P	$1,500	4/26/2012	WCSK	2WD, 93 PTO hp, PS, 2 hyd., PTO, 18.4-38 rear, needs work
970			G	$4,500	3/24/2012	SWMI	Agri King, cab, 3 pt., dual hyd., 540/1,000 PTO, 18.4x34 rear tires
970		5,300	G	$6,700	3/24/2012	NEIN	One owner, original, runs
970		9,300	G	$3,200	3/21/2012	ECMN	Duals, loader, 14.9x38, 3 pt., quick hitch, 540/1,000 PTO, 2 hyd.
970			G	$8,000	2/20/2012	WCWI	Agri King, power steering, new clutch, weights
970		4,250	F	$4,000	12/1/2011	SEMN	Cab, PTO, 3 pt., diesel, rock box, Peterson duals
970			F	$1,750	9/16/2011	ECND	2WD, cab, PTO
970			G	$5,800	3/19/2011	NCPA	Cab
970		7,751	G	$3,700	3/18/2011	SWIL	2 hyd., dual PTO, Westendorf loader, QT, wobble stick, runs well
970			G	$2,850	12/18/2010	ECMI	
970		5,025	G	$8,500	7/29/2010	WCMN	Agri King, cab, 1070 motor w/ 1,000 hours, PTO, 3 pt., 2 hyd., cab, air, heat
970		7,740	G	$10,500	4/21/2010	SESK	2WD, Leon 650 loader, 3 hyd., PS
990	1976	2,322	G	$5,250	7/31/2013	ECND	2 hyd., 3 pt., 540/1,000 PTO, 6' bucket, cab
990			G	$1,900	6/8/2013	NEND	Adj. front, PTO, 3 pt., front weights, 540/1,000 PTO
995	1975	3,743	G	$6,000	4/16/2012	SCSK	2WD, Case IH front-end loader, 3 pt., 540 PTO, 2 hyd., 16.9x30 rear, 3 rib front, 5' bucket
1030	1967	4,557	G	$1,900	3/15/2014	WCIL	Diesel, cab, 2 hyd., 540 PTO, 3 pt., 18.4x38 rear tires
1030	1968	3,067	G	$1,400	12/4/2010	SEWY	WF, diesel, 3 pt.
1030	1969	2,450	G	$3,500	7/31/2013	ECND	2 hyd., 3 pt., 1,000 PTO
1030			G	$3,200	12/20/2013	SCSD	Wheatland, rebuilt engine
1030			G	$2,200	5/8/2013	Online	*BigIron.com,* item in Nebraska, 540 PTO
1030			G	$6,000	3/23/2013	NEIN	Diesel, standard, original, runs
1030			G	$6,500	2/7/2013	NEIN	Comfort King, year round cab, 24.5x32 rear tires, 2 hyd.
1030		3,027	G	$6,500	2/7/2013	NEIN	Western Special, cab, 24.5x32
1030		3,819	G	$2,600	1/28/2012	ECMO	
1030			G	$4,000	12/9/2011	SWKY	
1030		1,799	G	$3,000	8/11/2011	WCMN	Diesel, 2 hyd., 3 pt., PTO, rock box, duals
1030			G	$1,500	5/7/2011	SWMB	2WD, cab, blade
1030			G	$1,200	11/18/2010	SEOK	Cab
1030		4,535	F	$805	6/23/2010	Online	*BigIron.com,*item in Nebraska, 6 cyl. diesel engine, rear tires 23.1x30 rice, front tires 10x16, 540 PTO, ran when parked, middle of restoration, bad seat, some glass in cab broken
1070	1971	6,210	G	$5,900	8/29/2013	NWIA	Cab, heat, PS, 3 hyd., 3 pt., 540 PTO, front weights, 18.4x38 band duals
1070	1971	7,500	G	$6,000	4/1/2011	NCMN	PS, Koyker loader, 4 tine grapple

Case

Model	Year	Hours	Condition	Price	Date	Area	Comments
1070	1972	4,394	G	$5,250	1/25/2014	WCIN	Cab, PS, 2 hyd., front weights, less than 350 hours on major OH
1070	1972	10,220	G	$4,800	2/6/2013	SESD	Engine OH about 6,000 hours ago
1070	1972	11,754	G	$5,700	10/27/2011	NWND	One owner, recent repairs, cab, heat, PS, 540/1,000 PTO, 2 hyd., 18.4x38 tires
1070	1972	5,653	G	$2,250	7/22/2010	ECND	2 hyd., 3 pt., 540 PTO
1070	1973	9,505	F	$6,250	6/21/2013	ECAB	2WD, 101 PTO hp, Case 6 cyl. diesel, partial PS, dual PTO, 2 hyd., 23.1x34 rear, 3 rib front
1070	1974	7,854	G	$5,050	4/12/2014	SEKS	6 cyl. diesel, PS, cab, radio, tilt wheel, WF, 3 pt., dual hyd., console control, 540/1,000 PTO, 107 PTO hp, 18.4x38 rubber, clamp-on dual hubs, 7' Hi-Master quick detach loader
1070	1974	7,952	G	$7,000	4/25/2013	SWSK	2WD, 85 drawbar hp, 8F/2R, dual PTO, 18.4x38 singles
1070	1974	5,260	G	$5,650	2/21/2012	Online	*IQBID.com* dealer sale, 2WD, 12 speed, 2 hyd., 3 pt., quick hitch, 540/1,000 PTO, 18.4x38 rears, 11x16 fronts
1070	1974	3,801	G	$2,850	4/13/2011	Online	*BigIron.com,* item in Texas, diesel, 2 hyd., 1,000 PTO
1070	1974	8,833	F	$2,200	12/4/2010	SEWY	WF, diesel, Case loader, 7' bucket
1070	1975	5,708	G	$10,750	2/15/2012	Online	2WD, Koyker K5 loader, 12 speed PS, 451 diesel, 120 hp, duals, 540 PTO, cab, heat, air
1070	1975	9,330	G	$5,750	12/17/2010	WCIL	PS, 2 hyd., 18.4x34 and 10x16 tires, duals, 540/1,000 PTO
1070	1975	9,145	G	$5,500	4/19/2010	SCMB	Canadian, 3 pt., duals, 2 hyd., dual PTO
1070	1976	12,000	F	$4,750	6/20/2013	ECSK	2WD, Case 70 front-end loader, 6' bucket, 101 PTO hp, 2 hyd., 20.8x34 rear, 11x16 SF, PS weak
1070	1976	7,955	F	$3,600	4/4/2011	SWSK	2WD, 100 PTO hp, dual hyd. and PTO, snap on duals
1070	1977	8,428	G	$4,550	3/5/2014	Online	*BigIron.com,* item in Nebraska, 12F/4R PS, diesel, 2 hyd., 3 pt., drawbar, 540/1,000 PTO, new batteries, new block heater
1070	1977	9,094	F	$6,900	4/11/2013	WCSK	2WD, Case 90 series front-end loader, 101 PTO hp, PS, dual PTO, 2 hyd., 23.1x34 rear tires, 4 rib front, front end loader w/ bucket, complete engine OH at 8,000 hours
1070	1977	7,773	G	$10,500	5/4/2011	WCSK	2WD, 108 PTO hp, PS, 2 hyd., dual PTO, 4 rib front
1070	1977	5,300	G	$5,026	4/13/2011	Online	*BigIron.com,* item in Nebraska, 4 range PS, 2290 Case 504 turbo diesel, 2 hyd., 540/1,000 PTO, 3 pt., new tach 2002, tank engine heater, heat, air
1070	1977	9,200	G	$4,500	4/19/2010	SCMB	Canadian, loader, duals, 2 hyd., dual PTO

Case

Model	Year	Hours	Condition	Price	Date	Area	Comments
1070	1978	7,922	F	$4,500	6/20/2013	ECSK	2WD, Case 70 front-end loader, 6' bucket, 101 hp PTO, 85 hp drawbar, 2 hyd., 18.4x34 rear, 11x6 SF, PS weak
1070	1978	7,612	G	$8,500	5/5/2012	SWSK	2WD, Ezee-On front-end loader, 108 PTO hp, PS, 2 hyd., 18.4-33 rear, 11x16 front
1070	1978		G	$5,300	5/26/2010	ECSD	Westendorf WL40 loader
1070	5800	3,690	G	$1,977	3/14/2012	ECND	PS, 3 hyd., 3 pt., PTO, 18.4x34 rear tires
1070			G	$1,900	3/26/2014	ECMS	
1070		7,000	G	$6,000	1/1/2014	SWOH	Cab, duals
1070			F	$1,250	12/20/2013	SCSD	Transmission problems, 18.4x34
1070			G	$2,750	12/20/2013	SCSD	Demonstrator
1070		5,513	G	$3,700	12/18/2013	Online	*BigIron.com,* Agri King, 2 hyd., 3 pt. drawbar
1070		8,320	G	$3,300	9/25/2013	SEMN	SN 8657797
1070		409	G	$2,530	8/28/2013	Online	*PurpleWave.com,* item in Missouri, 451 cu. in. 6 cyl. diesel, PS, cab, heat, front/rear lights, 3 pt., drawbar, 2 rear hyd., 10x16 front tires, 18.4x34 rear tires
1070		3,628	F	$3,500	8/24/2013	NWIL	2 hyd., cab, 18.4x34 rear tires, one brake hangs up, shift linkage loose, air does not work
1070		8,108	G	$3,601	6/12/2013	Online	*BigIron.com,* item in South Dakota, 12F/4R, 6 cyl. diesel
1070			F	$2,750	4/16/2013	SESK	2WD, Fabco rotary front-mounted snowblower, 108 PTO hp, PS, 2 hyd., PTO, 23.1x30 rear
1070			G	$5,900	3/9/2013	WCPA	Open station, WF, standard
1070		5,913	G	$9,500	12/8/2012	ECIA	Agri King diesel, factory cab with air, needs recharged, 3 pt., 18.4x38, has new battery and alternator
1070			G	$2,700	11/28/2012	ECND	12 speed, 3 hyd., 540/1,000 PTO
1070			G	$5,100	8/22/2012	Online	*BigIron.com,* item in Nebraska, loader, PS, diesel, grapple, 2 hyd., Fasse valve for loader
1070		6,762	G	$8,200	8/22/2012	Online	*BigIron.com,* item in Kansas, partial PS, 6 cyl. diesel, 90 hp, 2 hyd., 540/1,000 PTO, 4 speed ranges, 3 PS gears in each range, 3 pt.
1070		4,160	G	$6,100	8/13/2012	ECIL	Fender tractor, 18.4x34 tires, front and rear weights, one owner
1070			G	$7,600	4/23/2012	WCSK	2WD, 100 hp, dual PTO, PS, 20.8x38 rear rubber, dual hyd., not used in past 6 years
1070			F	$4,000	4/7/2012	SCOK	
1070			G	$2,400	3/24/2012	SEMN	Duals, rock box, 3 pt., quick attach
1070		4,375	G	$6,500	3/24/2012	NEIN	3 pt., PTO, dual hyd., original, runs
1070		5,598	G	$3,250	12/22/2011	Online	*IQBID.com,* 2WD, cab, PS, 2 hyd., 540 PTO, rock box
1070		5,598	G	$6,100	12/22/2011	Online	*IQBID.com,* cab, PS, 3 pt., 540 PTO, 2 hyd., rock box

Case

Model	Year	Hours	Condition	Price	Date	Area	Comments
1070			G	$3,350	12/15/2011	WCIL	Agri King, fully equipped cab, 18.4x34 rear tires, 2 hyd., 540 PTO
1070		7,677	G	$2,300	11/9/2011	Online	*BigIron.com,* item in Montana, 2WD, 12F 3 speed PS, 451 cu. in., 6 cyl. diesel, 108 hp, 1 hyd., 540 PTO, tilt wheel
1070			G	$2,500	9/14/2011	Online	*BigIron.com,* item in Colorado, loader, 6 cyl. diesel, parts, 5072 Du-al loader, 8' bucket, 3 pt.
1070		4,100	G	$5,750	4/23/2011	SESK	2WD, 12 speed, dual speed PTO, dual hyd., cab, air, heat, rear single tires,
1070		201	G	$9,127	3/23/2011	Online	*BigIron.com,* item in Nebraska, Du-Al 3100 loader, quick attach 8' bucket, 3 speed, PS, 6 cyl. diesel, 2 hyd., 540 and 1,000 PTO, cab, WF, 3 pt. hitch, engine block heater
1170		9,972	F	$2,300	4/3/2013	Online	*BigIron.com,* item in Nebraska, 18.4x38 rear tires, 11x16 front tires, 2 hyd., 540 PTO, engine has a miss, new batteries
1170		1,471	F	$6,000	2/9/2013	SWOH	Duals, weights
1170			P	$2,300	1/31/2012	NEIN	Not running
1170			P	$1,100	9/3/2010	NEIN	Cab, dead row, needs work and may not run or drive, as is
1175	1973	5,743	G	$3,500	8/20/2013	WCIL	Diesel, 2 hyd., 1,000 PTO, 20.8x38 tires
1175	1973	4,106	G	$4,500	7/22/2010	ECND	2 hyd., 3 pt., 540 PTO, Du-Al 3100 loader
1175	1974	11,986	G	$7,600	4/30/2013	WCSK	2WD, 125 PTO hp, 2 hyd., PTO, standard, 18.4x38 rear, 3 rib front
1175	1974	3,870	G	$12,750	4/23/2012	WCSK	2WD, 125 hp PTO, standard, 2 hyd., dual PTO, 10.8x38 near new, new rib front
1175	1977	3,185	G	$6,000	8/14/2010	NCIL	Diesel, cab, air, heat, 18.4x38 tires
1175			G	$3,500	11/20/2013	SESD	Cab, air, heat, 3 pt., duals
1175		2,041	G	$5,170	10/16/2013	Online	*PurpleWave.com,* item in Kansas, 6 cyl. diesel, PS, 540 PTO, drawbar
1175		5,508	F	$2,505	7/9/2013	Online	*IQBID.com,* 2 hyd., 3 pt., 540/1,000 PTO
1175			G	$8,400	2/20/2012	WCWI	Agri King, new clutch and hyd. pump
1175			F	$2,500	3/1/2011	NCKS	Open station
1175		4,109	G	$6,750	10/30/2010	WCOH	Cab, air, heat, diesel, new rear rubber, duals
1200			F	$2,500	8/6/2011	WCIL	4WD, 3 pt., 220 Cummins, diesel
1210		4,339	G	$1,650	8/28/2013	Online	*PurpleWave.com,* item in Missouri, 4 cyl. diesel, manual, 3 pt., 1 hyd., 265/75Rx16 front tires, 18.4x30 . rear tires
1210		5,461	G	$3,650	8/7/2013	Online	*IQBID.com,* open station, PS, diesel, 2 hyd., 3 pt., 540/1,000 PTO, quick attach loader, grapple forks, 18.4x30 rear tires, less than 200 hours on major OH
1210		1,771	G	$4,000	4/29/2011	NEOH	Case David Brown 1210

Case

Model	Year	Hours	Condition	Price	Date	Area	Comments
1210		4,468	F	$4,000	5/21/2010	Online	*IronPlanet.com,* item in Oregon, open operator station, 4 cyl. manual, 11Lx15SL front tires, 18.4-30 rear tires, shift, 3 pt., drawbar, 55" Hedge-master mower, 78" stick, 110" boom
1270	1972	8,220	G	$3,700	12/30/2010	ECMN	Cab, 4 hyd., 3 pt., 1,000 PTO
1270	1973		G	$2,805	5/9/2012	Online	*BigIron.com,* item in Nebraska, 12F/4R, 451 cu. in. turbo, 6 cyl. diesel, 109 drawbar, 127 hp PTO, 2 hyd., 1,000 PTO, cab, 3 pt., hour meter not working
1270	1973		G	$3,750	4/23/2012	WCSK	2WD, 2 hyd., PTO 1,000, 18.4x38 duals, PS 12/3
1270	1974		G	$7,000	12/1/2010	ECND	12 speed PS, 4 hyd., 3 pt., 540/1,000 PTO, 18.4x38 hub duals
1270			G	$3,500	8/24/2013	SEMN	Cab, 3 pt., dual hyd. PTO, 18.4x38
1270		8,600	G	$2,750	6/7/2013	NESD	Cab, 3 pt., PTO
1270		5,000	G	$1,900	2/23/2013	ECMI	WF, 3 pt., PTO, 2 hyd., no cab, 18.4x38 rear tires
1270			G	$4,900	6/30/2012	SESK	Diesel, cab, air, PS, dual hyd., PTO, 3-year-old tires
1270			G	$5,500	7/27/2011	ECND	PS, 2 hyd., 3 pt., 1,000 PTO, hub duals
1270		4,852	F	$2,500	5/11/2011	Online	*BigIron.com,* synchro transmission, 6 cyl. diesel, 2 hyd., 1,000 PTO, CAT III 3 pt. hitch, glass missing from rear window
1370	1972	4,626	G	$1,760	5/30/2012	Online	*PurpleWave.com,* item in Kansas, 6 cyl., 504 turbo engine locked up, PS, 2 rear hyd.
1370	1972		F	$2,700	8/27/2011	WCIL	Diesel, duals, weights
1370	1973	3,508	G	$4,700	2/12/2013	WCIL	20.8x38 rear tires, 4 hyd., 1,000 PTO
1370	1973		F	$3,250	11/30/2011	SEMN	20.8x38 tires
1370	1973	7,454	G	$4,500	3/19/2011	SEWY	WF, diesel, 3 pt., front weights
1370	1974	8,300	F	$4,800	3/14/2012	ECND	3 pt., PTO, Du-Al 400 loader, PTO pump
1370	1975	10,960	G	$6,901	8/6/2013	Online	*IQBID.com,* 155 hp, 12 speed PS, cab, air, 2 hyd., 3 pt., 1,000 PTO, Allied 895 loader, grapple
1370	1975	5,406	G	$6,650	6/5/2013	Online	*BigIron.com,* item in Iowa, PS 12F/3R, 6 cyl. turbo diesel
1370	1975	6,702	G	$3,500	11/6/2012	ECOK	Cab, air, PS, 3 pt. PTO
1370	1975	4,524	G	$6,800	8/22/2012	Online	*BigIron.com,* item in Colorado, 2WD, partial PS, 6 cyl. diesel, 130 hp, 2 hyd., 1,000 PTO, Allied 790 loader, 7' bucket
1370	1975	8,149	G	$4,000	12/7/2010	SEIA	Fully equipped cab, 20.8Rx38 rear tires, clamp-on duals, 11x16SL front tires, 2 hyd., 1,000 PTO, 3 pt.
1370	1976	7,896	G	$6,000	6/27/2012	NCND	3 speed PS, 4 hyd., 3 pt., 1,000 PTO, rock box, 20.8x38 band duals, long axle
1370	1976	3,498	G	$12,000	4/27/2012	ECSK	2WD, Leon 808 front-end loader, 155 hp PTO, 12 speed PS, 1,000 PTO, 2 hyd., 20.8x38 rear tires, 4 rib front tires, 8' bucket

Case

Model	Year	Hours	Condition	Price	Date	Area	Comments
1370	1976	6,607	G	$5,600	12/17/2010	WCIL	20.8-38 tires, 2 hyd., 1,000 PTO, duals
1370	1977	6,377	G	$3,400	2/22/2014	ECMI	Diesel, 3 pt., PTO, quick hitch, cab, 20.8x38 rear duals
1370	1977		G	$4,100	2/13/2014	SWMI	Cab, loader attachment, 3 pt., PTO, rear duals
1370	1977	8,291	G	$7,000	12/27/2012	NCIA	2 hyd., 3 pt., PTO, 18.4Rx42 tires, extra front lights, air converted to 134, SN 8818077
1370	1978	4,260	G	$3,500	1/16/2013	SENE	*AuctionTime.com,* item in Indiana, 130 hp, 2WD, SN 8833267
1370	1978	5,811	G	$7,920	8/15/2012	Online	*PurpleWave.com,* item in Kansas, 6 cyl. diesel, 160 hp, PS, air, heat, spring seat, 3 pt., drawbar, 1,000 PTO, dual rear hyd., exterior work lights, 86" wheelbase
1370	1978	5,585	G	$5,250	8/24/2011	SCMI	Cab, 20.8x38 axle duals, 3 pt., 2 hyd.
1370		1,663	G	$7,975	3/5/2014	Online	*BigIron.com,* item in Wyoming, 4 range 3 speed PS, 6 cyl., diesel, 2 hyd., dual hubs
1370			G	$5,100	2/26/2014	NCMO	Good tires
1370		6,600	G	$9,000	1/1/2014	SWOH	Duals 50%, cab, air, heat
1370			G	$1,600	12/20/2013	SCSD	Cab, good rubber, Du-Al 3150 loader
1370			G	$1,700	12/20/2013	SCSD	Cab, air, 1,000 PTO, 4 hyd., like new 20.8x38
1370			G	$2,800	12/20/2013	SCSD	Cab, air, PS, 1,000 PTO
1370			G	$5,500	12/20/2013	SCSD	Cab, air, PS
1370		6,431	G	$6,000	12/20/2013	SCSD	PTO, 2 hyd., loader, grapple
1370		9,760	G	$2,000	12/18/2013	Online	*BigIron.com,* PS, 2 hyd., hyd. drawbar, 3 pt., 1,000 PTO
1370			G	$4,000	12/5/2013	SCIA	
1370		9,799	G	$3,300	12/3/2013	NEND	12 speed, PS, 2 hyd., PTO, 20.8x38 dual tires
1370		4,252	P	$2,250	8/20/2013	WCIL	Diesel, cab, 2 hyd., 1,000 PTO, 18.4Rx38 tires, front weights, transmission out
1370		6,125	G	$2,000	7/10/2013	NCND	Cab, 2 hyd., 1,000 PTO, dual rear wheels
1370			G	$3,000	3/20/2013	SWMI	
1370			G	$6,150	3/9/2013	WCPA	Cab, WF, PS, new 18.4x38 rubber duals
1370		4,823	G	$2,750	12/13/2012	WCIA	12 speed, PS, 3 hyd., 1,000 PTO, 24.5x32 singles, SN 8750614
1370			G	$6,750	11/24/2012	WCIL	Loader
1370		5,900	G	$6,500	10/20/2012	ECIL	Cab, duals, 1,000 rpm, PTO, front weights, dual hyd.
1370		6,711	G	$3,000	8/16/2012	Online	*IQBID.com,* item in Minnesota, 2 hyd., 1,000 PTO, 20.8x38 band duals, 14Lx16.1 tires
1370			P	$3,750	6/3/2012	WCMN	Rough, Agri King, cab, PS, 3 pt., band duals, 2 hyd., 1,000 rpm PTO
1370		9,846	G	$2,750	5/30/2012	Online	*PurpleWave.com,* item in Kansas, 6 cyl., PS 12 speed

Case

Model	Year	Hours	Condition	Price	Date	Area	Comments
1370		8,438	G	$6,600	5/9/2012	Online	*BigIron.com,* item in Wyoming, 12 speed, 4 speed w/ 3 speed PS, 6 cyl. turbo diesel, 135 hp, 2 hyd., 1,000 w/ 540 adaptor PTO, 3 pt., link, swing drawbar, baler pan
1370		9,983	P	$2,000	3/14/2012	ECND	12 speed, PS, 2 hyd., 3 pt., PTO, 20.8x38 rear tires, 11x16 fronts, does not run
1370			G	$2,800	1/31/2012	NEIN	
1370		5,269	G	$4,750	12/22/2011	Online	*IQBID.com,* cab, air, heat, 3 pt., dual PTO, 2 hyd.
1370		5,310	G	$4,600	12/14/2011	WCMN	2WD, 18.4-38 duals, PS, 3 pt., PTO, 2 hyd.
1370			F	$2,000	12/9/2011	NENE	
1370		3,228	G	$3,300	11/9/2011	Online	*BigIron.com,* item in Nebraska, tach does not work, 6 cyl. diesel, 1,000 PTO, 2WD, two 12V batteries, inside wheel weights
1370			G	$6,000	3/25/2011	SCWA	
1370			G	$6,000	3/25/2011	SCWA	
1370		5,192	G	$5,500	1/29/2011	ECMO	3 pt., 1,000 PTO, 2 hyd., cab, air, heat, eyelets for duals, new turbo 1 year ago
1370		7,000	G	$4,500	12/17/2010	WCIL	Agri King, 18.4-38 duals, 2 hyd., 1,000 PTO, 1,000 hours on major OH, cab
1370		3,700	G	$3,600	11/27/2010	ECIA	Cab, air, heat, 3 pt., PTO, duals, weights
1370			F	$4,700	4/21/2010	SESK	2WD, PS, duals, 2 hyd., nice shape
1470	1970	8,343	G	$5,000	6/20/2012	SESD	4WD, 2 hyd., bareback, 18.4x34 tires, runs, original
1470	1972	11,000	G	$4,350	6/22/2011	Online	*BigIron.com,* item in Oklahoma, Traction King, 8F/2R, 504 diesel, 172 hp, 2 hyd., crab steer, air works, always shedded
1570	1976	6,153	G	$8,655	7/9/2013	Online	*IQBID.com,* Spirit of '76, PS, 3 pt., PTO, dual tires
1570	1977	9,039	G	$4,400	2/5/2014	SESD	2 hyd., 3 pt., PTO, PS, 280/85Rx38 duals
1570	1977		F	$4,000	5/24/2012	SCMI	Cab, 2 hyd., duals
1570			G	$4,250	9/28/2013	SWMN	3 pt. hitch, 20.8Rx38 tires SN 8830493
1570			G	$2,500	8/15/2013	ECMN	Cab, air, heat, PS, 4 hyd., 3 pt., PTO
1570		3,199	E	$12,000	8/13/2012	ECIL	One owner, 18.4x38 duals, quick hitch, front fenders
1570		4,080	G	$4,010	8/8/2012	Online	*BigIron.com,* item in Nebraska, PS, diesel, 2 hyd., 1,000 PTO, duals, 3 pt., heat, air not working, power steering has leak
1570			G	$3,200	8/24/2011	ECMN	
1570			G	$3,850	8/24/2011	ECMN	
1570		4,000	G	$4,200	7/30/2011	ECMO	
1570			G	$5,250	3/19/2011	NCPA	No cab

Case

Model	Year	Hours	Condition	Price	Date	Area	Comments
1570		4,204	F	$2,100	3/5/2010	NCMO	Cab, air, heat, 2 hyd., 3 pt., PS, good tires
2290	1978	6,096	G	$4,510	5/16/2012	Online	*PurpleWave.com,* item in Oklahoma, A504BDT diesel, manual, enclosed cab
2290	1978	8,098	F	$3,500	4/17/2010	ECNE	Cab, PS, 2 hyd., 3 pt.
2390	1978	5,390	G	$13,000	12/1/2011	ECND	PS, 3 pt., 1,000 PTO, 3 hyd., duals, rock box
2470	1973	4,371	F	$4,000	10/24/2012	NECO	Diesel, 4x4, 3 pt., duals, JD 10' bulldozer
2470	1974	8,190	F	$2,600	7/27/2011	ECND	Traction king
2470	1975	6,860	G	$2,250	6/13/2013	SEAB	4WD, 174 PTO hp, 12F/2R partial PS, 2 hyd., 20.8x34 singles
2470	1976	6,600	F	$14,000	6/10/2013	WCSK	4WD, 174 PTO hp, dual hyd., 1,000 PTO, Firestone 20.8x38 rear
2470	1976	5,145	G	$4,400	4/6/2011	Online	*PurpleWave.com,* item in Oklahoma, 4WD, 6 cyl. turbo diesel, 174 hp, range PS
2470	1976		G	$6,250	11/3/2010	NEND	4WD, cab, air, heat, PS, 2 hyd., 1,000 PTO, duals, one owner, recent engine work
2470	1977		F	$3,750	11/22/2011	NCMN	4WD, 2 hyd., 3 pt., PTO, duals
2470	1977		F	$4,800	4/1/2011	NCMN	4WD, 3 pt., PTO, 2 hyd., 18.4x34 rubber, factory duals
2470		5,876	G	$6,500	1/4/2014	ECOH	
2470		6,580	G	$2,700	12/4/2013	Online	*BigIron.com,* item in Nebraska, PS, 6 cyl. diesel, 18.4x34 rear tires, 18.4x34 front tires, 175 hp, 2 hyd., drawbar, duals all around
2470			F	$5,000	9/6/2013	ECSD	4WD, dozer blade, head gasket leaking
2470			G	$2,200	6/26/2013	Online	*BigIron.com,* item in Kansas, 4x4, 6 cyl., 4 hyd., drawbar, 3 pt.
2470		146	F	$7,260	10/10/2012	Online	*PurpleWave.com,* item in Kansas, 4WD, actual hours unknown, 6 cyl. diesel, replacement engine
2470		1,291	G	$3,700	5/23/2012	Online	*BigIron.com,* item in Kansas, 4WD, 12F/2R PS, diesel, 175 hp, 2 hyd., no PTO, cold assist starting, rear steering Leon dozer blade, runs
2470			G	$7,100	3/19/2011	NCPA	
2470			F	$3,700	3/16/2011	NWIA	Bald tires, rough, ran
2470			F	$4,500	11/26/2010	WCOH	3 pt., 500 hours on OH
2470		4,694	G	$2,500	3/18/2010	SEIN	4WD, Traction King, 3 pt., quick hitch, 2 hyd.
2670	1975		G	$4,250	7/31/2013	ECND	4 hyd., no 3 pt., 12' dozer, 20.8x34 duals, 1,000 hours on engine OH, 800 hours on PS OH
2670	1976	5,190	F	$4,100	3/8/2014	NEMO	4WD, 3 pt., 2 hyd., 1,000 hours on OH
2670	1976	4,903	G	$7,400	5/9/2012	Online	*BigIron.com,* item in Nebraska, 4x4, 4 range, 3 speed PS, diesel, 154 drawbar, 174 PTO hp, 2 hyd., 1,000 PTO, crab steer, duals, air, 12' Degelman dozer blade

Case

Model	Year	Hours	Condition	Price	Date	Area	Comments
2670	1976		G	$5,000	8/3/2011	ECND	4WD, cab, air, heat, PS, 3 pt., 1,000 PTO, 2 hyd., 18.4x34 singles, 8' twin fan front mount snowblower
2670	1976	5,922	F	$2,001	6/22/2011	Online	*BigIron.com,* item in Nebraska, 4 range, 3 speed PS, 6 cyl. diesel, 2 hyd., 1,000 PTO, 3 pt., missing third link, swinging drawbar, front window broken
2670	1977	6,137	F	$3,500	11/22/2011	NCMN	4WD, 2 hyd., duals, no 3 pt. or PTO, cracked glass, no cab insulation
2670	1977	13,173	G	$3,050	6/22/2011	Online	*BigIron.com,* item in Nebraska, PS, 6 cyl. diesel, 2 hyd., 1,000 PTO, 3 pt., missing third link, front aux. hyd., swinging drawbar
2670	1977		G	$4,750	8/11/2010	ECMN	4WD, cab, air, heat, PTO, duals
2670	1978	6,236	G	$5,750	3/31/2012	SWSK	4WD, 12' Leon dozer, 220 hp, 4 hyd., 1,000 PTO
2670		4,638	G	$5,500	3/13/2014	SCID	4x4, 12 speed, 1,000 PTO, 4 hyd., direct pull, 18.4x34 rubber, duals
2670		13,175	G	$3,601	1/22/2014	Online	*BigIron.com,* item in Nebraska, 20.8x34 rear tires, duals
2670		6,340	G	$2,600	7/17/2013	Online	*BigIron.com,* item in Wyoming, 4 range, 3 speed PS
2670		8,770	G	$5,060	9/12/2012	Online	*PurpleWave.com,* item in Kansas, 504 6 cyl. diesel, PS 12 speed
2670		7,900	G	$3,400	1/28/2012	ECMO	4WD, 2 hyd., lights work, AC comp locked up, left rear wheel seal has slight leak
2670			G	$3,200	9/17/2011	ECMN	
2670			P	$3,200	4/20/2011	NWMI	4WD, traction king, diesel, cab, bareback, PS, 18.4x34 duals, bad front differential
2670			F	$3,750	11/29/2010	ECIA	4WD, blade
2670		4,175	F	$3,600	4/1/2010	NCIN	Duals, 3 pt. quick hitch, 4 hyd.
2870	1977	4,452	G	$10,120	11/30/2011	Online	*PurpleWave.com,* item in Kansas, 4WD, 6 cyl. diesel, 300 hp, 4WD, hyd. 4 wheel steering, air, heat, AM/FM, extra lights, 3 pt., drawbar, 1,000 PTO
2870			P	$2,200	12/18/2013	Online	*BigIron.com,* item in Nebraska, for parts, does not run, 6 cyl. diesel, 4 hyd., has 12' push blade, 3 pt., no wheels
2870		6,194	F	$6,000	8/16/2012	Online	*IQBID.com,* item in Minnesota, 4WD, cab, air, heat, 4 hyd., 3 pt., 3rd arm, 24.5-32 w/ band duals
2870			G	$6,000	3/22/2012	ECMN	3 hyd., 3 pt.
C	1930		F	$2,750	8/14/2012	Online	*PurpleWave.com,* item in Kansas, 4 cyl. gas, manual, crank start, drawbar, all steel wheels, steel seat needs repair
C	1937		G	$4,000	5/7/2010	NEAR	
C			F	$775	10/2/2010	ECMN	WF, unstyled
CC	1930		G	$750	6/23/2010	Online	*BigIron.com,* item in Kansas, gas, made in the 1930s, SN missing, complete other than tires and seat

TRACTORS

Case

Model	Year	Hours	Condition	Price	Date	Area	Comments
CC	1936		G	$2,275	5/19/2012	SWMI	NF, 13.9x36 tires, fenders, flat spoke wheels, power lift, PTO, restored w/ new Case gray paint and decals
CC	1937		G	$1,700	10/23/2010	SCPA	
CC			F	$1,200	6/20/2012	SESD	Gas, on rubber, older restoration, should run
CO	1937		G	$1,750	10/23/2010	SCPA	
D	1948		G	$1,800	10/7/2011	NWSD	PTO, hyd., restored
D	1948		E	$1,900	10/7/2011	NWSD	PTO, hyd., very straight, very nice, runs
D	1951		G	$900	9/21/2013	SEMN	Standard, WF, fenders
D			E	$2,700	8/24/2013	SEMI	Restored, automotive paint
D			G	$1,300	9/22/2012	NEOR	
D			G	$950	4/10/2010	ECON	
DC	1950		G	$1,000	9/21/2013	SEMN	WF
DC	1950		G	$800	2/17/2011	WCNE	Gas, SF, 3 pt., hyd.
DC	1952		G	$1,250	8/24/2013	WCMN	New paint restoration, WF
DC			G	$1,500	10/22/2011	NECO	
DC			G	$2,000	8/7/2010	SEWI	
DC			F	$800	5/26/2010	ECSD	Eagle hitch
DC4	1950		G	$1,100	10/7/2011	NWSD	Older restoration, PTO, sheet metal and rubber are good
DC4			G	$2,500	8/24/2013	SEMI	Weights, hand clutch, WF
DC4			G	$1,200	4/23/2012	WCSK	
DC4			G	$1,400	7/17/2010	SCON	Canadian sale
DC4			G	$1,300	4/17/2010	SESK	PTO
DO	1951		G	$1,150	6/15/2013	WCMI	WF, 9.13x36 tires, SN 5509542 DO
L	1937		E	$2,750	10/24/2012	NECO	Rebuilt Wheatland, gas
L	1937		F	$935	8/14/2012	Online	*PurpleWave.com,* item in Kansas, 4 cyl. gas, 3 speed, 7.5x16 fronts, 14.9x28 rear tires, clutch has been replaced
L	1938		E	$1,250	4/10/2010	NCOK	Electric start, LP, PTO, 15x28 rear tires, two owners
L			G	$1,870	11/3/2011	Online	*PurpleWave.com,* item in Kansas
LA	1947		G	$1,375	2/9/2011	Online	*PurpleWave.com,* item in Kansas, 4 cyl. propane, 4 speed, 540 PTO, 1 hyd., 18.4x30 rear tires
LA	1948		F	$880	3/27/2013	Online	*PurpleWave.com,* item in Kansas, 4 cyl. gas, manual
LA	1948		E	$6,750	10/7/2011	NWSD	Restored, 3 cyl. Detroit engine, PTO hyd.
LA			G	$1,320	8/28/2013	Online	*PurpleWave.com,* item in Kansas, 4 cyl. gas, manual, 540 PTO, 2 rear hyd., 7.5x18 front tires, 16.9x30 rear tires, small leak in radiator
LA			G	$1,150	6/22/2013	SEMN	LP, WF
LA			G	$1,750	9/22/2012	NEOR	LP
LA			F	$1,900	8/14/2010	SEMN	
LA			G	$900	5/1/2010	SENE	
RC	1934		G	$2,200	9/1/2011	WCMN	SF, Waukesha engine, PTO, fenders, belt pulley, all steel wheels, original unrestored

Case

Model	Year	Hours	Condition	Price	Date	Area	Comments
RC	1936		G	$3,000	5/19/2012	SWMI	SF, over top steering, 11x36 Wards Riverside tires, fenders, factory round spoke rear wheels
RC			F	$1,265	11/3/2011	Online	*PurpleWave.com,* item in Kansas
S	1945		G	$1,600	10/7/2011	NWSD	Standard, PTO, restored
S	1949		G	$4,600	6/11/2010	SEAB	Gas, PTO, belt pulley, original rear rubber, rear weights, new paint, parts book
S	1953		G	$3,350	6/15/2013	WCMI	WF, restored, 13.6x28 tires, SN 5300609-S
S			G	$1,150	6/8/2013	NEND	Styled, standard tread, starter, good rear rubber, cast front wheels
SC	1943		G	$950	10/2/2010	SWWI	
SC	1945		G	$1,100	4/13/2011	Online	*BigIron.com,* item in Nebraska, 4F/1R, 4 cyl. gas, 540 PTO, 7' blade attach, new tires in '10
SC	1945		F	$2,600	5/7/2010	NEAR	
SC	1952		G	$3,350	5/19/2012	SWMI	WF, 11x38 tires, fenders, live power, Case Eagle hitch, top link, hyd., restored w/new paint and decals
SC	1952		G	$1,050	3/26/2011	NECO	WF, gas, new paint
SC			G	$1,100	8/24/2013	SEMI	Pulling tractor
SC			G	$1,100	11/24/2012	WCIL	
SC			G	$1,100	9/22/2012	NEOR	
SC			G	$800	8/31/2011	SEMN	
SC			F	$1,800	10/6/2010	WCSD	WF, 3 pt., Farmhand F11B loader, did not run
SC			G	$1,500	9/18/2010	ECMO	
SC			G	$1,450	5/22/2010	SEMN	Looked good, nice paint
SC			G	$900	5/1/2010	NCOH	Good tin, runs well
V	1941		G	$2,100	6/11/2010	SEAB	Optional electric start and lights, new front rubber
VA			G	$825	7/17/2010	SCON	Canadian sale, on steel
VAC	1946		G	$3,900	6/29/2011	NEND	NF, good rubber, stored inside
VAC	1949		G	$1,600	10/7/2011	NWSD	Restored, PTO, not perfect but pretty darn nice (description on the sale bill), runs
VAC	1950		G	$1,100	8/29/2013	NWIA	2WD, 4 speed, 12V, 540 PTO, rear weights, 12.4x28 tires, new brakes
VAC	1951		G	$901	3/27/2013	Online	*BigIron.com,* item in Kansas, 4 speed, 4 cyl.
VAC	1951		G	$775	6/22/2011	Online	*BigIron.com,* item in Nebraska, 4F/1R, 4 cyl. gas, 540 PTO, Eagle hitch, new left rear tire
VAC	1951		F	$950	3/19/2011	SEIA	Eagle hitch
VAC	1951		G	$4,000	5/7/2010	NEAR	
VAC	1952		G	$1,500	6/22/2011	Online	*BigIron.com,* item in gas, 12V conversion, new gauges, new mainfold, no leaks, 3 pt. adj. hitch, new head gaskets
VAC			F	$1,100	7/27/2013	NEIN	NF, 3 pt., Eagle hitch, PTO, drawbar
VAC			G	$2,200	2/6/2013	SESD	WF, Eagle hitch, fenders
VAC			G	$950	7/10/2010	SEIA	5' belly mower

Case

Model	Year	Hours	Condition	Price	Date	Area	Comments
VAC			G	$1,500	6/23/2010	Online	*BigIron.com,* item in Nebraska, gas converted to alternator, 11.2/10x54 new rear tires, 6x16 new front tires, 540 PTO
VAC			F	$800	5/1/2010	SENE	
VAC			G	$1,300	5/1/2010	SENE	
VAH	1956		G	$3,100	9/1/2011	Online	*IQBID.com,* WF, PTO, high crop, good tires, older restoration
VAH			G	$2,650	6/15/2013	WCMI	WF, power lift toolbar, 12.4x6 tires
VAO			F	$1,300	7/27/2013	NEIN	Orchard tractor, repainted, WF
VC			G	$950	12/4/2013	ECIN	
VC			G	$800	6/8/2013	NEND	NF, PTO, kept indoors
N/A	1919		G	$32,000	7/22/2011	SEMN	Steam engine, 50 hp, 150 PSI, hyd. tested 190 PSI, Baker valves
N/A	1922		G	$20,000	7/22/2011	SEMN	Steam engine, 65 hp, good engine and gears, Baker valves, needs boiler work
N/A	1950		G	$2,200	5/7/2010	NEAR	
N/A	1965	3,911	G	$2,200	3/22/2012	ECMN	WF, gas, 3 pt., top link, good tin, new seat

Cockshutt

Model	Year	Hours	Condition	Price	Date	Area	Comments
20			G	$1,050	6/8/2013	NEND	NF, starter, lights, 2 speed rear axle, belt pulley, PTO, rare
20			G	$7,250	10/23/2010	SCPA	
30	1947		G	$798	5/30/2012	Online	*PurpleWave.com,* item in Kansas
30	1947		E	$4,500	8/6/2011	NCIA	Gambles Farmcrest model, restored
30	1947		G	$6,250	10/23/2010	SCPA	Standard
30	1947		F	$1,050	10/2/2010	SWWI	Custom-built model 32 loader
30	1947		G	$1,000	6/11/2010	SEAB	Gas, belt pulley, PTO
30	1948		G	$1,600	8/24/2013	WCMN	New paint
30	1948		G	$1,925	6/11/2010	SEAB	PTO, belt pulley, new and reconditioned parts
30	1950		G	$1,200	8/6/2011	NCIA	Fenders, belt pulley
30			F	$4,500	4/16/2014	ECAB	2WD, 12.4x38 rear, 6V electrical, pully hooked to front mount welder
30			G	$900	5/11/2013	NCOH	Repainted, runs
30			G	$1,500	5/11/2013	NCOH	Belt pulley, repainted, runs
30			G	$3,200	5/11/2013	NCOH	Repainted, runs
30			F	$800	10/2/2010	ECMN	WF
30			G	$1,300	10/2/2010	ECMN	NF
30			P	$800	9/3/2010	NEIN	Dead row, needs work and may not run or drive as is
30			F	$1,500	8/21/2010	NCOH	Loader, not run in 10 years, rust/mice/squirrels had set in
30			F	$797	5/26/2010	Online	*PurpleWave.com,* item in Kansas, 1947-48, Buda 4 cyl. gas, belt pulley, live PTO, not stuck but has not run in 3 years, one rear wheel needs replacing

Cockshutt

Model	Year	Hours	Condition	Price	Date	Area	Comments
30			G	$1,300	5/1/2010	SENE	
35	1956		G	$4,000	8/6/2011	NCIA	Black Hawk, WF, restored
35			G	$1,150	6/11/2010	SEAB	Gas, hyd., PTO, belt pulley
40	1951		G	$2,000	8/24/2013	WCMN	Buda diesel, new paint restoration
40			G	$800	8/24/2013	NWMO	
40			G	$1,850	7/22/2013	SWSK	2WD, gas, live PTO, 13.6x38 rear, 6 cyl. gas, belt pulley
40			G	$2,975	4/24/2013	Online	*BigIron.com,* item in Nebraska, does not run
40			G	$1,500	6/9/2012	ECNE	Gas, PTO, hyd., runs
40			F	$900	8/6/2011	NCIA	
40			G	$3,000	4/29/2011	SWSK	2WD, gas, PTO, hydraulics
40			G	$1,750	10/2/2010	SWWI	Block has been welded
40			G	$1,000	4/21/2010	SESK	2WD, belt pulley, 3 pt., hydraulics, PTO, 3 pt. sickle mower
50	1953		G	$5,400	10/7/2011	NWSD	PTO, hydraulics, restored, diesel
50	1955		G	$7,000	8/6/2011	NCIA	Restored
50			G	$1,250	6/20/2012	SESD	Gas
50			G	$2,400	6/20/2012	SESD	Diesel
60			G	$3,750	9/4/2010	NEIN	
70	1941		G	$7,500	10/23/2010	SCPA	Standard
70			G	$1,300	11/13/2010	NCIA	Side panels
540	1958		G	$6,100	10/7/2011	NWSD	3 pt., PTO, power steering, WF, restored

I've had so much fun the past five years traveling the country shooting auction video for Machinery Pete's YouTube channel (www.youtube.com/machinerypete). One of the most fun days I spent on the auction trail was a warm and sunny Saturday on Oct. 1, 2011, at an Oliver and Cockshutt collector auction for Ed and Mary Ann Schulte of Manchester, Iowa.

On this sale was the 1963 Cockshutt 660 gas tractor pictured here, which is one of only 15 built. Ed had documented his 660 was the 13th built and rolled off the line in Ontario on Feb. 21, 1963. Bidding was hot and heavy, starting at $10,000 and racing past $20,000 in no time. It wound up selling for $28,000 to Gerald Capek, who was from Milligan, Neb., and drove a great distance just to bid on the 660.

PETE'S PICK

I interviewed Gerald after the sale to ask how he felt. "I could have bought a Harley," he said. Then he smiled. He was a happy buyer on his way home to Nebraska with a very rare Cockshutt tractor.

TRACTORS

Cockshutt

Model	Year	Hours	Condition	Price	Date	Area	Comments
540			G	$4,000	10/23/2010	SCPA	Utility
550	1959		G	$5,000	8/20/2013	WCIL	Gas, 1 hyd., 3 pt., 540 PTO, 15.5x38 tires
550	1959		G	$2,900	10/7/2011	NWSD	Restored, WF, diesel, 3pt., PTO, power steering, spin-out rims
550			G	$3,500	3/23/2013	NEIN	3 pt., PTO, repainted, runs
550			G	$2,400	3/24/2012	NEIN	Gas, standard, fenders, WF, PTO, original, runs
550			F	$1,000	6/23/2010	Online	*BigIron.com,* item in Nebraska, 4 cyl. gas, 1 hyd., 540 PTO, 12V system, left front spindle bent
550			P	$1,150	5/26/2010	ECSD	Gas, stuck
560	1961		F	$2,750	6/20/2012	SESD	Diesel, WF, Wheatland, 18.4x34 tires, wheel weights, PS, live PTO, fenders, runs, diesel pump rebuilt in 2011
560	1969		G	$3,000	10/7/2011	NWSD	Restored, PTO, hyd., power steering
560	1969		G	$3,200	10/7/2011	NWSD	Standard, PTO, hyd., power steering, restored
570	1959		G	$3,000	10/7/2011	NWSD	Diesel, WF, PTO, hyd., power steering, restored
570			G	$3,500	3/24/2012	NEIN	Standard, hyd., PTO, rear weights, WF, fenders, repainted, runs
570			P	$1,650	9/3/2010	NEIN	Diesel, dead row, needs work and may not run or drive, as is
660	1963		E	$28,000	10/1/2011	ECIA	Restored, 1 of only 15, 155 cu. in., hyd., PTO, cast rear wheels, gas, new tires
770	1960		G	$10,000	8/7/2010	WCMN	Wheatland gas, engine rebuilt
770	1963		G	$5,100	5/26/2010	ECSD	Wheatland, completely restored
1550			G	$6,200	3/24/2012	NEIN	Diesel, STD, PTO, hyd., runs
1550			G	$9,000	6/19/2010	SWIL	Running, restored, lights, deluxe seat, row crop
1600			G	$1,600	4/6/2013	SWSK	2WD, gas
1600			G	$5,000	9/4/2010	NEIN	Diesel
1600			G	$3,100	5/26/2010	ECSD	Diesel
1650			G	$2,200	8/8/2012	Online	*BigIron.com,* item in Illinois, Wheatland, diesel, 540 PTO, no 3 pt., WF
1650		8,299	G	$3,900	4/30/2012	SESK	2WD, diesel, PTO, hyd., wooden cab enclosure, belly pulley, new radiator
1650			G	$3,250	3/24/2012	NEIN	Diesel, STD, PTO, hyd., fenders, rear weights, runs
1650		2,304	G	$2,200	4/18/2011	WCSK	Case front-end loader, 2 hyd., 540 PTO
1750			G	$4,000	3/24/2012	NEIN	Diesel, standard, cab, excellent original, runs
1750		3,285	G	$6,700	4/18/2011	WCSK	82 hp, over/under Hydra-Power driveshift, new batteries, loader, quick detach bucket
1850			G	$9,200	6/30/2012	SESK	FWA, cab, hyd., new clutch, like new rear rubber
1850		1,988	G	$2,500	4/18/2011	SESK	2WD, 2 hyd., PTO, diesel, 6 speed Hydra-Power driveshift

Cockshutt

Model	Year	Hours	Condition	Price	Date	Area	Comments
1850			G	$4,000	5/26/2010	ECSD	Wheatland
1900			G	$5,100	4/18/2011	WCSK	105 hp, 2 hyd., 540 PTO, 453 Detroit motor, multipower, tilt steering
1900		5,429	G	$7,000	4/24/2010	SESK	FWA, diesel
1950		3,668	G	$11,000	3/27/2014	ECNE	GM diesel, Hydra-Power drive, fenders with fuel tanks, 2 hyd., PTO
1950			G	$13,000	10/2/2010	SESK	FWA, Ezee-On front-end loader, SN 68135415, fresh rebuilt and reconditioned engine with 0 hours
1950			G	$4,700	4/1/2010	SEAB	Diesel, Continental cab, PTO, hyd., 18.4x34 rear tires
E3	1948		G	$2,805	10/22/2013	Online	*HansenAndYoung.com,* E15AS hitch-mounted sickle mower
Super 570D			P	$2,000	5/26/2010	ECSD	Stuck

Co-Op

Model	Year	Hours	Condition	Price	Date	Area	Comments
2			G	$3,000	6/5/2010	WCMO	
3	1950		G	$5,000	8/7/2010	WCMN	Gas, engine rebuilt
3			G	$5,100	12/10/2013	WCWI	WF, PTO, 12V, belt pulley, new fronts, complete restoration
3			G	$2,600	9/22/2012	NEOR	WF, rear fenders
3			G	$950	8/25/2011	ECND	Electric start, PTO, belt pulley, full fenders, rear weights, 14.9x30 rear wheels, loose
3			G	$1,800	6/5/2010	WCMO	
30	1948		G	$1,325	8/6/2011	NCIA	WF
30	1951		G	$3,600	8/7/2010	SEWI	153/30 hp 4 cyl. engine built by Buda, new paint

---

Disney released its blockbuster animated movie *Frozen* in late November 2013. I saw the movie, enjoyed it, and then felt frozen myself, attending three machinery auctions during the two weeks that followed.

One was in southeast Minnesota, one was in northeast Iowa, and the third was in west-central Wisconsin on Dec. 10, 2013. At the December auction in Wisconsin, I think air temp was 10 to 15 below zero. At least it was bright and sunny, but it was just C-O-L-D. Despite the cold temperatures, the bidding was hot on the restored Co-Op No. 3 tractor pictured here. It sold for $5,100.

PETE'S PICK

TRACTORS

Co-Op

Model	Year	Hours	Condition	Price	Date	Area	Comments
C			F	$850	8/6/2011	NCIA	SN C54-431, original
E2	1952		G	$4,850	8/6/2011	NCIA	WF, 3 pt., restored
E3	1948		G	$3,750	8/6/2011	NCIA	WF
E3	1949		G	$1,300	6/15/2013	WCMI	NF, 12.4x38 tires, wheel weights
E3			G	$4,000	6/22/2013	SEWA	NF, 4 cyl., gas
E3			G	$1,600	6/15/2013	WCMI	WF, 14.9x38 tires, wheel weights
E3			G	$1,400	6/1/2013	SEMN	12.4x38 tires, NF, PTO
E3			G	$2,050	5/11/2013	NCOH	Repainted, runs
E3			F	$1,100	10/2/2010	ECMN	NF
E4	1951		G	$2,750	8/6/2011	NCIA	WF
E4			G	$2,000	12/15/2012	WCMI	Gas, NF, drawbar hitch, restored
E4			F	$925	6/23/2010	Online	*BigIron.com,* item in Nebraska, 6 cyl. gas, 15.5x38 rear tires, 6x16 front tires, WF, runs, water pump leaks
E4			G	$1,400	6/5/2010	WCMO	Diesel
N/A	1977	6,355	G	$7,750	4/16/2014	ECAB	2WD, diesel, PS with Hi/Lo, cab, dual PTO, 2 hyd., 18.4x38 duals

David Brown

Model	Year	Hours	Condition	Price	Date	Area	Comments
880	1963		E	$3,250	8/20/2011	NWOH	3 pt., utility tractor
885	1975	1,792	F	$3,900	6/20/2013	ECSK	2WD, 43 PTO hp, 540 PTO, 3 pt., 13.6x28 rear tires
885			G	$1,750	2/25/2012	WCMI	WF, diesel, 3 pt., PTO, 1 hyd., 13.6x28 rear tires
885			G	$2,250	4/2/2011	SWSK	2WD, front-end loader, 43 PTO hp, diesel, 3 pt., 540 PTO
889			F	$825	11/20/2010	SCKY	
990	1970		E	$6,500	3/24/2012	SEOH	Select-a-Matic Livedrive 12, SN 825586

Every day I scan upcoming auction sale bills from around the U.S. and Canada thinking, "Hmm, what do we have today, and what looks interesting?"

PETE'S PICK

Any time I see a David Brown tractor coming up for sale, that catches my eye.

In the past few years, one of the very nicest ones I've run across on the auction market was this 1970 David Brown 990 at a March 24, 2012 farm auction in southeast Ohio. It sold for $6,500, which earned the highest sale price I've seen on a 990 model.

David Brown

Model	Year	Hours	Condition	Price	Date	Area	Comments
990	1974		G	$2,900	10/16/2013	SWSK	2WD, front-end loader, 52 PTO hp diesel, 3 speed, 3 pt., 2 hyd., 16.9-30 rear tires, 540 PTO, 5' bucket
990	1974	3,893	G	$3,300	11/9/2011	Online	*BigIron.com,* item in Montana, 12 speed, 2WD, 4 cyl., diesel, 65HP, 1 hyd., 540 PTO, Case 56L, loader
990		4,000	G	$4,750	12/8/2011	NEND	2-stage clutch, 3 pt., PTO, 626 loader
990			G	$1,000	6/5/2010	NCTN	Select-A-Matic
990A			G	$2,100	3/28/2012	ECND	Front-end loader
995			G	$2,250	1/28/2012	ECMO	2WD, dual PTO, 1 hyd.
995			G	$2,400	1/21/2012	NEMS	
1210	1976	3,690	G	$5,300	2/1/2011	NEIN	
1210		5,028	G	$3,000	8/3/2011	ECND	Diesel, aftermarket cab, 3 pt., PTO, 2 hyd., 18.4x34 rear tires
N/A	1975		G	$3,300	4/18/2011	WCSK	2WD, diesel, rebuilt 310 hours ago, 3 pt.

Deutz

Model	Year	Hours	Condition	Price	Date	Area	Comments
60-06	1973	7,604	G	$2,200	8/20/2013	WCIL	Open station, 1 hyd., 540 PTO, 18.4x30 tires near new, front weights
D40061977			G	$2,100	4/1/2011	Online	*AuctionTime.com,* item in Illinois, transmission good, PTO good
N/A	1961		G	$7,500	8/7/2010	SEWI	Tractors supplied by Deutz but sold through the Canadian Cooperative Implements Limited (CCIL), 80 hp, new green paint, WF

One thing I've always really enjoyed is comparing auction sale prices on similar items sold at different times. That way I can see if they are up or down, by how much and start figuring out why. At a Nov. 18, 1999 farm auction in northwest Minnesota in the Red River Valley, a 1978 Deutz D100-06 in good condition, front-wheel assist, with 7,050 hours, cab and 18.4x38 band duals sold for $6,200. Now compare that to this 1979 Deutz D100-06 front-wheel assist tractor (pictured) with no cab, no duals and 6,790 hours sold at a southeast Iowa farm auction on June 2, 2012 for $11,250.

It's plain and simple. These good condition tractors from the '70s are just worth more money now than then.

PETE'S PICK

Eagle

Model	Year	Condition	Price	Date	Area	Comments
H 16-30		G	$24,000	9/21/2013	WCNY	
6A	1939	G	$12,500	10/23/2010	SCPA	
N/A		G	$26,000	9/9/2010	NWWI	40 hp

Earthmaster

Model	Year	Condition	Price	Date	Area	Comments
N/A	1947	G	$4,000	8/24/2011	ECMN	Wide gauge, hyd. power lift, fenders, new 8.3x24 rubber

Emerson Brantingham

Model	Year	Condition	Price	Date	Area	Comments
12-20		G	$15,000	9/21/2013	WCNY	Model AA, original, needs fenders, has extra lugs with it
12-20		G	$15,000	9/9/2010	NWWI	

Empire

Model	Year	Condition	Price	Date	Area	Comments
88-90		G	$3,700	6/5/2010	WCMO	

Ferguson

Model	Year	Hours	Condition	Price	Date	Area	Comments
20			G	$1,400	6/5/2010	NETN	12V ignition
35			G	$1,050	8/22/2012	Online	*BigIron.com,* item in Nebraska, gas, 11.2x28 rear tires, 6x16 front tires, loader, front pump, PTO
35			G	$1,000	8/13/2011	WCIL	Bush Hog loader, 13.6x28 tires, 540 PTO
35			G	$3,700	5/7/2011	SESK	Gas, 3 pt., PTO, front-end loader
F-40	1957		F	$8,100	9/14/2013	NEKS	Row crop, 3 pt., live power, 6/2, 540 PTO, SN RGM403744, tires original and needed to be replaced, 3 bidders bidding war on this tractor
F-40			G	$5,400	9/4/2010	NEIN	
F-40		3,988	F	$1,900	5/7/2010	WCOH	Selector valve
TE-20			G	$2,900	8/24/2013	SEMN	3 pt., engine OH, SN TE37562
TE-20			E	$3,200	4/26/2013	ECAB	13.6x28 rear tires, 6x16 front tires
TE-20			F	$850	4/10/2013	NETX	Gas, runs
TE-20			G	$2,750	4/15/2011	SESK	4 cyl. gas, 3 pt., 540 PTO
TO-20	1948		G	$2,500	10/7/2011	NWSD	3 pt., PTO
TO-20	1949		G	$1,400	8/24/2013	WCMN	New restoration and paint
TO-20	1949		F	$1,550	4/27/2011	NECO	Gas, WF, 3 pt.
TO-20	1949		G	$2,550	4/11/2011	Online	*AuctionTime.com*

Ferguson

Model	Year	Hours	Condition	Price	Date	Area	Comments
TO-20			G	$925	2/22/2014	NEIN	Gas, 3 pt., PTO
TO-20			G	$2,200	8/26/2013	NWWI	
TO-20			G	$1,800	3/22/2012	ECMN	Restored, 540 PTO, 12.4x28 rears, 4x19 fronts
TO-20			G	$1,400	12/28/2011	Online	*BigIron.com,* item in Wyoming, utility, 4 speed manual, 4 cyl. Ford gas, 3 pt., 540 PTO
TO-20			G	$975	9/14/2011	Online	*BigIron.com* auction, item in Colorado, overhead valve engine, 540 PTO, 3 pt. hitch
TO-20			F	$2,750	9/4/2010	NEIN	
TO-20			G	$1,200	5/7/2010	WCOH	Original
TO-30	1950		G	$2,900	10/23/2010	SCPA	
TO-30	1953		G	$1,350	8/24/2013	WCMN	New paint
TO-30	1954		F	$1,400	6/22/2011	NECO	Gas
TO-30			G	$3,500	6/15/2013	WCOH	High-speed transmission, new tires, 3 pt., repainted, runs
TO-30			G	$4,600	6/15/2013	WCOH	Repainted, new tires, 3 pt., runs
TO-30			G	$2,000	3/2/2013	NCWI	Firestone 13.6x28 tires, front guard, lights, 3 pt., PTO, nice, original
TO-30			G	$1,700	12/3/2011	ECNE	
TO-30			F	$800	11/22/2011	WCIL	SN 50656
TO-30			G	$1,610	10/15/2011	ECND	*IQBID.com* auction, compact, 2WD, PTO, 3 pt., fast hitch, new battery and seat cover, runs and drives great
TO-30			G	$2,500	8/20/2011	NWOH	Ferguson
TO-30			G	$1,300	8/13/2011	WCIL	12.4x28 rear tires, 540 PTO
TO-30			G	$1,100	3/15/2011	WCIL	540 PTO
TO-30			G	$1,500	3/5/2011	SEMN	Gas, WF, 540 PTO, 3 pt., new battery, new tires
TO-30			G	$1,300	12/30/2010	ECMN	Gas, WF, 3 pt., 540 PTO
TO-30			G	$1,400	11/13/2010	NCIA	
TO-35	1952		E	$4,400	6/8/2013	NEIA	PS, parade ready, WF, 3 pt., SN SGMI82004
TO-35	1955		G	$1,502	4/3/2013	Online	*BigIron.com,* item in Kansas, 6F/2R, 4 cyl. gas, 12.4x28 rear tires, 6x16 front tires, 32 claimed hp, 3 pt., Dearborn loader, 40x24 bucket
TO-35	1955		F	$2,000	6/9/2011	SWSK	32 PTO hp, Continental 4 cyl. gas, standard, 3 pt., mower, plow, disk
TO-35	1957	422	G	$1,550	6/12/2013	Online	*BigIron.com* auction, item in Wisconsin, loader, 6F/2R transmission, 2.2L, gas, 33 hp
TO-35			G	$2,100	10/18/2012	WCMI	Hyd. bucket loader, 3 pt., PTO
TO-35			G	$2,100	1/21/2012	SEVA	
TO-35			P	$1,700	12/3/2011	NCOH	As is, barely running, loader
N/A	1952		P	$1,110	6/14/2010	Online	*BigIron.com,* item in Nebraska, 4 cyl. gas Continental motor, left rim rusty, rear fenders bad

Flour City

Model	Year	Condition	Price	Date	Area	Comments
40-70	1917	E	$375,000	9/21/2013	WCNY	

Okay, I admit it. Machinery Pete didn't even know there was such a thing as a Flour City tractor. That is until a Sept. 21, 2013 collector auction in western New York caught my eye. Actually more than just the tractor brand name caught my eye. My eyeballs about popped out of my head when I saw what this amazing 1917 Flour City 40-70 tractor sold for…$375,000. Wow!

PETE'S PICK

The $375,000 price is in fact the highest auction sale price I've seen on any tractor in my 25 years of compiling auction price data. Yep, that is even beyond what the glitzy, computerized, GPS-laden new models of today go for. So score one for the rare antiques. Flour City, I know about you now.

Ford

Model	Year	Hours	Condition	Price	Date	Area	Comments
2N	1941		G	$875	5/8/2013	Online	*BigIron.com,* item in Missouri, 540 PTO
2N	1943		G	$900	10/3/2013	NCIN	
2N	1943		G	$1,150	10/27/2012	NEIA	3 pt. rear bucket
2N	1944		F	$1,100	1/30/2012	NEIA	
2N	1945		G	$600	8/20/2013	WCIL	Grill guard
2N	1946		G	$1,155	11/28/2012	Online	*PurpleWave.com,* item in Kansas, 4 cyl. gas, 3 pt., 540 PTO, front work lights, weak clutch
2N	1946		G	$1,265	8/31/2011	Online	*PurpleWave.com,* item in Kansas, 4 cyl., 3 pt., 540 PTO
2N	1946		G	$1,300	4/13/2011	Online	*BigIron.com,* item in Nebraska, 3F/1R Hi/Lo, 4 cyl. gas, 540 PTO, 12V electronic ignition
2N	1946		G	$850	6/11/2010	SEAB	Converted 12V, new tires, rear rims, brakes
2N	1947		G	$1,500	9/7/2011	SEND	3 speed, Hi/Lo, 3 pt., PTO, 11x2x28 rears
2N			G	$1,100	1/28/2012	ECMO	
2N			F	$1,200	9/7/2011	SEND	3 speed, Hi/Lo, 3 pt., PTO, 12x4x28 rears
2N			E	$1,400	7/17/2010	SCON	Canadian sale, on steel
2N			F	$1,900	6/5/2010	SEMN	Loader
340A	1974		G	$5,170	9/14/2011	Online	*PurpleWave.com,* item in Kansas, Ford 3 cyl.
8N	1930		G	$1,050	3/24/2012	SETN	New battery, new fuel line throughout, no key-toggle switch

Ford

Model	Year	Hours	Condition	Price	Date	Area	Comments
8N	1940		G	$1,300	5/19/2012	SWMI	8N with 9N engine, 9.5x24 tires, fenders, 3 pt.
8N	1946		G	$1,200	7/25/2013	WCSK	New brakes, running
8N	1947		G	$2,000	3/22/2014	NETN	New paint
8N	1947		F	$900	7/17/2013	NEND	3 pt., PTO
8N	1947		G	$1,550	7/17/2013	NEND	New paint, 3 pt., PTO
8N	1947		G	$1,045	8/22/2012	Online	*PurpleWave.com,* item in Kansas, Ford 2.0L, 4 cyl., manual, 3 pt.
8N	1947		G	$2,900	6/20/2012	SESD	
8N	1947		G	$1,100	5/19/2012	SWMI	WF, 11x28 tires, fenders, 3 pt.
8N	1947		E	$2,800	4/10/2010	NCOK	One owner, 3pt., PTO, new rear tires
8N	1948		G	$1,155	5/30/2012	Online	*PurpleWave.com,* item in Kansas, Flathead 4 cyl. gas, manual, 540 PTO, direct drive, 3 pt.
8N	1948		G	$1,540	5/30/2012	Online	*PurpleWave.com,* item in Kansas, Flathead 4 cyl. gas, manual, 540 PTO, 3 pt., front lights work
8N	1948		G	$2,200	3/28/2012	ECND	3 pt., drawbar, PTO
8N	1948		F	$800	1/30/2012	NEIA	Gas
8N	1948		G	$2,100	12/7/2011	NCIA	Restored
8N	1948		G	$1,900	9/1/2011	WCMN	3 pt., PTO, complete rebuilt engine, original unrestored, all new rubber

On a beautiful autumn afternoon on Oct. 22, 2011, I pointed the Machinery Pete pickup down I-90 from my home in Rochester, Minn. to the Lacrescent, Minn. area. There was a small collector auction with mostly antique cars but also a beautifully restored 1949 Ford 8N (see picture). As the bidding rolled along on the 8N (it eventually sold for $3,900) my mind drifted back to the previous fall.

In October 2010, I paid a visit to then 95-year-old Harold Brock of Waterloo, Iowa. Harold went to work for Ford as an apprentice engineer in 1929. He actually worked directly with the great man Henry Ford himself. Harold was very generous with his time and told me about the development of the 8N. He shared this cute story. Harold was the reason 8Ns are their iconic red and gray color scheme. As the story goes, the engineers had a vote on the colors and made Harold the tabulator. Harold's wife Kathleen had a beautiful red and silver dress he liked very much, so he may have ignored the votes and proclaimed red and gray.

Harold Brock passed away Jan. 2, 2011. I am so thankful I was able to meet him and spend a wonderful afternoon talking tractors with him.

PETE'S PICK

TRACTORS

Ford

Model	Year	Hours	Condition	Price	Date	Area	Comments
8N	1948		G	$1,501	6/8/2011	Online	*BigIron.com,* item in Nebraska, 4 speed, top link, new radiator, recent tune up
8N	1948		G	$1,200	3/17/2011	ECMN	12V
8N	1948		G	$1,550	10/17/2010	ECIN	
8N	1949		G	$800	3/26/2014	Online	*BigIron.com,* item in New Mexico, 3 speed manual
8N	1949		G	$3,050	8/24/2013	WCMN	New paint, 3 pt. mounted Ford 1R corn picker
8N	1949		G	$1,100	8/14/2013	WCMN	Original owner, gas, 11x28 tires, PTO
8N	1949		G	$1,265	8/14/2013	Online	*PurpleWave.com,* item in Kansas, 4 cyl. gas, 3 pt., 540 PTO
8N	1949		F	$1,000	4/3/2013	Online	*BigIron.com,* item in Kansas, 3F/1R Sherman, 4 cyl. gas, 12.4x28 rear tires, F78x14 front tires, 27 claimed hp, 3 pt.
8N	1949		G	$2,200	3/28/2012	ECND	3 pt., PTO, Woods 5' belly mower
8N	1949		E	$3,900	10/22/2011	SEMN	Reconditioned, Sherman step up, mint condition
8N	1949		F	$1,100	8/6/2011	NCIA	Front pump loader
8N	1949		G	$1,100	4/11/2011	Online	*AuctionTime.com*
8N	1949		G	$1,300	3/26/2011	SEWI	
8N	1950		F	$900	8/27/2013	NCIA	Tach, 3 pt.
8N	1950	1,772	G	$3,000	9/7/2011	SEND	Side distributor, 3 pt., PTO, hyd. loader, 12x4x28 rears
8N	1950		G	$1,700	8/25/2011	ECND	3 pt., PTO, 11.2x28 rears, runs
8N	1951	109	G	$2,400	4/24/2013	Online	*BigIron.com,* item in Kansas, Sherman step up, 8F/2R, 4 cyl.
8N	1951	2,678	G	$3,100	11/10/2012	WCIL	540 PTO, gas
8N	1951		G	$2,255	5/30/2012	Online	*PurpleWave.com,* item in Kansas, Flathead 4 cyl. gas, manual, 540 PTO, drawbar, 3 pt., front work lights, 11.2x28 rear tires
8N	1951		G	$1,400	3/22/2012	ECMN	3 pt., fast hitch, 540 PTO, hyd. pump, brush guard, tractor jacks, chains and side distributor, 12.4x28 rears
8N	1951		G	$3,300	8/24/2011	ECMN	3 pt., PTO, original rear wheels, new 11.2x28 rubber
8N	1951		G	$2,250	9/25/2010	ECIA	Factory sun shade
8N	1952	5,194	G	$1,155	10/30/2013	Online	*PurpleWave.com,* item in Kansas, 4 cyl. Flathead gas, 4 speed manual, 3 pt.
8N	1952		E	$3,750	6/20/2013	ECSK	2WD, 4 speed, 23 hp drawbar, 27 hp PTO, HD PTO, completely restored, new tires and paint and engine
8N	1952		G	$1,700	4/11/2013	NCMI	Gas, 3 pt., PTO
8N	1952		G	$3,800	4/1/2013	WCIL	2-owner, nice parade tractor
8N	1952		G	$2,600	3/16/2013	NEIL	OH, mower, signed by Harold Brock on rear left fender (Harold Brock was apprentice engineer with Henry Ford in 1929 as a designer of 8N and 9N. He's the reason they are red/gray color)

Ford

Model	Year	Hours	Condition	Price	Date	Area	Comments
8N	1952	1,400	G	$2,357	8/22/2012	Online	*BigIron.com,* item in Nebraska, 4 speed OD, 4 cyl. gas, 540 PTO, 3 pt., converted TO 6V alternator, side distributor, original 2 pt. drawbar
8N	1952		G	$2,000	12/7/2011	NCIA	Henry backhoe
8N	1952		G	$2,200	9/7/2011	SEND	4 speed, side distributor, 3 pt., PTO, 12x4x28 rears
8N	1952		G	$3,400	9/7/2011	SEND	Side distributor, 4 speed, 3 pt., PTO, Fast Hitch, 11x2x28 rears
8N	1952		G	$1,750	8/13/2011	WCIL	11.2x28 tires, PTO, runs well
8N	1952		G	$3,800	5/7/2011	WCSD	Completely restored, 3pt., new tires, runs great
8N	1952		G	$3,000	4/13/2011	Online	*BigIron.com,* item in Nebraska, 11.2x28 tires, 4-ply front tires, restored
8N	1952		G	$1,600	12/17/2010	WCIL	Blade, 540 PTO, 11.2x28 tires
8N	1952		G	$2,100	8/7/2010	SEWI	Original Funk conversion, new tires and Sherman OD
8N	1952		F	$1,000	5/1/2010	NCOH	Side distributor at tach original, does not run
8N	1953		G	$3,500	3/2/2010	ECIL	Hyd. loader, rear counter weights
8N	1954		G	$1,900	10/11/2011	Online	*BidNow.US,* item in Michigan, 3 pt. 5' blade, 4x19 front tires, 11.2x28 rear tires, 3 pt., electric starter, new tach, PTO
8N	1954		G	$1,815	7/28/2010	Online	*PurpleWave.com,* item in Kansas, 4 cyl. 25 hp gas, 4 speed, 3 pt., 540 PTO
8N	1956		G	$1,500	7/25/2013	WCSK	2WD, 4 new tires, used no oil, 3 pt.
8N			G	$1,050	4/3/2014	NEIN	14.9x24, 540 PTO, no top link, WF, grill guard
8N			G	$2,100	3/8/2014	NWLA	3 pt., gas
8N			G	$1,625	1/4/2014	ECOH	Restored
8N			F	$800	12/12/2013	Online	540 PTO, 13.6x28 tires, 3 pt.
8N			F	$1,050	11/23/2013	WCIL	Not running
8N			G	$2,400	11/9/2013	SWON	High crop conversion, factory shade, 3 pt., PTO, 42" tires, no SN
8N			G	$4,200	11/9/2013	SWON	6 cyl., Funk conversion, 3 pt., PTO, tach, no SN
8N			G	$6,000	11/9/2013	SWON	Flat V8, Ford 800 hood, 3 pt., no SN
8N		1,584	F	$880	10/30/2013	Online	*PurpleWave.com,* item in Oklahoma, 4 cyl. gas, 4 speed, 3 pt., 540 PTO
8N			F	$1,073	10/16/2013	Online	*PurpleWave.com,* item in Kansas, 4 cyl. gas, 4 speed, 3 pt., PTO, 205/70Rx15 front tires, 13.6x28 rear tires, battery missing, starts hard, needs work
8N		241	G	$1,375	10/8/2013	Online	*PurpleWave.com,* item in Nebraska, Ford 2.0L, 4 cyl. gas, 23 hp, constant mesh
8N			G	$1,000	9/28/2013	SWMN	11x28, good tin
8N			G	$1,050	9/12/2013	SEIA	3 pt., 540 PTO
8N			G	$2,250	9/6/2013	NCOH	3 pt., 11.2x28 rubber, runs, clean
8N			G	$907	8/26/2013	NWWI	New tires, runs great, new brakes, 3 pt. arms just quit working

TRACTORS

Ford

Model	Year	Hours	Condition	Price	Date	Area	Comments
8N			G	$800	8/20/2013	WCIL	540 PTO, 3 pt.
8N			G	$1,100	7/10/2013	NETX	Canopy
8N			G	$1,900	6/26/2013	Online	*BigIron.com,* item in Oklahoma, 4F/1R, 4 cyl.
8N			G	$800	6/22/2013	SEMN	3 pt., PTO, 11.2x28 tires
8N			F	$1,200	6/20/2013	ECSK	2WD, 23 hp drawbar, 27 hp PTO, 540 PTO, 3 speed, 3 pt.
8N			G	$1,350	6/19/2013	Online	*BigIron.com,* item in Nebraska, 4 speed, 4 cyl. gas, 540 PTO
8N			G	$850	5/22/2013	Online	*BigIron.com,* item in Kansas, manual 3 speed, 4 cyl., 3 pt.
8N			G	$3,250	5/11/2013	NCOH	6 cyl., conversion, repainted, new tires, 3 pt., blade, runs
8N			G	$852	4/24/2013	Online	*BigIron.com,* item in South Dakota, loader, 4F/1R, 4 cyl. gas
8N		4,490	F	$2,010	4/10/2013	Online	*BigIron.com,* item in Nebraska, 4 speed, 4 cyl. gas, 11.2x28 rear tires, 6x16 front tires, 3 pt.
8N			F	$1,400	3/28/2013	SCMN	WF, fenders, PTO
8N			G	$1,500	3/23/2013	NEIN	3 pt., repainted, runs
8N			G	$1,600	3/7/2013	SEIA	
8N			G	$1,075	3/2/2013	ECMN	Good rubber
8N			G	$1,525	3/2/2013	ECMN	Good rubber
8N			G	$1,550	2/23/2013	SCIN	
8N			G	$800	2/12/2013	WCIL	
8N			G	$850	2/12/2013	WCIL	
8N			G	$950	2/7/2013	SEAR	Gas, PTO
8N			G	$3,300	2/6/2013	SESD	
8N			G	$1,300	12/14/2012	SWKY	
8N			G	$1,400	12/6/2012	Online	IQBID.com
8N			G	$1,400	12/6/2012	SEIA	PTO, 3 pt.
8N			G	$2,750	11/28/2012	Online	*PurpleWave.com,* item in Kansas, 4 cyl. gas, manual, spring suspension seat, Davis 100 loader, 3 pt., 540 PTO, rear wheel weights, front blade
8N			G	$1,500	11/17/2012	SWMN	
8N			G	$875	10/24/2012	WCWI	
8N			G	$1,800	9/14/2012	NCVA	New paint, rear blade
8N			G	$6,000	9/13/2012	SEIA	Restored Flathead, V8, factory tri power, Sherman OD, 3 pt., PTO
8N		2,929	P	$1,150	9/12/2012	Online	*IQBID.com,* item in Minnesota, 3 pt., PTO, 11.2x28 tires, has not been run in 3 years, turns over but will not start
8N		1,932	G	$1,430	9/12/2012	Online	*PurpleWave.com,* item in Kansas, 4 cyl. gas, manual
8N			G	$3,100	8/8/2012	Online	*BigIron.com,* item in Kansas, 4F/1R, 4 cyl. gas, 540 PTO, new starter, generator and gas tank, just repainted
8N			G	$2,500	8/4/2012	ECMN	Fenders, 12.4x28 tires, 4 speed, 3 pt., runs
8N			F	$975	7/28/2012	SCNE	
8N			G	$1,300	7/27/2012	SWKY	

Ford

Model	Year	Hours	Condition	Price	Date	Area	Comments
8N			P	$1,025	7/24/2012	NCIA	Bad motor, loader sold separate for $150
8N			G	$1,100	7/18/2012	ECND	3 pt., good 11.2x28 tires
8N			G	$1,650	6/28/2012	Online	*PurpleWave.com,* item in Kansas, 4 cyl. gas, 4 speed, 3 pt., 540 PTO
8N			G	$2,000	6/20/2012	ECIL	
8N			G	$1,700	6/13/2012	Online	*BigIron.com,* item in Colorado, 4F/1R, gas, 540 PTO, 3 pt., Howse 5' mower
8N			G	$1,875	5/23/2012	Online	*BigIron.com,* item in Nebraska, 4 speed OD, 4 cyl. gas, 540 PTO, WF, 3 pt., drawbar
8N			G	$1,650	5/9/2012	Online	*PurpleWave.com,* item in Kansas, gas, Hi/Lo, 4F/1R, 540 PTO, 3 pt., 12.4x28 rear tires, 6x16 front tires
8N			G	$1,500	4/20/2012	WCSK	Front-end loader, 3 pt., 540 PTO
8N			G	$2,300	4/13/2012	SWSK	2WD, 27 hp, gas, 3 pt., 540 PTO, 12.4x28 rear
8N			G	$1,325	4/9/2012	ECSD	LP, WF, new rear tires
8N			G	$2,800	3/24/2012	NEIN	Repainted, new tires, runs
8N			G	$3,400	2/4/2012	ECTX	3 pt., 540 PTO
8N			G	$1,000	1/28/2012	ECMO	
8N			G	$1,200	1/28/2012	ECMO	
8N			G	$1,400	1/28/2012	ECMO	
8N			P	$800	1/27/2012	SEAL	
8N		7,380	G	$1,550	1/18/2012	Online	*BigIron.com,* item in Nebraska, 4 cyl., less than 200 hours on OH, gas, 540 PTO, fenders, 3 pt., 6V, new seat cover
8N			F	$1,200	1/11/2012	Online	*BigIron.com,* item in South Dakota, 6' loader, 5 speed, 4 cyl. gas, PTO, 6V battery system, 3 pt., exhaust leak
8N			F	$1,300	12/10/2011	SEIA	Utility
8N			G	$1,210	12/7/2011	Online	*PurpleWave.com,* item in Kansas, 4 cyl. gas, 4 speed, 3 pt., 540 PTO, 6V electric
8N			F	$1,400	12/3/2011	NCOH	New radiator and brakes
8N			F	$1,100	10/7/2011	NWSD	6 cyl., conversion, not running
8N			G	$1,300	9/17/2011	SEND	3 pt., PTO, 4 speed, looked good, steering arms altered
8N			G	$1,600	7/30/2011	ECMO	
8N			G	$2,200	7/27/2011	ECND	90% restored, new rubber
8N			F	$1,400	6/18/2011	SESK	4 cyl. gas, 3 pt., PTO
8N			G	$2,250	6/4/2011	ECIN	WF, gas
8N			G	$2,750	5/7/2011	SESK	Gas, 3 pt., saw mandrel
8N			G	$1,700	4/23/2011	WCMI	Gas, good tires, nice paint, 3 pt., PTO
8N			G	$1,600	4/13/2011	Online	*BigIron.com,* item in Nebraska, rear tires 12.4x26, front tires 6x16
8N			G	$2,300	3/26/2011	WCOH	Gas, WF
8N			G	$1,500	3/24/2011	ECMT	3 pt., PTO
8N			F	$900	3/19/2011	ECIA	
8N			G	$1,050	12/30/2010	ECMN	3 pt.
8N			G	$2,700	12/11/2010	NCOH	Very nice rubber

Ford

Model	Year	Hours	Condition	Price	Date	Area	Comments
8N			G	$1,000	12/4/2010	SEMN	5' sickle mower, new starter, new battery, 3 pt., WF, gas, unknown hours
8N			F	$900	12/2/2010	ECWY	4 cyl. gas, 3 speed, 3pt., 540 PTO, 11.2x28 tires
8N			P	$1,200	11/20/2010	SEIA	Does not run
8N			F	$1,200	11/17/2010	ECMS	6 cyl., Funk conversion
8N			F	$1,750	11/17/2010	ECMS	
8N			G	$3,750	11/17/2010	ECMS	
8N			P	$850	11/13/2010	WCMN	Needs work
8N			G	$2,100	11/6/2010	SEMN	Front bumper
8N			F	$1,100	10/16/2010	SEIA	2 sold on this sale - each for $1,100
8N			F	$1,100	10/16/2010	SEIA	2 sold on this sale - each for $1,100
8N			G	$2,000	9/4/2010	NEIN	Cut away
8N			G	$13,000	9/4/2010	NEIN	V8 conversion
8N			P	$1,300	9/3/2010	NEIN	Funk conversion, 6 cyl., gas, dead row, needs work and may not run or drive, as is
8N			P	$2,200	9/3/2010	NEIN	6 cyl. gas, dead row, needs work and may not run or drive, as is
8N			F	$1,200	8/24/2010	NEMO	Fenders, 3 pt., 540 PTO
8N			F	$800	8/19/2010	Online	*IronPlanet.com,* item in Kansas
8N		3,669	G	$1,760	7/28/2010	Online	*PurpleWave.com,* item in Kansas, 4 cyl. gas, WF, hyd., replaced alternator and battery
8N			G	$2,650	6/11/2010	SEAB	Gas, 3 pt., PTO, 6V, sandblasted, painted, OH, new rear tires, rims, tubes, carb, plugs, points, distributor, starter
8N			G	$800	6/5/2010	WCMO	
8N			G	$1,300	6/5/2010	WCMO	
8N			F	$1,475	6/5/2010	NEIN	12V ignition
8N			F	$1,600	6/5/2010	SEMN	Hyd. loader
8N			G	$1,600	6/5/2010	NETN	
8N			F	$1,800	6/5/2010	SEMN	3 pt.
8N			F	$2,000	6/5/2010	SEMN	3 pt.
8N		2,200	G	$2,090	5/26/2010	Online	*PurpleWave.com,* item in Kansas, 4 cyl. gas, 1 rev. gear, 3 pt., 540 PTO
8N			G	$1,250	5/7/2010	WCOH	Previous OH
8N			G	$1,800	5/1/2010	SENE	
8N			F	$2,600	4/17/2010	SESK	PTO, 3 pt., restored
8N			G	$2,200	4/16/2010	SESK	2WD, factory 3 pt., good rubber
8N			G	$1,700	4/10/2010	NCTN	
8N			G	$1,600	3/16/2010	SEND	
8N			G	$800	3/5/2010	SEWA	
8N			G	$1,045	2/24/2010	Online	*PurpleWave.com,* item in Kansas, 3 pt., PTO
8N			G	$1,265	2/24/2010	Online	*PurpleWave.com,* item in Kansas, 3 pt., 540 PTO, gas
8N			G	$1,485	2/24/2010	Online	*PurpleWave.com,* item in Kansas, 4 cyl. gas, 3 speed, 540 PTO, new 12V system
8N			G	$1,265	1/27/2010	Online	*PurpleWave.com,* item in Kansas, 3 pt., 540 PTO, 4 cyl. gas

Ford

Model	Year	Hours	Condition	Price	Date	Area	Comments
8N			G	$1,800	1/2/2010	NCIN	Turf tires
9N	1939		G	$982	6/21/2011	Online	*BidNow.US,* new paint job, last fall hyd. work, runs
9N	1940		G	$900	7/17/2013	NEND	3 pt., PTO, SN 34198
9N	1940		G	$1,550	7/17/2013	NEND	3 pt., PTO, SN 22857
9N	1940		G	$1,025	8/25/2011	ECND	3 pt., PTO, factory tall 4x19 fronts, 9.5x32 rears, runs
9N	1941		G	$1,925	9/27/2013	Online	*PurpleWave.com,* item in Oklahoma, Ford 4 cyl. Flathead gas, Sherman manual, Hi/Lo, differential lock, spring seat, 12V system, 3 pt., 540 PTO, 10 gal. fuel tank
9N	1941		G	$1,000	3/5/2011	NWMO	
9N	1942		G	$1,300	8/10/2011	Online	*BigIron.com,* item in Nebraska, 3 speed, OD, 4 cyl. gas, 540 PTO, 6V system, front bumper guard, front lights, 3 pt., hitch and stabilizer
9N	1942		F	$950	6/22/2011	NECO	Gas, Wagner loader
9N	1943		G	$1,100	11/9/2013	SWON	On steel, 3 pt., PTO
9N	1943		G	$1,100	11/9/2013	SWON	On steel, 3 pt., PTO, SN 124228
9N	1944		F	$675	9/13/2012	Online	*IQBID.com,* item in Iowa
9N	1946		G	$1,100	6/22/2011	Online	*BigIron.com,* item in Nebraska, 3F/1R, Ford 4 cyl. gas, 540 PTO, 3 pt., 7' IMCO rear blade
9N	1950		F	$1,200	9/7/2011	SEND	3 speed, 3 pt., PTO, Farmhand loader, 12x4x28 rears
9N			G	$1,350	3/4/2014	SWMN	12.4x28 rear tires, 15" front tires, gas, converted to 12V, 3 pt., PTO, no top link
9N			G	$900	2/22/2014	SCNE	
9N			G	$800	1/4/2014	WCNY	
9N			G	$1,000	11/9/2013	SWON	On Arps half tracks, no SN
9N			G	$2,500	7/25/2013	WCSK	Front-end loader, 3 pt., rear rubber good, 11.2x28
9N			G	$1,150	6/22/2013	SEWA	4 cyl. gas, crank start and electric starter, rear 3 pt., PTO
9N			G	$800	6/20/2013	ECSK	Rebuilt starter, fresh tune up, slight rear end leak, good rubber front and rear
9N			G	$1,150	5/11/2013	NCOH	3 pt., original, runs
9N			G	$3,500	3/23/2013	NEIN	Restored, runs
9N			G	$1,200	12/13/2012	WCIA	
9N			F	$1,475	6/7/2012	NEIN	
9N			G	$1,025	7/30/2011	ECMO	Finish mower, 3 pt. blade
9N			G	$1,300	6/22/2011	Online	*BigIron.com,* item in Nebraska, manual, 4 cyl. gas, 3 pt., new 6V battery, undercarriage low muffler, 3 pt. missing top link, new seat cover, manual, 3F/1R, front grill guard with hitch
9N			G	$900	3/5/2011	SEMN	Gas, 540 PTO, 3 pt., fenders
9N			F	$950	11/18/2010	SEOK	
9N			P	$850	11/13/2010	WCMN	Needs work
9N			G	$2,900	9/4/2010	NEIN	
9N			G	$1,000	8/7/2010	SEWI	Restored in 2002, complete mechanical restoration

Ford

Model	Year	Hours	Condition	Price	Date	Area	Comments
9N			G	$2,800	7/22/2010	ECND	3 pt.
9N			G	$1,200	6/26/2010	NCMD	
9N			G	$1,000	6/11/2010	SEAB	Gas, 3 pt., PTO, 12V, sandblasted, painted, OH, new hyd. pump, steering wheel, 3 pt. arms and level crank, plugs, battery
9N			G	$1,000	5/1/2010	SENE	
9N			G	$1,200	4/10/2010	SCMN	3 speed, loader, snow and manure buckets, 3 pt., weight box
600	1954		G	$1,500	4/11/2011	Online	*AuctionTime.com,* 2WD
600	1954		G	$2,000	5/1/2010	NCOH	3 pt., PTO, new battery, runs, works
600	1955		F	$1,600	10/24/2012	NECO	Gas, WF, 3 pt.
600	1956		E	$3,200	9/14/2011	NWIL	Gas, restored, good tires
600	1957		G	$2,100	8/24/2013	WCMN	Looks like original
600	1957	633	G	$1,600	3/26/2011	NECO	WF, 3 pt., gas
600		3,468	G	$1,900	8/29/2013	NWIA	WF, gas, 12 speed, OD, 3 pt., fenders, 13.6x28 tires
600			G	$900	7/27/2012	SWKY	
600			P	$2,500	4/26/2012	WCSK	3 pt., PTO, housing needs repair, 12.4x28 rear
600			G	$3,250	3/28/2012	ECND	Loader, recently painted, recent OH, excellent oil pressue, good rubber
600			F	$2,400	1/28/2012	SEAB	
600			G	$1,400	10/27/2011	NETX	Gas, 3 pt.
600			F	$1,300	10/22/2011	ECTX	Loader
600			G	$1,851	4/27/2011	Online	*BigIron.com,* item in Wyoming, 5 speed, 4 cyl. gas, 3 pt., drawbar
600			G	$2,200	3/19/2011	SEIA	
600			G	$3,800	12/21/2010	ECMI	
600			G	$2,250	10/16/2010	SEIA	New rear rubber
601	1961		G	$2,600	4/11/2013	NCMI	Gas, power steering, 3 pt., PTO, Freeman 2000 hyd. loader, SN 138068
601			G	$1,250	8/4/2012	SWKY	
601			G	$1,150	7/28/2012	SWTN	Workmaster
601			G	$3,200	12/1/2011	NEIN	Workmaster, front-end loader, 13.6x28 rear tires, hood guard
601			G	$850	10/28/2011	NETX	Open station, gas
601			G	$2,900	9/7/2011	SEND	1 hyd., 3 pt., PTO, 12x4x28 rears, restored
601			G	$1,850	4/16/2011	SCWI	Select-O-Speed, belly mower, gas, PS, 3 pt., PTO
601		800	G	$1,524	3/23/2011	Online	*BigIron.com,* high-crop, 4 cyl., gas, 540 PTO
601			G	$2,800	11/17/2010	ECMS	
640			G	$1,500	11/9/2013	SWON	3 pt., PTO, SN 121530
640			G	$2,600	1/31/2012	NEIN	Loader, power steering, original
640			G	$3,000	9/7/2011	SEND	3 pt., PTO, 12x4x28 turf tires
641	1960		F	$1,350	12/17/2010	WCIL	540 PTO
641	1961	6,616	F	$2,000	6/14/2010	Online	*BigIron.com,* item in Nebraska, 4 speed, 4 cyl. gas, 540 PTO, 3 pt., new battery

Ford

Model	Year	Hours	Condition	Price	Date	Area	Comments
641			G	$1,400	7/27/2012	SWKY	
641		2,768	G	$1,815	6/28/2012	Online	*PurpleWave.com,* item in Kansas, 4 cyl. gas, 4 speed manual, 3 pt., 540 PTO
641			G	$2,100	5/7/2010	WCOH	Loader, 40" bucket
661			G	$5,100	4/20/2012	WCSK	3 pt., 540 PTO, 1 hyd., 13.9x28 rear tires, 3 rib front
670	1960		G	$1,450	6/22/2011	NECO	Gas, Select-O-Speed, SF, 3 pt.
672	1959	912	G	$2,251	4/13/2011	Online	*BigIron.com,* item in Nebraska, 12.4x28 rear tires, 5.5x16 front tires
800	1954	713	G	$2,400	2/17/2011	WCNE	Gas, 3 pt., WF
800	1955		E	$5,000	7/27/2013	WCIL	Diesel, SN 20347, WF, PS, recent professional overhaul done at Hills Ford-New Holland dealership, Mt. Sterling, Ill., hyd. loader
800	1955		G	$3,050	8/6/2011	NCIA	Utility, 3 pt.
800	1957	5,362	G	$1,900	1/26/2011	NECO	WF, gas, 3 pt.
800			G	$1,600	3/22/2014	SWMI	4 cyl. gas, 5 speed, WF, 3 pt., PTO, 11.2x28 rear tires
800			G	$1,300	1/4/2014	WCNY	
800			G	$2,750	1/4/2014	ECOH	Restored
800			G	$1,000	12/19/2013	SCNY	
800			F	$1,500	11/9/2013	SWON	3 pt. not working, PTO, no SN
800			F	$1,870	10/8/2013	Online	*PurpleWave.com,* item in Kansas, Ford 4 cyl. gas, 10F/2R, 3 pt., 540 PTO, 13.6x28 rear tires, brakes are weak
800			G	$2,200	9/12/2013	SEIA	
800			G	$3,700	3/16/2013	SEMN	WF, 3 pt., hyd. PTO
800			G	$4,290	11/28/2012	Online	*PurpleWave.com,* item in Kansas, 4 cyl. gas, manual, spring suspension seat, Ford loader, 540 PTO, 3 pt., front hyd., rear wheel weights
800			F	$1,760	10/31/2012	Online	*PurpleWave.com,* item in Oklahoma, 4 cyl. gas, manual, 3 pt., top link, 540 PTO
800			G	$2,200	12/8/2010	ECND	Loader, factory weights, power steering, 3 pt.
800			G	$2,000	8/9/2010	WCMO	
800			G	$1,500	6/5/2010	NETN	
800			E	$2,850	5/15/2010	NEND	Factory 3 pt. hitch, 540 PTO, stored inside
800		2,442	G	$3,300	4/28/2010	Online	*PurpleWave.com,* item in Kansas, 4 cyl. 172 gauge, 1 hyd.
800			G	$1,600	4/10/2010	ECON	
800			G	$1,550	3/6/2010	NEMO	Gas, 14.9x28 tires, 3pt.
801	1955		G	$4,500	9/21/2013	SEMN	Master PS, 117 hours on rebuilt engine, like new 13.6x28 tires and rims on rear
801		2,505	G	$1,540	8/28/2013	Online	*PurpleWave.com,* item in Missouri, 4 cyl. gas, manual, 3 pt., drawbar, 6.5x16 front tires, 12.4x28 rear tires, clutch issue with PTO
801			G	$900	7/27/2012	SWKY	
801			G	$1,300	12/9/2011	SWKY	

Ford

Model	Year	Hours	Condition	Price	Date	Area	Comments
801			G	$3,700	6/30/2011	ECMO	Powermaster, 13.6x28 rear tires, 3pt., PTO, 1 hyd., straight and original!
801			F	$1,575	6/29/2011	WCIL	Gas, loader, weights, 5' rotary mower
801			G	$2,900	5/7/2011	SESK	2WD, gas, Select-O-Speed, PTO, 3 pt., front-end loader
850	1954		G	$1,350	2/27/2014	NWNE	Gas, WF, 3 pt.
850	1956	5,425	G	$2,300	12/8/2010	NECO	WF, gas, 3 pt.
850			G	$2,700	11/27/2010	SEMN	3 pt., PTO, hyd., back blade, 14.9x28 tires
860	1955		G	$4,200	3/28/2013	SCMN	WF, restored, 800 decals, fenders, PTO
860			G	$3,750	3/24/2012	NEIN	Unreadable tag, repainted, power steering, live PTO, live hyd., runs
860			G	$2,000	5/7/2010	WCOH	Live PTO, good sheet metal, 5 speed, jumps out of third gear
861	1954		G	$1,500	4/11/2011	Online	*AuctionTime.com*
861	1960		G	$3,000	1/28/2012	ECMO	Hours unknown, recent OH, Powermaster, live power
861			G	$2,700	8/24/2013	SEMN	Powermaster, 3 pt., hyd., PTO, 13.6x28
861			G	$4,200	8/24/2013	NWIL	Diesel, 4 new tires
861		2,829	G	$6,000	8/9/2013	SWOH	Powermaster
861			G	$4,900	9/29/2012	WCWI	Restored, parade ready, Powermaster
861			G	$2,850	3/17/2012	WCOH	
861			F	$1,600	8/23/2011	NCIA	Gas, 3 pt., fence row sprayer unit and 150 gal. tank
861			G	$2,600	6/5/2010	ECMN	Gas, 12V
900	1955		G	$2,500	4/18/2011	WCSK	3 pt., 38 hp, gas, engine rebuilt, blade, cultivator, pallet fork, post hole auger, 6" and 9" bits
900	1960	949	G	$1,900	3/26/2011	NECO	WF, gas, 7' 3 pt. blade
900			G	$1,705	8/26/2013	NWWI	
900		323	G	$2,420	9/14/2011	Online	*PurpleWave.com,* item in Kansas
901	1954		G	$2,250	8/24/2013	WCMN	Select-O-Speed, new paint, 3 pt.
901	1957	3,366	G	$2,801	5/23/2012	Online	*BigIron.com,* item in South Dakota, diesel, Select-O-Speed, 10F/2R gears, 1 hyd., 3 pt., 540 PTO, new battery, 6' Borngaars box blade
901	1958		G	$3,100	9/19/2013	SWIA	47 hp, 2WD, rear tires: singles, loader
901	1958		G	$1,400	11/9/2012	NEAR	Powermaster, 4 cyl. diesel, 3 pt., 540 PTO
901	1958		G	$3,700	7/10/2010	SEIA	Powermaster, NF, 5 speed, live power 3 pt., power steering
901	1959		G	$1,900	11/9/2013	SWON	Powermaster diesel, power steering, 3 pt., PTO
901	1959		G	$1,900	11/9/2013	SWON	Powermaster diesel, tricycle, power steering, 3 pt., PTO, SN 47090
901	1959		G	$4,000	3/17/2012	WCOH	Tricycle, NF, Select-O-Speed
901	1959		F	$1,000	9/11/2010	SEIA	WF, Freeman 2000 loader
901	1960		F	$2,250	4/20/2011	NWMI	Diesel, Select-O-Speed, WF, 14.9x28 tires, fenders, fresh paint
901	1962	8,251	G	$3,960	6/8/2010	Online	*PurpleWave.com,* item in Kansas, 4 cyl. gas, 8' Sunmaster belly mower

Ford

Model	Year	Hours	Condition	Price	Date	Area	Comments
901		1,265	G	$2,800	9/22/2012	NCCO	Powermaster, WF
901		8,183	G	$1,150	6/23/2010	Online	*BigIron.com,* item in Nebraska, auto 10 speed, diesel, 540 PTO, 2 pt., electric start
901			F	$3,200	6/23/2010	Online	*BigIron.com,* item in Nebraska, Select-O-Speed, 4 cyl gas, 13.6x28 rear tires, 5.5x16 front tires, 540 PTO, tractor was restored by the second owner of 30 years (seller)
960			G	$3,400	9/15/2012	SCMN	NF
961			G	$3,750	3/23/2013	NEIN	High crop, 3 pt., diesel, repainted, runs
961			G	$2,700	1/28/2012	ECMO	Gas, 3 pt. blade, manual
961			P	$900	11/19/2010	SENE	Standard, needs work
961			G	$1,500	6/5/2010	ECMN	12V conversion, gas, WF, recently OH
971	1959		G	$1,300	5/23/2012	Online	*BigIron.com,* item in South Dakota, Select-O-Speed, 4 cyl. gas, 1 hyd., 540 PTO, 3 pt., runs, shedded
971			G	$3,465	8/26/2013	NWWI	50 hp, gas, live power, many new or rebuilt parts, tires 90%, 1 arm loader, Select-O-Speed
981	1958		F	$975	10/7/2011	NWSD	Select-O-Speed, PTO, trans. out, tin is pretty good, rubber pretty good
1164	1978	3,100	G	$5,000	8/16/2012	Online	*IQBID.com,* item in Minnesota, 4WD, open station, 2 hyd., 3 pt., 1,000 PTO, no top link, 18.4x30 tires
1520	1974	1,852	G	$2,960	5/8/2013	Online	*IQBID.com,* HST utility, 2WD, 3 cyl. hydro, 23 hp, 3 pt., 540 PTO
1600	1978	428	G	$2,700	4/20/2011	NWMI	2WD, diesel, 11.2x24 tires, 3 pt., PTO, 1 hyd.
2000	1964		G	$1,700	11/2/2010	ECOK	Super Dexta, diesel, 3 cyl., 42 hp, 3 pt., PTO, rebuilt engine
2000	1970		G	$4,800	8/14/2013	WCMN	Live PTO, 3 pt., 1 hyd., gas, good rubber
2000	1972		G	$3,500	11/25/2013	SCIA	
2000	1972		G	$3,000	12/14/2012	SWKY	Diesel
2000	1974	4,287	G	$2,750	11/13/2013	Online	*PurpleWave.com,* item in Kansas, 3 cyl. gas, 540 PTO, 3 pt.
2000	1974		G	$3,200	3/24/2012	SETN	Rebuilt motor
2000			G	$2,250	3/26/2014	ECMS	2WD
2000			G	$2,300	3/26/2014	ECMS	
2000			G	$2,250	3/22/2014	NETN	3 cyl. diesel, PS, good rubber
2000			G	$2,600	1/4/2014	WCNY	1 hyd., 3 pt., PTO
2000			G	$1,250	8/24/2013	SWWI	Unrestored
2000			G	$3,300	4/26/2013	SWKY	Gas
2000			G	$2,900	3/23/2013	NEIN	Gas, 3 pt., fenders, repainted, runs
2000			G	$5,500	3/23/2013	NEIN	Low hours, offset, original, runs
2000		477	G	$5,610	2/19/2013	NWWI	Diesel, Koyker 210 loader, 3 pt., quick attach bucket
2000			G	$2,700	11/6/2012	ECOK	3 pt. PTO, ROPS, gas, 12.4x28 rubber
2000			G	$2,750	10/31/2012	Online	*PurpleWave.com,* item in Oklahoma, 4 cyl. gas, manual, Ford loader, 3 pt., top link, 540 PTO

Ford

Model	Year	Hours	Condition	Price	Date	Area	Comments
2000		1,497	G	$3,100	7/25/2012	Online	*BigIron.com,* item in Nebraska, gas, 12.4x28 tires, 3 pt., 540 PTO, over running clutch, 1 rear hyd., front lights, new steering wheel
2000			G	$1,900	6/29/2012	NETX	36 hp, 3 cyl. diesel, 2WD, open station, 12.4x28 tires
2000			G	$2,860	5/30/2012	Online	*PurpleWave.com,* item in Oklahoma
2000			G	$2,500	3/24/2012	SETN	Power steering
2000			G	$4,100	2/4/2012	ECSC	Diesel
2000			G	$2,100	2/2/2012	NEIN	12.4x28 rear tires, 3 pt.
2000		1,950	G	$1,750	12/9/2011	SWKY	Gas
2000		755	G	$2,640	8/31/2011	Online	*PurpleWave.com,* item in Kansas, 4 cyl. gas, 36 hp, 4 speed, PTO
2000			F	$3,750	3/19/2011	NCPA	
2000			G	$3,500	11/20/2010	NCLA	Diesel, 3 pt.
2000			F	$2,100	4/9/2010	WCFL	
3000	1967	6,913	G	$3,750	8/13/2011	WCIL	Utility tractor, loader, 13.6/12x28 turf tires, 3 pt., PTO
3000	1968		G	$3,000	8/14/2013	WCMN	2WD, good rubber, gas, 3 pt., PTO, 1 hyd.
3000	1969	3,047	G	$4,900	9/17/2011	NEIA	Gas, WF, 3pt., 13.6x28 rear tires, 80 hours on OH, new rear tires, chains
3000	1970	3,261	G	$4,000	11/10/2012	WCIL	ROPS, canopy, 3 pt., 540 PTO, gas
3000	1970	6,218	G	$1,750	3/20/2012	WCIL	Gas, 13.6x28 rear tires, 540 PTO
3000	1971	6,467	G	$2,000	12/12/2012	SEIA	loader
3000	1972	2,433	F	$4,730	6/8/2010	Online	*PurpleWave.com,* item in Kansas, 3 cyl. gas, 540 PTO, 3 pt., no 3rd link, needs battery
3000	1974		G	$3,410	1/19/2010	Online	*PurpleWave.com,* item in Kansas, 3 cyl. diesel, 540 PTO
3000	1975		G	$2,600	4/11/2013	NCMI	Gas, power steering, new 13.6x28 tires, 1 hyd., 3 pt., PTO
3000			G	$2,000	3/26/2014	ECMS	2WD
3000			G	$2,800	3/8/2014	NWLA	Diesel, PS
3000			G	$2,800	3/8/2014	NWLA	Diesel, PS
3000		1,334	G	$1,900	2/22/2014	NEIN	Loader, diesel, PTO
3000		2,054	F	$2,860	12/17/2013	WCMI	3 pt., rear tires 13.6/12x28
3000		2,676	G	$1,750	8/24/2013	NWMO	Diesel, Select-O-Matic, 3 pt., 540 PTO, new rear tires, one owner
3000		3,830	G	$1,900	4/10/2013	NETX	12.4x28
3000			G	$3,000	1/19/2013	NEMS	
3000			G	$2,900	12/14/2012	SWKY	
3000			F	$1,400	12/8/2012	ECTX	Diesel, 13.6x28 rear tires, 5.5x16 front tires, 3 pt., PTO, rough
3000		3,118	G	$3,750	8/4/2012	NEAR	3 cyl. gas, 3 pt., 540 PTO
3000			G	$2,300	7/28/2012	NWSC	Diesel
3000		3,500	G	$3,350	7/11/2012	WCIL	New pistons and rings, all new tires, good paint, gas
3000			F	$3,050	6/7/2012	NEIN	Loader
3000			G	$2,500	3/24/2012	SWMI	3 pt., loader attach, PTO, WF, gas, 14.9x24 rear tires, tire chains

Ford

Model	Year	Hours	Condition	Price	Date	Area	Comments
3000			G	$1,250	2/18/2012	SWAR	
3000			G	$3,700	1/21/2012	NEMS	
3000			G	$2,300	12/17/2011	SEFL	Diesel
3000			G	$2,750	12/9/2011	SWKY	Diesel
3000			G	$5,250	11/19/2011	SEIA	WF, 3 pt., Hi/Lo, 2 hyd.
3000			G	$5,600	10/27/2011	NETX	
3000		3,125	G	$2,200	9/7/2011	SEND	Open station, 8 speed, 1 hyd., 3 pt., PTO, 13x6x28 rears
3000		4,183	G	$2,000	5/13/2011	ECMS	
3000			G	$3,000	5/13/2011	ECMS	New rear tire
3000		3,540	G	$2,500	4/16/2011	SCWI	Utility, gas
3000			G	$2,900	4/11/2011	Online	*AuctionTime.com*
3000		3,652	G	$1,750	11/20/2010	SCKY	
3000			G	$2,250	11/20/2010	NCLA	3 pt., diesel
3000			G	$2,000	11/18/2010	SEOK	
3000			G	$2,600	11/18/2010	SEOK	
3000		1,664	G	$5,100	9/2/2010	ECND	3 pt., PTO
3000			G	$3,950	8/9/2010	WCMO	Tires 75%
3000		4,029	E	$8,200	7/17/2010	NCIL	Gas, PS, 3 pt., rear weights, Ford hyd. loader, 14.9x28 tires
3000		1,686	G	$1,700	6/5/2010	NETN	
3000		1,710	G	$2,300	6/5/2010	NETN	
3000		3,655	G	$2,900	5/22/2010	SEMN	Gas, WF, 3pt., PTO, 13.6x28 turf tires
3000		4,100	G	$3,500	5/7/2010	WCOH	Gas, OH, power steering, repaint
3000		2,115	F	$1,500	5/4/2010	WCOK	Diesel, 3 pt., PTO, does not run
3000			G	$3,500	4/10/2010	ECON	
3000			F	$2,500	4/9/2010	WCFL	
3000			G	$3,300	2/24/2010	Online	*PurpleWave.com,* item in Missouri, Ford 3 cyl., 3 pt., 540 PTO, 40" bucket
3000			F	$3,250	1/9/2010	ECTX	Diesel, loader, no power steering, 3pt., PTO, shows 2,992 hours (not correct)
3400	1972		G	$3,850	3/15/2011	WCIL	540 PTO, gas
3400		5,236	G	$1,450	3/26/2014	Online	*BigIron.com,* item in New Mexico, loader, manual, 16.9x24 rear tires, 7.5x16 front tires, gas, 3 pt.
3400			G	$1,150	1/17/2014	SEOK	
3400		3,971	G	$2,860	2/1/2012	SEND	Utility, gas, loader
3400			G	$4,125	12/6/2011	Online	*BidNow.US,* loader tractor, forks and bucket, ballast box, 14x24 rear tires
3400			G	$2,500	3/19/2011	SEIA	Industrial, loader
3400			P	$1,450	1/29/2011	ECMO	Industrial, industrial loader
3400			G	$1,950	11/20/2010	NCLA	Gas, 3 pt.
3400			G	$1,800	11/17/2010	ECMS	
3400			G	$2,250	5/7/2010	WCOH	Gas, power steering
3400		5,097	G	$4,950	1/19/2010	Online	*PurpleWave.com,* item in Kansas, 3 pt., 540 PTO, 3 cyl. gas, rear axle weights
3500		3,403	G	$1,550	9/12/2013	SEIA	Loader tractor, gas, 16.9x24 rears
3500			G	$3,650	3/19/2011	SEIA	Industrial

Ford

Model	Year	Hours	Condition	Price	Date	Area	Comments
3600	1977		G	$5,060	2/26/2014	Online	*PurpleWave.com,* item in Kansas, Ford 3 cyl. diesel, manual, spring suspension seat, 3 pt.
3600	1978	1,121	F	$1,705	9/26/2012	Online	*PurpleWave.com,* item in Kansas, Ford 3 cyl. gas, 34 hp, manual
4000	1960	600	G	$1,300	9/22/2010	NECO	WF, gas, 3 pt., loader
4000	1962	2,810	F	$2,500	12/1/2012	SEWY	Diesel, WF, no 3 pt., Ford loader, needs hyd. pump
4000	1962	2,155	G	$3,500	5/4/2010	WCOK	Power steering, 3 pt., PTO, 1 hyd., Ezee-On loader
4000	1964	3,017	F	$1,700	12/1/2012	SEWY	Diesel, WF, 3 pt.
4000	1964		F	$2,500	9/14/2012	NCVA	Diesel, Select-O-Speed, loader
4000	1964		F	$1,350	8/6/2011	NCOK	NF, 3pt., PTO
4000	1964		G	$3,200	3/24/2011	NCMI	Select-O-Speed, good tires, 3 pt., PS, 540 PTO, 1 hyd.
4000	1964		G	$3,700	3/5/2011	NWMO	NF, Select-O-Speed
4000	1965		G	$2,000	6/29/2012	NETX	55 hp, gas, 2WD, open station, new 13.6x28 tires, new paint
4000	1966	399	F	$1,800	12/1/2012	SEWY	Gas, WF, 3 pt.
4000	1966	316	F	$1,870	9/26/2012	Online	*PurpleWave.com,* item in Kansas, gas, 8 speed manual, 3 pt., no top link, NF, power steering
4000	1966	1,077	P	$1,550	11/26/2011	WCOH	Rough, gas, PS, runs, WF
4000	1969		G	$2,200	4/27/2013	ECMI	Diesel, 2WD, PS, 3 pt., PTO, 1 hyd., 13.6x36 tires, SN 245345
4000	1969		G	$3,500	11/19/2011	SEIA	Gas, 540/1,000 PTO, 3 pt., new rear rubber, quick attach loader
4000	1973		G	$2,800	1/29/2014	Online	*BigIron.com,* item in Nebraska, manual Hi/Lo, 3 cyl. diesel, 50 PTO hp, 1 hyd., 540 PTO, Du-Al loader, 5' bucket, PTO hyd. pump, 3 pt.
4000			G	$2,000	3/26/2014	ECMS	
4000		1,783	G	$1,750	3/22/2014	NETN	Gas, 5 speed
4000			G	$2,300	12/20/2013	SCSD	WF, PS, Du-Al 320 loader, 6' bucket
4000			F	$2,900	8/24/2013	SWOH	Gas, runs
4000			G	$3,500	8/24/2013	NWMO	Diesel, 3 pt., aux. hyd., 13.6/12x36 tires 75%, SN 208831
4000			F	$3,000	7/27/2013	WCIL	WF
4000			G	$1,900	3/22/2013	WCMI	60 hp 4 cyl. gas, WF, 3 pt., live PTO, 16.9x28 rear tires
4000		4,044	G	$4,300	3/16/2013	SEMN	Gas, WF, Ford 1 arm hyd. loader, 3 pt., PTO
4000			G	$4,000	1/7/2013	SWOH	3 cyl. gas, 14.9x30 tires, 3 pt., 540 PTO
4000			G	$2,800	12/14/2012	SWKY	Diesel
4000		2,888	G	$3,500	9/13/2012	Online	*IQBID.com*, item in Iowa, industrial, loader, 16.9x24 rears
4000		1,127	G	$2,420	8/15/2012	Online	*PurpleWave.com,* item in Kansas, 4 cyl., manual, 3 pt., drawbar, 540 PTO, dual rear hyd., 16 gal. fuel tank, 62" wheelbase
4000		3,225	G	$3,300	8/4/2012	NEAR	3 cyl. diesel, 3 pt., 540 PTO
4000			G	$5,700	8/1/2012	NEOK	Loader

Ford

Model	Year	Hours	Condition	Price	Date	Area	Comments
4000			F	$3,600	6/13/2012	NEWI	Gas, 3pt., 540 PTO
4000			G	$3,900	6/13/2012	NWMN	Utility, 3 pt., PTO
4000			G	$1,600	3/24/2012	SWMI	4 cyl. diesel, WF, drawbar, 3 pt., PTO, 14.9x28 rear tires
4000			G	$3,500	3/24/2012	SWLA	
4000			G	$2,325	2/18/2012	ECIL	Gas, loader
4000			G	$11,000	1/28/2012	ECMO	
4000		3,759	G	$2,000	5/13/2011	ECMS	Diesel, Select-O-Speed
4000		5,500	G	$3,400	3/19/2011	NEMI	Diesel, good 16.9x30 tires, 1 hyd., PS, PTO, 3pt.
4000		4,835	G	$3,650	11/20/2010	SCKY	
4000			G	$1,600	11/18/2010	SEOK	
4000			G	$3,100	11/18/2010	SEOK	Loader
4000			G	$5,000	11/18/2010	SEOK	L18 loader and boom
4000			G	$2,400	6/5/2010	NCTN	
4000			G	$3,700	5/26/2010	ECSD	Ford 727 loader, gas
4000			G	$2,900	5/7/2010	WCOH	Gas, 1 hyd.
4000		4,540	G	$3,250	5/7/2010	WCOH	Repaint, new power steering pump
4000			G	$3,900	5/7/2010	WCOH	Diesel, repaint, transmission repaired, 1 hyd., new tires
4000			F	$1,150	4/9/2010	WCFL	
4000			F	$3,300	1/30/2010	WCIL	WF, 3 pt., 250 hours on motor
4100			G	$6,950	11/20/2010	SCKY	Bush Hog 2346 loader, 1 hyd.
4100			G	$8,300	11/18/2010	SEOK	4x4, Westendorf loader
4110			G	$850	6/5/2010	NCTN	
4500			G	$1,700	3/30/2013	SCMN	Industrial tractor and loader, 3 pt., PTO, HD loader
4500			F	$4,500	3/20/2013	SCMN	Loader, backhoe, 6' bucket
4500			G	$2,100	2/25/2012	WCMI	Industrial loader, Bradco pounder, diesel, 4 cyl., 16.9x24 tires
5000	1965	133	G	$3,500	4/17/2013	Online	*BigIron.com,* item in Kansas, Select-O-Speed, 10F/2R auto, 2WD
5000	1965	3,999	G	$3,700	3/27/2013	Online	*BigIron.com,* item in Nebraska, Select-O-Speed transmission
5000	1966	1,879	G	$4,000	12/8/2012	ECIA	Gas, WF, like new 15.5x38 front tires, 8 speed, super sharp, new paint
5000	1966		G	$4,700	8/16/2012	Online	*IQBID.com,* item in Minnesota, 2WD, WF, diesel, M&W turbo, 3 pt., PTO, rock box, 15.5x38 tires with band duals
5000	1966		G	$3,700	6/6/2011	SWSK	2WD open station, 53 PTO hp, Select-O-Speed, 3 pt., 540 PTO, 1 hyd., 3 rib front, engine rebuilt recently
5000	1967	4,170	G	$2,700	11/26/2013	ECND	Gas utility, 3 pt., PTO, 2 hyd., 16.9x30 rear tires, weight box
5000	1967		G	$2,900	8/22/2012	ECMN	Loader, 7' bucket, Select-O-Speed
5000	1968		G	$5,900	4/11/2013	NCMI	Diesel, 16.9x38 tires, 3 pt., PTO, 300 hours on OH, Ford 747 hyd. loader w/ bucket, SN C215977
5000	1968	7,600	F	$1,600	4/3/2013	NCMI	Diesel, 4th gear and reverse gone, Select-O-Speed, rear weights, runs and drives
5000	1968	8,332	G	$3,900	3/19/2011	SEWY	WF, diesel, 3 pt., no cab

Ford

Model	Year	Hours	Condition	Price	Date	Area	Comments
5000	1969		G	$4,300	8/15/2012	SCMN	Gas, 3 pt., 1 hyd., 18.4x34 tires, SN C241021
5000	1972	2,228	G	$4,620	10/16/2013	Online	*PurpleWave.com,* item in Kansas, 4 cyl. turbo diesel, 8 speed, 540 PTO
5000	1975	3,322	G	$4,950	3/4/2014	SWMN	WF, diesel, 2 hyd., 3 pt., PTO, Ford loader, 6' bucket, 16.9x30 tires
5000			G	$3,200	3/26/2014	ECMS	2WD, canopy
5000		5,391	G	$3,900	3/22/2014	NWMO	WF, 16.9x30 rubber, full hyd. loader and material bucket
5000			G	$4,000	1/4/2014	WCNY	Fender tractor, 3 pt., PTO
5000			G	$3,700	1/1/2014	SWOH	Select-O-Speed
5000		4,000	G	$4,300	12/26/2013	Online	*BigIron.com,* item in Colorado, PS, 4 cyl. diesel, 15.5x38 rear tires, 7.5-16 front tires, 1 hyd., 540 PTO, PS, 3 pt.
5000		688	G	$3,465	10/28/2013	NWWI	Diesel, WF, 3 pt., PTO
5000			F	$1,800	6/10/2013	WCSK	Diesel, 3 pt., belt pulley
5000		3,400	G	$8,800	3/23/2013	NEPA	Diesel
5000		4,820	G	$5,250	3/21/2013	ECIL	2WD, loader, no cab
5000		5,105	G	$5,600	3/16/2013	SEMN	Diesel, WF, rock box, 3 pt., dual hyd., PTO
5000			G	$6,800	12/14/2012	SWKY	Loader
5000			G	$5,500	8/4/2012	SWKY	
5000			F	$3,600	6/13/2012	NEWI	Diesel, mounted loader, 15.5x38 tires 90%
5000		2,065	G	$2,090	5/9/2012	Online	*PurpleWave.com,* item in Kansas, hour meter inoperable, 4 cyl. gas, 8F/2R, differential lock, spring ride seat, 12V system, 3 pt., drawbar, 540 PTO
5000			G	$4,700	2/24/2012	NETX	50 hp, diesel, row crop, 2WD, open station, 18.4x34 tires
5000		7,129	G	$6,500	5/19/2011	SWMT	3 pt., PTO, 18.4x30 tires, 60 hp, sold w/ Du-Al 325 loader, grapple
5000		6,380	G	$12,500	4/26/2011	ECSK	2WD, Leach loader, 53 PTO hp, diesel, 3 pt., hyd., 72" bucket, single bale spike, 10 sq. bale forks
5000			F	$4,000	2/21/2011	NEMO	15.5x38 rear tires, 7.5x16 front tires, rear weights, 3pt., 540 PTO, 1 hyd., loader, bucket
5000		6,000	G	$3,500	2/17/2011	NWIA	Diesel, no cab, 3 pt., 1 hyd., 4 speed Hi/Lo
5000			G	$7,750	11/20/2010	SCKY	Bush Hog 2846QT loader, cab, 2 hyd.
5000			G	$4,500	11/18/2010	SEOK	
5000		435	F	$5,280	7/28/2010	Online	*PurpleWave.com,* item in Kansas, diesel, rear rim rusted through, 3 pt., front weights
5000			F	$4,500	6/5/2010	NETN	Kelly front
5000		4,751	G	$4,600	6/5/2010	NETN	
5000		870	G	$2,860	5/26/2010	Online	*PurpleWave.com,* item in Missouri, Ford 3.6L, 47 hp diesel, hyd. PU
5000		3,081	G	$3,900	5/7/2010	WCOH	OH, repaint
5000			P	$3,100	4/9/2010	WCFL	Select-A-Speed, salvage
5600	1977	4,132	G	$8,000	9/21/2013	SWOH	Canopy, weights

Ford

Model	Year	Hours	Condition	Price	Date	Area	Comments
5600	1977		G	$4,070	9/10/2013	Online	*PurpleWave.com,* item in Kansas, 4 cyl., manual, 7.50Rx16LT front tires, 16.9x30 rear tires
6000	1963	2,597	G	$2,035	9/26/2012	Online	*PurpleWave.com,* item in Kansas, Ford 4.0L,, 6 cyl. diesel, 60 hp, PS, 3 pt., 540 PTO
6000	1963	1,251	G	$2,970	5/9/2012	Online	*PurpleWave.com,* item in Kansas, Ford 6 cyl., 66 hp, Select-0-Speed, 3 pt., 540 PTO
6000			F	$1,800	6/20/2012	SESD	Diesel, Commander, 15.5x38 tires, WF, rear fenders, 3pt., PTO, runs
6000			G	$1,400	10/2/2010	SWWI	Select-0-Speed, doesn't run
6600	1975	5,025	G	$3,700	12/12/2012	SEIA	2WD
6600	1976	3,645	F	$6,000	6/20/2013	ECSK	2WD, Workmaster 800 front-end loader, 70 PTO, 4 cyl. diesel, standard, 540 PTO, 2 hyd., 3 pt., 6' bucket, 18.4x34 rear tires, 4 rib front
6700	1978	5,242	G	$7,040	5/9/2012	Online	*PurpleWave.com,* item in Kansas, diesel, 8F/2R, air, heat, spring ride seat, tilt wheel, AM/FM/cass., exterior lights, windshield wiper, 3 pt., drawbar, 540 PTO
7000	1972	3,461	G	$5,300	3/15/2011	WCIL	Diesel, 540 PTO
7000	1975	3,493	G	$5,500	2/25/2012	NETX	WF, 2WD, 2 hyd., 16.9x34 rear tires, 10x16 front tires, SN C452634
7000	1975		G	$5,600	4/7/2011	WCMI	One owner, diesel, 16.9x38 tires, 540/1,000 PTO, 2 hyd.
7000	1975		G	$5,600	1/29/2011	ECMO	2WD, diesel, Ford 7210 loader
7000		6,800	G	$5,500	7/11/2013	SCMN	2WD, cab, heat, 3 pt., PTO, rock box, 1 owner, diesel
7000			P	$1,300	6/13/2012	NWMN	Diesel, for parts, cab, 3 pt., PTO, needs transmission work
7000			G	$2,900	6/13/2012	NWMN	Cab, 3 pt., PTO, 3 hyd., Great Bend loader, bucket
7000			G	$4,300	3/20/2012	WCIL	Row crop
7000			G	$6,200	2/25/2012	WCMI	777B loader, cab, heat, WF, 3 pt., PTO, 3 remotes, 16.9x28 tires, duals
7000		3,000	F	$5,350	11/12/2011	WCKY	Canopy, R1 rubber, weights, SN 80874
7600	1977		G	$6,900	3/19/2011	ECIA	Loader
7700	1976	6,835	G	$7,900	1/1/2011	ECKS	2WD, cab, tires 10%
7700	1978	5,125	G	$5,625	6/5/2013	Online	*BigIron.com,* item in Nebraska, row crop, 16F/4R, 256 cu. in. 4 cyl. turbo
8000	1969	6,699	F	$3,000	11/22/2011	NCMN	2WD, cab, standard, 2hyd., 3 pt., 540/1,000 PTO,
8000	1972		F	$2,900	4/8/2011	SWMN	Diesel, cab, 3pt., PTO, 2 hyd., 16 speed, Du-Al 340 loader, 18.4x38 tires
8000			G	$5,100	2/26/2014	NCMO	Rebuilt trans., clean
8000		5,867	G	$7,100	12/18/2013	Online	*BigIron.com,* 8 speed, 6 cyl. diesel, 540 PTO, 2 hyd.
8000			F	$1,400	9/6/2013	ECSD	3 pt., diesel, PTO needs work
8000			G	$2,200	7/10/2013	NETX	Cab, air, 2WD, loader, SN C337866
8000			F	$5,400	4/27/2013	NWMO	No dual power

Ford

Model	Year	Hours	Condition	Price	Date	Area	Comments
8000		7,259	F	$5,000	3/16/2013	SEPA	Weights
8000			G	$1,400	8/4/2012	SWKY	
8000			G	$4,500	8/4/2012	ECMN	2 hyd., 3 pt., 540 PTO, dual power, 16 speed
8000		4,605	F	$4,200	3/24/2012	NWMO	Diesel, dual power, 3 pt., wheel weights, Westendorf WL42 full hyd. loader, 2 prong bale spear, dash gauges do not work
8000		3,651	G	$5,250	2/25/2012	NETX	2WD, WF, hyd., 18.4x38 rear tires, 10x16 front tires
8000		2,892	G	$2,200	5/13/2011	ECMS	
8000			F	$3,750	11/29/2010	ECIA	
8000			G	$5,000	5/1/2010	SETX	
8600	1975		G	$9,750	1/28/2012	ECMO	Westendorf TA28 loader, cab, air, heat
8600	1976	5,508	G	$3,900	8/20/2013	WCIL	Cab, 2 hyd., 540 PTO, 18.4x38 rear tires, axle mount duals, front weights
8600			G	$4,750	12/30/2013	SEMN	
8600		6,770	G	$4,500	1/9/2013	Online	*BigIron.com,* item in Minnesota, 2WD, 8 speed, dual power transmission, diesel, 18.4x38 rear tires, 10x16 front tires, 2 hyd., PTO, 3 pt., turbo
8600		7,118	G	$4,840	11/28/2012	Online	*PurpleWave.com,* item in Missouri, Ford 6 cyl. diesel, manual, spring seat, drawbar, 3 pt., 540/1,000 PTO, 2 rear hyd., 8 suitcase weights, power adj.
8600			F	$4,400	3/10/2012	NCOK	2WD, WF, cab, air
8600			G	$8,750	3/3/2012	SEMN	2WD, open station, diesel, 18.4x38 duals, front weights, 2 hyd., 3pt., 540 PTO, new 2 speed
8600			F	$2,700	2/24/2012	NETX	OROPS
8600			G	$8,000	1/28/2012	SEAB	18.4x38 tires, Koyker 400 loader, bucket
8600		2,823	G	$6,200	3/23/2011	Online	*BigIron.com,* 6 cyl. diesel, 540 PTO, 3 pt.
9000			G	$2,000	2/4/2012	ECSC	
9600	1969		G	$3,000	7/27/2011	ECND	2 hyd., 3 pt., 540 PTO, good fronts
9600	1973	4,953	F	$5,400	11/22/2011	NCMN	2WD, cab, standard, 2 hyd., 3 pt., 540/1,000 PTO, large inside rear wheel weights
9600	1974	7,516	F	$3,000	8/27/2011	NCIN	Cab, WF, 3 pt., 2 hyd.
9600	1975		G	$2,800	2/25/2012	WCMI	3 pt., PTO, cab, no doors, broken glass, 2 hyd., WF, diesel, 18.4x38 rear tires, power steering hose leak, manifold gaskets
9600	1975	5,877	G	$5,610	11/30/2011	Online	*PurpleWave.com,* item in Missouri, Ford 6.6L, 6 cyl. turbo diesel, 135 PTO hp
9600	1976	3,407	F	$2,860	8/15/2012	Online	*PurpleWave.com,* item in Illinois, Row Crop, Ford 6 cyl. diesel, 43 gal. fuel capacity, manual dual power, air, heat, radio, all non-operational, spring seat, block heater

Ford

Model	Year	Hours	Condition	Price	Date	Area	Comments
9600	1976	5,410	G	$3,850	8/31/2011	Online	*PurpleWave.com,* item in Kansas, Ford 6 cyl. diesel, 135 hp, 540 PTO
9600	1976	5,600	G	$4,800	7/30/2011	ECMO	Dual PTO, 2 hyd., 3 pt.
9600		5,295	G	$2,725	4/17/2013	Online	*BigIron.com,* item in Nebraska, manual 8 speed, 4 speed dual power, 401 cu. in. engine
9600			G	$1,700	12/14/2012	SWKY	Cab, duals
9600			G	$5,100	6/9/2012	ECNE	Factory cab, PTO, dual hyd., runs
9600			G	$2,900	6/2/2012	SEMN	Cab, bad transmission
9700	1977	10,471	G	$4,500	3/31/2012	SWSK	2WD, 135 hp, 16 speed, 23.1x34 rubber
9700	1977	8,218	G	$8,800	1/29/2011	ECMO	540 PTO, 3 pt., duals, 134A air, 50 hours on new clutch, 1,500 hours on OH
A	1930		G	$5,500	6/27/2013	*Online*	*IQBID.com,* item in Iowa, runs, spoke wheels, new parts
A	1931		G	$1,500	6/27/2013	*Online*	*IQBID.com,* item in Iowa, frame, cab, fenders, other miscellanous parts
NAA	1953		G	$3,750	9/19/2013	SWIA	Golden Jubilee, 20 hp, 2WD, 1 hyd., good rubber, 540 PTO
NAA	1953		G	$1,450	9/12/2013	SEIA	Golden Jubilee factory package, Superior loader and Sherman backhoe, new front and rear tires, front pump and carborator rebuilt
NAA	1953		G	$1,600	9/12/2013	SEIA	Golden Jubilee factory package, Superior loader and Sherman backhoe, new rims on rear, new tires on front and rear
NAA	1953	255	G	$2,310	8/21/2013	Online	*PurpleWave.com,* item in Kansas, Golden Jubilee, Ford 4 cyl. OH valve gas, manual, spring suspension seat, Wagner Works loader, 3 pt., 540 PTO
NAA	1953		G	$1,500	7/31/2013	ECND	Golden Jubilee, open station, 3 pt., PTO
NAA	1953		G	$2,100	12/14/2012	SWKY	Golden Jubilee
NAA	1953		G	$4,600	9/15/2012	SCMN	Golden Jubilee, fenders, 3 pt., factory WF, repainted
NAA	1953		F	$1,700	6/29/2012	NETX	Golden Jubilee, 27 hp, gas, 2WD, open station, 11.2x28 tires, 5' rotary mower
NAA	1953		F	$1,300	8/6/2011	NCIA	Golden Jubilee, loader
NAA	1953		G	$3,100	7/16/2011	NEKS	Golden Jubilee, gas, SN NAA55230, 12V, 4 speed, 12.4x28 tires
NAA	1953		F	$1,700	11/17/2010	SCMT	Golden Jubilee, 3 pt., PTO
NAA	1953		G	$4,750	10/23/2010	SCPA	Golden Jubilee
NAA	1953		G	$6,000	8/7/2010	SEWI	Golden Jubliee
NAA	1953		G	$1,600	7/10/2010	SEIA	Golden Jubilee, new clutch, second owner, factory hand clutch (non-working)
NAA	1953		G	$5,600	4/24/2010	SEMN	Golden Jubilee, WF, 3 pt., one owner, straight tin, threadbare paint, above average, if painted it would have been a 9 out of 10
NAA	1953		G	$2,600	2/20/2010	NCIL	Golden Jubilee, 3 pt., gas

Ford

Model	Year	Hours	Condition	Price	Date	Area	Comments
NAA	1954		G	$2,000	8/24/2013	WCMN	Golden Jubilee, new paint
NAA	1954		G	$2,750	3/16/2013	SEMN	Golden Jubilee, WF, 3 pt., PTO, Kosh belly mount sickle mower, 13.4x28 tires
NAA	1954	179	G	$1,430	8/14/2012	Online	*PurpleWave.com,* item in Kansas, Golden Jubilee, 4 cyl. gas, 4 speed, 540 PTO, 6V style, missing top link, 6.5x16 fronts, 12.4x28 rears
NAA	1954		G	$1,705	8/14/2012	Online	*PurpleWave.com,* item in Iowa, Golden Jubilee, 4 cyl. gas, manual, spring seat, 3 pt., 540 PTO, front bumper with ball, 5.5x16 fronts, 11.2x28 rears, fully operational
NAA		739	G	$4,500	3/26/2014	Online	*BigIron.com,* item in Nebraska, Golden Jubilee
NAA		3,880	G	$1,600	3/13/2014	SCID	Golden Jubilee, gas, 4 speed, 540 PTO, 11.2x28 rubber
NAA			G	$3,000	2/5/2014	SESD	Golden Jubilee, WF
NAA			G	$1,800	1/25/2014	NCOH	Golden Jubilee, 3 pt., good rear rubber, blue paint, grill guard hitch and clean
NAA			G	$3,000	11/9/2013	SWON	Golden Jubilee, 3 pt., PTO, no SN
NAA			G	$1,800	9/25/2013	SEMN	Golden Jubilee, SN 1949
NAA			G	$1,300	9/12/2013	SEIA	Golden Jubilee, 3 pt., 540 PTO
NAA			F	$2,300	2/12/2013	WCIL	Golden Jubilee
NAA		512	G	$1,900	2/7/2013	NEIN	Golden Jubilee, gas
NAA		2,605	G	$1,250	12/12/2012	SEIA	Golden Jubilee, 2WD
NAA			P	$1,000	12/1/2012	NCOH	Golden Jubilee, not running
NAA			G	$1,200	11/24/2012	WCIL	Golden Jubilee
NAA			G	$2,000	1/31/2012	NEIN	Golden Jubilee, loader
NAA			G	$4,000	12/6/2011	Online	*BidNow.US,* item in Michigan, Golden Jubilee, converted to 12V starting, 3 pt., PTO, new rear tires
NAA			G	$2,400	12/1/2011	ECND	Golden Jubilee, runs and operates very well
NAA			F	$2,600	10/22/2011	ECTX	Golden Jubilee, backhoe and front blade
NAA		1,153	G	$2,600	9/14/2011	Online	*BigIron.com,* item in Colorado, Golden Jubilee, 4 cyl., restored, golden edition, converted 12V
NAA			G	$2,800	11/20/2010	SCKY	Golden Jubilee
NAA			P	$900	10/7/2010	NCOH	Golden Jubilee, for parts
NAA			G	$1,500	6/5/2010	NETN	Golden Jubilee
NAA			G	$2,100	5/26/2010	ECSD	Golden Jubilee, gas
NAA			G	$4,300	5/22/2010	SEMN	Golden Jubilee, WF, 3pt., newer 12.4x28, 3 custom pipes extruding up from engine
NAA			G	$2,900	4/10/2010	ECON	Golden Jubilee
NAA			P	$925	4/9/2010	WCFL	Golden Jubilee

Fordson

Model	Year	Hours	Condition	Price	Date	Area	Comments
Dexta	1958	3,882	G	$2,860	8/22/2012	Online	*PurpleWave.com,* item in Kansas, Ford Perkins 3 cyl., 32 hp, manual Hi/Lo, 3 pt., drawbar
Dexta	1962		G	$1,100	10/28/2011	NETX	39 hp diesel, open station, 6F/2R, 11.2x28 tires
Dexta	1963		G	$2,500	7/30/2011	ECMO	Diesel, 1 hyd., 3 speed Hi/Lo
Dexta			G	$1,100	11/18/2010	SCMS	Block, injector pump, clutch, pressure plate all new
Dexta			G	$4,700	9/4/2010	NEIN	
Major	1948		G	$1,375	2/1/2012	SEND	3 pt., PTO
Major	1954		G	$2,500	10/7/2011	NWSD	3 pt., PTO
Major	1956		G	$1,200	4/2/2011	ECMN	Rebuilt engine and fuel system
Major	1957		G	$800	8/24/2013	WCMN	Straight tin
Major	1958		G	$1,500	6/20/2012	SESD	Diesel, WF, 3pt., 2 hyd., rear wheel weights, good running order
Major	1961		F	$3,000	5/2/2012	WCSK	53 hp PTO, 4 cyl. diesel, 3 pt., 1 hyd., 3 rib front
Major			G	$1,900	1/4/2014	WCNY	
Major			F	$1,100	3/26/2013	ECND	Diesel, 3 pt., PTO, not running
Major			F	$3,000	4/7/2012	ECSK	Clutch, sleeves and pistons all new, side panels
Major			G	$1,600	3/24/2012	NEIN	Diesel, unreadable, 3 pt., PTO, repainted, runs
Major			G	$3,500	9/4/2010	NEIN	Diesel
Major			G	$1,100	6/11/2010	SEAB	Gas, PTO, belt pulley, type 7-7 high speed transmission, new rear rubber
Major			G	$1,900	6/11/2010	SEAB	Diesel, belt pulley, 3 pt., PTO
Major			G	$2,050	6/11/2010	SEAB	Diesel, belt pulley, 3 pt., new rear rubber
Power Major	1959	222	F	$950	5/25/2011	NECO	WF, diesel, 3 pt.
Power Major		8,987	G	$975	1/25/2012	Online	*BigIron.com,* item in Nebraska, 3.6L, diesel, 6F/2R, 4 cyl., 540 PTO, drawbar only, set of duals
Power Major			F	$1,018	1/11/2012	Online	*PurpleWave.com,* item in Kansas, 4 cyl. diesel, 3 speed Hi/Lo, 540 PTO, 3 pt., weak injector pump, no brakes

Gibson

Model	Year	Hours	Condition	Price	Date	Area	Comments
D			G	$1,000	6/5/2010	WCMO	Stick steer
N/A			G	$1,151	9/14/2011	Online	*BigIron.com,* item in Colorado, gas, runs, rear hitch, blades
N/A			F	$1,000	7/17/2010	NEMT	
N/A			G	$4,100	6/5/2010	WCMO	
N/A			G	$1,000	1/30/2010	NETX	

Graham Bradley

Model	Year	Hours	Condition	Price	Date	Area	Comments
N/A	1938		G	$10,000	10/23/2010	SCPA	NF

Greyhound

Model	Year	Hours	Condition	Price	Date	Area	Comments
25-52	1928		G	$50,000	9/21/2013	WCNY	Thresherman's special

Hart-Parr

Model	Year	Hours	Condition	Price	Date	Area	Comments
70	1935		G	$5,200	6/30/2012	NEIA	Early model, 40" wheels, rebuilt and painted
12-24			G	$5,250	9/21/2013	WCNY	Looks complete, full steel, SN 42463
12-24			G	$13,000	9/9/2010	NWWI	
12-25			G	$22,000	9/21/2013	WCNY	Repainted, SN 8405
18-27	1934		G	$1,900	6/30/2012	NEIA	Complete OH
18-36	1928		E	$7,000	6/11/2010	SEAB	On steel, belt pulley, older restoration
18-36	1929		F	$5,390	11/3/2011	Online	*PurpleWave.com,* item in Kansas, 2 cyl., 36 belt hp, 18 drawbar hp
18-36	1929		G	$5,500	9/1/2011	WCMN	Rebuilt engine and lubricator, unrestored
18-36	1929		G	$6,000	9/1/2011	WCMN	Very good, very straight
18-36			G	$7,500	10/12/2013	NEOH	Parade rubber
18-36			F	$2,000	10/7/2011	NWSD	Been in a fire, built from 1926 to 1930
18-36			G	$5,750	9/4/2010	NEIN	
18-36			G	$5,000	7/10/2010	SEIA	
18-36			G	$8,000	4/21/2010	SESK	On steel
22-40			G	$10,000	9/21/2013	WCNY	Fairly complete, no fenders, industrial rubber front and rear, one missing front tire, SN 70161
22-40			G	$11,000	9/21/2013	WCNY	Nice, complete, on original hard rubber rears with cast fronts
28-44			G	$4,000	3/18/2011	NWIA	14x30 rubber, spoke wheels, one owner, running order
28-50	1929		G	$11,750	10/12/2013	ECOH	
28-50			G	$5,000	9/21/2013	WCNY	Canopy, large radiator, road lugs, rough, SN 71507
30-60	1915		G	$135,000	9/21/2013	WCNY	

PETE'S PICK

The Richard Bauman Oliver collector auction on Oct. 12, 2013 in Sterling, Ohio was quite a sale. Here's the Hart-Parr 18-36 that sold for $7,500 at this sale. That's the third highest auction price I've seen in the past 18 years. He also had a 1929 Hart-Parr 28-50 that sold for $11,750. Other highlights included the 1951 Oliver 66 row crop high clearance and a rare 1966 Oliver 1650 HFWA tractor. Both sold separately for $30,000.

Heider

Model	Year	Hours	Condition	Price	Date	Area	Comments
N/A	1920		F	$8,250	4/14/2014	SCSK	Steel wheels

Huber

Model	Year	Hours	Condition	Price	Date	Area	Comments
25-50	1927		G	$6,400	7/25/2013	WCSK	2WD, steel-wheeled, 4 cyl. gas, belt pulley, 2F/1R, complete, HD
40-62			G	$11,000	6/5/2010	WCMO	
HS			G	$3,600	6/5/2010	WCMO	
LC	1937		G	$7,500	9/1/2011	WCMN	NF, gas, PTO, older restoration, 14x24 rubber on spokes
LC			G	$5,000	6/5/2010	WCMO	Open post
Light 4			G	$19,000	9/21/2013	WCNY	Cross motor, nice original, fairly complete, missing radiator
Super 4			G	$16,000	9/21/2013	WCNY	Cross motor
N/A	1936		G	$8,000	10/23/2010	SCPA	
N/A	1938		G	$5,750	10/23/2010	SCPA	
N/A			G	$15,000	9/9/2010	NWWI	Steam engine
N/A			P	$2,600	9/3/2010	NEIN	Loader, dead row, needs work and may not run or drive, as is

International Harvester Company

Model	Year	Hours	Condition	Price	Date	Area	Comments
15	1908		G	$170,000	9/14/2013	SWMN	On steel, 15 hp gas single cyl. engine, friction drive, make and brake ignition, open tower cooling, canopy, restored and in running condition, in family for many years
100	1955		P	$1,800	2/22/2014	NWNJ	Farmall, rusted
100	1956		G	$2,650	12/3/2011	NCIN	2000 Woods 59" finish mower
100	1956		G	$6,500	3/26/2011	SEWI	Farmall, WF, 1pt.
100			G	$2,100	9/21/2013	SWOH	Farmall, cultivators, side dresser
100			F	$2,600	2/4/2012	ECSC	Farmall
100			G	$2,400	9/14/2011	Online	*BigIron.com,* item in Colorado, Farmall, 6 cyl. diesel, 4 hyd., 540 PTO, 4 hyd.
100			G	$2,400	6/5/2010	WCMO	Farmall, cultivators, 1 pt.
100			G	$2,000	4/10/2010	ECON	Farmall, cultivator
100			G	$5,500	3/5/2010	NENE	Hydro, cab, 3 pt., PTO
130	1957		G	$4,400	7/16/2011	NEKS	Gas, SN 2407, restored, engine OH, hyd. lift, rear weights, new Firestone 11.2x24 tires, International Harvester 105 mid mount 5' sickle mower, new sections and guards
130			G	$4,000	3/22/2013	NWMN	Farmall, repainted, runs
130			G	$1,500	8/4/2012	NEAR	4 cyl. gas
130			P	$1,800	6/9/2012	ECNE	High clearance, PTO, hyd. lift, not running, complete
140	1957		G	$1,300	8/25/2011	ECND	WF, loose PTO, 1R, cultivator, 11.2x24 rears, runs
140	1960		G	$3,200	7/16/2011	NEKS	Farmall, gas, SN 10073, restored, WF, belt pulley, new Titan 11.2x24 tires

International Harvester Company

Model	Year	Hours	Condition	Price	Date	Area	Comments
140	1961		G	$1,100	2/23/2013	ECMI	Side-mounted sickle bar mower, new tires
140			G	$1,875	10/26/2013	SCKY	Ran good, good paint, cultivator sold separate for $425 (good)
140			G	$2,750	6/22/2013	SESC	Farmall
140			G	$3,200	6/22/2013	SESC	Farmall, cultivator, rebuilt lift
140			G	$4,250	6/22/2013	SESC	Farmall, cultivator disk
140			G	$2,750	4/26/2013	SWKY	Cultivators
140			G	$3,800	4/26/2013	SWKY	Side dresser, cultivators, bracket top
140			G	$3,400	4/6/2013	NWNC	Cultivator
140			G	$3,250	3/2/2013	NETN	Farmall, side dresser, drawbar
140			G	$3,300	12/14/2012	SWKY	Cultivators
140			G	$1,100	11/24/2012	WCIL	
140			G	$2,000	8/4/2012	SWKY	Farmall, cultivator
140			G	$1,250	7/27/2012	SWKY	Woods L59 mower
140			G	$2,300	7/27/2012	SWKY	
140			P	$1,300	6/9/2012	ECNE	1 pt. fast hitch, motor stuck
140			G	$2,500	6/7/2012	NEIN	
140			G	$5,000	2/25/2012	NETX	WF, 1R, planter, cultivator, fertilizer distributor
140			G	$1,300	4/2/2011	SEMN	Farmall, WF, belly mower
140			G	$3,400	11/20/2010	NCKY	Cultivators, side dresser single plow
140			G	$6,400	10/16/2010	NCTN	Late '70s model, full set of cultivators, drawbar
140			G	$2,000	9/4/2010	SEVA	Farmall, 4 cyl., gas
140			G	$5,060	4/28/2010	Online	*PurpleWave.com*, item in Kansas
140			G	$3,950	4/3/2010	NENC	Farmall, converted to 12V
140			G	$1,800	1/30/2010	NETX	Farmall
154	1969		F	$825	7/28/2010	Online	*PurpleWave.com*, item in Kansas, low boy, 3 speed, 72" mower deck

In 1908 my grandfathers were 1 and 7 years old. It's mind blowing to see a 105-year-old tractor in great running condition, but that was the case with a restored 1908 International Harvester model 15 tractor on steel with a one-cylinder gas engine and friction drive. It sold at a Sept. 14, 2013, auction in southwest Minnesota. My auctioneer friend Dan Pike with Dan Pike and Associates Auction Co. sold the tractor, and they were kind enough to shoot video for our Machinery Pete YouTube channel. The bidding opened at $50,000 and quickly was up to $85,000. It went all the way up to $170,000! The buyer was from Belgium. Now that was an exciting auction.

PETE'S PICK

International Harvester Company

Model	Year	Hours	Condition	Price	Date	Area	Comments
154			G	$1,000	6/1/2013	SEMN	Turf tires
200	1955		G	$1,100	12/6/2012	Online	*IQBID.com*, Farmall
200	1955		G	$1,100	12/6/2012	SEIA	Farmall
200	1955		G	$1,700	12/30/2010	ECMN	Farmall, NF, Summers 1360C mower
200			G	$1,500	2/25/2012	WCMI	Farmall, broom attach, gas, WF, 11.2x36 rear tires
200			G	$2,500	1/8/2011	SEPA	Fast hitch, straight original, new rear tires
230	1957		G	$1,800	7/30/2011	ECMO	New tires and paint, runs perfect
230	1957		F	$1,900	2/25/2011	NENC	Fertilizer hoppers, cultivators, 3 pt., SN 3066J
230			F	$1,600	11/12/2011	WCMI	Farmall, NF, PTO, fast hitch, 1 hyd., 11.2x36 rear tires, not restored
230			G	$2,200	9/24/2011	WCSD	NF
240	1958		G	$1,800	1/16/2013	Online	*AuctionTime.com,* item in Indiana, 30 hp, 2 WD, SN 612
240	1959		G	$3,500	8/20/2013	WCIL	Gas, 3 pt., 540 PTO
240	1960	2,379	G	$2,200	12/4/2010	SEWY	WF, 2 pt., gas
240	1968		G	$2,600	6/20/2012	SESD	WF, gas, 2 pt.
240			G	$1,200	1/4/2014	WCNY	Fenders, fast hitch, PTO
240		2,718	G	$2,500	10/3/2013	NCIN	Farmall, fast hitch, 11.2x36
240			G	$5,600	5/11/2013	NCOH	Repainted, 3 pt., fenders, runs
240		2,427	G	$2,310	9/12/2012	Online	*PurpleWave.com,* item in Kansas, 4 cyl. gas, manual
240			G	$1,450	7/28/2012	SWTN	As is, Bush Hog mower
240			F	$2,500	11/12/2011	WCMI	Farmall, fast hitch 2 hyd., 12.4x36 rear tires, not restored, NF
240			G	$4,750	11/12/2011	WCMI	Farmall, fast hitch, 2 hyd., WF, 12.4x36 rear tires
240			G	$1,500	11/18/2010	SEOK	Loader
240		2,289	G	$4,200	6/5/2010	NWIA	Series A, loader, box scraper
284	1977		G	$4,000	3/30/2012	SEND	Gas, 4 speed Hi/Lo, hyd., 3 pt., PTO, diff. lock
300	1954		G	$2,400	2/8/2014	NWIL	Gas
300	1955		E	$6,000	3/15/2014	ECMD	Farmall, NF, gas, local, used only to plant and pull grain drill,TA good, engine strong, power steering, fast hitch with correct hyd. leveling cyl. mount, 2 hyd.
300	1955		G	$3,500	1/29/2014	Online	*BigIron.com,* item in Kansas, 15.5x38 rear tires, 5.5x16 front tires, 5F/1R, 2 pt. fast hitch, 540 PTO, 12V system, alternator
300	1955		E	$4,100	6/8/2013	NEIA	Fast hitch, NF, parade ready
300	1955		G	$3,000	11/24/2012	SCIA	NF, standard drawbar, TA has been rebuilt and works good, SN 19286, 13.6x38 Firestones, like new front rubber, straight tinned, looks sharp, painted like a 350
300	1955		G	$1,300	9/14/2011	Online	*BigIron.com,* item in Nebraska, Farmall, 5 speed, TA, 4 cyl. gas, 37 drawbar hp, 2 hyd., 540 PTO, converted to 12V, live hyd., independent PTO, flip seat

International Harvester Company

Model	Year	Hours	Condition	Price	Date	Area	Comments
300	1955		G	$1,600	9/9/2011	ECND	NF, 1 hyd., PTO
300	1955		F	$1,600	7/13/2011	WCMN	McCormick Farmall, TA, NF, been repainted, new front tires
300	1955		G	$1,500	4/11/2011	Online	*AuctionTime.com*
300	1955		F	$1,400	11/20/2010	SEIA	Farmall, loader
300	1955		G	$2,550	6/23/2010	NCIA	Fenders, repainted last year
300	1956		G	$1,850	8/23/2012	SWMN	NF, 1 hyd., live hyd., 13.6x38 tires, SN 25764, 1 owner
300	1956		F	$2,300	11/22/2011	WCIL	Gas, 3 pt., hyd. loader
300	1956		G	$1,700	8/13/2011	WCIL	Quick hitch, 540 PTO, 14.9x24 tires
300	1956		G	$2,300	5/25/2011	Online	*BigIron.com,* item in Kansas, hour meter broken, 5 speed, 4 cyl. International Harvester gas, 1 hyd., 2 axle, 540 PTO, starts and runs, TA
300	1956		G	$2,250	3/15/2011	WCIL	NF, 1 hyd., runs
300	1956		F	$1,100	6/23/2010	Online	*BigIron.com,* item in Nebraska, 5F/ 1R, International Harvester C-169 gas, rear tires 13.6x28, front tires 6.5x16SL, live power hyd., single axle, WF, engine OH 2 years ago
300	1968		G	$1,600	11/3/2012	SWMI	4 cyl. gas, WF, drawbar, PTO, hyd. set up for loader, wet lines, 3 pt. fast hitch
300			G	$1,300	4/3/2014	NEIN	Farmall
300			G	$4,000	12/30/2013	SEMN	
300			G	$1,165	12/18/2013	Online	*BigIron.com,* item in Nebraska, 5 speed TA, 4 cyl. gas, 540 PTO, tricycle front end, inside rear wheel weights, muffler is broken
300			G	$1,250	12/7/2013	SEMN	Loader
300			G	$1,400	12/4/2013	ECIN	Farmall, 13.6x38 tires, gas
300			G	$1,200	9/12/2013	SEIA	Fast hitch, 540 PTO, 2 hyd., WF, good TA and live power, live hyd., PS
300			G	$2,050	8/24/2013	SEMI	Farmall, NF, new rubber
300			G	$1,300	8/15/2013	ECMN	Farmall, NF
300			G	$2,500	8/14/2013	WCMN	WF, 3 hyd., good torque, PS, original International Harvester front end
300			G	$2,100	6/1/2013	SEMN	Sickle mower
300			G	$950	5/29/2013	Online	*BigIron.com,* item in Nebraska, 4 cyl. gas, 540 PTO
300			G	$1,200	5/25/2013	NWMO	Farmall, WF, hyd. post lifter, gas
300			G	$3,500	4/24/2013	Online	*BigIron.com,* item in Nebraska, TA
300			G	$4,800	3/23/2013	NEIN	Gas, repainted, new torch, fast hitch, fenders, PS, runs
300			G	$3,600	9/15/2012	SCMN	Farmall, NF, front and rear wheel weights
300			G	$2,850	8/30/2012	SEMN	PS, like new rubber
300			G	$900	7/28/2012	NWSC	Farmall
300			G	$1,700	6/9/2012	ECNE	Gas, factory WF, fast hitch, hyd., motor locked up
300			G	$2,800	5/26/2012	ECPA	Gas, 13.6x38 tires, drawbar, 540 PTO, 1 set rear weights, fenders, factory tool box

International Harvester Company

Model	Year	Hours	Condition	Price	Date	Area	Comments
300			F	$1,200	4/4/2012	WCMN	Farmall, gas, power steering, 2 pt., all original
300			F	$1,500	12/30/2011	NCIA	Woods 72" belly mower, SN 12404, NF
300			F	$1,800	12/1/2011	SEMN	Paulson loader, chains
300			F	$1,900	10/6/2011	SEMN	18.4x26 turf tires, set of lug tires, 3 pt., PTO
300			G	$1,800	8/24/2011	ECMN	2WD, No. 33 loader, hyd. bucket, good rubber, Schwartz WF, good clutch and TA, 2 pt., blade
300			G	$950	7/30/2011	ECMO	Farmall, gas, WF
300			G	$2,800	7/28/2011	NESD	TA, 2 hyd., PTO, WF
300			F	$900	6/17/2011	SWMN	New Idea hyd. loader, NF, road chains
300			G	$3,250	9/4/2010	NEIN	Farmall, high crop
300			P	$900	9/3/2010	NEIN	Farmall, LP, fast hitch, dead row, may not run or drive, as is
300			G	$1,000	7/10/2010	SEIA	New TA and clutch last winter, OH recent 6-7 years
300			G	$8,000	6/19/2010	SWIL	Farmall, running, unrestored, original, lights, rebuilt head, all new fluids
300			F	$825	5/7/2010	NEAR	
330	1958	1,933	G	$5,500	7/14/2012	NWIA	International Harvester loader, WF, snow bucket, sharp, rare
330			P	$1,500	12/6/2012	SEIA	Farmall, loader, does not run
340	1958		E	$10,400	5/26/2012	ECPA	Diesel, TA, 13.9x36 tires, 2 pt., 540 PTO, front weights, fast hitch, 1 set rear weights, sharp looking
340	1959	3,312	G	$2,500	6/16/2010	SEND	Gas, WF, open station, TA, 5 speed, 1 hyd., fact hitch, PTO, fenders
340	1960	1,248	G	$6,500	8/15/2013	ECMN	Adj. WF
340	1960	3,383	G	$1,500	6/22/2011	NECO	Gas, SF, 2 pt.
340	1960	3,383	F	$1,500	5/25/2011	NECO	Gas, WF, 2 pt.
340	1963		G	$1,710	5/11/2011	Online	*BigIron.com,* 4 cyl. gas, front weight, power steering, 3 pt.
340		7,752	G	$2,000	3/15/2014	WCIL	Gas, International Harvester hyd. loader and 5' bucket
340			G	$3,950	9/12/2013	NCIA	Gas, fast hitch, Freeman loader, hyd. bucket
340			F	$2,500	2/22/2013	NWIN	Fork lift, power steering, weights
340			G	$1,700	10/20/2012	SEWY	3 pt.
340			G	$3,400	9/15/2012	SCMN	Row crop, NF, fenders
340			G	$4,300	6/27/2012	NCND	Power steering, PTO, 1 hyd., Leon quick attach loader
340			G	$1,925	5/30/2012	Online	*PurpleWave.com,* item in Kansas
340			G	$2,025	3/24/2012	ECKS	Farmall, NF, tires 90%, 2 pt.
340			G	$4,100	12/3/2011	ECNE	WF
340			G	$1,400	11/18/2010	SEOK	Farmall
340		2,545	G	$1,400	11/13/2010	ECTX	Diesel
340			G	$2,500	9/4/2010	NEIN	High crop
340			G	$11,250	9/4/2010	NEIN	Diesel, low production
340			P	$800	9/3/2010	NEIN	High crop, dead row, needs work, may not run or drive, as is

International Harvester Company

Model	Year	Hours	Condition	Price	Date	Area	Comments
340			P	$1,350	9/3/2010	NEIN	Dead row, needs work and may not run or drive, as is
340			G	$2,600	5/22/2010	SEMN	Did not start, battery dead, shedded but not used for years, NF, PTO, 12.4x36 tires, hyd., fast hitch
350	1956		F	$975	6/14/2010	Online	*BigIron.com,* item in Oklahoma, 2WD, 10F/2R, 41 hp, 540 PTO, WF
350	1957	3,921	G	$2,420	10/23/2013	Online	*PurpleWave.com*, item in Iowa, International Harvester 2.9L,4 cyl. gas, TA
350	1957	4,924	G	$2,600	8/20/2013	WCIL	Loader
350	1957		G	$4,400	2/6/2013	Online	Item in Illinois, Farmall, NF, 2 pt., live hyd. PTO, 12.4x38 tires, body shop paint, sharp, SN 1311
350	1957	1,066	F	$1,200	10/24/2012	NECO	Gas, WF, 3 pt., loader, 3 pt. 8' blade
350	1957	3,314	G	$2,035	8/14/2012	Online	*PurpleWave.com,* item in Kansas, Farmall, gas, manual, TA, 540 PTO, drawbar, live hyd., rear hyd., rear wheel weights, 6x16 fronts, 13.6x38 rears
350	1957		G	$1,300	7/18/2012	ECND	WF, gas, 12V, PTO, 2 hyd., working TA, quick hitch, low hours
350	1957		G	$4,500	7/14/2012	NWIA	Diesel, new TA, clutch, new cyl., not repainted
350	1957	1,660	E	$8,000	7/14/2012	NWIA	Diesel, NF, side pulley, good TA, clutch, 2nd owner
350	1957		G	$8,600	6/30/2012	NEIA	Fast hitch, diesel, NF
350	1957	3,217	G	$5,700	4/23/2012	WCSK	Western special, gas, TA, hydro touch system, independent PTO, deluxe cushion seat with arm rest pad, new radiator, thermostat
350	1957	5,124	G	$5,000	9/9/2011	ECND	WF, TA, 1 hyd., PTO, restored, runs
350	1957	4,417	G	$3,250	9/1/2011	WCMN	Wheatland, special, gas, PTO, good TA, wheel weights, original/unrestored
350	1957		G	$4,500	8/25/2011	ECND	Wheatland, special, gas, TA, 2 hyd., PTO, 14.9x28 rears, older restoration, good runner
350	1957		G	$6,900	8/24/2011	ECMN	WF, PTO, TA, fast hitch, fenders, power slide wheels, new 13.6x38 rubber
350	1957		F	$2,400	7/16/2011	NEKS	Gas, SN 2268, original, good TA, Schwartz WF, PTO, 2 pt., PS wheels, wheel weights, new Titan 13.6x38 tires
350	1957		F	$775	6/22/2011	NECO	Gas, WF, 3 pt.
350	1957		G	$1,800	6/22/2011	NECO	Gas, SF, 2 pt.
350	1957		F	$1,900	5/25/2011	NECO	Gas, SF, 2 pt.
350	1957		G	$1,750	8/26/2010	ECIL	Gas, TA
350	1958		G	$2,300	8/20/2013	WCIL	NF, TA is out
350	1958		E	$8,000	7/14/2012	NWIA	Diesel, WF, new TA, clutch
350	1958		G	$2,650	5/26/2012	ECPA	High-Utility, TA, 13.6x38 tires, 2 pt. fast hitch, 540 PTO, 1 set rear weights, fenders
350	1958		F	$775	11/15/2011	Online	*IQBID.com,* Farmall, WF, 2 hyd., 3 pt., torque needs work, 13.6x38 tires
350			G	$5,750	1/24/2014	NCNE	Farmall
350			F	$1,800	11/26/2013	SEIA	Farmall, original, has not run for a while

International Harvester Company

Model	Year	Hours	Condition	Price	Date	Area	Comments
350			G	$1,600	10/3/2013	NCIN	Loader, backhoe
350			G	$3,000	9/12/2013	SEIA	NF, 540 PTO, 1 hyd., new tires
350			G	$1,900	9/7/2013	SEMN	Gas, NF, TA, 13.6x38 tires, 540 PTO
350			G	$2,800	7/31/2013	ECND	Open station, 2 hyd., 3 pt., PTO
350			G	$4,250	11/13/2012	NCIA	Farmall
350			G	$3,500	9/15/2012	SCMN	Row crop, NF, fenders
350			G	$1,550	8/21/2012	WCIL	Loader
350			G	$2,200	8/21/2012	WCIL	Loader
350			F	$1,700	6/20/2012	SESD	NF, gas
350			P	$1,550	6/9/2012	ECNE	Diesel, hyd., PTO, NF, motor locked up
350			G	$2,800	6/9/2012	ECNE	Factory WF, PTO, hyd., runs
350			G	$3,400	6/9/2012	ECNE	WF, PTO, hyd., repainted, runs
350			F	$3,600	6/9/2012	ECNE	Diesel, factory WF, PTO, hyd., good rear rubber, not running
350			G	$4,500	5/26/2012	ECPA	Diesel, 13.6x38 tires, 2 pt., 540 PTO, 2 set rear weights, fenders, factory tool box, engine block heater
350			G	$2,800	3/24/2012	NEIN	LP, original, fast hitch, 1 of 242 built, runs
350			G	$3,800	3/24/2012	NEIN	High-Utility, gas, original, fenders, fast hitch, front weights, hyd., rear weights, runs
350			G	$4,750	3/24/2012	NEIN	Gas, power steering, fast hitch, fenders, repainted, runs
350			F	$2,700	12/3/2011	NCOH	Loader
350			F	$1,500	12/17/2010	WCIL	
350			F	$2,900	12/16/2010	NWIA	Du-Al loader
350			F	$1,600	11/13/2010	WCMN	Good TA, fast hitch, High-Utility, WF
350			G	$4,900	9/4/2010	NEIN	High-Utility, LP, rare, low production
350			G	$5,700	9/4/2010	NEIN	Diesel,
350			G	$13,000	9/4/2010	NEIN	Farmall, gas, high crop
350			G	$23,000	9/4/2010	NEIN	Farmall, diesel, high crop
350			F	$2,200	8/7/2010	SEWI	Farmall, LP, NF, flat tire in front
350			G	$1,225	7/10/2010	SEIA	Row crop, aftermarket, 3 pt.
350			G	$3,300	5/26/2010	ECSD	
350			G	$3,750	5/26/2010	ECSD	Diesel
350			G	$3,600	2/26/2010	SEMN	Farmall loader
354	1972		G	$2,600	6/29/2012	NETX	35 hp gas, 2WD, open station, 13.6x28 tires, Freeman 3000 loader, 60" bucket, 2 hyd.
384	1978	3,891	G	$1,500	11/9/2010	NWMS	Standard diesel, 35 hp, 3 pt., 540 PTO
400	1948		G	$1,100	12/4/2013	ECND	Farmall loader, OH 4 years ago, needs radiator shield
400	1955		E	$6,600	3/15/2014	ECMD	Gas, good TA, strong engine, WF, 70% rubber, fast hitch, professionally restored and painted, SN 16693
400	1955		G	$6,850	4/17/2013	Online	*BigIron.com,* item in Nebraska, 2WD, row crop, 5F/1R
400	1955		F	$1,000	8/8/2012	SEND	Farmall, WF, belt pulley, TA, 1 hyd., PTO pump, non-runner
400	1955		G	$1,250	7/18/2012	ECND	WF, gas, 12V, PTO, 2 hyd., working TA, quick hitch, low hours

International Harvester Company

Model	Year	Hours	Condition	Price	Date	Area	Comments
400	1955		G	$3,600	7/30/2011	NCIA	NF, power steering, diesel
400	1955		G	$2,500	8/7/2010	NWOH	Restored, rebuilt engine, good 14.9x38 rubber, new paint
400	1956		G	$5,300	12/16/2013	ECIL	Gas, WF, canopy, 3 pt., PTO, Bush Hog 1400 loader, 1 owner, 14.9x38 rear tires, SN 39395
400	1956	6,770	G	$1,200	1/28/2012	ECMO	Farmall
400	1956		G	$1,900	7/30/2011	ECMO	PS, fast hitch, TA is out
400	1956		G	$4,400	3/26/2011	SEWI	WF
400	1956		G	$3,100	1/25/2011	NCIL	Gas, row crop, fenders, belt pulley
400	1957		G	$4,100	4/1/2014	WCMN	Farmall, WF, TA, PTO, 3 pt., cast iron rims, 14.9x38 tires, power steering
400	1957		G	$1,300	8/22/2012	ECMN	Farmall
400			G	$1,200	9/6/2013	ECSD	WF, loader
400			G	$800	7/17/2013	Online	*BigIron.com,* item in Iowa, 540 PTO, engine locked up, tins
400			G	$1,200	6/1/2013	SEMN	Farmall, WF, good TA
400			G	$2,550	5/15/2013	Online	*BigIron.com,* item in Kansas, loader, 4 cyl.
400			G	$2,950	12/10/2012	ECIL	NF, TA, power steering, 3 sets rear weights, good rubber, new rod and main bearings
400			G	$4,000	12/10/2012	ECIL	LP, NF, power steering, TA, 2 sets of rear weights, OH March 2012
400			G	$2,900	12/7/2012	NCIN	Gas, NF, fenders, 1 set rear weights, power steering
400		3,267	F	$2,310	9/26/2012	Online	*PurpleWave.com,* item in Kansas, gas, TA, 540 PTO, 2 hyd., 15.5x38 rear
400			G	$2,601	8/22/2012	Online	*BigIron.com,* item in South Dakota, manual, 4 cyl. gas, 55 hp, 3 hyd., 540 PTO, live power, TA, power steering, Du-Al 150 loader, 8' Farmhand bucket
400		4,673	G	$1,200	7/25/2012	Online	*BigIron.com,* item in Nebraska, Farmall, 4 cyl. gas, 1 hyd., 540 PTO, TA, rear wheel weights, drawbar
400			G	$1,000	6/9/2012	ECNE	Diesel, hyd. PTO, runs, rough condition
400			P	$1,200	6/9/2012	ECNE	Diesel, NF, PTO, hyd., not running
400			G	$2,500	6/9/2012	ECNE	LP, SF, no PTO, hyd., runs
400			G	$4,000	5/26/2012	ECPA	Diesel, 13.6x38 tires, 2 pt., 540 PTO, 1 set rear weights, fenders, front tilt hyd. drawbar
400			G	$1,625	4/9/2012	ECSD	Diesel, NF, 75% restored, starts easily
400			G	$3,100	3/24/2012	NEIN	Diesel, repainted, new tires, PTO, hyd., runs
400			G	$3,000	2/4/2012	ECTX	Farmall, 3 pt.
400			F	$1,450	10/29/2011	ECMN	Loader
400			G	$2,000	9/14/2011	Online	*BigIron.com,* item in Colorado, Farmall, 4 cyl. gas, runs, 5' bucket, new tires
400			F	$925	4/27/2011	Online	*BigIron.com,* item in Nebraska, Farmall, 540 PTO, 1 hyd. hose, loose engine, 12V, rusted out, ran when parked, belt pulley, missing front hood tin work
400			G	$1,600	3/23/2011	ECMN	Farmall, new tires, restored

International Harvester Company

Model	Year	Hours	Condition	Price	Date	Area	Comments
400			G	$5,700	9/4/2010	NEIN	Farmall, all-fuel, high crop
400			G	$9,250	9/4/2010	NEIN	Farmall, diesel, high crop
400			P	$1,200	9/3/2010	NEIN	Diesel, dead row, needs work and may not run or drive, as is
400			P	$1,500	9/3/2010	NEIN	Farmall, LP, fast hitch, dead row, needs work and may not run or drive, as is
400			G	$2,500	8/7/2010	SEWI	Diesel, recent tune up, runs excellent, all original, new paint, good TA
400		1,300	G	$4,400	6/11/2010	SEAB	Diesel, hyd. PTO, weights, original
400			G	$2,100	6/5/2010	WCMO	Farmall loader
400			G	$1,850	5/26/2010	ECSD	Gas
404	1958		G	$2,400	5/26/2012	ECPA	Gas, 13.6x28 tires, 2 pt., fenders, 540 PTO
404		2,920	G	$4,400	6/22/2013	SEMN	WF, 2 speed, 3 pt., PTO, 11.2x36, SN 1283
404			G	$1,000	6/7/2013	NEAR	4 cyl. gas, 540 PTO, 3 pt., 1 hyd., SN 10950J
424		2,840	G	$3,200	4/3/2014	NEIN	International Harvester 200 loader, 13.6x28 tires, 1 hyd., 540 PTO, no drawbar
424			G	$1,400	1/4/2014	WCNY	Snow blade, finish mower, 3 pt., PTO
424			G	$2,145	10/28/2013	NWWI	International Harvester 2000 loader, gas
424			G	$3,600	3/30/2013	NWIL	Gas, straight, original, runs, drives
424			G	$1,900	11/9/2012	NEAR	4 cyl. diesel, 13.6x28 rears, 3 pt., 540 PTO
424			G	$1,000	2/4/2012	NEAR	4 cyl. gas, 3 pt., 540 PTO, 12.4x28 rears
424			G	$3,250	8/31/2011	SEMN	12.4x28 tires
424			F	$1,900	11/18/2010	SEOK	Loader
424			F	$2,400	6/5/2010	NETN	
434	1968		F	$800	7/16/2011	NEKS	B434, diesel, 3 pt., 540 PTO, original, 13.6x36 tires, SN B24025, not running
434			G	$4,500	9/4/2010	NEIN	
444	1969	2,569	G	$1,710	7/11/2012	Online	*BigIron.com,* item in Missouri, loader and box blade, 4 speed Hi/Lo, 4 cyl. gas, 40 hp, 1 hyd., 540 PTO, WF, power steering, grill guard, electric fuel pump
444	1969		G	$4,900	7/16/2011	NEKS	Gas, SN03312, restored, 3 pt., 1 hyd., 540 PTO, front frame weights, 13.6x28 rear tires
444			G	$2,400	2/10/2014	NEMO	Restored gas
444			G	$1,100	1/4/2014	WCNY	3 pt., PTO
444			G	$1,000	5/13/2011	ECMS	Gas
444		2,083	G	$3,200	4/11/2011	Online	*AuctionTime.com*
444		1,743	G	$7,370	5/26/2010	Online	*PurpleWave.com,* item in Kansas, 4 cyl. gas, 3 pt., 540 PTO
450	1957		E	$10,000	3/15/2014	ECMD	Gas, 306 cu. in., 85 hp, professionally built engine, new TA and clutch and bearings in transmission and rear assembly, fast hitch, fenders, WF, new 16.9x38 rear tires

International Harvester Company

Model	Year	Hours	Condition	Price	Date	Area	Comments
450	1957		F	$1,900	12/6/2013	NWIA	Farmall, International Harvester 2001 hyd. loader, 13.6x38 rubber, Schwartz WF
450	1957		G	$6,250	10/12/2013	NESD	Diesel, torque, WF, 14.9x38 rear tires, SN 18094
450	1957		G	$6,000	6/30/2012	NEIA	Factory hitch, diesel, power steering, NF
450	1957	4,131	G	$5,800	5/26/2012	ECPA	Diesel, TA, 15.5x38 tires, drawbar, 540 PTO, 2 sets rear weights, original tool box, fenders
450	1957		G	$2,500	9/9/2011	ECND	Belt pulley, TA, 1 hyd., PTO, belt pulley, fenders, runs
450	1957		G	$2,700	8/6/2011	NCIA	Farmall, PS, fenders
450	1957		G	$2,900	7/30/2011	ECMO	Gas
450	1957	4,942	F	$1,850	5/11/2011	Online	*BigIron.com,* 4 speed manual, 4 cyl. gas, 60 hp, 1 hyd., 540 PTO, Farmhand F25 loader, window cracked, 9' bucket, grapple
450	1957		F	$1,400	3/19/2011	SEWY	Gas, WF, 3 pt. Du-Al 325 loader
450	1957	3,420	G	$2,900	3/15/2011	WCIL	Farmall, 540 PTO, NF
450	1957		G	$3,400	6/23/2010	SEND	Gas, WF, power steering, Du-Al 350 loader, bucket, grapple, hay basket
450	1958	1,131	G	$2,700	12/10/2013	WCWI	Schwartz WF, 1 hyd., new TA, power steering, wheel weights, restored
450	1958		G	$3,500	8/24/2013	WCMN	Koyker loader, fast hitch, good TA, WF
450	1958		G	$4,400	2/6/2013	Online	Item in Illinois, Farmall, NF, 2 pt., power steering, fenders, 15.5x38 tires, SN 23857
450	1964		G	$4,100	9/6/2013	NCOH	Gas, International Harvester WF, clam shell fenders, 3 pt., 2 hyd., 988 hours on OH, rear weights, sharp
450			F	$5,100	12/14/2013	ECPA	Bad TA, NF, fast hitch
450		9,489	G	$2,500	8/27/2013	NWIA	Fast hitch, 13x36 tires, band duals, 1 hyd.
450			G	$1,700	7/17/2013	Online	*BigIron.com,* item in Iowa, 4 cyl. diesel, 1 hyd., 540 PTO, WF, 2 pt., drawbar
450			G	$2,200	6/22/2013	SEWA	Farmall, 4 cyl., diesel , direct start, rear 3 pt.hitch and PTO, SN 6756
450			G	$1,610	5/1/2013	Online	*BigIron.com,* item in Kansas, 5 speed, 4 cyl. gas, 540 PTO
450			E	$5,000	3/23/2013	SWOH	Restored, TA, PS, live PTO, NF
450			G	$1,000	3/7/2013	SEIA	Farmall, gas, NF, 540 PTO, 15.6x38 rear tires
450			G	$4,000	2/6/2013	NCIL	Gas, NF, International Harvester 2000 loader, nice, fenders sold separate for $1,900...wow!
450			G	$2,400	1/16/2013	Online	*AuctionTime.com,* item in Iowa, 49 hp, 2WD, SN 14671
450			G	$3,600	12/7/2012	NCIN	NF, fast hitch, fenders, PS, 2 sets rear weights
450			G	$1,601	8/8/2012	Online	*BigIron.com,* item in Nebraska, Farmhand F11C loader, manual, gas, 2 hyd., 540 PTO, 8.5' bucket grapple cyl. no fork, PTO hyd. pump

International Harvester Company

Model	Year	Hours	Condition	Price	Date	Area	Comments
450			G	$2,600	3/24/2012	NEIN	LP, original, fast hitch, 1 of 1019 built, runs
450			G	$3,100	3/24/2012	NEIN	Diesel, fast hitch, power steering, repainted, PTO, hyd., runs
450			E	$6,250	3/24/2012	NEIN	Diesel, WF, fast hitch, fenders, repaint, runs
450			G	$1,750	3/20/2012	WCIL	Farmall
450			G	$1,350	1/28/2012	ECMO	
450		7,189	G	$2,000	8/25/2011	ECND	Farmall, diesel, NF, TA, PTO, wheel weights, 15.5x38 rear, loose, ran when parked
450		5,146	G	$3,350	11/27/2010	SEMN	WF, fast hitch, hyd., 15.5x38, new paint
450			G	$2,750	9/11/2010	SEIA	Farmall
450			G	$17,500	9/4/2010	NEIN	Farmall, high crop
450			P	$1,600	9/3/2010	NEIN	Farmall, spin out rims, dead row, needs work, may not run or drive, as is
450			G	$6,000	6/19/2010	SWIL	Farmall, running, restored, PTO, hyd., TA, lights, new seat suspension
450			F	$1,700	6/5/2010	SEMN	NF, good tires
450			G	$2,500	5/8/2010	WCTN	
450			G	$2,500	4/10/2010	SEMN	Farmall, WF
454	1967		G	$2,900	1/29/2011	ECMO	Diesel
454	1971	2,084	G	$3,080	8/28/2013	Online	*PurpleWave.com,* item in Missouri, International Harvester 4 cyl. gas, 4 speed manual, power steering, 3 pt., 540/1,000 PTO, drawbar, blinkers, fenders, minor dents
454	1972	3,126	G	$3,500	8/23/2010	WCIL	Gas, 2 hyd., 540 PTO, 3 pt., GB 700 Job Master loader
454			G	$1,800	12/5/2013	NEIN	
454			G	$4,300	8/4/2012	ECMN	3 pt., WF, 12 speed
454		2,300	G	$3,000	1/28/2012	ECMO	PS, diff. lock, live dual PTO, power brakes, manual
454			F	$900	10/22/2011	ECTX	
454		3,473	G	$3,900	4/10/2010	ECON	Loader
460	1957		G	$1,900	2/1/2011	NEIN	Gas, fast hitch, Kelly loader, original
460	1958		G	$2,500	5/5/2012	NCKS	Gas, 2 pt. hitch, 540 PTO, excellent 18.9x28 rear tires
460	1959	4,582	G	$2,375	12/4/2013	Online	*BigIron.com,* item in Nebraska, Farmall, row crop, 5F/1R, TA, 6 cyl. gas, 45 drawbar, 49 PTO rated hp, Schwartz WF, engine block heater
460	1959	3,185	G	$5,750	2/19/2011	ECNE	Gas, WF, 2 pt., Farmhand-11 loader
460	1959		G	$3,800	12/3/2010	WCIL	3 pt. conversion
460	1959		G	$4,000	2/20/2010	NCIL	2 pt., PTO, TA, fenders, International Harvester 2000 loader
460	1960		G	$3,300	12/13/2013	NCMO	Diesel, WF, fast hitch, new paint, parade ready
460	1960		G	$2,601	5/23/2012	Online	*BigIron.com,* item in Iowa, Farmall 5' loader backhoe, Hi/Lo, 6 cyl. gas, 61 hp

International Harvester Company

Model	Year	Hours	Condition	Price	Date	Area	Comments
460	1961	5,559	G	$2,500	7/13/2011	Online	*BigIron.com,* item in Nebraska, Farmall, 5F/1R, TA, 6 cyl. gas, 540 PTO, TA works, 2 pt. fast hitch, fuel gauge inoperable, rear cement weights
460	1962	2,491	G	$4,600	4/13/2012	ECNE	Gas, SN J27756 S-Y-CC, WF, 6 cyl., 2 pt., PTO, 1 hyd., 14.9x38 rear tires, 2 rear wheel weights each side, Farmhand F11 loader, 5' bucket
460	1962		G	$5,250	7/14/2011	SWMN	Good rubber, WF, gas, fast hitch, SN 29784-S-Y-CC
460	1962		G	$2,200	3/15/2011	WCIL	NF, fast hitch, 540 PTO
460	1962	1,400	G	$3,700	2/20/2010	NCIL	Gas, NF, 3 pt., fenders
460	1963		F	$1,900	7/21/2012	ECIN	Gas, NF, fast hitch
460			G	$3,000	3/22/2014	SWMI	Farmall, 2WD, 1 hyd., fast hitch, 540 PTO, WF
460			G	$4,900	2/5/2014	SESD	WF
460			G	$6,100	2/5/2014	SESD	Wheatland
460			G	$2,365	10/10/2013	Online	*HansenandYoung.com,* item in Wisconsin, WF, recent OH, Paulson hyd. header
460		2,145	F	$2,200	9/7/2013	SEMN	Gas, NF, faded, fast hitch, 14.9x38 tires, 540 PTO, 1 hyd., not showing correct hours, weak TA
460		9,545	G	$2,500	9/7/2013	SEMN	Gas, NF, weak TA, fast hitch, 14.9x38 tires, 540 PTO, 1 hyd.
460			G	$2,800	8/15/2013	ECMN	NF
460			G	$5,500	3/23/2013	NEIN	High-Utility, original, runs
460			G	$2,600	2/23/2013	ECMI	Gas, WF, PTO, 13.6x38 tires, Freeman loader attached
460			F	$2,800	2/16/2013	NEIA	Gas, NF
460		7,974	G	$3,100	2/16/2013	SENE	Gas, NF, JD 45 loader, fast hitch
460		3,536	G	$3,700	2/7/2013	NEIN	Gas, 14.9x28 tires 50%, hyd. loader, 6' bucket, 540 PTO, fast hitch
460		3,536	G	$3,700	2/7/2013	NEIN	Gas, loader
460		5,000	G	$3,000	2/6/2013	SESD	High crop, 1 of 345 built
460			F	$4,300	2/6/2013	Online	Item in Illinois, diesel, power steering, good TA, 2 pt., 14.9x38 tires, rear weights, blown head gasket
460			G	$3,500	11/13/2012	NCIA	Loader
460		2,054	F	$1,980	7/25/2012	Online	*PurpleWave.com,* item in Kansas, International Harvester 3.9L, 6 cyl. diesel, 61 hp, manual, 23 gal. fuel tank, 3 pt., 540 PTO, 78" wheelbase
460		6,877	G	$3,500	7/14/2012	NWIA	Gas, new TA, clutch, NF
460			P	$1,200	6/9/2012	ECNE	Gas, aftermarket WF, motor stuck
460			G	$2,200	6/9/2012	ECNE	Hyd., PTO, NF, fast hitch, original, runs
460			F	$2,000	6/7/2012	NEIN	
460			G	$4,805	5/23/2012	Online	*BigIron.com,* item in Nebraska, 5 speed, 6 cyl. diesel, 1 hyd., 540 PTO, tach. does not work
460		3,810	F	$2,210	5/8/2012	Online	*IQBID.com,* gas, 3 pt., PTO, Du-Al hyd. loader, new 13.6x38 tires, new brakes, seat, steering wheel, manifold, newly rebuilt carburator

International Harvester Company

Model	Year	Hours	Condition	Price	Date	Area	Comments
460		2,244	G	$4,000	4/25/2012	Online	*BigIron.com,* item in Nebraska, NF, 1 hyd., 540 PTO, quick hitch
460		2,738	F	$1,500	3/24/2012	SETX	WF, low profile, 1 hyd., 540 PTO, 3 pt. hitch, diesel, 50 hp, new injection pump
460			F	$1,600	11/30/2011	ECND	Industrial loader
460			G	$1,100	9/14/2011	Online	*BigIron.com,* item in Colorado, 6 cyl. gas, ran when parked, mid-hyd.
460			P	$1,100	8/20/2011	NEMN	Gas, industrial, Wagner hyd. loader, needs hyd. work, has noise in rear end, moves forward and back, but loader does not raise
460			G	$2,500	8/11/2011	WCMN	Farmall, gas, hyd. loader, 3 hyd., power steering, fast hitch
460		5,917	G	$3,800	7/28/2011	NESD	Farmall, 1 hyd., PTO
460			G	$1,251	6/21/2011	Online	*BidNow.US,* Farmall, 6 cyl., gas, 13.6x38 tires, no smoke
460			G	$1,700	4/16/2011	ECMI	Farmall, diesel, fast hitch, PS, WF, triple axle
460			G	$3,200	4/16/2011	ECMI	Farmall, gas, Du-Al hyd. loader, 72" material bucket, nice paint, drawbar hitch, good sheet metal
460			G	$3,800	4/2/2011	SEMN	Gas, 3 pt., loader
460		5,234	F	$1,900	2/8/2011	ECNE	Diesel, NF, 5,234 hours showing on tach., 13.6x38 rear tires, 6x16 front tires, 2 pt., Farmhand F11 loader
460			F	$1,400	12/17/2010	WCIL	WF
460			G	$3,200	11/20/2010	NCOH	Gas, row crop, fast hitch
460			G	$3,900	9/4/2010	NEIN	Farmall, high crop, 2 pt.
460			G	$1,225	6/23/2010	Online	*BigIron.com,* item in Nebraska, 5F/1R TA, 6 cyl. diesel, rear tires 16.9x38, front tires 6.5x16, 540 PTO, power steering, 2 pt. fast hitch
460		4,991	G	$2,900	6/23/2010	Online	*BigIron.com,* item in Nebraska, 5 speed, 6 cyl., 1 hyd., 540 PTO, hyd. drawbar lift, WF
460		500	G	$1,550	6/5/2010	ECMN	Farmall, gas, good TA
460			G	$2,100	6/5/2010	SEMN	WF, fast hitch, PTO
460			F	$950	5/26/2010	ECSD	Gas, Johnson loader
464	1974	2,841	G	$4,300	3/20/2013	SWMI	Diesel, 3 pt., orchard and regular fenders
464	1976	1,348	G	$2,585	8/15/2012	Online	*PurpleWave.com,* item in Kansas, International Harvester 4 cyl. gas, manual, spring seat, 3 pt., 540 PTO, 1 rear hyd., Land Pride rotary mower
464		1,272	G	$4,650	10/19/2012	ECIL	WF, 3 pt., weights, 2 hyd., 14.9x28 tires, GB 666 loader, 60" hyd. bucket, original
464		2,057	G	$1,950	2/4/2012	NEAR	3 cyl. diesel, 3 pt., 540 PTO
464			G	$4,000	11/20/2010	SCKY	International Harvester 2200 loader, 2 hyd.
464			G	$3,000	11/18/2010	SEOK	
464		3,220	G	$3,630	1/19/2010	Online	*PurpleWave.com,* item in Kansas, 4 cyl. gas, 3 pt., 540 PTO

International Harvester Company

Model	Year	Hours	Condition	Price	Date	Area	Comments
504	1958		G	$3,100	5/26/2012	ECPA	Gas, 14.9x38 tires, 3 pt., 540 PTO, 1 set rear weights, 1 set front weights, 1 bolt-on front weight
504	1958		G	$4,200	5/26/2012	ECPA	Gas, WF, 13.6x38 tires, 2 pt. drawbar, 540 PTO, fenders
504	1962	2,146	G	$2,100	12/26/2013	Online	*BigIron.com,* item in Iowa, Farmall, row crop, 5F/1R, TA, 2.5L, 4 cyl., 13.6x38 rear tires, 6x16 front tires, 40 hp, 2 hyd., 3 pt., 6' Westendorf bucket on loader, rear wheel weights
504	1963		G	$4,100	11/23/2010	NCIA	Diesel, WF, 3 pt., 13.6x38 tires
504	1964		G	$3,400	2/8/2014	NECO	SF, 3 pt., PTO, electric start, good rubber, PS, diesel, hyd. 1 set
504	1964		G	$3,200	11/23/2010	NCIA	Gas, WF, fast hitch, 13.6x38 tires
504	1967	3,637	G	$6,700	4/17/2013	Online	*BigIron.com,* item in Iowa, loader, 5F/1R
504			G	$1,800	12/18/2013	Online	*BigIron.com,* item in Nebraska, row crop, manual 5 speed, 4 cyl. LP, 18.4x38 rear tires, 6x16 front tires, 1 hyd., 540 PTO, 3 pt.
504			G	$4,000	12/5/2013	SCIA	Gas, low profile, 3 pt., loader
504		2,472	G	$1,700	8/24/2013	SEMN	NF, fast hitch, PTO, hyd., 13.6x38
504			G	$7,500	3/23/2013	NEIN	Gas, high crop, repainted, new tires, fenders, runs
504			G	$1,300	2/22/2013	SWKY	Farmall, diesel, NF
504		9,395	G	$4,900	10/13/2012	NCCO	Gas, 3 pt.
504			P	$3,900	6/9/2012	ECNE	Diesel, high clear, 3 pt., hyd., no PTO, fenders, motor stuck
504		2,013	G	$3,750	6/2/2012	SEMN	Farmall, NF, 3 pt., good TA
504			G	$4,600	3/10/2012	NWIL	2 pt. fast hitch, 3 pt. conversion, International Harvester 2000 loader, manure and snow buckets, low hours
504			G	$1,700	3/1/2012	NWTX	Farmhand loader
504			G	$3,400	12/7/2011	NCIA	Restored
504			G	$2,150	8/27/2011	NEIA	Gas, NF, TA out, major engine oil leaks, straight tin
504		3,976	G	$5,600	8/27/2011	SEND	Farmall, original WF, power steering, 3 pt., PTO, gas, original fenders
504			F	$2,800	4/11/2011	NEIA	Gas
504			G	$2,750	12/30/2010	ECMN	Farmall, NF, 1 hyd., 540 PTO, new paint
504			F	$2,150	12/17/2010	WCIL	Runs
504			G	$3,200	11/23/2010	NCIA	
504			G	$4,100	11/23/2010	NCIA	
504			G	$4,200	9/4/2010	NEIN	
504			P	$800	9/3/2010	NEIN	High crop, dead row, needs work, may not run or drive, as is
504		3,358	G	$2,900	3/18/2010	SEIN	WF
544	1958		G	$6,700	5/26/2012	ECPA	Hydro, gas, 13.6x38 tires, drawbar 3 pt., 540 PTO, 1 set rear weights, fenders, front weight bracket
544	1968	6,917	G	$3,700	12/18/2013	Online	*BigIron.com,* item in Nebraska, 5 speed, TA, 4 cyl. gas

International Harvester Company

Model	Year	Hours	Condition	Price	Date	Area	Comments
544	1968	6,871	G	$2,300	7/27/2011	Online	*BigIron.com,* item in Nebraska, Farmall, 10F/2R, 4 cyl. gas, 53 hp, 1 hyd., 540 PTO, 12V, power steering
544	1969		G	$5,060	11/30/2011	Online	*PurpleWave.com,* item in Oklahoma, hours unknown, 4 cyl. gas, 74" bucket, 3 pt., drawbar, 540 PTO
544	1970	4,307	G	$8,300	11/25/2013	SCIA	Hydro, fast hitch, ROPS, canopy
544	1971	4,870	G	$33,000	11/9/2013	SEIA	Estate auction, 2 brothers bidding against each other, dad bought new, SN 23004880014976
544			G	$7,300	12/5/2013	SCIA	Gas, Great Bend loader
544		1,948	G	$7,300	6/16/2012	WCSD	3 pt.
544			F	$2,600	3/19/2011	NEMI	Gas, hyd. loader, material bucket, 3 pt., 540 PTO, PS, hours unknown
544			G	$4,600	3/19/2011	NCPA	Gas, NF
544			G	$2,800	9/4/2010	NEIN	Farmall, high crop
560	1958		F	$1,000	12/1/2012	NWIL	Gas, NF, loader
560	1958		G	$5,600	5/26/2012	ECPA	Diesel, 16.9x38 tires, 2 pt., 540 PTO, front weight bracket, 1 set rear weights, side mount step
560	1958		F	$2,675	5/19/2012	WCIL	Farmall, International Harvester 2000 loader, fast hitch, NF
560	1958		F	$1,500	11/30/2011	SEMN	Gas, WF
560	1958		G	$2,900	7/16/2011	NEKS	Gas, SN 4806, original, 2 pt., Schwartz WF, good TA, press steel wheels, new Goodyear 16.9x34 tires
560	1958		G	$3,200	4/11/2011	Online	*AuctionTime.com*
560	1958		F	$2,250	8/24/2010	NEMO	Schwartz WF, 540 PTO, fast hitch with drawbar, 3 hyd.
560	1959		G	$2,500	4/4/2014	SESD	
560	1959		G	$1,750	7/31/2013	ECND	Farmall, WF, single hyd., PTO, Du-Al 300 loader, PTO hyd. pump, 8' bucket
560	1959		G	$3,400	3/20/2013	SWMI	Gas, NF
560	1959		F	$2,500	8/6/2011	NCIA	
560	1959		G	$2,200	4/15/2011	NEND	Farmall
560	1959		G	$2,700	4/23/2010	NENE	WF
560	1960		E	$9,000	3/15/2014	ECMD	Mounted 2MHD corn picker, gas, restored and painted prior to picker being mounted, 70% rubber, good TA, strong running, picker OH, new bearings and chains
560	1961	4,564	G	$1,800	7/3/2013	Online	*BigIron.com,* item in Iowa, 5F/1R, 6 cyl.
560	1961	2,632	G	$1,400	2/12/2013	WCIL	18.4/15x34 rear tires, 540 PTO
560	1961		G	$2,000	8/18/2012	ECNE	Diesel, 1 owner, 15.5x38 rubber, duals, WF, 2 pt.
560	1961	5,577	G	$1,100	5/23/2012	Online	*BigIron.com,* item in Wyoming, 5 speed, 6 cyl. diesel, 540 PTO, 3 pt., third link, missing front end cover
560	1961		F	$1,900	12/3/2011	NEMO	Diesel, NF, 18.4Rx38 tires, fast hitch, 2 hyd., 540 PTO, SN 37352
560	1961		G	$7,600	3/19/2011	ECIA	WF, fast hitch, International Harvester 2000 loader
560	1961	8,158	G	$1,800	9/22/2010	NECO	WF, diesel, 2 pt.

International Harvester Company

Model	Year	Hours	Condition	Price	Date	Area	Comments
560	1962		E	$7,000	3/15/2014	ECMD	Diesel, NF, rebuilt engine, new hyd. pump, rebuilt TA, new 16.9x38 tires on Power adj., fast hitch, front weight box, professionally restored and painted, fenders
560	1962		G	$2,900	9/12/2013	NCIA	Gas, WF, fast hitch
560	1962	9,813	G	$1,800	8/20/2013	WCIL	Diesel, WF, 1 hyd., fast hitch, 16.9x38 tires
560	1962	4,978	G	$3,550	7/11/2012	Online	*BigIron.com,* item in Iowa, 5F/1R TA, 6 cyl. diesel, single axle, 540/1,000 PTO, quick attach 2 pt.
560	1962		G	$1,550	6/27/2012	Online	*BigIron.com,* item in Nebraska, 5 speed, TA, 6 cyl. diesel, 1 hyd., 540 PTO, power steering, rear wheel weights
560	1962	3,191	G	$6,800	5/26/2012	ECPA	Diesel, TA, 15.5x38 tires, 2 pt., 540 PTO, 1 set front weights, 1 set rear weights
560	1962	6,222	G	$2,500	5/23/2012	Online	*BigIron.com,* item in Kansas, Farmall, 5F/1R, LP, 60 hp, 1 hyd., single axle, 540 PTO, WF, Super K Koyker 5' loader
560	1962	3,264	G	$3,300	11/12/2011	SEIA	WF, gas, 3 pt., 15.5x38 tires
560	1962		G	$2,750	8/20/2011	SCMI	Diesel, NF, fast hitch, 1 hyd., NF
560	1962		G	$3,250	8/20/2011	SCMI	Diesel, WF, fast hitch, 1 hyd.
560	1962		G	$4,350	1/25/2011	NCIL	Gas, NF, fenders, 2 pt. hitch
560	1962		E	$8,400	9/9/2010	SCIA	Diesel, front fenders, WF, 2 pt., fast hitch, 2nd owner, radio, 15.5x38 tires
560	1962	1,375	G	$3,700	2/20/2010	NCIL	NF, 2 hyd., fenders, 2 pt. fast hitch
560	1963	1,237	G	$2,201	4/3/2013	Online	*BigIron.com,* item in Kansas, 5F/1R, 6 cyl. gas, 15.5x38 rear tires, 235/85xR16 front tires, 60 claimed hp, 1 hyd., 2 pt. fast hitch, 900 Hi-Master
560	1963		G	$1,600	8/7/2010	WCMN	Loader, LP, engine good
560			F	$3,250	3/1/2014	SEMN	Diesel, WF, fast hitch, hyd., PTO, 15.5x38 tires, new paint
560		4,763	G	$5,400	1/24/2014	NCNE	WF, diesel, 5 speed, TA, 15.5x38 rear tires, 9.5Lx14 front tires, 540 PTO
560			G	$1,500	12/30/2013	SEMN	WF, Farmall, diesel
560			G	$1,805	12/18/2013	Online	*BigIron.com,* item in Nebraska, gas, 11.5x38 rear tires, 9.5Lx15 front tires, WF, rear extra wheel weights, single rear hyd., 2 pt. lift, 8' Farmhand loader, 3-tine grapple
560		3,789	G	$1,550	12/5/2013	WCMN	2WD, WF, gas, fast hitch, 15.5x38 tires
560			G	$2,025	12/3/2013	NEND	Farmall, WF, gas, 2WD, 1 hyd., 540 PTO
560		4,864	G	$1,925	9/25/2013	Online	*PurpleWave.com,* item in Kansas, Farmall, 6 cyl. diesel, 5 speed, power steering, 2 pt., drawbar, rear hyd., 6.5x16SL front tires
560			G	$1,350	9/12/2013	SEIA	WF, TA, 2 pt., 2 hyd., PTO
560			G	$1,500	9/12/2013	SEIA	WF, 3 pt., PTO, front loader forks
560			G	$1,650	8/24/2013	SEMN	WF, fast hitch, PTO, hyd., 15.5x38
560			E	$3,900	8/24/2013	SEMI	Farmall, gas, restored, WF, fast hitch, wheel weights

International Harvester Company

Model	Year	Hours	Condition	Price	Date	Area	Comments
560			G	$1,300	7/10/2013	Online	*BigIron.com,* item in Nebraska, 5 speed, 6 cyl. diesel, 1 hyd., 540 PTO
560			G	$2,600	7/10/2013	Online	*BigIron.com,* item in Nebraska, 5 speed, TA, 6 cyl. diesel
560			F	$2,750	7/10/2013	NCIA	Gas
560			G	$2,900	7/10/2013	NCIA	Diesel
560			G	$8,500	6/15/2013	WCOH	Gas, fenders, weights, new tires, PS, restored, runs
560			G	$2,800	6/1/2013	SEMN	Farmall, gas, WF, quick hitch, loader, new tires
560			G	$3,000	4/13/2013	SEMN	Farmall, gas, fast hitch, 18.4x34 tires 75% good, TA
560		2,519	G	$4,300	4/6/2013	SEMN	Gas, WF, fast hitch, wheel weights
560			G	$1,125	3/30/2013	NWIL	Farmall, gas, NF, hyd. loader, runs, drives
560			G	$2,600	3/23/2013	NEIN	Gas, fenders, new tires, runs
560			G	$2,800	3/23/2013	NEIN	Gas, standard, repainted, weights, runs
560			G	$3,000	3/16/2013	NEIL	Diesel
560			G	$3,000	3/2/2013	NEIA	Farmall, fenders
560			F	$2,800	2/16/2013	SENE	Gas, NF
560			P	$3,200	2/16/2013	NEIA	Diesel, rough, WF, 2 pt.
560			G	$5,500	2/16/2013	NEIA	Gas, NF, 2 pt.
560			P	$1,200	11/24/2012	SEMN	NF, not running, needs head gasket
560			G	$3,250	9/15/2012	SCMN	NF, fast hitch
560		4,617	G	$1,600	9/14/2012	ECMN	Farmall, International Harvester gas, live PTO, drawbar, 5 speed, hyd., front and rear lights, WF, PS
560		6,850	G	$1,601	8/22/2012	Online	*BigIron.com,* item in Nebraska, Farmall, diesel, 18.4x34 rear tires, 6x16 front tires, 540 PTO
560			G	$2,000	8/21/2012	WCIL	Farmall
560		2,061	G	$2,200	8/16/2012	Online	*IQBID.com,* item in Minnesota, gas, WF, 1 hyd., hyd. pump on 540 PTO, 16.9x38 tires, 85% rubber, 9.5Lx15 tires
560			G	$1,500	8/14/2012	Online	*IQBID.com,* item in Minnesota, Farmall, WF, gas, 2 hyd., 540 PTO, 18.4x34 tires
560			G	$3,200	6/9/2012	ECNE	LP, fast hitch, PTO, hyd., runs, original
560			G	$3,850	6/9/2012	ECNE	Diesel, fast hitch, belt pulley, hyd., PTO, original, runs
560			G	$3,600	5/23/2012	Online	*BigIron.com,* item in Nebraska, 5 speed, 6 cyl. diesel, 2 hyd., 540 PTO, fenders, back tire has sidewall cracks
560			F	$1,200	3/24/2012	SWMI	6 cyl. gas, NF, drawbar, 15.5x38 rear tires, TA, rebuilt, works
560			G	$2,700	3/22/2012	ECMN	2 hyd., fast hitch, 540 PTO, good TA, new clutch and radiator
560		4,573	F	$3,200	1/24/2012	NWWI	Gas, SN 60334S-Y-CC, 18.4x34 tires on pressed steel, after market WF, bad torque
560			F	$2,500	12/9/2011	NENE	WF, duals
560			G	$3,000	12/1/2011	WCMN	Farmall, gas, WF, bare back, Du-Al 320 hyd. loader

International Harvester Company

Model	Year	Hours	Condition	Price	Date	Area	Comments
560			G	$1,400	8/31/2011	SEMN	Farmall
560			G	$1,900	8/13/2011	WCIL	Gas, 15.5x38 rear tires, 1 hyd., 540 PTO, 3 pt.
560		7,400	G	$2,000	8/13/2011	WCIL	Farmall, 1 hyd., 15.5x38 rear tires, aftermarket 3 pt.
560			G	$3,400	8/13/2011	WCIL	WF, Farmall, Westendorf loader, 15.5x38 tires
560			G	$2,000	7/26/2011	ECND	Farmall, NF, Schwartz 20' jib boom, 3 stage high lift ram and hyd.
560		3,549	G	$6,160	6/29/2011	Online	*PurpleWave.com,* item in Kansas, 72 hp, TA, workhorse 800 loader, 540 PTO, 3 pt., rear hyd.
560		3,885	G	$2,100	3/18/2011	SWIL	1 hyd., 3 pt., 540 PTO, complete OH, 2 owners
560			G	$3,100	3/18/2011	SWIL	Gas, quick hitch, tricycle
560			P	$1,650	3/15/2011	WCIL	540 PTO, does not run
560			F	$2,500	1/29/2011	ECMO	International Harvester 2000 loader, gas, TA, power steering has hyd. leak
560		2,980	G	$2,700	12/17/2010	WCIL	Repainted, gas, 540 PTO, NF, 15.5x38 and 6.50x16 tires
560			G	$2,000	12/4/2010	SEMN	Diesel, fenders, fast hitch, 540 PTO, 1 hyd., good paint
560			F	$1,800	11/29/2010	ECIA	Gas, fast hitch
560		7,223	G	$2,600	11/27/2010	SEMN	NF, gas, PTO, hyd., good tires
560			G	$2,800	11/20/2010	NWIA	Diesel, Du-Al loader, WF, 2 pt., chains
560			E	$7,000	11/13/2010	NCIA	Restored front to back, new radiator, motor, clutch and TA
560			G	$1,800	9/11/2010	SEIA	Diesel
560			G	$2,200	9/11/2010	ECIA	WF, fast hitch
560			G	$2,200	9/11/2010	SEIA	Farmall
560			G	$6,250	9/4/2010	NEIN	Farmall, high crop
560			G	$1,800	8/11/2010	ECMN	Valve job just completed
560			G	$3,400	8/7/2010	SEWI	Wheatland, diesel, WF, belt pulley, new paint, TA 100%, originally out of North Dakota
560			G	$2,850	6/5/2010	ECMN	Farmall, diesel
560			G	$2,700	5/26/2010	ECSD	
560			F	$1,400	5/15/2010	SEKS	Gas, WF, tires 75%, 2 pt.
560		3,055	G	$3,000	4/10/2010	ECON	
560			G	$3,100	4/3/2010	ECMN	Turbo diesel, NF, fast hitch, single hyd.
560			F	$2,400	1/30/2010	WCIL	WF, 2 pt.
574	1973	3,030	F	$4,400	12/1/2012	SWMO	
574	1973		G	$3,600	4/1/2011	Online	*AuctionTime.com,* item in Arkansas, 67 hp, 2WD, 540 PTO, original, straight sheet metal, runs and drives great, 1 hyd.
574	1974		G	$6,800	7/16/2011	NEKS	Diesel, SN 107792, restored, excellent motor, rear end gone through, 1 hyd., 3 pt., Coop 13.6x38 tires, a real show tractor
574	1974	3,212	G	$3,250	4/9/2011	WCNE	WF, diesel, 3 pt. Farmhand 226 loader
574	1974		G	$4,100	9/11/2010	ECIA	Quick attach loader and bucket

International Harvester Company

Model	Year	Hours	Condition	Price	Date	Area	Comments
574	1975		G	$2,700	6/29/2012	NETX	67 hp, 2WD, OROPS, 14.9x28 tires, 8F/4R transmission, 1 rear hyd., starter problems
574	1977	4,300	F	$5,700	12/13/2012	NWIL	International Harvester 2250 loader, 6' bucket, gas
574		2,715	F	$1,600	10/3/2013	NCIN	Gas
574		6,016	G	$1,800	10/3/2013	NCIN	Diesel, 16.9x30, 1 hyd., aux. fuel tank
574		3,939	G	$4,500	9/12/2013	SEIA	International Harvester 2000 loader, hydro
574			G	$4,500	8/24/2013	SEMN	Gas, International Harvester 1850 hyd. loader, 3 PT, hyd. PTO, 14.9x28
574			P	$1,000	4/26/2013	SWKY	Gas, bad engine
574			G	$3,200	4/26/2013	SWKY	
574			G	$4,400	3/30/2013	SCMN	International Harvester 2200 loader, 3 pt., PTO, gas
574		2,533	G	$6,900	2/22/2013	NWIN	2WD, gas, loader, 3 pt., hyd., PTO, power steering, original
574		2,849	G	$5,250	2/19/2013	WCOH	Gas, 13.6x28 tires, loader
574			G	$6,800	1/7/2013	SWOH	Diesel, 3 pt., 540 PTO, 16.9x30 tires, International Harvester 2250 loader
574			G	$6,250	10/27/2012	WCOH	Gas, International Harvester 2250 loader
574		1,193	G	$4,100	10/24/2012	WCWI	16.9x28 tires
574			G	$2,700	1/28/2012	ECMO	Great Bend 800 loader, 1 hyd.
574			G	$6,900	8/29/2011	WCWI	Gas, WF, nice
574		3,273	G	$3,900	4/14/2011	NCND	Gas
574			G	$2,300	1/29/2011	ECMO	New batteries, runs
574		3,150	F	$4,000	12/11/2010	NCOH	Gas, 3pt., 8 speed, rear weights, SN 2310016V106220, 16.9x28 Kelly Springfield rear tires at 99%, joystick, 62" Mount-O-Matic, loader SN 0810100C00164
574		4,058	G	$4,400	11/20/2010	SCKY	1 hyd.
574			F	$4,900	11/20/2010	NCOH	International Harvester loader
574			F	$1,900	11/18/2010	SEOK	
600	1956	4,159	G	$2,700	8/25/2011	ECND	Diesel, standard, hand clutch, PTO, belt pulley, fenders, rear weights, 18.4x34 rears, loose, ran when parked
600			G	$3,800	9/1/2011	WCMN	Wheatland, diesel, 1 hyd., 12V, power steering, lights, wheel weights
606	1963		G	$5,000	7/16/2011	NEKS	Diesel, SN 1923X-Y-FF, restored, 540 PTO, no TA, 3 pt., 1 hyd., swept back front axle, Goodyear 14x26 tires
606	1964	1,364	G	$3,850	10/31/2012	Online	*PurpleWave.com,* item in Kansas, 3.6L, 6 cyl. gas, TA, 540 PTO, 3 pt., rear hyd., front hyd.
606	1964		G	$4,350	2/20/2010	NCIL	High speed reverse, TA, International Harvester 2000 loader, gas
606	1966		G	$4,350	2/20/2010	NCIL	Gas, WF, 3 pt.
606		4,905	G	$6,650	3/5/2014	Online	*BigIron.com,* item in Nebraska, 5 speed TA, 6 cyl., 14.9x28 rear tires, 6.5x16 front tires, gas, single hyd., 540 PTO, 3 pt.

International Harvester Company

Model	Year	Hours	Condition	Price	Date	Area	Comments
606			G	$3,700	3/2/2013	ECMN	Loader, good rubber
606			G	$2,700	10/24/2012	WCWI	
606			G	$3,700	1/31/2012	NEIN	Freeman loader
606			G	$3,500	5/7/2011	SWMB	3 pt., hyd., 60 hp, gas
606			G	$5,400	4/24/2010	SESK	2WD, gas, PTO, hyd.
650	1958	4,186	G	$4,100	8/25/2011	ECND	Diesel, standard, hand clutch, 1 hyd., PTO, power steering, 18.4x34 tires, loose, ran when parked
650			G	$4,900	10/3/2013	NCIN	
650			G	$5,500	9/12/2013	SEIA	WF, power steering, 1 hyd., PTO, new rear tires
650			G	$5,000	3/24/2012	NEIN	Diesel, repainted, power steering, PTO, hyd., runs
650			G	$5,000	3/24/2012	NEIN	LP, standard, original, PTO, hyd., power steering, excellent tires, very straight, runs
650			G	$2,500	1/28/2012	ECMO	LP
650		3,656	G	$2,750	12/15/2011	Online	*IQBID.com,* diesel, 1 hyd., live hyd., PTO, 18.4x34 rears
650		2,374	F	$2,700	9/15/2011	Online	*IQBID.com,* standard, diesel, PTO, 1 hyd., restored
650		2,524	F	$2,900	6/6/2011	SWSK	2WD, 62 PTO hp, gas start up, engine seized
650			G	$6,500	6/19/2010	SWIL	Gas, unrestored, original
656		657	G	$3,850	11/30/2011	Online	*PurpleWave.com,* item in Kansas, 6 cyl., Kelby loader, 540 PTO
656	1960		G	$4,900	5/26/2012	ECPA	Diesel, 15.5x38 tires, 2 pt. drawbar, 540 PTO, 1 set rear weights, fenders, tool box
656	1965		G	$3,100	9/12/2013	NCIA	Gas, WF, fast hitch
656	1965	6,871	G	$4,100	5/1/2013	Online	*BigIron.com,* item in Nebraska, loader, hydro, 6 cyl. diesel
656	1965		F	$4,300	11/22/2011	WCIL	Gas, 2 hyd., 540 PTO, New Idea 504 loader, hyd. material bucket
656	1965	5,138	G	$3,900	11/12/2011	SEIA	Gas, hydro drive, fast hitch, 15.5x38 tires
656	1965	9,522	G	$3,000	12/4/2010	SEWY	WF, 3 pt., diesel
656	1965	5,685	G	$3,250	12/4/2010	SEWY	WF, diesel, 3 pt.
656	1966		G	$4,500	11/30/2013	SCIL	WF, loader, SN 21051
656	1966	5,202	G	$3,400	3/28/2013	Online	*IQBID.com,* item in North Dakota
656	1966		G	$5,750	2/6/2013	SESD	Diesel, Farmhand 11 loader, fast hitch
656	1966	2,106	G	$3,200	11/20/2012	NEND	Gas, open station, 2 hyd., 540 PTO, JD 148 loader bracket, rear weights
656	1966		G	$2,750	8/21/2012	WCIL	
656	1966		F	$2,200	5/19/2012	WCIL	Gas, good tires
656	1966	4,317	G	$5,687	5/9/2012	Online	*BigIron.com,* item in Nebraska, Farmall, diesel, 2 hyd., 540 PTO, 2 pt., new batteries and flow plugs, rear wheel weights
656	1966	5,747	G	$6,850	2/14/2012	WCNE	Gas, 2 pt., Farmhand F11 black stripe loader, grapple head, grain scoop
656	1967	7,919	G	$2,200	8/14/2013	WCMN	Gas, 2 PT, fender, TA works, WL40 loader, WF

International Harvester Company

Model	Year	Hours	Condition	Price	Date	Area	Comments
656	1967	7,751	F	$4,070	9/26/2012	Online	*PurpleWave.com,* item in Iowa, gas, 3 pt., 540 PTO, < 150 hours on recently replaced tires
656	1967		G	$3,900	3/21/2012	ECMN	WF, 2 hyd.
656	1967	4,435	G	$4,350	11/14/2011	ECIL	Gas, SN 29177, row crop, 15.5x38 tires, 3 pt. inserts and top link, weights
656	1967	2,743	G	$2,100	6/6/2011	SWSK	Farmall, Western special, 2WD, 64 PTO hp, 540 PTO, 2 hyd., Mintoba cab
656	1967		G	$4,400	8/28/2010	WCIL	WF, 15.5x38 rear tires, OH, gas
656	1968	6,109	G	$5,000	2/5/2014	SESD	Hydro, gas, WF, 1 hyd., 2 pt., 15.5x38
656	1968		G	$2,700	1/28/2012	ECMO	
656	1968	9,976	G	$2,400	12/22/2011	Online	*IQBID.com,* NF, diesel, open station, canopy, roll bar, 2 hyd., 540 PTO, third arm, 40% rubber
656	1968		G	$5,000	7/16/2011	NEKS	Hydro, High-Utility, gas, SN 10204, original, 3 pt., 1 hyd., 540 PTO, Firestone 15.5x38 tires
656	1968		G	$6,000	7/16/2011	NEKS	Hydro, Gas, SN 35648, original, WF, 3 pt., dual mid hyd., Goodyear 16.9x38
656	1968	5,097	G	$4,000	4/11/2011	Online	
656	1968	7,352	G	$4,800	5/1/2010	ECMN	Gas, cab, heat, 3 pt., single PTO, 2 hyd., flat top fenders, rear wheel weights, 16.9x38 tires, new 7.5x16 fronts, Schwartz all hyd. loader, snow bucket
656	1968	6,597	G	$5,100	2/23/2010	NWOH	Open station, gas, hydro, WF, 15.5x38 tires, duals
656	1969		G	$8,000	4/18/2013	WCMN	Diesel, hydro, open station, WF, PS, 3 pt., 18.4x34 tires, SN 40900
656	1969	6,863	G	$4,300	2/6/2013	SESD	Gas, Du-Al 3000 loader, 2 pt., 15.5x38 tires
656	1969		F	$2,300	11/30/2011	SEMN	Gas, WF, 18.4x38 tires
656	1969		G	$4,500	1/29/2011	ECMO	WF, 2 pt. and 3 pt. adapter, 2 hyd.
656	1970	6,381	G	$8,300	9/14/2011	Online	*BigIron.com,* item in Nebraska, Farmall, 5 speed, TA, 6 cyl. diesel, 63 PTO hp, 2 hyd., 3 pt., WF, set of heavy rear wheel weights, left steering arm is welded to spindle, bucket, Farmhand F11 loader, push blade
656	1972	8,000	G	$3,600	4/25/2013	WCMI	Farmall, gas, 3 pt., 13.6x38 tires, SN49468
656	1972		G	$4,000	6/23/2010	SEND	Gas, WF, 3 pt., good rubber and tin
656	1972		G	$5,500	2/20/2010	NCIL	Hydro, WF, fenders, 3 pt., 2 hyd., PS, original paint, gas
656	1973	6,140	F	$2,000	6/20/2013	ECSK	2WD, front-end loader, 63 PTO hp, bale spear, 2 hyd., 18.4x34
656	1973		F	$3,000	4/24/2013	SWSK	2WD, Du-Al front-end loader, 63 PTO hp, 18.4x34 rear
656		5,000	G	$5,500	3/30/2013	NEIA	Diesel
656		9,357	G	$2,710	3/19/2014	Online	*BigIron.com,* item in Nebraska, manual, 6 cyl. gas
656		6,700	G	$7,600	3/19/2014	Online	*BigIron.com,* item in Nebraska, hydro, 6 cyl.

International Harvester Company

Model	Year	Hours	Condition	Price	Date	Area	Comments
656		4,591	F	$1,550	3/15/2014	WCIL	Gas, hydro, 2 hyd., 540 PTO, 3 pt., 15.5x38 rear tires, engine is good, hydro is out
656			F	$3,500	2/26/2014	NCMO	Gas, loader
656			G	$3,200	2/22/2014	SCNE	NF, LP, fenders, 2 pt.
656		6,451	G	$2,100	12/18/2013	Online	*BigIron.com*
656		8,950	G	$4,000	9/28/2013	SWMN	WF, gas, 15.5x38, 3 pt.hitch, International Harvester quick attach loader, SN20189
656		5,961	F	$4,750	9/7/2013	SEMN	Gas, WF, fast hitch, cab, good TA, 540 PTO, 16.9x34 tires, Schwartz QT 1800 loader, SN 11948
656		7,486	G	$2,700	8/24/2013	SEMN	Gas, WF, 3 PT, dual hyd., PTO, 15.5x38, SN24500284042693
656		7,768	G	$1,500	7/10/2013	Online	*BigIron.com,* item in South Dakota, 5 speed, 6 cyl. gas, 540 PTO, salvage
656		5,340	G	$4,200	6/13/2013	Online	*IQBID.com,* diesel, WF, open station, 2 hyd., 3 pt., no top link, 540 PTO, 16.9x38 tires, transmission needs rebuilding
656			G	$4,050	6/11/2013	Online	*IQBID.com,* single hyd., 3 pt., PTO, Du-Al 340 loader, grapple
656		8,438	G	$4,250	6/1/2013	SEMN	Diesel, 16.9x38 tires, 540 PTO, 3 pt., square fenders
656		8,736	G	$3,050	5/8/2013	Online	*BigIron.com,* item in Nebraska, 6 cyl.
656		5,177	G	$4,500	3/30/2013	NEIA	Diesel, WF
656			F	$5,750	3/23/2013	SWON	Low profile
656			G	$3,250	3/22/2013	NESD	2 pt., PTO, good tires
656		6,801	G	$2,950	3/8/2013	SWMN	Gas, single hyd., 3 pt., PTO, 15.5x38 tires
656			G	$3,100	3/2/2013	NCWI	Farmall, diesel, WF, hyd., PTO, 14.9x38 tires
656		5,400	G	$6,000	2/6/2013	SESD	Westendorf loader, gas, 16.9x30 tires
656		8,220	G	$4,100	12/12/2012	WCIL	Open station, fenders, 3 pt.
656			G	$1,625	11/3/2012	SWMI	6 cyl. gas, WF, hydro, 3 pt., PTO, canopy, 16.9x30 rears
656			G	$6,100	10/18/2012	WCNE	Hydro, row crop, WF, 3 pt., couldn't read the hour meter
656		7,575	G	$3,750	10/13/2012	NCCO	Fast hitch, diesel
656			G	$4,000	9/15/2012	SCMN	Hydro, WF, 3 pt., fenders
656			G	$5,100	9/15/2012	SCMN	Hydro, factory WF, new rubber, fenders, repainted, 2 hyd., 3 pt.
656			G	$7,000	9/15/2012	SCMN	WF, 3 pt., fenders
656		5,859	G	$6,250	9/13/2012	Online	*IQBID.com,* item in Iowa, Farmall, Westendorf WL21 loader, 15.5x38, 2 hyd., 540 PTO, 3 pt.
656			F	$3,300	8/22/2012	NCIA	Gas, SN 209643, 3 pt., PTO, WF, 15.5x38 tires
656		7,129	G	$3,400	6/7/2012	NEIN	NF
656			G	$3,150	3/24/2012	SWMI	3 pt., PTO, WF, gas, hyd., 15.5x38 rear tires
656		5,300	G	$3,000	3/22/2012	ECMN	3 pt., PTO, fenders
656			G	$2,900	2/18/2012	ECIL	Farmall, gas, WF

International Harvester Company

Model	Year	Hours	Condition	Price	Date	Area	Comments
656		3,300	G	$3,100	1/28/2012	ECMO	Gas
656			G	$4,200	1/28/2012	ECMO	Diesel
656		9,958	F	$2,400	12/22/2011	Online	*IQBID.com,* 2WD, gas, 2 hyd., fast hitch, PTO, needs work
656			F	$1,900	10/29/2011	ECMN	Gas
656		4,568	G	$5,000	8/13/2011	WCIL	Hydro, gas, 2 hyd., 540 PTO
656		6,848	G	$4,400	8/6/2011	SCMN	6 cyl. gas, WF, open station, TA works, 1 hyd., 540 PTO, SN 25992, 15.5x38 rear tires
656			G	$2,800	7/30/2011	ECMO	International Harvester 2000 loader
656			G	$3,500	7/30/2011	ECMO	Gas, NF, 3 pt., good TA
656			G	$3,900	7/30/2011	ECMO	Du-Al 345 loader
656			G	$4,200	7/30/2011	ECMO	Gas
656		6,062	G	$3,550	5/11/2011	Online	*BigIron.com,* Farmall, hydro, 6 cyl. diesel, 540 PTO, WF, 2 front and 1 rear hyd., drawbar, engine block heater
656			G	$3,750	5/7/2011	WCSD	Diesel, 3 pt., 2 hyd., 540 PTO, brand new torque, 18.4x34 tires
656			G	$4,300	5/7/2011	WCSD	Hydro, gas, new seat, excellent tires, Farmhand F10 loader
656		6,445	G	$3,700	4/27/2011	Online	*BigIron.com,* item in Nebraska, hyd., gas, Dyna Torque rear tires, 3 sets of aux. hyd. valves, power steering, live 3 pt., 12V, push rod cover gasket leaking
656			G	$3,750	4/16/2011	ECMI	Gas, row crop, open station, triple axel, 3 pt., WF, 1 hyd., 540 PTO, nice rubber
656		7,802	G	$4,300	3/17/2011	ECMN	WF, factory 3 pt., single hyd.
656			G	$4,350	3/15/2011	WCIL	Gas, 540 PTO, 2 hyd., International Harvester loader
656			G	$5,000	3/15/2011	ECNE	WF, 3 pt.
656			F	$3,300	12/11/2010	NCOH	60 hp., WF, SN 2450126U045401, 15.5x38 Titan rear tires, 75% tread, diesel, 3 pt. 540 PTO, hydro
656			G	$3,050	11/8/2010	SCWI	Gas, hydro, Allied loader, 7' bucket
656			E	$3,000	10/23/2010	NCMD	Cab, loader and manure bucket
656			G	$4,500	9/4/2010	NEIN	Farmall, high crop, 3 pt.
656			G	$6,400	9/4/2010	NEIN	Gas
656			P	$900	9/3/2010	NEIN	High crop, dead row, needs work, may not run or drive, as is
656			G	$4,800	8/9/2010	WCMO	Hydro, high clearance, diesel
656			G	$2,300	6/5/2010	NWIA	Loader, gas motor
656		721	G	$4,750	6/5/2010	NWIA	M&W turbo, NF, 700 hours on OH, good clutch and torque
656			F	$2,800	3/5/2010	NCMO	Gas, gear drive, 3 pt., WF
656			F	$5,000	3/5/2010	NCMO	Gas, Westendorf loader, Schwartz WF, gear, 3 pt.
660	1960	1,182	G	$2,400	9/22/2010	NECO	Wheatland, diesel, PTO
660	1962		G	$2,500	4/24/2013	SWSK	2WD, 95 hp, TA works
660	1963		F	$16,000	9/8/2012	NECO	Rare gas burner, not restored, in its work clothes, Du-Al 3100 loader, 2,500 hours showing, tach. did not work

International Harvester Company

Model	Year	Hours	Condition	Price	Date	Area	Comments
660			G	$1,600	10/20/2012	SEWY	Add-on, turbo kit
660			F	$2,400	9/16/2011	ECND	Engine gone through, TA is a bit weak, diesel
660			G	$3,700	6/5/2010	ECMN	Farmall, gas, new TA, restored
666	1973	8,000	G	$6,750	2/8/2014	NECO	3 pt., diesel, 2 hyd. sets, PTO, WF, front weight box, Year-A-Round cab, good rubber
666	1973		G	$3,100	9/12/2013	SEIA	Gas, WF, 3 pt., no third link, 2 hyd., 16.9x38
666	1973		G	$3,000	7/17/2013	Online	*BigIron.com,* item in Iowa, 291 gas, 66 hp, 1 hyd.
666	1973	9,108	G	$5,200	12/22/2011	Online	*IQBID.com,* cab, 3 pt., PTO, 2 hyd.
666	1973		G	$3,700	8/28/2010	WCIL	Hydro, gas, WF, 2 hyd., good 15.5x38 tires, 2 years hours on OH
666	1975	4,374	G	$4,950	10/31/2012	Online	*PurpleWave.com,* item in Kansas, 6 cyl. diesel, 69 hp, TA, Schwartz loader, 72" bucket, 3 pt., drawbar, 540 PTO
666	1975	3,400	G	$3,700	3/14/2012	ECND	WF, gas, open station, 2 hyd., 3 pt., PTO, electronic ignition, 15.5x38 rears
666	1975	9,024	G	$5,400	12/22/2011	Online	*IQBID.com,* ROPS, 3 pt., 540 PTO, 2 hyd., canopy, rock box
666	1976	9,000	F	$6,000	11/22/2011	WCIL	540 PTO, 2 hyd., International Harvester 2250 loader
666	1976		G	$8,100	2/20/2010	NCIL	Diesel, WF, fenders, 3 pt., 1 hyd.
666	1978		G	$2,600	12/4/2013	ECND	Du-Al loader, 540 PTO
666		4,838	G	$4,800	1/4/2014	ECOH	Gas
666		2,755	G	$1,766	6/26/2013	Online	*BigIron.com,* item in Nebraska, hydro, does not run
666		7,038	G	$6,600	1/7/2013	SWOH	Farmall, 15.5x38 tires, 3 pt., 540 PTO, International Harvester 2350 loader
666			G	$1,900	3/24/2012	NEIN	Diesel, high crop, older repaint, runs
666			G	$4,400	1/31/2012	NEIN	
666			F	$2,500	1/17/2012	SCKS	WF, 2 hyd., 540 PTO, 3 pt., 3rd link
666			G	$8,500	12/3/2011	NCIL	WF, 3 pt., 540 PTO, 2 hyd., diesel
666			G	$5,200	12/1/2011	WCMN	WF, 3 pt. hyd. loader
666			G	$5,600	3/19/2011	SEIA	Gas
666		5,971	G	$3,800	3/15/2011	WCIL	540 PTO
666			G	$4,600	1/8/2011	ECMI	
666			F	$5,200	10/23/2010	SWWI	WF, cab
666			G	$3,100	9/4/2010	NEIN	Farmall, high crop
666			P	$2,800	9/3/2010	NEIN	3 pt., dead row, needs work and may not run or drive, as is
666			G	$3,950	8/9/2010	WCMO	Gas, International Harvester loader, not quick attach
666		9,650	G	$4,200	4/1/2010	NCIN	Gas, 540 PTO, 1 hyd.
674	1973	3,674	G	$6,500	8/20/2011	SCMI	International Harvester 2250 loader, 14.9x30 tires, 3 pt., gas, 1 hyd.
674	1974		G	$4,250	3/15/2014	WCIL	Gas, 1 hyd., 540 PTO, 3 pt., 16.9x30 rear tires, one owner, Great Bend 800 Work Master loader, 5.5' bucket with forks

International Harvester Company

Model	Year	Hours	Condition	Price	Date	Area	Comments
674	1975		G	$3,500	8/16/2012	Online	*IQBID.com,* item in Minnesota, cab, gas, 1 hyd., 3 pt., PTO, no top link, no drawbar, loader, 16.9x30 rears, 65% rubber, hours unknown
674	1977	3,876	G	$2,350	12/11/2013	Online	*BigIron.com,* item in Illinois, 8F/4R, International Harvester engine, 3 pt. 16.9x30 rear tires, 2 hyd., drawbar, end loader ready, OH in 2009
674		5,326	G	$4,250	12/10/2013	WCWI	Canopy, 1 hyd., 3 pt., PTO, bar axle
674		2,948	G	$7,000	8/24/2013	NWIL	Diesel, 16.9x30 rears, 2250 Mount-O-Matic loader
674		3,893	G	$5,800	3/30/2013	NEIA	Diesel
674			G	$5,170	3/27/2013	NWWI	3 pt., dual hyd., WF, 18.4x30 rear tires, 540 PTO
674			G	$5,300	3/23/2013	NEIN	Gas, 3 pt., hyd., loader bucket, forks, runs
674			G	$4,300	1/21/2013	NCIA	Gas, F348 Farmhand loader, joystick
674		5,585	G	$7,500	11/24/2012	SEIA	Diesel, WF, Westendorf loader
674			G	$2,000	7/27/2012	SWKY	
674			G	$7,500	2/6/2012	ECIL	Front loader, 4 speed Hi/Lo.
674			G	$3,800	1/28/2012	ECMO	
674			F	$3,750	12/15/2011	WCIL	Diesel tractor, 16.9x28 tires, 1 hyd., 540 PTO and sells complete, International Harvester 2250 loader
674			G	$5,500	5/7/2010	WCOH	1 hyd., repaint
674		2,751	G	$3,000	5/4/2010	WCOK	Diesel, 3 pt., PTO, rebuilt topside
674			F	$3,750	1/9/2010	ECTX	Loader, diesel, spear on loader
686	1976		F	$4,100	4/15/2014	SWSK	2WD, 66 PTO hp, 2 hyd., 18.4x34 rear, Ezee-On FEL brackets, Charlynn tank, hour meter not working
686	1977		G	$5,300	2/22/2014	NEIN	2 hyd., 3 pt., PTO
686	1977	2,149	G	$10,100	2/1/2011	NEIN	Fender
686	1978		G	$4,650	3/15/2014	WCIL	
686	1978		G	$7,400	2/15/2010	ECIL	Fender, 2 hyd., 18.4x34 rear tires, New Idea loader with hyd. bucket off 560
706	1963	4,924	G	$5,600	1/18/2012	Online	*BigIron.com,* item in Nebraska, Farmall, 8 speed manual, 6 cyl. diesel, glow plugs, 67 drawbar hp, 72 PTO hp, 2 hyd., WF, 16F/4R
706	1963		E	$5,400	7/16/2011	NEKS	Gas, SN 37633, restored, 3 pt., 1 hyd., good TA, Goodyear 18.4x34 tires
706	1964	9,335	G	$1,786	6/5/2013	Online	*BigIron.com,* item in Nebraska, Hi/Lo 4 speed
706	1964		G	$4,800	7/16/2011	NEKS	Diesel, SN 9808, restored, WF rebuilt, 2 pt., dual mid hyd., single rear hyd., German diesel, new 18.4x34 Firestone tires
706	1964		G	$3,250	9/11/2010	ECIA	WF, 3 pt., 1,000 hours on OH
706	1965	2,964	F	$3,654	12/18/2013	Online	*BigIron.com,* item in Iowa, Farmall, Stanhoist loader, 806 gas motor, 89 hp, 2 hyd., 8' bucket, press plate, clutch replaced

International Harvester Company

Model	Year	Hours	Condition	Price	Date	Area	Comments
706	1965	5,240	F	$2,800	4/13/2013	SCMI	Farmall, diesel, bad TA and rear end gear, good 15.5x38 tires, rear weights, 1 hyd., fast hitch, SN 22597
706	1965	6,858	G	$3,700	3/27/2013	Online	*BigIron.com,* item in Minnesota, 4 speed Hi/Lo, International Harvester 263 6 cyl.
706	1965	5,147	G	$2,250	8/13/2011	WCIL	Gas, TA out, new brakes, clutch and rear main seals, fast hitch, single rear hyd., 540 PTO
706	1965	4,974	G	$2,000	4/11/2011	Online	*AuctionTime.com,* MFWD
706	1965	1,756	F	$3,700	1/20/2010	ECNE	Diesel, Schwartz WF, M&W turbo, 16.9x34 rear tires, 9.5Lx15 front tires, 1 hyd., 540/1,000 PTO, 2 pt. fast hitch, rear fenders
706	1966		G	$4,100	6/13/2012	SWOH	Diesel, WF
706	1966	9,061	G	$2,200	3/22/2012	ECMN	Factory WF, 1 hyd., 3 pt., no arms, 540/1,000 PTO
706	1966	4,419	G	$2,550	3/20/2012	WCIL	Gas, 16.9x34 rear tires, 540/1,000 PTO, 1 rear hyd.
706	1966		G	$5,250	3/20/2012	WCIL	Gas, 16.9x34 tires, 540/1,000 PTO, 1 hyd., WF
706	1966		G	$3,000	11/22/2011	WCIL	Gas, WF, SN 354575Y
706	1966	2,977	G	$8,800	9/2/2011	ECIL	Diesel, 2 pt., dual PTO, hyd.
706	1966	3,070	E	$6,500	8/20/2011	NWOH	Gas, 3 pt., flat fenders, WF, duals, front weights
706	1966		E	$8,900	8/20/2011	NWOH	Gas, flat fenders, 3 pt., WF, duals, two 200 gal. saddle tanks, 3 pt. Century sprayer light bar, 60' booms, hyd. pump
706	1966		G	$2,850	3/15/2011	WCIL	Gas, 540/1,000 PTO
706	1966		G	$2,750	3/5/2011	SEMN	Farmall, gas, WF, fast hitch, 2 hyd., 540/1,000 PTO
706	1966	4,587	E	$5,750	4/24/2010	NWMO	WF, gas, 2nd owner, OH, SN 32954, front and rear weights, good rubber, sound torque, 2 pt. quick hitch
706	1966		G	$3,750	2/20/2010	NCIL	Gas, NF, flat top fenders, dual PTO, 2 hyd., 3 pt., good torque
706	1967		F	$3,400	12/27/2012	NCIA	Gas, International Harvester 2000 loader, SN 41014, fast hitch, 540/1,000 PTO, 16.9x34 tires, 3 pt., Year-A-Round cab, WF
706	1967	7,770	G	$7,100	7/10/2012	NCIA	German diesel, open station, WF, 1,000 PTO, 3 pt., Westendorf WL42 loader
706	1967	5,760	G	$2,100	6/27/2012	Online	*BigIron.com,* item in Nebraska, Hi/Lo, 291 gas, 67 hp, 2 hyd., 7' bucket, loader pins are loose
706	1967	6,056	F	$5,600	11/3/2011	ECIL	German diesel, fenders, SN 41065, Goodyear 18.4x34 tires, 2 hyd., #3000 hyd. loader, 8' bucket, needs fuel pump work
706	1968	6,483	G	$4,250	2/8/2014	NWIL	No TA, gas, all new tires
706			G	$3,800	2/26/2014	NCMO	Gas
706		4,120	G	$2,250	12/4/2013	ECIN	

International Harvester Company

Model	Year	Hours	Condition	Price	Date	Area	Comments
706			G	$3,100	9/12/2013	SEIA	WF, 3 pt., 540/1,000 PTO, 2 hyd., recent paint, OH 60 hours ago
706			G	$4,000	9/7/2013	ECIA	Gas
706			G	$7,250	7/31/2013	ECND	2 hyd., live PTO, 2 pt. International Harvester fast hitch with arms, Buhler Allied H695 quick attach loader, dirt and snow buckets
706		7,900	G	$5,000	7/27/2013	NCIA	Farmall, Hiniker cab, 2 hyd., 2 pt., 540/1,000 PTO, Westendorf WL21 loader, 16.9x34 tires, chains, adj. width hubs
706		6,708	F	$1,825	7/9/2013	Online	*IQBID.com,* gas, WF, PS, 3 pt., 540/1,000 PTO, Du-Al 345 loader, 72" bucket, bale spear
706		7,901	G	$5,000	6/27/2013	Online	*IQBID.com,* Hiniker cab, 2 hyd., 2 pt., 540/1,000 PTO, Westendorf WL21 loader, 16.9x34 tires, chains, adj. width hubs, SN 29226
706			G	$2,000	6/22/2013	SEMN	18.4x34, WF, gas, 3 PT, no arms, hyd. PTO, hyd. loader, 7' bucket
706			G	$2,800	6/22/2013	SEMN	WF, 3 pt., dual PTO, hyd. 18.4x34
706			G	$2,607	6/12/2013	Online	*BigIron.com,* item in Iowa, 2WD, manual 4 speed Hi/Lo, TA, 6 cyl.
706			G	$3,500	6/7/2013	NESD	Diesel, 3 pt., PTO, Farmhand F-11 loader
706			G	$5,115	4/23/2013	Online	*HansenandYoung.com,* item in Wisconsin, restored
706			G	$4,600	3/23/2013	NEIN	Gas, WF, fenders, weights, repainted, 3 pt., runs
706			G	$3,900	3/22/2013	NWMN	Fender, 3 pt., dual hyd., dual PTO, original, runs
706			G	$4,000	3/22/2013	NESD	Gas, WF, new clutch, F10 loader, engine work has been done
706			F	$3,750	3/21/2013	ECIL	Gas, machinery boom, counter weight, narrow prop front
706		4,406	G	$2,950	3/7/2013	SEIA	Farmall, diesel, 3 pt., 540/1,000 PTO, 2 hyd., WF, 56 series shifter, 18.4Rx34 rears
706		5,443	G	$3,300	3/7/2013	SEIA	3 pt., 540/1,000 PTO, 2 hyd., 18.4x34 rears
706			G	$3,500	11/13/2012	NCIA	Gas, flat fenders
706			F	$3,400	11/7/2012	NEND	Gas, WF, PTO, loader, grapple
706		7,711	G	$2,950	10/13/2012	NCCO	Gas, fast hitch
706			G	$2,500	9/13/2012	SEIA	
706		3,226	F	$2,100	8/11/2012	NWIA	Gas, WF, Year-A-Round cab, 16.9x34 tires, 3 pt., manual
706			G	$1,900	8/4/2012	SWMN	Farmall, Hiniker cab, 18.4x34 rubber, rock box, 3 pt., 540/1,000 rpm PTO
706			G	$3,000	7/18/2012	ECND	3 pt., 540/1,000 PTO, nearly new tires, Du-Al loader, forks and bucket
706			G	$4,100	3/24/2012	NEIN	Gas, standard, 3 pt., original, runs
706			G	$1,500	2/18/2012	SWAR	Pecan shaker attached
706			F	$1,750	12/9/2011	NENE	
706			F	$4,100	12/9/2011	NENE	

International Harvester Company

Model	Year	Hours	Condition	Price	Date	Area	Comments
706			F	$2,500	9/16/2011	ECND	Gas, cab, WF, PTO, 3 pt.
706			G	$3,000	8/31/2011	ECMN	Loader
706			F	$2,600	8/27/2011	NEIA	WF, gas, rough cab, straight tin
706		3,225	G	$4,200	8/6/2011	NEIA	German diesel, NF, 3 pt., runs 2 hyd., 16.9Rx34, new PTO and pump 2 years ago, handy chore tractor
706			F	$3,100	7/27/2011	ECND	2 hyd., 540/1,000 PTO, fenders
706			F	$775	4/27/2011	Online	*BigIron.com,* item in Nebraska, standard, LP, 1 hyd., 540/1,000 PTO, for parts, NF, some parts missing
706			G	$5,500	4/23/2011	WCMI	Diesel, WF, 3 pt., dual PTO, 1 hyd., good tires
706			G	$1,200	4/16/2011	SESK	Farmall, 2WD, D engine, standard, single hyd., dual speed PTO
706			G	$3,400	3/5/2011	SEMN	Farmall, gas, cab, 540/1,000 PTO, 2 hyd., 3 pt.
706			G	$2,000	1/29/2011	ECMO	Farmall, diesel, fast hitch
706			G	$2,900	1/29/2011	ECMO	Farmall, 2 pt., WF, gas, tight steering
706			G	$4,600	1/29/2011	ECMO	3 pt., dual PTO, diesel, 2 hyd., 3 pt.
706			G	$5,800	1/29/2011	ECMO	OH, new paint, 3 pt., dual PTO
706		5,240	G	$3,000	12/4/2010	SEMN	Farmall, gas, WF, fast hitch
706			G	$3,900	12/4/2010	SEMN	Farmall, gas, WF, cab, fast hitch, 540 PTO, very clean
706			G	$4,200	11/27/2010	ECIA	Farmall, Hiniker cap, 3 pt. PTO, gas, complete OH 1,300 hours ago
706			G	$1,950	11/20/2010	SCKY	Farmall
706			G	$1,750	11/13/2010	ECTX	Farmall
706			G	$4,400	9/4/2010	NEIN	Farmall, high crop, 3 pt.
706		5,460	G	$2,250	8/11/2010	ECMN	Farmall, diesel, NF, 1 hyd., 3 pt., PTO
706			G	$9,000	6/19/2010	WCIA	Loader
706			F	$1,500	6/5/2010	SEMN	Fast hitch
706			G	$3,000	6/5/2010	ECMN	Gas, WF, loader
706			G	$2,600	5/5/2010	SEIA	Farmall
706		4,543	G	$5,170	4/28/2010	Online	*PurpleWave.com,* item in Kansas, Great Bend loader
706			G	$5,200	4/3/2010	ECMN	Dual hyd.
706			G	$2,000	3/12/2010	SEIA	
756	1967	9,927	G	$5,600	5/2/2011	WCSK	2WD, Leon front-end loader, diesel, dual PTO, 2 hyd., 18.4x34 RR, 12V conversion, 5' bucket
756	1968	6,103	G	$5,400	4/21/2011	WCMI	Farmall, diesel, WF, 2 hyd., 3 pt., PTO, duals
756	1968	9,708	G	$5,100	2/19/2011	ECNE	Diesel, WF, 3 pt., Ezee-On loader
756	1968	7,192	G	$3,500	12/30/2010	ECMN	WF, 2 hyd., 540/1,000 PTO, fast hitch
756	1969	7,973	G	$9,000	3/1/2014	SEMN	Diesel, rock box, 3 pt., 2 hyd., dual PTO, good 16.9x38 tires, newer paint, SN 16238S-Y
756	1969	4,875	G	$8,500	9/10/2011	ECIA	German diesel, NF, 16.9x38 tires, 3 pt.
756	1969	4,879	G	$2,900	3/15/2011	WCIL	2 hyd., 540/1,000 PTO
756	1969		G	$4,900	6/5/2010	NWIA	Gas, Westendorf WL40 loader, quick attach
756	1970		G	$3,850	4/25/2012	Online	*PurpleWave.com,* item in Missouri

International Harvester Company

Model	Year	Hours	Condition	Price	Date	Area	Comments
756	1971		G	$5,500	3/15/2011	WCIL	Diesel, 3100 Du-Al loader, material bucket, 2 hyd., 540/1,000 PTO
756	1973	4,703	G	$3,900	12/30/2010	ECMN	WF, cab, 2 hyd., 3 pt., 540/1,000 PTO, weights
756			G	$3,000	3/15/2014	WCIL	Gas, 2 hyd., 540/1,000 PTO, 3 pt., 16.9x38 rear tires, Great Bend hyd. loader, 5.5' bucket
756		6,594	G	$5,435	12/26/2013	Online	*BigIron.com,* item in Illinois, 2 range 16F/8R, International Harvester 6 cyl. German diesel, 118.4Rx34 rear tires, 9.5Lx15 front tires, 76 hp, dual, draft control, hyd., drawbar and 3 pt., 540/1,000 PTO
756			G	$4,750	12/5/2013	SCIA	Diesel, cab, fast hitch
756		676	G	$5,250	9/12/2013	SEIA	NF, German diesel, no third link
756		2,829	F	$3,750	7/27/2013	WCIL	Gas, tires are fair, loader, SN13881S-X, loader SN2000U-1111
756		1,830	G	$5,850	6/12/2013	Online	*BigIron.com,* item in Colorado, 2 hyd.
756			G	$4,000	2/6/2013	SESD	Gas
756		6,800	G	$6,000	9/29/2012	WCNE	German diesel, 3 pt., Leon 10' dozer
756			G	$8,500	11/27/2011	ECIA	Gas, 3 pt., 2 hyd., NF
756			G	$4,200	8/31/2011	SEMN	Farmall, 18.4x34 tires
756			G	$6,900	3/15/2011	ECNE	German diesel, 3 pt., new clutch and TA
756			G	$4,800	1/29/2011	ECMO	WF, 3 pt., International Harvester loader
760	1966	6,489	G	$7,400	5/22/2013	Online	*BigIron.com,* item in Nebraska, 16F/4R, 263 cu. in. gas
766	1971	7,450	G	$8,000	8/6/2011	SWMN	
766	1972		G	$7,200	12/10/2010	NCMI	Diesel, open station, 18.4x38 good tires, 2 hyd., Power Beyond, 3 pt., dual PTO
766	1973	5,264	G	$11,000	2/9/2013	SENE	WF, 2 hyd., 3 pt., 16.9x38 tires
766	1973	7,972	G	$6,100	3/3/2011	ECMI	Diesel, ROPS, canopy, WF, 2 hyd., dual PTO, 18.4x34 tires
766	1973	7,972	G	$6,100	3/3/2011	WCMI	Diesel, TA, 1 owner, ROPS, canopy, WF, 2 hyd., dual PTO
766	1973		G	$7,400	2/1/2011	NEIN	Year-A-Round cab
766	1975	6,231	G	$8,700	8/20/2013	WCMN	Diesel, rock box, tach. hard to read, 2 hyd., 2 PTO, 3 pt., 18.4x34 tires, SN 2490187U015392
766	1976	3,101	G	$15,000	11/22/2011	WCIL	Black stripe, 2 hyd., 540/1,000 PTO, flat top fenders, straight and original
766			G	$13,000	1/24/2014	NCNE	Farmhand F236 loader, diesel, 18.4x38 rear tires, dual hyd., 540/1,000 PTO, rear wheel weights, fluid in tires, fenders
766		7,586	G	$5,600	8/22/2013	SEMN	SN 016444
766			G	$6,900	4/10/2013	NETX	Farmall, 660 Great Bend loader, canopy
766		5,633	G	$6,626	3/7/2013	SEIA	Cab, heat, single hyd., 3 pt., 540/1,000 PTO, 18.4x34 tires
766		5,014	G	$4,900	11/24/2012	SEMN	Diesel, fast hitch, dual hyd., dual PTO, 15.5x38 good rubber

International Harvester Company

Model	Year	Hours	Condition	Price	Date	Area	Comments
766		5,477	G	$7,750	8/16/2012	Online	*IQBID.com*, item in Minnesota, black stripe, cab, 2 hyd., dual PTO, third arm, rock box, 18.4x38 tires with hub duals, 9.5x15 tires, manual, 300 hours on OH
766		4,196	G	$12,000	8/11/2012	NWIA	Hiniker cab, manual trans., 18.4x34 rear tires
766			G	$10,000	2/28/2012	NEWI	Very late model black stripe, 540/1,000 rpm, good TA, front bracket, original
766		5,277	G	$3,300	1/31/2012	NEIN	Fender, dual hyd., dual PTO, fast hitch
766		4,545	G	$7,800	12/22/2011	Online	*IQBID.com*, Hiniker cab, new seat, 3 pt., dual PTO, 2 hyd., wheels weights
766			E	$14,000	11/23/2011	NCMO	Farmall, very low hours, family owned since new in 1974
766			G	$13,250	9/4/2010	NEIN	Rear weights, top link
766			G	$6,500	8/7/2010	WCMN	WF, dual hyd.
806	1963	4,459	F	$4,500	7/17/2013	SESK	2WD, 95 PTO hp, 28.1x30 rear, dual PTO, 2 hyd.
806	1963		G	$7,300	10/25/2012	SEMN	Diesel, low time on OH, dual PTO, 3 pt., 18.4x38 tires
806	1964	5,797	P	$3,000	8/27/2013	NCIA	Diesel, rough, open station, WF, 3 pt., extra valve
806	1964	6,318	E	$9,600	8/14/2013	ECIL	Gas, International Harvester 2350 hyd. loader with forks, 96" bucket, 3 pt., 2 hyd., dual PTO, 16.9x34 tires
806	1964	3,678	G	$4,900	4/10/2012	ECND	2 hyd., 540 PTO, rear weights
806	1964		G	$8,250	2/19/2012	NEIL	High hours, open station, diesel, WF, 3 pt., new tires and batteries, SN 10888, good TA
806	1964	6,900	G	$4,500	8/13/2011	WCIL	Diesel, 3 pt., 2 hyd., 18.4x34 rear tires
806	1964		G	$5,750	8/28/2010	WCIL	Diesel, turbo, NF, injection pump, 2 pt. fast hitch, cab, 18.4x34 rear tires
806	1964		F	$4,500	3/30/2010	ECND	TA, open station, WF, 2 hyd., 540/1,000 PTO
806	1965	8,074	F	$3,750	7/17/2013	SESK	2WD, Leon front-end loader, 95 PTO hp, dual PTO, 2 hyd., 18.3x34 rear, 6' bucket
806	1965	6,500	G	$7,000	4/7/2013	ECMN	Farmall, diesel, factory cab, 3 pt., dual hyd., WF, 540/1,000 PTO, 18.4x34 rear rubber good, rebuilt starter
806	1965		F	$3,300	5/19/2012	WCIL	Farmall, diesel, no cab, WF, tires cut for pulling
806	1965	4,501	G	$4,200	4/13/2012	ECNE	Diesel, WF, SN 201225, hour meter 1inoperable, TA, dual PTO, 1 rear hyd., 2 mid-mount hyd., 3 pt. quick hitch, 8.4x34 rear tires, 11Lx16 front tires
806	1965		G	$2,600	1/31/2012	NEIN	3 pt.
806	1965		G	$16,000	8/6/2011	SEWI	Wheatland, restoration by Midwest Tractor and Plow, rebuilt engine and clutch, all new rubber w/ vintage tread pattern, 2 hyd., 540/1,000 PTO, ether assist, cigarette lighter
806	1965	7,125	G	$4,000	3/18/2011	SWIL	Diesel, dual PTO, drawbar, TA doesn't work, 1 hyd., 3 pt., flat fenders

International Harvester Company

Model	Year	Hours	Condition	Price	Date	Area	Comments
806	1965	7,249	G	$3,350	2/26/2011	WCIL	Open station, diesel, 2 pt., dual PTO, 18.4x34 tires
806	1965	6,366	G	$4,100	2/19/2011	ECNE	Diesel, WF, 3 pt., open station
806	1966	6,174	G	$6,200	10/3/2013	NCIN	2WD, diesel, 18.4x34 tires 70%, fast hitch, 2R, 540/1,000
806	1966	8,914	G	$5,500	4/10/2012	ECND	Cornhusker 3 pt., 540/1,000 PTO, 2 hyd.
806	1966	4,449	G	$3,800	2/7/2012	WCOK	LP, 3 pt., PTO, 18.4x34
806	1966		G	$4,900	1/31/2012	NEIN	3 pt.
806	1966		G	$3,000	10/28/2011	NETX	95 hp, diesel, 18.4x38 tires, 1 rear hyd.
806	1966	6,125	G	$3,900	6/8/2011	Online	*BigIron.com,* item in Nebraska, turbo, 4 speed Hi/Lo, 6 cyl., 2 hyd., 540/1,000 PTO, 3 pt., 3 rear wheel weights
806	1966		G	$3,300	6/6/2011	SWSK	Diesel 2WD, 95 PTO hp, dual PTO, 2 hyd., 3 rib front, International Harvester cab
806	1966	3,300	G	$4,200	6/6/2011	SWSK	2WD diesel, 95 PTO hp, dual PTO, 2 hyd., 18.4x38, Excel cab
806	1966		G	$5,950	2/12/2011	SWOH	Diesel, WF, 2 hyd.
806	1967	2,997	G	$3,255	12/4/2013	Online	*BigIron.com,* item in Kansas, Farmall, manual plus TA, 6 cyl., 18.4x34 rear tires, 11Lx16 front tires, diesel, drawbar, 3 pt.
806	1967	8,533	G	$4,200	8/14/2013	WCMN	Diesel, WF
806	1967		G	$7,000	4/8/2013	SESK	2WD, 95 PTO hp, cab, air, heat, 3 hyd., dual PTO, 18.4x38 rear, 4 rib front, rear weights, bucket
806	1967	2,003	G	$4,500	2/6/2013	SESD	3 pt., 1 hyd., cab, 18.4x38
806	1967		G	$5,250	4/23/2012	WCSK	2WD, 95 hp PTO, diesel, dual PTO, 2 hyd., 18.4x38 rear
806	1967	6,843	G	$3,800	8/11/2011	WCMN	2 hyd., backhoe, 6 front. weights, flat top fenders
806	1967		F	$4,300	7/16/2011	NEKS	Wheatland, diesel, SN 7470, original, no TA, no PTO, 2 hyd., rear wheel weights, new 18.4x34 Goodyear tires
806	1968		G	$6,600	9/6/2013	NCOH	Diesel, TA, 2 hyd., 3 pt., 18.4x38 tires, square fenders, open station, clean
806			G	$5,000	3/22/2014	NEIA	Diesel, NF, flat fenders, 1 hyd., 856 shift kit, 2 pt., good rubber 18.4x34, tin excellent, SN 27584S-Y
806		6,160	G	$7,500	3/22/2014	NEIA	Diesel, NF, flat fenders, 1 hyd., 856 shift kit, 2 pt., good rubber 16.9x38, tin excellent, nice, OH 3 years ago, SN 27555S-Y
806			G	$4,250	2/4/2014	SEAR	Wheeled, 8 speed, 1 hyd., 3 pt., 540/1,000 PTO, 18.4x38 tires
806			P	$4,750	1/4/2014	ECOH	Farmall, diesel, cab, rough
806		8,771	G	$4,875	1/4/2014	ECOH	
806		6,181	G	$3,750	12/26/2013	Online	*BigIron.com,* item in South Dakota, 8F/4R Hi/Lo, International Harvester 6 cyl. diesel, 18.4x34 rear tires, 10x16 front tires, 2 hyd., 3 pt., Du-Al 330 loader, grapple, PTO pump, 7' bucket

International Harvester Company

Model	Year	Hours	Condition	Price	Date	Area	Comments
806			G	$2,800	12/20/2013	SCSD	Farmhand F11 loader
806		4,010	G	$4,000	9/12/2013	SEIA	Rebuilt motor, clutch and radiator
806		8,604	G	$4,000	9/12/2013	SEIA	WF, 540/1,000 PTO, 2 hyd.
806		1,591	G	$4,500	9/12/2013	SEIA	Fast hitch, 540/1,000 PTO, 2 hyd., 18.4x34, new front tires, WF
806		7,358	G	$3,360	9/9/2013	NWWI	Diesel, WF, 3 pt., like new 18.4x34 rear tires, 2 hyd., dual PTO
806		5,578	G	$6,400	9/7/2013	ECIA	
806			F	$2,900	9/5/2013	WCMN	2WD, diesel, 2 hyd., 540/1,000 PTO, rock box, 18.4x38 tires, needs hyd. work
806		3,990	G	$4,070	8/28/2013	Online	*PurpleWave.com,* item in Kansas, 6 cyl. diesel, 93 hp, manual, power steering, 540/1,000 PTO, drawbar, 2 rear hyd., rear wheel weights
806		5,869	G	$2,900	8/20/2013	WCIL	Diesel, 1 hyd., both PTO, 18.4x38 tires, missing 3 pt. arms
806			F	$6,750	7/19/2013	SWSK	2WD, Leon front-end loader, cab, 95 PTO hp, diesel, dual PTO, 18.4x34 rear tires, 7.5x20 front, 6' bucket
806		7,191	G	$3,200	7/17/2013	SESK	2WD, Schulte snowblower, dual PTO, 2 hyd., 18.4x34 rear, International Harvester 1066 cab, tire chains
806			F	$5,200	4/13/2013	SEMN	Diesel, open station, WF, fenders, good TA, PTO not working, knock rear end, duals, SN 8981 S-Y
806			G	$5,500	3/23/2013	NEIN	Diesel, standard, original, big rubber, weights, dual hyd., PTO
806			F	$4,500	2/23/2013	ECIN	NF
806			F	$2,100	2/22/2013	SWKY	Farmall, diesel, NF, ROPS
806			G	$3,500	2/7/2013	SEAR	Diesel, PTO
806		162	G	$3,500	2/7/2013	SEAR	Wheeled, diesel, PTO
806			G	$3,400	10/24/2012	WCWI	18.4x34, 3 pt., WF
806			G	$2,503	9/12/2012	Online	*IQBID.com,* item in North Dakota, Wheatland, 3 pt., 18.4x34 rears, 7.5x20 fronts
806		5,867	G	$4,100	8/22/2012	Online	*BigIron.com,* item in Nebraska, Farmall, 4 speed Hi/Low, diesel, 1 hyd., 540/1,000 PTO, 3 pt., heat
806		5,982	G	$2,000	8/16/2012	Online	*IQBID.com,* item in Minnesota, gas, 1 hyd., dual PTO, rock box, 16.9x34 with band duals
806		7,200	G	$4,300	8/16/2012	Online	*IQBID.com,* item in Minnesota, cab, air, heat, diesel, 2 hyd., fast hitch, PTO, 18.4x38 tires
806		5,574	G	$1,275	8/9/2012	Online	*IQBID.com,* item in Minnesota, diesel, Wheatland, cab, heat, 2 hyd., 540/1,000 PTO, 23.1x30 tires, no TA
806			G	$2,500	7/18/2012	ECND	Du-Al loader
806			F	$2,000	6/7/2012	NEIN	
806			P	$2,400	3/24/2012	SWLA	Farmall
806			G	$3,500	3/24/2012	NEIN	Wheatland, diesel, original, dual hyd., dual PTO, runs

International Harvester Company

Model	Year	Hours	Condition	Price	Date	Area	Comments
806			G	$4,400	3/24/2012	NEIN	Diesel, Year-A-Round cab, dual hyd., dual PTO, fast hitch, runs
806			G	$3,000	3/20/2012	WCIL	
806			F	$2,750	3/14/2012	ECND	WF, PTO, no 3 pt., Farmall
806			G	$3,500	3/14/2012	ECND	WF, 540/1,000 PTO, no 3 pt.
806			P	$5,800	2/25/2012	ECIA	Rough, 2 hyd., recent repairs
806			G	$2,800	2/2/2012	NEIN	Farmall, 2WD, gas, WF, 18.4x34 rear tires, fast hitch, 2 hyd., 540/1,000 PTO
806		5,280	G	$3,650	2/1/2012	SEND	Wheatland, diesel
806			G	$4,700	1/31/2012	NEIN	Dual hyd., diesel, dual PTO, rear weights
806			G	$4,500	1/28/2012	ECMO	
806			G	$3,200	12/1/2011	NEIN	Gas, WF
806			G	$7,250	11/23/2011	NCMO	Farmall, new style torque, new clutch
806		3,880	G	$5,500	8/6/2011	NEIA	Diesel, NF, standard drawbar, 18.4Rx34, over $9,000 spent on recent OH (motor, clutch, TA), good straight metal and paint, very clean
806		6,130	G	$2,750	3/15/2011	WCIL	1,000 PTO, fast hitch
806		6,129	F	$2,900	12/17/2010	WCIL	Gas, WF, fast hitch, adapter, 18.4x34 tires, 1,000 PTO
806			G	$1,800	9/11/2010	SEIA	Gas
806			G	$3,600	9/4/2010	NEIN	Wheatland, diesel
806			G	$6,200	9/4/2010	NEIN	Diesel, dual PTO
806			P	$1,100	9/3/2010	NEIN	Diesel, high crop, dual PTO, dead row, may not run or drive, as is
806		4,248	G	$4,400	8/11/2010	ECMN	Wheatland, dual PTO, good TA, front fenders, restored
806			G	$5,700	7/10/2010	SEND	Diesel, row crop, cab, 3 pt., low hours
806			G	$3,000	6/19/2010	SESK	2WD, diesel, 2 hyd., TA
806			G	$4,900	5/26/2010	ECSD	Diesel
806			G	$4,200	5/5/2010	SEIA	Farmall, diesel
806			G	$4,500	5/5/2010	SEIA	Farmall
806		4,295	F	$2,500	4/16/2010	SESK	2WD, 9' dozer blade, 2 hyd.
806			G	$4,000	2/11/2010	NENE	WF
806			G	$5,000	2/11/2010	ECIL	Turbo, fenders, WF, 2 pt. fast hitch, good TA, diesel
826	1970		G	$4,600	7/3/2013	Online	*BigIron.com,* item in Nebraska, 2WD, 16,253 miles, 358 cu. in., diesel 92
826	1970	6,535	G	$1,925	10/10/2012	Online	*PurpleWave.com,* item in Kansas, 6 cyl. diesel, hydro
826	1970	6,622	G	$4,775	4/25/2012	Online	*BigIron.com,* item in Nebraska, 16F/4R, diesel, 92 hp, 1 hyd., 540/1,000 PTO, fast hitch, drawbar
826	1970		G	$6,500	1/31/2012	NEIN	Cab, original
826	1970		G	$7,200	8/6/2011	NCIA	Diesel, WF, 3 pt.
826	1970		F	$8,000	7/16/2011	NEKS	Diesel, SN 11647, original, good TA, WF, dual PTO, 2 hyd., $4,000 spent on engine, 18.4x38 Goodyear tires
826	1970		G	$17,000	7/16/2011	NEKS	Gold Demonstrator, diesel, SN 11991, restored, WF, 1 hyd., 2 pt., 540 PTO, new 18.4x34 Firestone tires

International Harvester Company

Model	Year	Hours	Condition	Price	Date	Area	Comments
826	1970		G	$3,750	2/28/2011	SCMI	Diesel, WF, cab, 3 pt., 8 front, PTO
826	1970	4,355	G	$6,300	2/1/2011	NEIN	Fender, super nice
826	1970		G	$4,900	1/29/2011	ECMO	Factory WF, 3 pt., 358 German diesel
826	1970	8,738	F	$2,700	12/4/2010	SEWY	WF, diesel, 3 pt., cab
826	1970		G	$6,400	11/18/2010	ECND	WF, diesel, 2 hyd., Cornhusker 3 pt, 540/1,000 PTO, fenders
826	1970	8,288	G	$6,900	3/17/2010	WCMN	German diesel, 200 hours on OH, 3 pt., PTO
826		158	G	$3,600	12/4/2013	ECIN	18.4x34 tires, 2 hyd., 540/1,000 PTO, 3 pt.
826			G	$3,500	10/3/2013	NCIN	
826			G	$8,000	3/30/2013	NCPA	OH in 2011
826			G	$3,300	2/7/2013	SEAR	Diesel, PTO
826			G	$12,000	3/24/2012	NEIN	Factory Gold Demonstrator, 3 pt., dual PTO, hyd., new tires, fenders, runs
826		9,579	G	$7,000	3/22/2012	ECMN	German diesel, open station, 2 hyd., 3 pt., dual PTO
826		7,500	G	$6,200	8/6/2011	NEIA	Diesel, NF, gear shift, good clutch, TA, straight metal
826			G	$3,700	5/11/2011	Online	*BigIron.com,* hydro, diesel, 79 drawbar hp, 2 hyd., 540/1,000 PTO, no third arm, add on power steering pump
826		8,415	G	$7,200	3/26/2011	NCOH	Hydro, nice straight original, 18.4x34 Firestone Radials, 1 hyd., WF
826		8,397	F	$4,700	2/20/2011	SCPA	WF, 2 hyd., 540/1,000 PTO, diesel
826		7,852	G	$11,500	4/10/2010	ECON	PTO

Starting in 2008, "the new collector tractor" trend has reflected rising values on good condition original or restored models from the mid 1960s to mid 1970s.

The trend's arrival may have been trumpeted when a 1966 International 1206 with 3,696 hours sold for a record price of $32,250 at a Sept. 6, 2008, auction in west-central Iowa. The two hottest International models have been the 1206 and the 1468. The 1468 tractor was made from 1971 to 1974 only, and with its unique V8 engine, it sold for low prices for decades until exploding higher in the past four years. A beautifully restored 1973 International 1468 set a new record of $23,750 at a northeast Kansas auction July 16, 2011. That record stood until July 14, 2012, when a 1972 model with 3,869 hours went for $31,500 in northwest Iowa. Then, this record price held until the 1468 with 4,685 hours from northwest Ohio pictured here sold for $34,250 on an online farm auction Sept. 26, 2013 ($33,250 winning bid + $1,000 buyer's commission).

PETE'S PICK

International Harvester Company

Model	Year	Hours	Condition	Price	Date	Area	Comments
856	1967	4,510	G	$10,500	7/16/2011	NEKS	Wheatland, diesel, SN 7585, original, 2 hyd., wheel weights, 18.4x34 tires
856	1968		G	$6,500	7/25/2013	WCIL	Diesel, 18.4x38 rear tires, new front tires, 2 hyd., 1 owner, SN 16524S, rebuilt PTO, set of rear wheel weights, front weight bracket, rebuilt alt., runs
856	1968		F	$8,100	6/20/2012	ECIL	
856	1968	8,225	G	$4,900	2/25/2012	WCMI	100 hp diesel, 3 pt., dual hyd., Hi/Lo, 8F/4R, power steering, 540/1,000 PTO
856	1969	8,404	G	$5,000	2/22/2014	ECMI	Diesel, WF, 3 pt., PTO, 2 hyd., duals
856	1969	8,737	G	$4,100	7/18/2013	SCSK	2WD, 100 PTO hp, dual PTO, 2 hyd., 18.4x38 duals
856	1969	6,384	F	$4,350	4/3/2013	Online	*BigIron.com,* item in South Dakota, 4 speed Hi/Lo TA, diesel, 2 hyd., 2 pt., 540/1,000 PTO, rear wheel weights, tool box, 2 pt. missing, homemade canopy
856	1969	9,768	G	$3,800	2/6/2013	SESD	Diesel, 18.4x34 tires, fast hitch, 2 PTO, starts hard, Ride-N-Drive
856	1969		G	$5,100	6/13/2012	NWMN	540/1,000 PTO, 2 hyd., duals
856	1969		G	$5,200	8/11/2011	WCMN	WF, open station, 2 hyd., 3 pt., 540/1,000 PTO, like new
856	1969		G	$4,600	8/6/2011	NCIA	Diesel, WF, duals, 3 pt.
856	1969		G	$10,000	7/16/2011	NEKS	Diesel, SN 24323, restored, WF, good TA, 3 pt., dual PTO, 2 hyd., new Goodyear 18.4Rx34 tires, no front weights
856	1970	6,960	G	$11,000	11/10/2012	NWIA	Diesel, NF, 2 pt., 2 hyd., 18.4x38 rear tires, Year-A-Round cab, 1 owner
856	1970	9,207	G	$8,000	12/30/2011	NCIA	18.4x38 tires, 2 hyd., dual PTO, 3 pt., Hiniker cab, heat, M&W turbo
856	1971	5,180	G	$8,000	11/3/2011	ECIL	Diesel, cab, air, 3 pt., Firestone 15x38 tires, front and rear weights
856	1971		G	$9,900	7/16/2011	NEKS	High crop, diesel, SN 33960, restored, gear drive, front end rebuilt, TA rebuilt, 3pt, dual PTO, 1 hyd., new 20.8x38 Firestone tires
856	1971	4,400	G	$13,500	3/19/2011	ECIA	Dual PTO, WF
856	1977		G	$3,950	5/11/2011	Online	*BigIron.com,* 2WD, 407 diesel, 100 hp, 2 hyd., 540/1,000 PTO, 3 pt. Year Round cab, heat, WF
856		5,894	G	$8,750	3/22/2014	NEIA	Diesel, NF, flat fenders, 3 pt., 2 hyd., 18.4x38 tires, tin in great condition, SN 16199S-Y
856			G	$4,750	2/5/2014	SESD	WF
856		6,704	G	$13,750	1/14/2014	WCNY	OROPS
856			G	$5,201	12/11/2013	Online	*BigIron.com,* item in Nebraska, Hi/Lo 4 speed, 18.4x34 rear tires, 11Lx15 front tires, left side panel missing, Schwartz front end, TA not working, 3 pt., 2 hyd., 2 PTO 540/1,000
856		9,181	G	$7,750	9/26/2013	NWOH	Diesel, WF, 18.4x38 tires and axles duals, front and rear weights, 3 pt., dual PTO, 2 hyd., complete OH at around 5,000 hours

TRACTORS

International Harvester Company

Model	Year	Hours	Condition	Price	Date	Area	Comments
856		9,945	G	$6,000	9/12/2013	SEIA	Diesel, fast hitch, 540/1,000 PTO, 2 hyd., 18.4x38 tires
856		9,845	G	$4,672	9/9/2013	NWWI	Diesel, WF, 3 pt., dual hyd., dual PTO, 18.4x38 rear tires
856		8,238	G	$8,000	3/30/2013	NWIL	Diesel, 18.4x34 rears, 60% rubber, 2 sets rear wheel weights, front weight bracket, third link, new seat, 1 hyd.
856			G	$4,600	3/23/2013	NEIN	Runs
856		5,597	G	$4,400	3/7/2013	SEIA	Diesel, 540/1,000 PTO, 2 hyd., 3 pt., 18.4/15x34 rears
856		4,300	G	$13,100	2/16/2013	NEIA	Diesel, Comfort cab, heads and various valves redone, original hours
856			G	$5,600	2/7/2013	NEIN	Standard
856			G	$5,600	2/7/2013	NEIN	Wheatland, Day cab, 18.4x34, 2 sets hyd., 540/1,000 PTO, no 3 pt.
856		8,216	G	$3,900	11/24/2012	SEMN	Diesel, cab, fast hitch, hyd. dual PTO, 18.4x34 tires
856		8,400	G	$7,000	8/24/2012	SWMN	Open station, 3 pt., 2 hyd., 18.4x38 tires
856		9,721	G	$6,000	8/16/2012	Online	*IQBID.com,* item in Minnesota, 2 hyd., 3 pt., dual PTO, no top link, 18.4x38 tires
856			G	$5,250	8/4/2012	NEAR	6 cyl. diesel, 3 pt., 540/1,000 PTO, dual hyd.
856		6,500	G	$5,500	6/20/2012	ECIL	10x16 front tires, 18.4x38 rear tires, 3 pt., no top link, 2 hyd.
856			G	$6,700	6/7/2012	NEIN	Diesel
856			G	$3,800	6/2/2012	SEMN	3 pt., 2 hyd., 540/1,000 PTO
856		8,422	G	$5,150	4/25/2012	Online	*BigIron.com,* item in Nebraska, 8F/4R, TA, diesel, 2 hyd., 540/1,000 PTO
856		4,986	G	$7,700	3/20/2012	WCIL	Diesel, 18.4x38 rear tires, 540/1,000 PTO, 2 hyd.
856			G	$5,200	3/14/2012	ECND	Open station, 3 pt., PTO, high hours
856			G	$6,500	1/28/2012	ECMO	Good rubber, good TA, new clutch
856			G	$5,000	10/29/2011	ECMN	Dual hyd., fenders, diesel
856			G	$3,300	8/11/2011	WCMN	WF, 1 hyd., 3 pt., PTO, fenders
856			G	$4,900	4/2/2011	ECMN	
856			G	$5,500	3/19/2011	ECIA	
856		9,300	G	$9,000	2/26/2011	ECIA	Original, WF, 3 pt., 2 hyd., flat top fenders, upgraded steps, good straight metal, owner bought in 1984
856			G	$5,700	1/29/2011	ECMO	Diesel, 3 pt., good TA
856		10,346	G	$4,400	12/4/2010	SEMN	Diesel, 3 pt.
856		7,700	F	$4,500	11/13/2010	NCIA	Custom, 1 valve, dual PTO, torque out
856			G	$5,250	9/11/2010	ECIA	Farmall
856			G	$5,300	9/4/2010	NEIN	Standard
856		6,400	G	$9,000	9/2/2010	ECND	Open station, 2 hyd., 3 pt., PTO, fenders, Farmhand 235 quick attach loader, grapple
856			G	$5,000	8/9/2010	WCMO	
886	1976	6,805	G	$6,005	7/10/2013	Online	*BigIron.com,* item in Nebraska, 16 speed, D360 International Harvester 6 cyl.

International Harvester Company

Model	Year	Hours	Condition	Price	Date	Area	Comments
886	1976	2,806	G	$15,100	3/23/2013	SWOH	WF, diesel, SN 2490189U008839, TA, 3 hyd., 540/1,000 PTO, front and rear wheel weights cab, air, heat, AM/FM, block heater
886	1976	3,300	G	$13,500	12/7/2011	NCIA	One owner
886	1976	10,425	G	$8,000	3/31/2010	ECND	Cab, air, heat, 2 hyd., 3 pt., PTO, Allied 594 loader and 84" bucket, rebuilt engine and TA and clutch
886	1977		G	$7,000	4/3/2014	NEIN	4 post
886	1978	5,600	G	$14,000	9/28/2013	ECNE	3 pt., 2 hyd., cab, air, 540/1,000 PTO, Grammer air seat, Firestone 18.4x34 tires
886	1978	6,532	G	$10,800	2/6/2013	SESD	Cab, air, heat, 2 hyd., 3 pt., TA good, 18.4x34 tires, Ride-N-Drive
966	1971	1,638	F	$3,855	7/9/2013	Online	*IQBID.com,* Cozy cab, 2 hyd., 3 pt., 540/1,000 PTO
966	1971	4,078	E	$17,000	11/17/2012	NWIA	3 pt., 2 hyd., WF, new rubber, no cab, 16.9x38 tires 60%, SN 011615
966	1971	6,016	E	$15,000	7/14/2012	NWIA	Diesel, WF, rear fenders, complete OH
966	1971		G	$7,750	8/13/2011	WCIL	Diesel, 2 hyd., 540/1,000 PTO, new torque 800 hours ago, new batteries, cab, 18.4Rx34 rear tires
966	1971	8,883	G	$7,500	9/22/2010	NECO	WF, diesel, 3 pt., cab
966	1971	5,270	F	$5,250	2/16/2010	WCIL	Diesel, 2 hyd., 540/1,000 PTO
966	1972	6,678	P	$2,300	2/27/2014	NWNE	Diesel, WF, 3 pt., cab, front weights, runs
966	1972	8,566	G	$13,000	1/24/2014	NCNE	Front mount hyd. blade, 18.4x38 rear tires, 9-bolt duals and hubs, 10x16SL front tires, dual hyd.
966	1972	8,073	F	$4,750	12/10/2013	WCWI	Repaint, open station, 1 hyd., 540/1,000 PTO, flat top fenders
966	1972	4,660	E	$17,000	9/6/2013	SWIA	Diesel, open station, safe cab roll bar and sun shade, 2 hyd., 540/1,000 PTO, 16.9x38 rear rubber, International Harvester Loader, 6' bucket, SN U018880
966	1972		G	$6,000	6/13/2013	Online	*IQBID.com,* Westendorf TA29 quick attach loader, bucket, cab, 2 hyd., 3 pt., 540/1,000 PTO, 18.4x34 HUB duals, hours unknown
966	1972	7,961	G	$7,000	12/4/2010	SEWY	WF, diesel, 3 pt., cab, Du-Al 3100 loader, grapple
966	1973	6,450	F	$5,600	4/3/2013	Online	*BigIron.com,* item in IL, 4 speed Hi/Lo and TA, 18.4x34 rear tires, 11Lx15SL front tires, diesel, drawbar, 3 pt., PS needs repair, missing left door window and rear hitch window
966	1973		G	$13,000	2/6/2013	Online	Item in Illinois, hours unknown, 2 hyd., major engine OH, TA good, body shop paint, 18.4x38 good rubber, SN 2510175U018061
966	1973	9,806	G	$6,160	12/28/2011	Online	*PurpleWave.com,* item in Kansas, 6 cyl. diesel, 73" cab, air, heat, TA, 7' bucket loader
966	1973	5,861	G	$5,500	12/30/2010	ECMN	Cab, air, heat, 2 hyd., 3 pt., no top link, rebuilt engine, TA

International Harvester Company

Model	Year	Hours	Condition	Price	Date	Area	Comments
966	1974	3,274	F	$3,500	7/27/2013	WCIL	Diesel, cab, 3 pt.
966	1974	4,592	F	$7,000	6/25/2013	SWSK	2WD, 95 PTO hp, cab, 2 hyd., 540/1,000 PTO, air, radio, 4 rib front, 18.4x38 rear
966	1974		G	$5,100	1/31/2012	NEIN	Fender, original
966	1974		G	$3,400	1/28/2012	ECMO	Weak clutch, 18.4x34, 3 pt., 540 PTO, 2 hyd., manual
966	1974		G	$6,250	1/28/2012	ECMO	
966	1974	3,239	G	$11,250	12/17/2011	WCIL	WF, no cab, duals, weights
966	1974	5,628	G	$6,800	7/13/2011	Online	*BigIron.com,* item in Iowa, 100 hp, 2WD, 2 hyd.
966	1974		G	$6,500	4/15/2011	NEND	Cab, air, heat, Farmall, 3 pt., 540/1,000 PTO, 2 hyd., power beyond, front weights, good rubber
966	1974		F	$6,250	11/2/2010	ECOK	Cab, air, dozer blade
966	1974	5,547	F	$5,500	3/30/2010	ECND	2 hyd., 540/1,000 PTO, no 3 pt.
966	1975	8,500	G	$5,250	3/18/2011	SWIL	3 pt., 2 hyd., dual PTO
966	1976	6,523	G	$8,000	3/3/2012	SEMN	Black stripe, 3 pt., 2 hyd., 540/1,000 PTO, TA good, rebuilt injector pump, SN 32722
966	1976	4,000	G	$8,100	6/6/2011	SWSK	2WD, 16F/8R standard, dual PTO, 2 hyd., 3 rib front, factory duals
966		4,925	G	$16,750	3/7/2014	SCPA	TA, canopy, 20.8x38 radials, all original newer tires, farmer said "Turbo" decal from the factory but not a turbo
966		7,600	G	$17,000	3/7/2014	SCPA	Hydro, canopy, 7-year-old restoration
966		3,200	E	$21,000	3/7/2014	SCPA	Hydro, canopy, 3-year-old restoration
966		8,588	G	$6,930	9/9/2013	NWWI	WF, 2 hyd., 3 pt., dual PTO, 18.4x34 rear tires
966		4,777	G	$6,250	8/22/2013	SEMN	Cab, 5 front weights, 3 pt., 2 hyd., 540/1,000 PTO, SN 030373
966		7,179	G	$4,205	5/1/2013	Online	*BigIron.com,* item in Wyoming, 6 cyl. diesel, 2 hyd.
966		6,174	E	$8,400	4/6/2013	SEMN	Hiniker 1300 cab, air, duals, new style step, very good rubber, 540/1,000 PTO, 3 pt., 2 hyd., very sharp
966			G	$4,500	4/3/2013	Online	*BigIron.com,* item in Colorado, 8F/4R, TA, turbo, TA, 6 cyl. diesel, 540/1,100 PTO 2 hyd., 6.9x38 rear and 9.5x15 front tires
966			G	$4,100	3/30/2013	NESD	Cab, 2 hyd., 3 pt., 540/1,000 PTO, low hours
966			G	$7,300	3/30/2013	NWWI	3 pt., dual hyd., PTO, 18.4x34 tires
966		3,650	G	$10,000	3/22/2013	NWMN	Hyd., 3 pt., PTO, nice original, runs
966			G	$6,200	1/21/2013	NCIA	WF, diesel, Bush Hog loader
966			G	$3,500	12/12/2012	SESD	
966			G	$5,700	12/12/2012	SESD	
966			F	$8,750	11/23/2012	WCOH	OH 3 years ago, Westendorf TA-46B loader
966		5,731	G	$13,000	8/24/2012	SWMN	2 hyd., 3 pt., Year-A-Round cab, new 18.4x38 tires
966		6,605	G	$4,700	8/16/2012	Online	*IQBID.com,* item in Minnesota, cab, 2 hyd., 3 pt., dual PTO, no top link, 18.4x34 tires

International Harvester Company

Model	Year	Hours	Condition	Price	Date	Area	Comments
966		4,844	G	$4,300	8/8/2012	Online	*BigIron.com,* item in Nebraska, 2WD, 4 speed, diesel, 2 hyd., 540/1,000 PTO, 3 pt., heat, air
966			G	$4,300	7/28/2012	SWTN	4 post, 1 hyd.
966			F	$5,800	7/11/2012	NEWI	Fast hitch, good TA, 2 shafts, runs strong, kind of rebuilt from 3 tractors
966		7,194	G	$8,500	6/2/2012	SEMN	Diesel, 18.4x34 duals, flat top fenders, new seat, 540/1,000 PTO, 2 hyd.
966			G	$10,000	3/24/2012	NEIN	Black stripe, MFWD, cab, dual PTO, dual hyd., 3 pt., runs
966			G	$9,900	2/28/2012	NEWI	900 hours on reman., 18.4x38 tires, 540/1,000 rpm, rebuilt PTO
966			G	$3,400	2/25/2012	WCMI	Diesel, 1,000 PTO, no 540 shaft, good tires, 18.4x38 rear tires
966			G	$5,600	1/31/2012	NEIN	Dual hyd., dual PTO, 18.4x34 tires
966			G	$5,000	1/27/2012	SEAL	
966		6,601	F	$4,500	1/17/2012	SCKS	Fertilizer tanks, SN 2510161V0229
966			G	$8,000	12/17/2011	NETX	Buggy top and loader, 18.4x34 rear tires, 9.5Lx15 front tires, 1 hyd., 540/1,000 PTO, 3 pt. International Harvester 2355 front-end loader, bucket, joystick controls, new paint
966			F	$3,900	10/6/2011	SEMN	Cab, 540/1,000 PTO, 3 pt., 2 hyd.
966		12,040	G	$5,800	8/6/2011	NEIA	WF, 3 pt., 2 hyd., 18.4Rx38, looks and runs great, new clutch, TA is good
966			G	$7,100	3/9/2011	Online	*BigIron.com,* item in Wisconsin, hydro, diesel, 540/1,000 PTO, 3 pt. missing center link, 1 hyd., recently rebuilt hydro, new alternator, new muffler
966		7,500	F	$4,400	3/5/2011	SEMN	540/1,000 PTO, new tach., rock box, rear wheel weights, TA does not work
966		7,270	G	$10,000	3/3/2011	SEPA	No cab, 2 hyd., 18.4x38 tires at 25%, very nice original 1 owner
966			G	$7,800	2/22/2011	SEPA	Weights, black stripe, dual PTO, 2 hyd.
966			F	$5,800	2/8/2011	ECNE	Year-A-Round cab, 18.4x38 rear tires w/ 9 bolt duals and hubs, 11Lx15 front tires, 2 hyd., 540/1,000 PTO
966			G	$3,000	11/20/2010	NWSC	
966			G	$6,300	9/4/2010	NEIN	Dual hyd., dual PTO
966		3,277	G	$8,250	7/29/2010	WCMN	Hiniker cab, complete OH 300 hours ago, HUB duals, good rubber, 3 pt., 540/1,000 PTO, 1 hyd., 4 front weights
986	1976	6,810	E	$17,500	3/1/2014	NWPA	2WD, cab, air, all original, 2 hyd., 540/1,000 PTO, front and rear weights, 20.8x34 rears, nice, SN 09728
986	1976	8,578	G	$7,810	9/25/2013	Online	*PurpleWave.com,* item in Missouri, International Harvester diesel, 105 hp, TA, air, heat, spring seat, 3 pt., drawbar, 2 rear hyd., 540/1,000 PTO
986	1976	5,163	G	$7,400	3/20/2012	WCIL	18.4R3x4 rear tires, 540/1,000 PTO, 2 hyd., 10 front weights
986	1976	5,077	G	$12,000	11/22/2011	WCIL	Fully equipped cab, 540/1,000 PTO, good rear rubber

TRACTORS

International Harvester Company

Model	Year	Hours	Condition	Price	Date	Area	Comments
986	1976	3,750	G	$15,600	10/11/2011	Online	*BidNow.US,* 105 hp, 16.9x38 tires and duals, duals, complete OH at 2,500 hours, new clutch and air last year
986	1976	8,186	G	$7,000	12/8/2010	NECO	WF, diesel, Farmhand F236 loader and grapple
986	1976	7,822	G	$6,930	7/28/2010	Online	*PurpleWave.com,* item in Kansas, 16F/8R gears, cab, air, heat, hubs, 540/1,000 PTO, 2 hyd.
986	1977	7,129	G	$4,750	10/3/2013	NCIN	Cab, air, heat
986	1977	5,881	G	$6,050	8/28/2013	Online	*PurpleWave.com,* item in Missouri, 6 cyl. diesel, enclosed cab, front/rear work lights, 540/1,000 PTO, 3 pt., drawbar, 2 rear hyd., rear wheel weights, 10x16 front tires, 18.4x38 rear tires
986	1977	5,091	F	$13,000	4/11/2011	WCSK	2WD, 106 PTO, 3 hyd., duals, dual PTO
986	1978		G	$11,000	3/15/2014	NCOR	Cab
986	1978	8,350	G	$4,000	7/25/2013	WCSK	2WD, 106 PTO hp, cab, 18.4x38 rear, 2 hyd., dual PTO, 4 speed Hi/Lo
986	1978	2,450	G	$15,500	11/29/2012	ECIL	1 owner, 18.4x38 duals like new, 2 hyd., 10 front suitcase weights, 3 inter rim weights, SN 17481
986	1978		G	$10,750	2/25/2012	NETX	Cab, air, 2 hyd., 540/1,000 PTO, new 18.4x38 rear tires, 10x16 front tires, new paint
986	1978		G	$8,800	6/15/2011	NWMN	3 hyd., 3 pt., 540/1,000 PTO, front. suitcase weights, hub duals
1026	1970	10,124	G	$26,000	7/14/2012	NWIA	Gold Demonstrator, hydro, WF, rear fenders
1026	1970		F	$6,700	11/18/2010	ECND	Hydro, diesel, Cornhusker 3 pt., hydro and motor reworked, fenders, Du-Al 3000 loader, bucket, grapple
1026	1970		E	$15,500	8/21/2010	ECPA	Hydro, International Harvester 2355 loader, excellent tires, dual PTO, 2 hyd., repainted in 2002, pallet forks, bale spear, grapple, manure bucket
1026	1971	5,122	E	$22,500	8/23/2012	SWMN	Hydro, 2WD, diesel, cab, heat, 2 hyd., 18.4x38, 540/1,000 PTO, rock box, SN 2610150U008820
1026	1971		G	$9,101	6/27/2012	Online	*BigIron.com,* item in Iowa, Farmall, hydro, 6 cyl. turbo diesel, 112 hp, 2 hyd., WF, power steering
1026	1971		G	$4,000	4/9/2010	WCNE	Farmhand loader, bucket, grapple fork
1026		5,900	F	$17,000	10/26/2013	SEPA	Hydro, Golden Demonstrator, SN 8779, original GOLD, was painted red at some point but still has the gold paint and decals underneath the red, excellent 20x38 Firestone radial tires
1026			G	$10,200	5/22/2013	Online	*BigIron.com,* item in Nebraska, Farmhand F11 loader, hydro, 6 cyl. diesel
1026			G	$9,000	3/23/2013	NEIN	Farmall, hydro, dual PTO, dual hyd., original, runs
1026		7,200	G	$19,500	3/24/2012	NEIN	Demonstrator, original, dual PTO, dual hyd., cab, runs

International Harvester Company

Model	Year	Hours	Condition	Price	Date	Area	Comments
1026			G	$1,147	9/14/2011	Online	*BigIron.com,* item in Colorado, 6 cyl. diesel
1026		11,039	G	$3,100	4/27/2011	Online	*BigIron.com,* item in Wyoming, Farmall, hydro, 6 cyl. diesel, 2 hyd., 540/1,000 PTO, 3 pt., front weight bracket, cab, needs front grill, hydro is weak
1026		4,600	G	$11,400	2/26/2010	SEMN	Hydro, 3 pt., dual PTO, 5 hours on major hydro rebuild
1066	1971	2,793	G	$14,000	8/21/2012	WCIL	Farmall, cab, 18.4x38 tires
1066	1971		G	$2,250	5/4/2010	WCOK	Diesel, 3 pt., PTO, hours not available
1066	1971	2,940	G	$8,250	3/5/2010	NCMO	Cab, air, heat, 18.4x34 tires
1066	1972	3,343	G	$9,000	12/6/2012	Online	*IQBID.com,* open station, SN 2610159U016118
1066	1972	7,060	G	$5,000	11/28/2012	ECND	3 pt., PTO, newer clutch and TA, no cab, 18.4x38 singles
1066	1972		G	$9,750	6/13/2012	NWMN	MFWD, hyd. drive, cab, 3 pt., 540/1,000 PTO, 2 hyd., rock box, duals
1066	1972		G	$5,600	3/20/2012	WCIL	
1066	1972	5,479	G	$6,400	8/11/2011	WCMN	Cab, heat, 2 hyd., 3 pt., PTO, side tool boxes, front. weights, 9 bolt hub duals
1066	1972		F	$2,900	2/25/2011	NENC	Turbo, 1 hyd., straight shaft no TA, long axles, 540/1,000 PTO, sway bars
1066	1972	7,790	F	$4,250	11/19/2010	ECND	Open station, 2 hyd., 540/1,000 PTO, no 3 pt.
1066	1972		G	$13,100	5/26/2010	ECSD	Koyker K5 loader, 4,000 hours on OH
1066	1973	5,377	G	$8,401	1/22/2014	Online	*BigIron.com,* item in Wyoming, 6.8L, 6 cyl. diesel, 18.4x38 rear tires, 11Lx15SL front tires, 2 hyd., 540/1,000 PTO, 3 pt., no third link
1066	1973	6,353	G	$9,606	12/26/2013	Online	*BigIron.com,* item in Iowa, 414 engine, 18.4x38 rear tires, 10x16SL front tires, diesel, 125 hp, 4 hyd., 3 pt., 540/1,000 PTO, factory cab
1066	1973	894	G	$6,900	4/3/2013	Online	*BigIron.com,* item in IL, 4 speed Hi/Lo, TA, 18.4x38 rear tires, 10x16 front tires, diesel, drawbar, 11 front weights, 2 weights on each rear wheel, rear chains, duals
1066	1973		G	$7,000	4/2/2013	ECIA	Cab, 2 hyd., 3 pt., 540/1,000 PTO, good clutch and TA, OH
1066	1973	6,356	G	$7,950	8/8/2012	Online	*BigIron.com,* item in Kansas, hydro, diesel, 125 hp, 540/1,000 PTO, category 3, dual hyd., loader and bucket
1066	1973	6,742	G	$11,000	7/14/2012	NWIA	Diesel, WF, rear fenders, OH
1066	1973		F	$4,000	5/24/2012	SCMI	Cab, 2 hyd., 3 pt., duals
1066	1973	6,096	F	$5,000	1/30/2012	NEIA	Diesel
1066	1973		G	$7,750	12/30/2011	NCIA	20.8x38 tires, 3 pt., PTO, flat top fenders
1066	1973	8,502	G	$7,250	4/15/2011	NEND	Cab, air, heat, 3 pt., 540/1,000 PTO, 2 hyd., power beyond, front. weights, aux. fuel tank, new front tires
1066	1973		G	$4,900	4/13/2011	Online	*BigIron.com,* item in Texas, Farmall, diesel, 2 hyd., 1,000 PTO, back and side windows missing, blade

International Harvester Company

Model	Year	Hours	Condition	Price	Date	Area	Comments
1066	1973	6,058	G	$7,800	4/11/2011	Online	*AuctionTime.com*
1066	1973	5,500	G	$10,500	3/19/2011	ECIA	Open station, new TA, new paint
1066	1973		F	$2,500	12/2/2010	NWIA	18.4x38 tires, cab
1066	1974	8,000	G	$5,000	2/8/2014	NECO	3 pt., cab, 2 hyd., 2 PTO, one owner
1066	1974	5,537	G	$5,000	6/13/2013	Online	*IQBID.com,* turbo, Hiniker cab, 2 hyd., 3 pt., no top link, 540/1,000 PTO, 18.4x38 hub duals, OH 3 years ago
1066	1974		G	$8,500	12/13/2012	WCIA	2 hyd., 3 PT, 540/1,000 PTO, 18.4x38 tires, 50% rubber, new oil hyd. pump, new PTO clutch pack, Westendorf WL42 hyd. loader
1066	1974	2,400	G	$10,000	12/1/2012	NWIL	Diesel, Westendorf TA-28 Loader, bale spear
1066	1974		G	$7,000	11/22/2011	WCIL	Front weight bracket, all lights work, TA is good, 540/1,000 PTO, new fenders, seat and paint, all fluids and filters just changed, good turbo, 125 hp
1066	1974		G	$6,000	8/20/2011	WCIL	Open station, approx. 3 years on engine OH, recent clutch and PTO, new paint, 18.4Rx38 tires
1066	1974		G	$18,000	8/6/2011	SEWI	Complete restoration, engine OH, new TA, new clutch, new steering wheel, new rubber, reconditioned front end
1066	1974		G	$5,500	7/27/2011	ECND	No cab, 2 hyd., 3 pt., good TA
1066	1974		G	$6,500	4/14/2011	NCND	2WD, factory 3 pt., dual PTO, Allied loader, well maintained unit
1066	1974	2,433	G	$13,600	7/16/2010	SCIA	Hiniker cab, 18.4x38 duals,
1066	1974	634	G	$4,400	6/14/2010	Online	*BigIron.com,* item in Nebraska, meter has turned over, 4 speed Hi/Lo, DT414 diesel, 2 hyd.
1066	1975	8,400	G	$6,500	6/13/2013	Online	*IQBID.com,* cab, 2 hyd., 3 pt., no top link, 18.4x38 hub duals
1066	1975		G	$5,900	2/12/2013	WCIL	
1066	1975		G	$7,500	10/25/2012	SEMN	Open station, WF
1066	1975	5,130	G	$7,600	1/30/2012	NEIA	Diesel
1066	1975	8,577	G	$5,250	8/3/2011	ECND	Farmall, cab, 3 pt., 540/1,000 PTO, 2 hyd., front tank, good TA, oil records, 18.4x38 good tires
1066	1975	5,800	G	$7,300	7/30/2011	ECMO	
1066	1975	4,561	G	$11,250	3/15/2011	WCIL	Diesel, 2 hyd., 540/1,000 PTO
1066	1975	6,520	G	$8,200	2/1/2011	NEIN	Dual hyd., dual PTO, cab, motor OH, repainted
1066	1975		G	$8,850	10/23/2010	NCMO	
1066	1975	6,516	G	$8,100	9/9/2010	SCIA	Turbo, diesel, 18.4x38 tires, duals, radio, less than 200 hours on major OH, clean
1066	1975	4,561	G	$11,250	3/15/2010	WCIL	Diesel, 2 hyd., 540/1,000 PTO
1066	1976	8,683	G	$3,000	7/25/2013	WCSK	2WD, 116 PTO hp, 10x16 SL fronts, 18.4x38 rears, 3 hyd., dual PTO
1066	1976	2,032	G	$6,900	6/13/2013	Online	*IQBID.com,* cab, 2 hyd., 3 pt., no top link, 540/1,000 PTO, 18.4x38 hub duals, 2 years on motor OH
1066	1976	3,420	G	$8,300	3/15/2011	WCIL	2 hyd., 540/1,000 PTO, cab

International Harvester Company

Model	Year	Hours	Condition	Price	Date	Area	Comments
1066	1976	4,890	G	$8,000	4/9/2010	NWMN	2WD, cab, 2 hyd., 3 pt., 540/1,000 PTO, 730 hours on engine major OH
1066	1976	3,420	G	$8,300	3/15/2010	WCIL	Diesel, 2 hyd., 540/1,000 PTO, cab
1066		7,214	G	$5,500	4/3/2014	NEIN	2R, 540/1,000 PTO, 18.4x38 tires
1066			G	$4,800	3/26/2014	ECMS	Farmall
1066			G	$3,800	3/22/2014	NWMO	Front-end loader, 18.4x38 tires 75%, 540/1,,000 PTO, 3 pt.
1066			G	$7,500	2/26/2014	NCMO	Cab
1066			G	$8,600	2/5/2014	SESD	WF, cab
1066			G	$7,900	12/5/2013	SCIA	Cab
1066			G	$7,500	11/30/2013	SCIL	
1066			P	$4,500	11/19/2013	SCWI	Salvage, 18.4x38 duals, SN 37530
1066		8,830	G	$8,250	10/10/2013	Online	*HansenandYoung.com,* item in Wisconsin, new front tires, 3 pt., no cab, dual hyd., 800 hours on complete out of frame OH
1066		4,800	G	$11,000	5/11/2013	NCOH	Dual PTO, dual hyd., weights, new tires, repainted, new injection pump, runs
1066		5,560	G	$3,500	5/8/2013	Online	*BigIron.com,* item in Wyoming, 4 speed Hi/Lo turbo, 6 cyl. diesel
1066			F	$6,500	4/27/2013	ECMI	Hydro, diesel, cab, 20.8x38 tires 20%, PTO not functional, axle duals with being complete, 2 hyd.
1066			G	$5,300	3/2/2013	NCWI	Cab, 2 hyd., 540/1,000 PTO, 3 pt., 18.4x38 tires, noisy high range
1066		8,600	G	$5,300	3/2/2013	NCWI	Cab, heat, 20.8Rx38 tires, rear wheel weights, 540/1,000 PTO, 2 hyd., stationary drawbar
1066			G	$4,000	2/22/2013	SWKY	
1066		3,390	G	$3,000	2/7/2013	SEAR	Diesel, straight shift, PTO, dual 18.4x36 tires
1066			G	$20,500	2/6/2013	SESD	Diesel, HFWD, restored
1066			G	$6,100	12/12/2012	SESD	Cab
1066			G	$5,000	11/28/2012	ECND	Diesel, no cab
1066			G	$6,500	11/24/2012	WCIL	Open station, no TA, 18.4Rx38, 540/1,000, 2 hyd.
1066			G	$3,900	8/22/2012	ECMN	
1066		4,033	G	$8,000	8/16/2012	Online	*IQBID.com,* item in Minnesota, cab, air, heat, 2 hyd., dual PTO, 18.4x38 tires, completely repainted in 2000, 3 pt. blade, no drawbar
1066			G	$4,600	7/28/2012	SCNE	Diesel, 540/1,000 PTO, Ansel cab, 500 hours on complete OH
1066		3,800	G	$4,700	7/28/2012	SWTN	Canopy, duals
1066		7,525	F	$4,000	6/20/2012	ECIL	11x16.5 tires, 2 PTO, as is
1066		3,200	G	$10,400	6/20/2012	ECIL	Cab
1066		4,800	G	$10,150	4/4/2012	NWIA	
1066			G	$12,000	3/24/2012	NEIN	Restored, new tires, dual hyd., dual PTO, 3 pt., repainted, OH motor, new TA, runs
1066			G	$18,500	3/24/2012	NEIN	Hydro, dual PTO, restored, runs
1066			G	$6,000	3/22/2012	ECMN	Cab, 2 hyd., 3 pt., duals, 540/1,000 PTO

International Harvester Company

Model	Year	Hours	Condition	Price	Date	Area	Comments
1066		6,279	G	$6,700	3/20/2012	WCIL	
1066			G	$7,000	2/4/2012	ECSC	Duals
1066		3,116	G	$11,500	1/31/2012	NEIN	Cab, air, heat, excellent
1066		7,924	G	$6,750	12/22/2011	Online	*IQBID.com,* open station, 3 pt., dual PTO, 2 hyd.
1066		3,426	G	$9,500	12/1/2011	NEIN	18.4x38 tires, bolt-on duals, 10x16 front tires, 2 hyd., dual PTO, chrome stack
1066		8,664	G	$7,400	11/15/2011	Online	*IQBID.com,* cab, air, heat, turbo, 2 hyd., 3 pt., 540/1,000 PTO, Westendorf hyd. loader 8' bucket
1066		6,883	F	$7,600	10/6/2011	SEMN	Front weights, 3 pt., 540/1,000 PTO, 2 hyd., 18.4x38 tires, duals
1066			G	$4,500	9/16/2011	ECND	Cab, 3 pt., PTO, new rear tires
1066			G	$5,250	8/3/2011	ECND	Farmall
1066			G	$7,300	7/30/2011	ECMO	Manual
1066		4,000	G	$7,000	3/18/2011	SWIL	TA good
1066			G	$6,600	2/1/2011	NEIN	Black stripe, runs, rough
1066		9,000	G	$9,400	1/8/2011	SEPA	No cab, hours approx., dual PTO, no weights, 2 hyd., TA, 20.8x38 duals, needs all new tires, straight original
1066		7,221	G	$8,250	11/26/2010	WCOH	Turbo, axle duals, OH transmission 1,200 hours ago
1066			G	$7,100	11/20/2010	NCLA	Bush Hog loader, canopy
1066			P	$1,500	10/2/2010	SESK	
1066		6,543	G	$7,900	9/12/2010	WCIA	18.4x38 rear tires excellent, duals, 3 pt., 540 PTO
1066			G	$6,600	9/10/2010	Online	*IronPlanet.com,* item in New Jersey, Farmall
1066			G	$18,000	9/4/2010	NEIN	4x4, dual hyd., dual PTO
1066			P	$4,200	9/3/2010	NEIN	Cab, dual hyd., dual PTO, fast hitch, dead row, needs work and may not run or drive, as is
1066			G	$5,000	8/13/2010	Online	*IronPlanet.com,* item in Indiana
1066			F	$2,600	8/9/2010	WCMO	Duals, rough, runs
1066		6,300	G	$5,000	7/10/2010	SEND	Cab, air, heat, 3 pt., 18.4x36 hub duals
1066		3,186	G	$12,000	6/12/2010	NENE	2nd owner, owner put land into CRP back in mid 1980s and shedded tractor, cab, turbo, 18.4x38 tires
1066			F	$3,600	6/5/2010	NWIA	Cab, no 3 pt., clutch, TA and engine are strong, running
1066			G	$6,000	6/5/2010	NWIA	Good batteries, 3,750 hours on OH
1066		9,197	G	$7,250	6/5/2010	NWIA	2,500 hours on OH, new clutch and TA
1066			G	$4,700	5/26/2010	ECSD	Koyker K5 loader
1066			G	$5,300	5/5/2010	SEIA	
1066		8,036	G	$6,100	4/8/2010	WCMN	Diesel, cab, 2 hyd.
1066			G	$5,500	4/1/2010	NCIN	2 hyd., 540/1,000 PTO, open station
1086	1975	7,549	G	$9,800	2/27/2014	NWNE	Diesel, WF, 3 pt., cab
1086	1976	1,800	E	$23,000	9/6/2013	SWIA	3 hyd., axle mount duals, cab, 540/1,000 PTO, front weights
1086	1976	1,800	E	$24,500	9/6/2013	SWIA	Diesel, 3 hyd., 18.4x38 rear rubber, axle mount duals, cab, 540/1,000 PTO, front weights, SN 90079, black stripe

International Harvester Company

Model	Year	Hours	Condition	Price	Date	Area	Comments
1086	1976	5,757	G	$5,400	8/20/2013	WCIL	Cab, 2 hyd., both PTO, 18.4x38 tires, rust areas on cab
1086	1976	6,172	G	$18,500	2/14/2012	WCNE	WF, 3 pt., 3 hyd., 12 front weights, 540/1,000 PTO, new engine at 6,093 hours, new interior
1086	1976	4,365	G	$16,000	4/9/2011	SWSK	2WD, 130 PTO hp, TA, dual PTO and hyd., duals, aux. fuel tank, air, heater
1086	1977	3,164	G	$13,750	1/29/2014	Online	*BigIron.com,* item in Nebraska, Westendorf loader, grapple, and forks, 8F/4R, 6.8L, 6 cyl. turbo diesel, 131 PTO hp, 3 hyd., 540/1,000 PTO
1086	1977	6,467	G	$9,750	12/12/2013	Online	7' Westendorf loader, cab, diesel, 2 hyd., 3 pt., 540/1,000 PTO, 18.4x38 rears, 10x16 fronts
1086	1977	6,155	G	$11,000	12/4/2013	ECIN	Cab, air, heat
1086	1977	7,597	G	$8,100	7/25/2013	WCSK	2WD, 131 PTO hp, 540/1,000 PTO, 3 hyd., 18.4x38 rear, 4 rib fronts, duals
1086	1977	7,751	E	$18,250	1/12/2013	NCIL	Less than 3,000 hours on rebuilt International Harvester engine, mechanical diode TA and clutch, duals, new front rubber, super sharp
1086	1977	1,133	G	$5,000	12/1/2012	SEWY	Diesel, WF, 3 pt., cab
1086	1977	9,550	G	$15,500	11/24/2012	SEIA	Red Power, cab, air, heat, 18.4x38 tires, near new axle duals, SN 18850
1086	1977	6,425	G	$12,500	9/13/2012	SEIA	Duals sold separately
1086	1977	7,934	F	$7,000	8/22/2012	NCIA	Dual PTO, 18.4x38 duals
1086	1977	6,645	G	$3,900	8/21/2012	WCIL	
1086	1977	6,645	G	$4,400	3/20/2012	WCIL	18.4x38 rear tires, 540/1,000 PTO, 2 hyd.
1086	1977	9,385	G	$9,500	12/30/2011	NCIA	New clutch, transmission, bearings, and AC pump, 18.4x38 tires
1086	1977	8,687	G	$9,250	8/11/2011	WCMN	Cab, air, heat, 3 hyd., 3 pt., 540/1,000 PTO, quick hitch, rock box
1086	1977	7,184	G	$5,000	4/27/2011	Online	*BigIron.com,* item in Nebraska, 2 range 4 speed, International Harvester diesel, 2 hyd., 540/1,000 PTO, cab, air, heat, rear wheel weights, 9 bolt dual hubs, AM/FM/cass., block heater
1086	1977	4,515	G	$10,100	1/29/2011	ECMO	Cab, air, heat, axle mount duals, TA replaced at 3,200 hours, 8 front weights, top link
1086	1977	3,350	G	$12,400	8/27/2010	NWOH	Cab, 2 hyd., axle duals
1086	1978	5,625	G	$15,250	3/7/2013	ECIA	3 hyd., 3 pt., 540/1,000 PTO
1086	1978	6,500	G	$5,700	9/13/2012	SEIA	Duals
1086	1978	6,456	G	$8,750	9/13/2012	Online	*IQBID.com,* item in Iowa, 18.4x38 duals, 540/1,000 PTO, 2 hyd., duals
1086	1978	3,539	G	$19,275	4/25/2012	Online	*BigIron.com,* item in Nebraska, 8F/4R TA, diesel, 2 hyd.,540/1,000 PTO, ISO hyd. connections, 2 hyd., new battery
1086	1978	1,950	G	$19,000	12/7/2011	NCIA	One owner
1086	1978	4,382	E	$18,500	8/20/2011	NWOH	Cab, air, 2 hyd., dual PTO, hub duals, front weights
1086	1978		F	$6,600	7/27/2011	ECND	Cab, air, heat, TA, 3 pt.

International Harvester Company

Model	Year	Hours	Condition	Price	Date	Area	Comments
1086	1978		F	$6,000	2/17/2011	NWIA	Diesel, cab, air, heat, 3 pt., 2 hyd.
1086	1978	5,620	G	$12,300	2/1/2011	NEIN	Front/rear weights, very nice
1086	1978	11,000	G	$4,250	4/9/2010	WCNE	QR, TA, 3 pt., 3 hyd., duals, 131 hp
1086	1978	4,500	G	$8,550	2/15/2010	ECIL	Cab, air, 18.4x38 tires, axle duals
1206	1965	5,719	G	$7,000	3/20/2012	WCIL	
1206	1965		G	$14,500	10/12/2011	NWOH	
1206	1965		G	$8,000	7/16/2011	NEKS	
1206	1965		G	$11,750	8/7/2010	WCMN	
1206	1966	6,400	E	$24,500	11/2/2013	ECIA	Restored
1206	1966		E	$22,500	9/21/2013	SWIA	
1206	1966	6,303	G	$16,250	7/14/2012	NWIA	
1206	1966	9,222	G	$19,000	7/14/2012	NWIA	
1206	1966	5,489	G	$9,000	1/28/2012	ECMO	
1206	1966		G	$22,750	7/16/2011	NEKS	
1206	1966		E	$24,000	3/26/2011	SEWI	
1206	1967	6,648	G	$25,000	12/16/2013	ECIL	
1206	1967	5,087	G	$26,000	9/26/2013	NWOH	
1206	1967	7,700	G	$11,750	4/2/2013	ECIA	
1206	1967		F	$13,000	2/23/2013	ECIN	
1206	1967		G	$27,000	12/10/2012	ECIL	
1206	1967	6,807	G	$9,130	6/27/2012	ECKS	
1206	1967	8,387	G	$10,500	1/30/2012	NEIA	
1206	1967	3,200	E	$16,200	12/22/2011	ECMN	
1206	1967	6,730	G	$20,500	11/14/2011	ECIL	
1206	1967		G	$21,500	7/16/2011	NEKS	
1206	1967		G	$7,750	12/30/2010	ECMN	
1206			F	$42,000	3/26/2014	ECMS	Rare International Harvester 1206 Industrial, 1 of only 10 made, 1 of only 3 with TA, county owned
1206		1,936	G	$8,500	1/14/2014	WCNY	Online auction, item in New York, turbo diesel, block heater, 18.4x38 rear tires
1206			F	$4,750	2/6/2013	SESD	
1206			F	$12,500	12/29/2012	SWMI	
1206		4,020	G	$4,950	8/15/2012	ECKS	
1206			G	$12,500	8/4/2012	ECMN	
1206			G	$9,000	3/24/2012	NEIN	
1206			G	$10,500	1/28/2012	ECMO	
1206			G	$5,200	7/30/2011	ECMO	
1206			G	$11,500	7/30/2011	ECMO	
1206		10,776	G	$4,800	4/27/2011	Online	
1206			G	$10,250	11/13/2010	NCIA	
1206		3,300	G	$14,500	11/13/2010	NCIA	
1206			G	$27,000	9/4/2010	NEIN	
1206			G	$7,500	7/17/2010	SEIA	
1206			G	$11,000	6/19/2010	SWIL	
1206			G	$3,500	5/15/2010	SEKS	
1206		6,522	G	$8,300	4/3/2010	ECMN	
1256	1968	7,430	G	$10,500	4/17/2013	NWND	115 hp, PTO, 1 owner, owner paid $8,500 for it new

International Harvester Company

Model	Year	Hours	Condition	Price	Date	Area	Comments
1256	1968		G	$10,950	7/31/2012	SCMN	WF, 2 hyd., 3 pt.
1256	1968	9,511	G	$10,750	7/14/2012	NWIA	Diesel, turbo, 3 pt., 2 hyd., rear fenders
1256	1968	10,016	G	$13,200	7/14/2012	NWIA	Diesel, WF, rear fenders, new head gasket, HD, TA clutch
1256	1968		G	$4,200	3/15/2011	WCIL	Diesel, 3 hyd., 540/1,000 PTO
1256	1968		F	$5,500	3/30/2010	ECND	TA, open station, 2 hyd., 540/1,000 PTO
1256	1969	6,921	G	$6,900	3/14/2012	ECND	2 hyd., PTO, 16.8x38 rears, Koyker K5 loader, bale spear
1256	1969	7,000	G	$13,000	1/31/2012	NEIN	1 owner, excellent
1256	1969		G	$11,250	7/16/2011	NEKS	Diesel, SN 13506, restored, new TA, clutch, PTO OH, trans. gone through, WF, dual PTO, 3pt, 1 hyd., new 23.1x34 MaxiTrac tires, "Just like stepping up on a brand new one," said owner
1256		6,732	G	$9,100	3/26/2014	Online	
1256			G	$8,500	8/24/2013	SEMN	
1256			G	$8,500	8/15/2013	ECMN	
1256			G	$27,100	6/1/2013	NCON	Diesel, turbo
1256			G	$7,750	5/11/2013	NCOH	
1256		12,440	G	$7,300	3/7/2013	ECIA	
1256			G	$4,100	3/24/2012	NEIN	Standard, original, dual hyd., dual PTO, cab, runs
1256			G	$6,750	3/24/2012	SWMI	Diesel, 3 pt., 2 hyd., rear wheel weights, 540/1,000 PTO, 18.4x38 tires
1256		7,648	G	$13,000	1/31/2012	NEIN	Turbo, dual PTO, dual hyd., 3 pt., Hiniker cab, front/rear weights, 20.8x38 new tires
1256		5,862	G	$4,000	9/14/2011	Online	*DigIron.com,* itom in Colorado, turbo, 6 cyl., runs, 2 hyd., 540/1,000 PTO, 3 pt., 2 hyd.
1256			P	$6,750	3/5/2010	NEMO	Pro Stock pulling tractor, needs work
1456	1970	4,718	G	$16,250	7/14/2012	NWIA	Hyd. clutch, rear fenders, good TA
1456	1970		G	$6,500	6/13/2012	NWMN	2WD, cab, 3 pt., 540/1,000 PTO, 2 hyd.
1456	1970		E	$20,750	7/16/2011	NEKS	Diesel, SN 13276, restored, new TA, clutch, injection pump and injectors, front end rebuilt, rear end gone through, motor has 600-700 hours on major OH, 3 pt., dual PTO, 2 Hyd., new 20.8x38 Firestone tires, no front weights
1456	1970	6,830	F	$6,500	3/30/2010	ECND	White cab, WF, cab, 2 hyd., non factory 3 pt., 540/1,000 PTO
1456	1971	5,578	G	$13,500	8/20/2013	WCIL	2 hyd., 1,000 PTO, 18.4x38 tires
1456	1971		E	$14,500	11/13/2010	NCIA	Cab, very nice, original low hours
1456	1971	8,412	F	$6,750	3/30/2010	ECND	White cab, 2 hyd., 3 pt., 540/1,000 PTO
1456		8,687	G	$14,500	3/22/2014	NEIA	Turbo, diesel, WF, 3 pt., 2 hyd., PTO, flat top fenders, good rubber 20.8x38, good tin, nice sharp, complete OH 5 years ago, SN 2650005U010267
1456		6,051	G	$15,500	3/3/2014	NEKS	3 pt., TA, 1 owner
1456		4,924	G	$15,750	11/21/2013	WCIL	WF, cab, new clutch
1456		6,200	E	$20,500	11/2/2013	ECIA	Restored
1456			G	$14,000	6/22/2013	SEMN	Cab, 3 pt., dual hyd., dual PTO

International Harvester Company

Model	Year	Hours	Condition	Price	Date	Area	Comments
1456			G	$16,100	6/1/2013	SEMN	Good TA, 3 pt., tires like new, full cab, good glass
1456		7,826	G	$14,900	4/13/2013	SEMN	Cab, good TA, 540/1,000 PTO, 18.4x38 tires, duals, SN U014480
1456		8,904	G	$15,750	7/14/2012	NWIA	Rear fenders, hyd. seat, 3 pt., 2 hyd., WF
1456			G	$5,500	3/24/2012	NEIN	Original, 3 pt., fenders, PTO, hyd., runs
1456		5,311	G	$7,500	3/22/2012	ECMN	Factory WF, 2 hyd., 3 pt., 540/1,000 PTO, third arm
1456			G	$6,600	12/17/2011	NETX	Buggy top, fendered, 2 hyd., 3 pt., 540/1,000 PTO, front weights, 18.4x38 rear tires, 11L-15 front tires, hubs, no duals
1456			F	$5,250	9/17/2011	WCIL	Diesel, WF, cab, new tires
1456		6,700	G	$12,300	8/31/2011	ECMN	New TA 200 hours ago, new paint
1456			G	$5,200	1/29/2011	ECMO	Dual hyd., dual PTO, new PTO, hyd. fluid and filters
1456			G	$11,750	8/11/2010	ECMN	2 hyd., 3 pt., dual PTO, flat top fenders, new batteries, 9 bolt hub duals
1456			G	$24,250	8/7/2010	SEWI	Gold Demonstrator
1466	1971	7,628	G	$6,750	9/13/2012	SEIA	1,200 hours on OH, TA is out, 2 hyd.
1466	1971	5,500	P	$2,800	6/23/2010	SEND	Engine shot, turbo, cab, air, heat, 3 pt., front weights, hub duals (like new rubber), dual PTO
1466	1972	5,795	G	$10,000	9/6/2013	SEIA	20.8x38 tires, black stripe, 3 PT, 2 hyd., flat top fenders, 540/1,000 PTO, SN U010415
1466	1972	8,570	G	$8,200	11/17/2012	NWIA	White cab, 3 pt., 2 hyd., 18.4x38 tires, recent new torque and clutch
1466	1972		G	$4,250	6/13/2012	ECND	2 hyd., 3 pt., PTO, PTO needs work
1466	1972		G	$11,000	5/19/2012	NWMI	
1466	1972	2,999	F	$3,100	12/2/2010	ECWY	2 hyd., cab, 540/1,000 PTO, 18.4x38 tires
1466	1973	8,426	F	$3,300	3/12/2014	ECND	Open station, 3 pt., PTO and power steering need work
1466	1973	4,007	G	$9,500	8/21/2012	WCIL	Air doesn't work, TA good, 18.4x38 rear tires and duals
1466	1973		G	$14,000	7/16/2011	NEKS	Diesel, restored, good motor and TA, 2 hyd., 3 pt., dual PTO, new Firestone 18.4x38 tires
1466	1973	3,832	G	$6,350	3/15/2011	WCIL	540/1,000 PTO, turbo
1466	1973	8,573	G	$7,500	2/8/2011	ECNE	Turbo diesel, 18.4x38 rear tires w/ 9 bolt duals,11x16 4-ribbed front tires, 2 hyd.
1466	1974	6,546	G	$14,000	7/14/2012	NWIA	Good TA, diesel. 50% rear rubber, 80% front rubber, rear fenders
1466	1974		G	$7,500	12/30/2011	NCIA	18.4x38, cab, heat, PTO, 3 pt.
1466	1974	5,156	G	$6,000	10/27/2011	NWND	Cab, air, heat, Jobber 3 pt., 540/1,000 PTO, 2 hyd., duals, aux. fuel tank
1466	1974	5,320	G	$8,300	7/30/2011	ECMO	1,000 PTO, 3 pt., 3 Fasse hyd., remanufactured engine 1,100 hours, new TA, duals, one owner
1466	1974		G	$14,600	4/11/2011	Online	*AuctionTime.com*

International Harvester Company

Model	Year	Hours	Condition	Price	Date	Area	Comments
1466	1974		G	$5,400	1/29/2011	ECMO	New tires, clutch and press plate, paint, TA and seat, 500 hours on OH
1466	1974	6,000	G	$13,750	1/29/2011	ECMO	New TA, clutch, pressure plate and throw out bearing, new tires, seat and paint, 500 hours on complete OH
1466	1974	6,908	F	$6,100	8/24/2010	NEMO	Turbo, International Harvester cab, axle duals, 4 hyd., 540/1,000 PTO
1466	1975	7,738	G	$30,000	3/22/2014	NEIA	Diesel, black stripe, WF, Elwood front wheel assist, flat top fenders, 3 pt., 2 hyd., dual PTO, ROPS, canopy, 18.4x38 rear excellent, 13.6x24 front, completely gone through 3 years ago, paint/tin excellent
1466	1975	8,004	G	$14,500	1/24/2014	NCNE	Black stripe, 18.4x38 rear tires, dual hyd., 540/1,000 PTO, 3 pt., rear wheel weights
1466	1975		F	$6,700	4/3/2013	NCMI	1 owner, diesel, cab, TA, 20.8x38 tires, axle hubs, 12 front weights, weak dual PTO, 2 hyd.
1466	1975	4,228	G	$11,500	12/8/2012	ECIN	SN 2650129U028431, 11x16L front tires, 18.4x38 rear tires, 2 hyd., 540/1,000 PTO, front weights
1466	1975	5,900	G	$5,800	1/31/2012	NEIN	Cab
1466	1975	5,008	G	$4,500	2/19/2011	ECNE	Diesel, WF, 3 pt., cab
1466	1975	5,644	G	$4,250	12/4/2010	SEWY	WF, 3 pt., cab, diesel
1466	1976	4,076	G	$13,350	4/25/2012	Online	*BigIron.com,* item in Nebraska, 8F/4R TA, diesel, 2 hyd., 1,000 PTO, hyd. connections, new battery
1466	1976		F	$7,900	7/20/2011	NCIA	Cab, dual hub, 2 PTO, 2 hyd., front rock box, OH
1466	1976		G	$7,500	2/1/2011	NEIN	Black stripe, factory cab, air, heat
1466			G	$7,000	3/26/2014	ECMS	
1466		5,537	G	$9,000	3/22/2014	SWMI	Turbo, 6 cyl. diesel, WF, 2 hyd., 3 pt., 540/1,000 PTO, 2 front weights, 18.4x38 duals, 2 hours on major OH
1466			P	$1,900	12/20/2013	SCSD	Salvage, stuck engine
1466			G	$11,600	12/5/2013	SCIA	Duals, 1,000 hours on OH, front fuel cell, cab
1466			G	$4,750	9/12/2013	SEIA	3 pt., 540/1,000 PTO, 2 hyd., 18.4x38 tires
1466		8,898	F	$8,000	5/5/2013	WCMN	Little rough, turbo, diesel, cab, 2 hyd., 18.4x38 tires, 1,000 hours on OH
1466			G	$7,500	12/14/2012	SWKY	Duals
1466			G	$3,300	11/3/2012	SWMO	Runs well, used to bale fall hay
1466			G	$2,200	7/28/2012	SWTN	Dual hyd., cab
1466		2,500	G	$6,250	3/24/2012	NEIN	Dual hyd., dual PTO, original, runs
1466			G	$4,000	2/4/2012	NEAR	Farmall, diesel, 3 pt., 1,000 PTO, dual hyd., 18.4x38 rears, duals
1466			G	$6,950	10/15/2011	Online	*IQBID.com,* open station, turbo, 2 hyd., 3 pt., 540/1,000 PTO, flat top fenders, 9 bolt hub duals, 2350 loader, grapple
1466			G	$5,900	8/11/2011	WCMN	2WD, 2 hyd., 3 pt., PTO, open station

International Harvester Company

Model	Year	Hours	Condition	Price	Date	Area	Comments
1466	1974	5,951	G	$13,000	4/9/2011	SEMN	Turbo, open station, 540/1,000 PTO, 3 pt., 2 hyd., rock box, new clutch, 5 hours ago, new hyd. pump
1466		5,718	G	$10,000	3/19/2011	SEIA	
1466			G	$12,300	2/22/2011	SEPA	Weights, dual PTO, 2 hyd.
1466			G	$3,500	2/1/2011	NEIN	Not running
1466			G	$7,000	1/29/2011	ECMO	New TA, PTO has been rebuilt
1466			G	$6,200	12/18/2010	ECMI	Turbo
1466			G	$5,250	9/4/2010	NEIN	Dual PTO, dual hyd.
1466		4,600	G	$9,750	5/7/2010	WCOH	Turbo, 3 hyd., new inj pump, strong TA
1466			G	$2,250	4/9/2010	WCNE	Cab, synchro TA, 3 pt., 2 hyd., duals
1466		7,867	G	$5,300	4/3/2010	ECMN	Turbo, dual hyd.
1466			P	$7,600	4/3/2010	ECMN	Needs work, turbo diesel, dual hyd. new rubber
1466			F	$5,500	3/20/2010	WCOH	New TA and clutch, paint faded badly
1466			G	$7,200	2/11/2010	ECIL	Turbo, fenders
1468	1971	6,100	E	$16,000	11/13/2010	NCIA	All original, OH, new clutch, TA
1468	1972	4,067	G	$22,000	3/1/2014	SEMN	V8, Cozy cab, 1 owner, actual hours, 3 pt., 2 hyd., dual PTO, 20.8x38 axle mount duals, SN 2650119U007986
1468	1972	6,530	G	$15,500	3/23/2013	SWOH	Cab, ok appearance
1468	1972	5,981	G	$17,750	7/14/2012	NWIA	International Harvester cab with air, WF, rear cab bottom glass cracked
1468	1972	4,787	G	$22,000	7/14/2012	NWIA	Diesel, WF, rear fenders, HD, TA clutch
1468	1972	3,869	E	$31,500	7/14/2012	NWIA	Diesel, WF, rear fenders, HD TA, clutch, new paint
1468	1972	4,421	G	$14,000	8/25/2011	ECND	Factory cab, air, 2 hyd., 3 pt.,1,000 PTO, tilt steering, 18.4x38 singles, good runner
1468	1973		F	$19,300	12/28/2012	WCIL	V8, TA weak, open station, 20.8x38 tires, restoration started
1468	1973		E	$23,750	7/16/2011	NEKS	Diesel, SN 9124, new engine, TA, clutch, injection pump, rear end gone through, hardly any hours since restoration and engine work on new tach., hyd. seat, tilt steering, 3 pt., 1,000 PTO, new 18.4x38 Goodyear tires, new tractor, no front weights
1468	1974		F	$19,500	5/22/2012	NEIA	Diesel, WF, cab, 20.8x38 tires, duals, International Harvester V8 engine, 135 hp, 16F/8R speed, in storage for 10 years, attached 35 gal. saddle fuel tanks, SN 9967
1468	1974	5,316	G	$22,000	11/14/2011	ECIL	Cab, V8 engine, 18.4Rx38 tires, 2 hyd., weights, new bearings, clutch and TA
1468		4,685	E	$34,250	9/26/2013	NWOH	V8 diesel, 1 owner, 540 cu. in., cab, 18.4x38 tires and axle duals, dual PTO, 3 pt., 2 hyd., aux. fuel tanks, online only farm sale, purchase price $33,250 +1,000 buyers fee
1468			G	$17,250	3/24/2012	NEIN	Original, 3 pt., 2 hyd., single PTO, cab, runs
1468			G	$26,000	3/24/2012	NEIN	MFWD, dual PTO, 2 hyd., 3 pt., nice original, rear weights, runs

International Harvester Company

Model	Year	Hours	Condition	Price	Date	Area	Comments
1468			G	$9,600	9/4/2010	NEIN	2 hyd.
1468			G	$10,200	9/4/2010	NEIN	Front weights, dual PTO, top link, 2 hyd.
1468		5,834	G	$17,000	3/13/2010	WCIL	18.4Rx38 tires, 2 hyd., 3 pt.,
1486	1976		G	$5,350	12/12/2013	Online	
1486	1977	1,305	G	$4,200	2/5/2014	SESD	WF, 2 hyd., 2 PTO diesel, 3 pt., no top link, 18.4x38 tires
1486	1977		G	$5,800	11/26/2013	ECND	Cab, air, heat, 3 pt., PTO, 2 hyd., 20.8x38 duals, 2,767 hours on engine major OH
1486	1977	4,911	G	$5,000	9/12/2013	SEIA	3 pt., no third link, 540/1,000 PTO, 2 hyd., 20.8xR38 rear tires
1486	1977	6,023	F	$7,150	9/26/2012	Online	*PurpleWave.com,* item in Kansas, 3 pt., 540/1,000 PTO, cab, air, heat, 2 hyd., wheel weights, 20.8x38 rear tires, leaks hyd. oil at underside pan
1486	1977	709	E	$23,000	8/4/2012	WCIA	Diesel, cab, air, heat, radio, 3 pt., 18.4x38 tires, SN 18565
1486	1977	1,934	G	$6,100	11/23/2011	Online	*BigIron.com,* item in Wyoming, hour meter not working, Hi/Lo 4 speed, diesel, Firestone tires, 540/1,000 PTO, block heater
1486	1977	4,617	G	$11,000	4/28/2010	Online	*PurpleWave.com,* item in Kansas, 6 cyl. diesel, 8F/4R gears, International Harvester 2450 loader bucket, 2 hyd., 146 PTO hp
1486	1978	3,088	G	$19,250	9/12/2013	NCIA	Cab, front and rear weights, duals
1486	1978		G	$7,400	3/22/2013	WCIL	Fully equipped cab, 18.4xR38 rear tires, axle mount duals, 11x16 front tires, 2 hyd., 540/1,000 PO
1486	1978	1,995	G	$9,750	6/28/2012	NEND	Cab, air, heat, 3 pt., 540/1,000 PTO, 3 hyd., hand duals, front weight, tach. was replaced
1486	1978		G	$10,750	3/3/2012	SEMN	Cab, air, heat, 20.8x38 tires, 2 hyd., 3 pt., 540/1,000 PTO, 300 hours on new clutch and TA, 2,000 hours on engine OH, SN 18351
1486	1978		G	$13,250	12/28/2011	SEMN	Cab, air, heat, 2 hyd., 3 pt., 540/1,000 PTO, 4 front weights, 20.8x38 tires 65%, SRC 436B remfg. engine, clutch/TA/PTO all new rebuild
1486	1978	5,653	G	$15,750	3/15/2011	WCIL	Diesel, duals, 2 hyd., 540 PTO, front weights, air, OH
1486	1978	1,051	F	$4,750	2/19/2011	ECNE	Diesel, front weights, duals
1566	1975	5,200	F	$8,750	2/23/2013	ECIN	SN 2650125U007225, cab, duals, new front tires
1566	1975		G	$3,410	10/10/2012	Online	*PurpleWave.com,* item in Missouri, hours unknown, International Harvester 6 cyl. diesel, 156 hp, manual, canopy
1566	1976	2,919	G	$14,500	11/14/2011	ECIL	400 hours on new bearings, clutch, TA and pump, cab, good 18.4x38 tires w/ axle duals and cast iron hubs, 2 hyd., weights
1566		4,274	G	$8,000	12/10/2013	WCWI	Repainted, black stripe, open station, 2 hyd., 3 pt., 540/1,000 PTO, PTO, flat top fenders, repainted, black stripe, new TA

TRACTORS

International Harvester Company

Model	Year	Hours	Condition	Price	Date	Area	Comments
1566		6,204	G	$5,900	12/5/2013	SCIA	Estate tractor, clean
1566			G	$7,500	12/5/2013	SCIA	Duals, cab, front fuel cell, approximately 500 hours on new engine
1566			G	$5,250	8/24/2013	SEMN	Cab, 3 pt., dual hyd., dual PTO, 18.4x38 tires
1566			G	$7,260	8/23/2013	Online	*PurpleWave.com,* item in Oklahoma, Farmall, 7.1L, 6 cyl. diesel, 175 hp, 3 pt., quick attach, 540/1,000 PTO, 105" wheelbase, dual hyd.
1566		5,029	G	$6,750	6/1/2013	SEMN	20.8xR38 rubber, 540/1,000 PTO, 3 hyd., 3 PT
1566			G	$6,700	12/13/2012	WCIA	Cab, 2 hyd., 3 PT, 1,000 PTO, 20.8x38 tires, 65% rubber, TA out, SN265015U0023
1566		6,378	G	$6,000	11/24/2012	SEMN	Black stripe, cab, 3 pt. dual hyd., PTO, wheel weights, aux. front fuel tank
1566			F	$3,500	3/24/2012	SETX	Diesel, 1,000 rpm PTO, dual valves, 3 pt., rears 60%
1566		5,094	G	$5,500	1/31/2012	NEIN	Dual hyd., quick coupler
1566		5,111	G	$4,000	9/14/2011	Online	*BigIron.com,* item in Colorado, 2 hyd., 540 PTO, 3 pt., setup for duals, 10 suitcase weights, runs
1566			G	$5,700	4/12/2011	Online	*IQBID.com,* cab, air, heat, 2 hyd., 3 pt., PTO, front weights, duals
1566			G	$5,060	4/28/2010	Online	*PurpleWave.com,* item in Missouri, 6 cyl. 161 hp diesel, 3 pt., 2 hyd., rear wheel weights
1568	1974		E	$24,000	11/2/2013	ECIA	Factory cab, 2nd owner in 1979
1568	1974	2,600	E	$41,500	11/2/2013	ECIA	Restored, original hours, super sharp
1568	1974	2,532	G	$19,000	7/14/2012	NWIA	Duals, International Harvester cab, no PTO, 2 hyd.
1568	1974	1,832	G	$24,000	7/14/2012	NWIA	Cab, duals, PTO
1568	1974	2,410	G	$22,500	7/16/2011	NEKS	Diesel, SN 7305, restored, 3 pt., good TA, no PTO, new 20.8x38 Firestone tires, low SN
1568	1974		G	$23,000	7/16/2011	NEKS	Diesel, SN 7531, restored, complete engine OH, new TA, injection pump and injectors rebuilt, rear end gone through, 3 pt., 1,000 PTO, new Firestone 20.8x38 tires
1568	1975	4,853	G	$20,500	6/13/2012	NWMN	V8, cab, air, heat, 3 pt., 1,000 PTO, 2 hyd.
1568	1975		E	$22,000	7/16/2011	NEKS	Diesel, SN 7884, restored, injection pump rebuilt, new TA and clutch, rear end serviced, made to start on 4 and run on 8, 1,000 PTO, 3 pt., 2 hyd., new 20.8x38 Firestone tires, no front weights
1568			G	$18,250	9/4/2010	NEIN	Twin turbo, suitcase weights
1586	1975	9,153	G	$7,810	7/28/2010	Online	*PurpleWave.com,* item in Kansas, new turbo 10 hours ago, planetary gears replaced, air, 1,000 PTO, 11 suitcase weights
1586	1976		G	$7,700	12/6/2012	SEIA	18.4x38 duals, 10 front weights, 1,000 PTO, 3 hyd., 3 pt.

International Harvester Company

Model	Year	Hours	Condition	Price	Date	Area	Comments
1586	1976	4,000	G	$8,500	12/8/2010	ECND	3 pt., PTO, very nice
1586	1977	7,479	G	$5,000	12/4/2013	ECIN	Cab, air, heat
1586	1977	5,158	F	$4,600	3/26/2011	SEIL	Duals (1 new), tach. broke fall 2009
1586	1977	6,110	G	$8,600	2/26/2011	WCIL	Cab, 3 pt., 2 hyd., 2 pair inner wheel weights, 12 front weights., 20.8x38 tires, axle duals
1586	1977	5,303	G	$8,000	12/4/2010	SEMN	3 hyd., 3 pt., duals, new rod and main bearing
1586	1977	4,670	G	$7,800	6/18/2010	SEIA	Fully equipped cab, 20.8x38 rear tires, axle duals, 11x16SL front tires, 2 hyd., 540/1,000 PTO, front, rear weights
1586	1978	1,780	G	$8,200	6/22/2011	Online	*BigIron.com,* item in Kansas, diesel, 540/1,000 PTO, TA kit has been removed, air, cab, bolt on duals
1586	1978	4,438	F	$4,300	6/9/2010	ECIA	
2400	1973	1,873	F	$900	2/7/2012	WCOK	Series A, 3 pt., PTO, gas
2424	1964	2,375	G	$1,705	8/14/2013	Online	*PurpleWave.com,* item in Kansas, 4 cyl. gas, manual, 3 pt.
2826	1970	4,856	G	$56,100	7/10/2012	Online	*PurpleWave.com,* item in Kansas, 1 of only 15 made, 6 cyl. manual, Great Bend 900 loader and 7' bucket, Saline County paid $9,607 new in 1970
4166	1972	3,592	G	$12,250	12/28/2011	Online	*BigIron.com,* item in Nebraska, 4x4, 8 speed manual, diesel, 130 drawbar, 150 PTO hp, 2 hyd., PTO, front hyd. lift dozer blade, steerable axles, hypoid drive
4166	1973	4,542	G	$9,800	9/28/2013	ECNE	4WD, 3 pt., 2 hyd., cab, air, Firestone 23.1x26 tires, less than 200 hours on remanufactured engine
4166	1974	3,526	G	$9,400	3/23/2013	SWOH	4WD
4166	1975		G	$4,700	9/11/2010	SEIA	
4166		3,150	G	$7,000	3/24/2012	NEIN	No tag, 4WD, 3 pt., nice original, runs
4166			G	$951	9/14/2011	Online	*BigIron.com,* item in Colorado, 6 cyl. diesel, for parts, rolled, no tires, 3 pt.
4186	1978	6	E	$36,500	8/20/2013	ECMI	4WD, SN 2960417U019086, shedded, full set of front weights, 3 pt., 2 hyd., Goodyear 23.1x26 tires
4366	1975	2,900	G	$7,000	3/21/2012	ECMN	Duals, 3 pt., 3 hyd., cab, air, heat, all new filters/oil
4366	1976	9,799	G	$4,750	11/26/2013	ECND	4WD, cab, air, heat, 3 hyd., 18.4x38 duals
4366	1976	9,789	G	$6,700	11/26/2013	ECND	4WD, cab, air, heat, 3 hyd., duals
4366		9,345	G	$3,900	6/19/2013	Online	*BigIron.com,* item in South Dakota, tach. not working, auto Allison 4 speed
4366			G	$7,000	12/1/2012	SWMO	4WD, 3 pt., runs, 18.4x38 tires outside, 24.5x32 tires inside
4366		8,363	G	$3,800	12/15/2011	Online	*IQBID.com,* 4WD, cab, air, heat, 3 hyd., 18.4x38 duals
4366		7,534	F	$2,750	6/29/2011	Online	*PurpleWave.com,* item in Kansas, 500 hours on OH, International Harvester DT466 6 cyl. diesel, 10 speed Hi/Lo, hyd. power steering, radiator leaks

International Harvester Company

Model	Year	Hours	Condition	Price	Date	Area	Comments
4366		3,900	F	$5,500	4/13/2010	NWWI	4WD, 200 hours on OH, 3 pt., new rubber, duals all around
4386	1976	5,454	G	$4,750	11/26/2013	ECND	4WD, cab, air, heat, factory 3 pt., 2 hyd., duals
A	1939		G	$1,775	7/9/2013	Online	*IQBID.com,* Farmall, WF, 60" mower, electric start
A	1939		G	$2,700	6/30/2012	NEIA	Farmall, good paint, runs
A	1940		G	$1,150	8/24/2013	WCMN	New paint
A	1941		G	$4,250	9/18/2013	ECMT	Farmall, fully restored, 9.5x24 rubber, PTO, belt pulley, runs on kerosene or gas, SN FAAA42211, WF, good runner
A	1941		G	$1,400	8/24/2013	WCMN	Industrial, new paint, rough hood
A	1941		G	$3,600	8/24/2011	ECMN	PTO, belt pulley, new 11.2x24 rubber
A	1941		G	$2,300	8/7/2010	SEWI	Farmall, restored by Joe's Auto Body
A	1942		G	$1,625	5/15/2013	Online	*BigIron.com,* item in Iowa, Farmall, 4F/1R, 4 cyl. gas
A	1944		G	$5,750	9/6/2012	Online	*IQBID.com,* item in Minnesota, complete restoration
A	1946		F	$1,900	7/17/2013	NEND	Farmall, WF, PTO, shop built 60" belly mower
A	1946		G	$3,750	7/17/2013	NEND	Farmall, WF, PTO, Woods 59" belly mower
A	1946		F	$1,400	5/19/2012	SWMI	Farmall, WF, 9x24 tires, fenders, belt pulley, wheel weights
A			G	$975	3/12/2014	Online	*BigIron.com,* item in Nebraska, Farmall, 4 speed, 4 cyl., 9x24 rear tires, 4x15 front tires, gas
A			G	$1,400	9/12/2013	SEIA	Farmall, PTO, belt pulley, rear wheel weights
A			G	$1,182	8/26/2013	NWWI	Farmall, runs, good sheet metal, electric start
A			G	$1,300	8/24/2013	SEMI	Farmall, wheel weights, mounted plow, cultivator
A			G	$1,000	7/17/2013	SESK	2WD
A			G	$1,700	6/8/2013	NEND	Farmall, PTO, WF, no starter
A			G	$1,250	3/23/2013	NCOH	Farmall, Woods mower
A			G	$1,800	2/16/2013	NEIA	Farmall
A			G	$2,100	2/6/2013	Online	Item in Illinois, Farmall, CaseIH 61 MS belly mower, new exhaust, intake manifold, carburetor kit, wheel weights
A			G	$1,800	9/22/2012	NEOR	Farmall, WF
A			G	$2,095	6/27/2012	Online	*BigIron.com,* item in Nebraska, Farmall, belly cultivator, 4F/1R, 4 cyl. gas, 540 PTO, WF, rear drawbar and weights
A			G	$1,400	3/24/2012	ECKS	Farmall, belly mower, WF, rear wheel weights, tires good, not restored
A			F	$1,450	10/22/2011	ECTX	Farmall, cultivator, plow
A			P	$900	9/17/2011	SEND	Farmall, tough looking, Woods belly mower, PTO, belt pulley drive, good runner
A			G	$1,000	6/18/2011	NEIA	Farmall, cultivator A
A			G	$2,700	4/16/2011	ECMI	Farmall, gas, new rear and front tires, drawbar hitch

International Harvester Company

Model	Year	Hours	Condition	Price	Date	Area	Comments
A			G	$1,600	4/11/2011	Online	*AuctionTime.com,* 2WD
A			F	$1,100	10/2/2010	ECMN	WF
A			G	$2,900	8/24/2010	NEMO	Farmall, WF, fenders, 540 PTO, drawbar
A			G	$1,600	8/14/2010	SEMN	Farmall, belly mower
A			G	$1,575	7/17/2010	SCON	Canadian sale, Farmall
A			G	$1,325	5/26/2010	ECSD	Belly mower
A			G	$2,900	5/1/2010	SENE	Farmall
A			G	$1,350	2/26/2010	SEMN	Farmall, belly mower
AV			G	$1,900	3/24/2012	NEIN	Farmall, high crop, new tires, repainted, rear weights, runs
B	1930		F	$850	9/22/2010	NECO	DF, gas, running
B	1940		G	$875	8/24/2013	WCMN	New paint
B	1940		G	$1,500	8/24/2013	WCMN	Woods L59 mower
B	1941		G	$1,150	7/10/2010	SEIA	Farmall, Art's Way 5' belly mower, 12V, original
B	1942		E	$2,500	10/7/2011	NWSD	Restored, Farmall, NF, PTO, runs like a top
B	1942		F	$900	9/22/2010	NECO	SF, gas, running
B	1943		F	$1,200	11/6/2012	ECOK	Farmall, restored
B	1945		G	$3,500	4/7/2013	ECMN	Farmall, PTO, wheel weights, retrofitted hyd. with reservoir, 12.4x24 rear rubber, chains, nice original metal
B	1945		G	$2,255	5/30/2012	Online	*PurpleWave.com,* item in Texas, Farmall
B	1945		E	$2,200	10/15/2011	ECIA	Row crop, parade ready, new Goodyear 9.5x24 tires
B	1947		E	$12,000	3/15/2014	ECMD	Parade tractor and cart, Farmall, rebuilt engine, overbore kit installed, trans/final drive has new bearings and seals, completely disassembled, rebuilt and re-assembled with fabricated Schwartz Wide
B	1947		G	$3,100	9/6/2012	Online	*IQBID.com,* item in Minnesota, WF, complete restoration
B	1947		E	$3,000	9/14/2011	NWIL	Farmall, gas, restored, good tires
B	1947		G	$3,100	7/16/2011	NEKS	Farmall, gas, SN 209566, restored, NF, wheel weights, new Firestone 11.2x24 tires
B	1948		G	$925	4/25/2012	Online	*BigIron.com,* item in South Dakota, 4 speed manual, 4 cyl. gas, 16 hp, 12V, alternator, NF, wheel weights
B			G	$2,600	12/19/2013	WCMN	Farmall, NF, 12V, Woods L306 mower, restored
B			G	$1,200	9/12/2013	SEIA	Farmall, NF, Rider seat, PTO, belt pulley
B			G	$1,200	9/12/2013	SEIA	Farmall, Woods belly mower
B			G	$2,000	9/12/2013	SEIA	Farmall, cultivator, NF, rider seat, Woods 59 belly mower
B			G	$1,550	8/24/2013	SEMN	Art's Way 72" belly mower, good rubber
B			G	$1,200	8/20/2013	WCIL	Farmall, NF
B			G	$1,000	7/27/2013	NCIA	Farmall, NF, 12V, 540 PTO, Woods 59" belly mower, Firestone 11.2x24 tires
B			G	$1,000	6/27/2013	Online	*IQBID.com,* Farmall, NF, 12V, 540 PTO, Woods 59" belly mower, Firestone 11.2x24 tires, SN 1064016

International Harvester Company

Model	Year	Hours	Condition	Price	Date	Area	Comments
B			G	$2,200	6/22/2013	SEMN	Farmall, NF, Woods 60" belly mower
B			G	$1,100	6/7/2013	NESD	
B			G	$3,000	5/5/2013	WCMN	Farmall, fenders, wheel weights, PTO, pulley, nice tin
B			G	$1,900	4/13/2013	SEMN	Farmall, NF, fenders, Woods 59" mower
B			G	$2,500	4/10/2013	SWMN	Farmall, SF
B			G	$2,700	4/10/2013	Online	*BigIron.com,* item in Nebraska, 4 speed, 4 cyl. gas, 11.2x24R rear tires, 4x15SL front tires, 540 PTO
B			G	$1,211	8/22/2012	Online	*BigIron.com,* item in Nebraska, Farmall, 4 speed, 4 cyl. gas, 540 PTO, new clutch, 59" Woods belly mower
B			G	$2,200	8/16/2012	Online	*IQBID.com,* item in Minnesota, Farmall, NF, 6V, 540 PTO, air ride seat, Woods 59" mower, fully restored, complete engine rebuild
B			F	$800	7/25/2012	SEND	Farmall, NF, Woods 59" mower deck, turf tires
B			F	$850	6/20/2012	SESD	Farmall, gas, Woods belly mower, 11.2x24 tires, need brakes, 3rd gear out
B			G	$1,800	6/20/2012	SESD	Farmall, belly mower, turf tires, runs
B			G	$2,200	10/29/2011	NEAR	Farmall
B			G	$2,000	7/27/2011	ECND	Ford shaft drive undermount mower, 12V system, runs and mows excellent
B			G	$1,500	6/18/2011	NEIA	Farmall
B			G	$1,100	4/13/2011	Online	*BigIron.com,* item in Texas, Farmall, 3F/1R, 4 cyl. gas, 28 hp, 540 PTO
B			G	$1,750	4/2/2011	ECMN	Farmall, NF, 5' Art's Way belly mower, newer paint, good condition
B			F	$1,000	3/19/2011	SEIA	Farmall, belly mower
B			G	$1,500	3/5/2011	SEMN	Farmall, gas, 540 PTO, NF, fenders, wheel weights, Woods belly mower
B		8,638	G	$1,200	12/15/2010	SEMI	Farmall, new 11.2x24 rear tires
B			G	$1,200	9/11/2010	ECIA	Farmall, Woods belly mower
B			G	$1,050	9/3/2010	SCMN	Farmall, NF, gas, converted to 12V, PTO, rear tires 85%
B			G	$1,100	7/10/2010	SEIA	Farmall, original
B			F	$826	6/23/2010	Online	*BigIron.com,* item in Nebraska, Farmall, gas, 9x24 rear tires, 6x15 front tires new, 540 PTO, WF, electric start (no battery), steering box cracked
B			F	$900	6/5/2010	SEMN	Woods 5' belly mower
B			G	$1,100	6/5/2010	ECMN	Farmall, new rear tires and OH motor
B			G	$2,000	6/5/2010	WCMO	Farmall
B			G	$2,700	5/22/2010	SEMN	Farmall, NF, Woods L59 belly mower, runs, looked good, new 9.5x24 tire
B			G	$1,700	5/1/2010	SENE	Farmall
B			F	$2,100	4/17/2010	NEIA	Farmall, NF, turf tires, Woods 60" mower deck, ran good
B			G	$1,300	4/1/2010	NCIN	Farmall, Woods 59 belly mower
BN	1952		F	$1,100	1/18/2013	WCOH	Farmall, 72" Woods belly mower, NF

International Harvester Company

Model	Year	Hours	Condition	Price	Date	Area	Comments
BN			G	$1,100	11/3/2012	SWMI	Farmall, NF, new 123 cu. in. gas, live hyd. and water pump, new brakes and seat, belt pulley, drawbar, PTO, snowplow
BN			G	$3,600	11/12/2011	WCMI	Farmall, Cultivision, PTO, 10x24 rear tires, NF
BN			G	$2,000	9/4/2010	NEIN	Farmall
C	1947		G	$1,000	1/28/2012	ECMO	Farmall, blade
C	1948		G	$900	9/12/2013	SEIA	5' Continental belly mower, 11.2x36 tires, NF
C	1948		G	$1,900	9/6/2012	Online	*IQBID.com,* item in Minnesota, WF, original condition
C	1949		G	$1,100	6/1/2013	SEMN	Farmall, NF
C	1949		G	$1,650	2/6/2013	Online	Item in Illinois, Farmall, PTO, fenders, belt pulley, SN 33534, body shop paint, nice
C	1949		G	$1,250	9/22/2012	WCMN	Farmall, NF, pulley, cultivator lift, nice tin
C	1950		G	$1,200	8/24/2013	WCMN	Older paint
C	1950		G	$1,900	4/14/2012	NEIA	Farmall, fenders, engine OH in 2006, new radiator in 2003, SN hard to read
C	1950		G	$800	8/25/2011	ECND	Farmall, NF, PTO, 11.2x36 tires, runs
C	1950		G	$1,800	8/6/2011	NCIA	Farmall, belly mower
C	1951		G	$850	5/25/2011	Online	*BigIron.com,* item in Nebraska, Super C, 4F/1R, 4 cyl. gas, 540 PTO, drawbar
C			G	$1,000	1/24/2014	NCNE	Farmall, WF, converted to 12V, 12.4x36 rear tires, 15" front tires, 540 PTO
C			G	$1,000	12/20/2013	SCSD	Farmall, Kosch side mount sickle bar mower
C			G	$907	10/28/2013	NWWI	Farmall, new paint
C			G	$1,150	10/3/2013	NCIN	Farmall, NF, belly mower, fenders
C			G	$1,076	9/9/2013	NWWI	Farmall, International Harvester loader, 1 set rear weights, belt pulley
C			G	$850	8/14/2013	WCMN	Farmall, NF, PTO, 2 hyd., electric start, 6' belly mower
C			G	$1,300	7/31/2013	ECND	NF, PTO, Art's Way 60" belly mower, hyd. lift
C			G	$800	6/1/2013	SEMN	Farmall, Woods 59" belly mower, 11.2x36 tires
C			G	$1,000	6/1/2013	SEMN	Gas
C			G	$1,200	6/1/2013	SEMN	NF, Woods 60" belly mower
C			G	$1,300	5/11/2013	NCOH	Farmall, fenders, Woods belly mower, belt pulley, older repaint, runs
C			F	$1,850	5/5/2013	WCMN	Farmall, PTO, pulley attachment, good 11.2x36 rubber
C			G	$1,500	3/30/2013	NWIL	Farmall, runs, drives, mechanically sound
C			G	$1,600	2/22/2013	SWKY	Farmall, cultivator
C			G	$1,400	12/7/2012	NCIN	Farmall, NF, fenders, excellent, rear rubber, repainted
C			G	$1,050	11/9/2012	NEAR	Farmall, 4 cyl. gas, 3 pt., 540 PTO, NF, 5' 3 pt. cutter
C			F	$1,300	9/13/2012	SEIA	Farmall
C			G	$950	8/14/2012	Online	*IQBID.com,* item in Minnesota, Farmall, NF, 12V, Woods 5' mower, 9.5x36 rears

International Harvester Company

Model	Year	Hours	Condition	Price	Date	Area	Comments
C			G	$2,420	8/14/2012	Online	*PurpleWave.com,* item in Kansas, Farmall, gas, manual, 540 PTO, drawbar, steel seat cushion, 5x15 front tires, 11.2x36 rear tires, fully restored
C			F	$800	6/20/2012	SESD	Farmall, NF, 11.2x26 tires, mower, shedded, should run
C			G	$1,100	6/9/2012	ECNE	PTO, hyd., raise, runs
C			G	$1,000	6/2/2012	SEMN	Farmall, 12V system, 11.2x36 tires, NF, runs
C			G	$825	5/9/2012	Online	*BigIron.com,* item in Missouri, Farmall, 4 speed manual, gas, 540 PTO, Woods 60" belly mower
C			G	$1,050	4/4/2012	WCMN	Farmall, NF
C			G	$2,500	3/24/2012	NEIN	Farmall, fenders, new tires, rear weights, 2 bottom mounted plow
C			G	$1,800	10/27/2011	NWND	Farmall, WF, PTO, recent OH and 12V system
C			G	$1,500	10/15/2011	Online	*IQBID.com,* Farmall, 4 cyl., PTO, rear belt pulley, 12V, 11.2x36 rear tires, restored
C			G	$1,200	4/2/2011	ECMN	Farmall, NF, newer paint
C			G	$1,900	2/14/2011	NEMO	Farmall, NF, 11.2-36 tires (like new), 72" belly mower
C			G	$2,000	11/13/2010	NCIA	Farmall, NF
C			F	$1,000	11/6/2010	SEMN	Farmall, NF, new rear rubber, bad clutch
C			G	$1,750	8/24/2010	NEMO	Farmall, NF, 540 PTO, nicely restored
C			G	$1,700	8/11/2010	ECMN	Farmall, NF, belly mower
C			G	$1,200	7/17/2010	SCON	Canadian sale, Farmall
C			G	$1,100	6/23/2010	Online	*BigIron.com,* item in Nebraska, Farmall, 4 speed with reverse, 4 cyl. gas, 540 PTO, has electric start, hyd. lift, belt pulley attachment without pulley
C			G	$2,400	6/12/2010	NENE	Farmall, NF, 6' belly mower, good rubber
C			G	$1,250	5/26/2010	ECSD	Belly mower
C			G	$1,600	5/26/2010	ECSD	NF
C			G	$1,300	5/1/2010	SENE	Farmall
C			G	$1,050	4/10/2010	ECON	Cultivator
Cub	1948		G	$1,500	10/7/2011	NWSD	Farmall, restored, PTO
Cub	1948		G	$2,000	7/16/2011	NEKS	Farmall, gas, SN 53991, original, motor OH, lights, Woods 4' mower, new Firestone 9.5x24 tires
Cub	1948		G	$1,600	8/24/2010	NEMO	Farmall, WF, fenders, newer restoration
Cub	1948		G	$1,750	5/1/2010	NCOH	Farmall, original tin, hyd., 42" belly mower
Cub	1949		G	$1,950	8/24/2011	ECMN	Farmall, new tires, wheels weights, front and rear, new paint, good runner
Cub	1950		E	$3,700	10/15/2011	ECIA	WF, parade ready, Firestone 8x24 tires
Cub	1950		G	$3,200	8/24/2011	ECMN	PTO, PS
Cub	1952		G	$1,300	8/25/2011	ECND	Farmall, PTO, 8.3x24 tires, International Harvester 5' sickle mower, runs, needs tune up

International Harvester Company

Model	Year	Hours	Condition	Price	Date	Area	Comments
Cub	1952		G	$1,800	7/9/2011	SWIL	Red, 9.5/9x24 rear tires, rear wheel weights, Woods 46" mower, runs great
Cub	1955		G	$3,750	9/6/2012	Online	*IQBID.com,* item in Minnesota, older restoration
Cub	1957		E	$3,000	3/15/2014	ECMD	Farmall, belly mount sickle mower, professionally restored, new rubber all around, SN 198816
Cub	1957		G	$3,000	10/23/2010	SCPA	Farmall mower
Cub	1959		G	$1,400	6/15/2013	WCMI	Farmall, WF, power lift, rear belt pulley, 8x24x tires, wheel weights, SN214251
Cub	1959		G	$2,500	3/19/2011	ECIL	Lo-Boy, Farmall, restored, new tires
Cub	1969		G	$1,500	7/9/2011	SWIL	Yellow/white, 60" mid-mount mower deck, 8.3x24 rear tires, runs great
Cub	1972		G	$2,000	3/26/2011	SEWI	Lo-Boy
Cub			G	$1,250	3/22/2014	SWMI	4 cyl. gas, WF, 5' Woods belly mower, 8.3x24 rear tires, tire chains
Cub			G	$1,000	2/5/2014	SESD	Farmall
Cub			G	$1,050	8/29/2013	NWIA	Farmall, WF, cultivator, sickle mower, plow, push blade
Cub			G	$1,265	8/28/2013	Online	*PurpleWave.com,* item in Kansas, Farmall, 4 cyl. gas, manual, PTO, 64" mower, 4x12 front tires, 8.3x24 rear tires
Cub			F	$1,050	8/24/2013	SWOH	Needs repair
Cub			G	$1,900	8/24/2013	SEMI	Farmall, belly mount sickle mower, front blade, wheel weights
Cub			G	$2,000	3/23/2013	NEIN	Low boy, deck, runs
Cub			G	$2,000	3/20/2013	SWMI	Lo-Boy, 60" mower, all repainted
Cub			G	$1,500	2/23/2013	ECMI	Farmall, gas, rebuilt motor, 9.5x24 rear tires, new tires
Cub			P	$1,400	12/6/2012	SEIA	Farmall, does not run
Cub			G	$800	12/1/2012	SWMO	Farmall, 5' belly mower
Cub			G	$1,000	11/3/2012	SWMO	Sickle mower, new paint, new tires, very nice, runs well, new pitmen for sickle mower
Cub			G	$1,600	9/22/2012	NEOR	Farmall, WF
Cub			G	$850	8/1/2012	NEOK	Low boy
Cub			G	$1,800	8/1/2012	NEOK	Farmall, belly mower
Cub			G	$2,000	3/31/2012	SWSK	2WD, hyd. pump adapted, hyd., 3 pt., PTO
Cub			G	$1,300	3/24/2012	NEIN	Farmall, PTO, original, runs
Cub			G	$1,500	3/17/2012	ECIN	Farmall
Cub			G	$2,100	3/14/2012	ECND	4 cyl. gas, Woods 60" belly mower, hyd. lift
Cub			G	$1,275	12/3/2011	NCOH	Farmall, belly mower
Cub			F	$1,870	11/3/2011	Online	*PurpleWave.com,* item in Kansas, WF
Cub			G	$1,800	10/29/2011	NEAR	Farmall
Cub			G	$2,200	8/20/2011	NEMN	Farmall, restored
Cub			G	$1,700	6/18/2011	NEIA	Farmall, row crop cultivator
Cub			G	$3,000	11/13/2010	NCIA	Farmall, WF
Cub			E	$2,000	10/23/2010	NCMD	Lo-Boy

International Harvester Company

Model	Year	Hours	Condition	Price	Date	Area	Comments
Cub			G	$1,700	10/2/2010	ECMN	Farmall
Cub			G	$1,850	10/2/2010	ECMN	Farmall, WF
Cub			F	$1,425	9/25/2010	NCNJ	Farmall, Lo-Boy, mower
Cub			F	$1,500	9/25/2010	NCNJ	Farmall, mower
Cub			G	$2,250	8/21/2010	NCNC	Farmall, runs great
Cub			G	$1,900	8/7/2010	SEWI	Farmall
Cub			G	$1,750	5/26/2010	ECSD	
Cub			G	$1,400	5/1/2010	SENE	Farmall
Cub			G	$1,300	4/10/2010	ECON	Farmall, blade
Cub			G	$1,300	4/9/2010	WCFL	Lo-Boy
F12	1932		G	$1,600	8/25/2011	ECND	Farmall, PTO, full steel, SF, 54" wheels, stuck, Waukesha model FL6D engine
F12	1933		G	$1,100	9/21/2013	SEMN	Farmall, tricycle
F12	1934		G	$850	8/25/2011	ECND	Farmall, SF, PTO, full steel, 54" steel wheels, loose, restored
F12	1934		F	$1,200	8/28/2010	WCIL	Farmall, SF, 12x38 rear tires
F12	1934		G	$1,400	7/10/2010	SEIA	Farmall, restored, on rubber
F12	1934		G	$1,300	5/7/2010	NEAR	Farmall
F12	1935		G	$1,800	6/30/2012	NEIA	Farmall, SF
F12	1935		G	$1,800	9/1/2011	WCMN	Farmall, NF, power lift, factory front, 38" rear cut offs, fenders, round spokes, new front and back tires, restored
F12	1935		G	$3,750	8/25/2011	ECND	Farmall, factory WF, PTO, 54" full steel
F12	1936		G	$2,250	9/18/2013	ECMT	Farmall, tricycle front, fully restored, PTO, belt pulley drive, 9.5x24 rubber, SN FS58313, good runner
F12	1936		G	$2,000	7/28/2012	SCTX	Farmall, for racing, modified for pulls
F12	1936		G	$15,500	6/30/2012	NEIA	Farmall, OH, painted, McCormick model 1M 1R mounted corn picker
F12	1937		F	$1,100	5/26/2012	ECPA	Farmall, gas, 9.5x40 tires (new and tubeless), 540 PTO
F12	1937		G	$1,450	11/12/2011	WCMI	Farmall, NF, PTO, 11.2x36 rear tires
F12	1937		F	$850	8/25/2011	ECND	Farmall, SF, full steel with lugs, 54" steel wheels, stuck
F12	1937		G	$1,200	8/25/2011	ECND	Farmall, NF, Farmall power lift, round spoke rears, loose, restored, mounted 2-way plow
F12			G	$1,000	2/22/2014	SCNE	Rubber, no tag, restored
F12			G	$1,300	8/24/2013	SEMI	Farmall, steel wheels, fenders, hyd. lift
F12			G	$800	5/11/2013	NCOH	SF, full steel, older repaint, runs
F12			G	$900	5/11/2013	NCOH	Repainted, cut down spoke wheels, runs
F12			F	$875	7/24/2012	NCIA	Farmall, engine free, shedded
F12			G	$1,150	5/19/2012	SWMI	Farmall, NF, 11.2x28 tires, round spoke front wheels
F12			G	$2,200	5/19/2012	NWMI	Farmall
F12			G	$1,200	12/28/2011	Online	*BigIron.com,* item in Nebraska, Farmall, 3F/1R, 113 cu. in., 4 cyl. gas, 540 PTO, 10 drawbar hp, 13 belt hp, 52" steel with lugs, engine is free
F12			F	$800	12/3/2011	NEMO	Farmall, on rubber, front and rear spokes, like new 11.2x36 tires, restored nicely and runs excellent

International Harvester Company

Model	Year	Hours	Condition	Price	Date	Area	Comments
F12			F	$800	10/29/2011	SEMN	Farmall, round spokes, sickle mower
F12			F	$1,100	10/29/2011	SEMN	Farmall, does not run, 2R cultivator
F12			G	$1,100	7/30/2011	ECMO	Farmall
F12			G	$975	8/24/2010	NEMO	Farmall, NF, rear spokes
F12			G	$1,200	4/24/2010	SEMN	Farmall, rear steel, will run, good paint, may need work but would pull start
F14	1938		G	$1,100	8/7/2010	SEWI	Farmall, partial restoration, runs, fresh paint and decals, original 40" tires, OD gear box
F14	1939		G	$1,400	6/30/2012	NEIA	Farmall, kerosene special, 40" rubber
F14	1939		G	$1,800	6/30/2012	NEIA	Farmall, round spoke wheels
F14	1939		G	$6,500	8/25/2011	ECND	Farmall, factory WF on rubber, PTO, power lift, factory electric start generator, cast wheels, radiator shutters, stuck
F14	1977	8,907	G	$10,756	7/10/2013	Online	*BigIron.com,* item in Nebraska, row crop, loader and disk, TA 16F/8R, 7.1L, 6 cyl. diesel, 2 hyd., 3 pt., 84" Westendorf loader
F14			G	$1,000	9/12/2013	SEIA	Steel rear wheels, SF rubber,
F14			F	$800	6/20/2012	SESD	Farmall, on rubber, flat spokes, should run
F14			G	$1,300	5/19/2012	NWMI	Farmall
F14			G	$1,350	11/12/2011	WCMI	Farmall, PTO, NF, hyd. lift, electric start, 10x38 rear tires
F14			G	$2,000	11/12/2011	WCMI	Farmall, PTO, SF, hyd. lift, 12.4x40 rear tires
F14			G	$2,500	9/4/2010	NEIN	Farmall, rare factory WF, full steel
F14			G	$1,700	8/24/2010	NEMO	Farmall, NF, rear spokes
F20	1932		G	$1,675	6/30/2012	NEIA	Farmall, steel wheels
F20	1933		G	$1,800	7/22/2011	SEMN	Farmall, power lift, shutters, cast rear on rubber, round spoke fronts, original unrestored, cultivator
F20	1934		G	$1,400	7/22/2011	SEMN	Farmall, on full steel with lugs, older restoration
F20	1935		G	$1,150	6/30/2012	NEIA	Farmall, spoke wheels
F20	1936		G	$2,750	6/22/2013	SEWA	Farmall, NF, 4 cyl., gas, crank start, right side belt drive, SN FA41247N
F20	1936		G	$2,100	8/25/2011	ECND	Farmall, narrow tread, SF on rubber, PTO, belt pulley, cast rear wheels, loose, older restoration
F20	1937		F	$925	6/30/2012	NEIA	Farmall, round spoke wheels
F20	1937		G	$1,550	5/7/2010	NEAR	Farmall
F20	1938		G	$1,200	8/21/2012	WCIL	Farmall
F20	1938		G	$1,000	6/30/2012	NEIA	Farmall, new paint
F20	1938		G	$1,350	6/30/2012	NEIA	Farmall, narrow tread
F20	1938		G	$1,600	9/9/2011	ECND	Farmall, NF, PTO, spoke wheels, restored
F20	1938		G	$2,900	8/25/2011	ECND	Farmall, factory WF, narrow rear tread, PTO, belt pulley
F20	1938		G	$5,400	7/16/2011	NEKS	Farmall, gas, SN FA-122810, restored, crank start, electric generator and lights, new tires

International Harvester Company

Model	Year	Hours	Condition	Price	Date	Area	Comments
F20	1938		G	$1,350	2/20/2010	NCIL	Farmall, V-belt fan, OD, restored, good rubber, gas
F20	1939		G	$1,200	5/19/2012	SWMI	Farmall, narrow tread, 12x36 tires, fast road gear
F20			G	$1,000	2/22/2014	SCNE	Rubber
F20			G	$800	9/12/2013	SEIA	NF, PTO, new front tires, hyd. pump
F20			G	$1,600	9/12/2013	SEIA	NF, PTO, self starter kit
F20			G	$975	8/24/2013	SEMI	Farmall, NF, restored
F20			G	$1,001	5/22/2013	Online	*BigIron.com,* item in Colorado, plow, 4 speed, 4 cyl. gas
F20			G	$920	4/24/2013	Online	*BigIron.com,* item in Nebraska, 4 cyl.
F20			P	$800	2/22/2013	NWIN	Farmall, not running, complete
F20			F	$900	2/12/2013	WCIL	Farmall
F20			G	$850	11/3/2012	SWMO	New paint, new tires on front, very nice, been in many parades, hand start only
F20			G	$800	12/3/2011	NEMO	Farmall, on rubber, front and rear spokes, like new 11.2x36 tires, restored nicely and runs excellent
F20			F	$1,000	11/12/2011	WCMI	Farmall, PTO, NF, 11.2x36 rear tires, not restored
F20			G	$1,300	11/12/2011	WCMI	Farmall, PTO, NF, belt pulley, electric start, foot brakes, 12.4x36 rear tires
F20			P	$1,000	3/5/2011	SEMN	Farmall, gas, NF, rear weights, front and rear spoke wheels, not running
F20			F	$1,250	9/4/2010	NEIN	
F20			G	$1,000	8/24/2010	NEMO	Farmall, NF
F30	1935		G	$1,100	5/19/2012	NWMI	Farmall
F30	1936		G	$3,500	9/8/2012	NECO	Farmall, shedded, NF, rear rubber poor but has set of steel rims
F30	1936		F	$800	7/22/2011	SEMN	Farmall, for parts
F30	1937		F	$908	8/14/2012	Online	*PurpleWave.com,* item in Kansas, Farmall, 20 hp gas, engine is stuck, drawbar, manual, PTO shaft, steel wheels, no lugs
F30	1937		G	$4,000	6/30/2012	NEIA	Farmall, 40" wheels, OH and painted
F30	1938		F	$3,700	8/25/2011	ECND	Farmall, NF, narrow tread, PTO, belt pulley, 12.4x40 rears on press steel, stuck
F30	1939		E	$14,000	6/30/2012	NEIA	Farmall, 40" wheels, complete OH and painted
F30			G	$1,100	2/22/2014	SCNE	Rubber, round spoke, no tag, restored
F30			G	$1,550	2/22/2014	SCNE	On rubber, round spoke, no tag, restored
F30			G	$2,900	10/3/2013	NCIN	Farmall
F30			G	$1,900	9/12/2013	SEIA	NF, PTO, new rear tires, spoke wheels
F30			G	$800	6/8/2013	NEND	Farmall, NF
F30			G	$1,250	4/24/2013	Online	*BigIron.com,* item in Nebraska, Farmall, 4 cyl.
F30			G	$2,025	3/7/2013	SEIA	Farmall, dual NF, PTO, belt pulley, all steel wheels
F30			G	$1,350	1/9/2013	Online	*IQBID.com,* NF, PTO, round spoke, 12.4x38 tires

International Harvester Company

Model	Year	Hours	Condition	Price	Date	Area	Comments
F30			G	$3,500	9/22/2012	NEOR	Farmall, new rubber, NF
F30			G	$2,000	6/20/2012	SESD	Farmall, mostly complete, factory duals, rear winch
F30			G	$8,000	3/24/2012	NEIN	Farmall, rare, restoration started, runs
F30			G	$925	12/28/2011	Online	*BigIron.com,* item in Kansas, Farmall, gas, steel rear tires, cracked manifold
F30			G	$3,200	7/22/2011	SEMN	Farmall, belt pulley, 2 speed, duck bill steering, skeleton wheels, lugs, round spoke front on rubber
F30			G	$1,550	8/24/2010	NEMO	Farmall, NF, rear spokes
F30			G	$800	6/5/2010	WCMO	Farmall, rear steel
H	1939		G	$1,500	3/15/2014	WCIL	Farmall, 540 PTO, 12.4x38 tires
H	1939		E	$3,800	9/14/2011	NWIL	Farmall, gas, restored, weights
H	1939		F	$1,100	8/25/2011	ECND	Farmall, SF, PTO, belt pulley, 51" full steel, stuck
H	1939		G	$1,800	8/25/2011	ECND	Farmall, factory WF, full steel, PTO, belt pulley, fenders, 51" steel, flat spoke, loose, runs
H	1939		G	$1,800	8/25/2011	ECND	Farmall, NF, belt pulley, full steel with lugs, 51" wheels, stuck
H	1939		G	$2,500	7/16/2011	NEKS	Farmall, gas, SN 8168, complete engine OH, NF, electric start and lights, multi fuel, fenders, original radiator shutters and controls work, new 13.6x38 Firestone tires
H	1939		G	$1,500	7/17/2010	SEIA	Farmall, low SN
H	1940		G	$2,100	8/24/2011	ECMN	NF, PTO, notched deck plate, fenders, new 12.4x38 rubber
H	1940		G	$950	12/30/2010	ECMN	Farmall, NF
H	1941		G	$2,500	9/9/2011	ECND	WF, PTO, Woods L306 belly mower, PTO
H	1941		G	$2,000	10/2/2010	SWWI	Farmall
H	1942		G	$1,075	8/24/2013	NWIL	Farmall, NF, fresh fluids, new electrical
H	1942		G	$1,750	8/6/2011	SWMN	Farmall
H	1944		G	$1,500	4/24/2013	Online	*BigIron.com,* item in Nebraska, Farmall mower, 5F/1R
H	1944		G	$2,600	8/24/2011	ECMN	Factory WF, PTO, fenders, new rubber
H	1944		G	$1,000	6/5/2010	NWIA	NF
H	1944		G	$2,225	6/5/2010	ECMN	Farmall, restored, new rubber
H	1944		G	$1,800	5/1/2010	ECMN	Farmall, Schwartz WF
H	1945		F	$850	7/25/2012	SEND	Farmall, NF
H	1945		F	$950	6/20/2012	SESD	Farmall, gas, homemade 2 pt., owned since 1960
H	1945		G	$2,300	2/18/2012	ECIL	Farmall, restored, 45 angle tires on rear, runs great
H	1945		F	$900	12/4/2010	SEWY	Double front, gas
H	1946		E	$3,000	3/15/2014	ECMD	Farmall, live hyd., NF, fresh paint, new tires, local tractor that has never been out of Dorchester County, MD, 12V conversion, SN 234211x1
H	1946		G	$770	10/17/2012	Online	*PurpleWave.com,* item in Kansas, Farmall, 4 cyl. gas, Farmhand loader 102"

International Harvester Company

Model	Year	Hours	Condition	Price	Date	Area	Comments
H	1946		G	$1,800	9/6/2012	Online	*IQBID.com,* item in Minnesota, WF, restored
H	1946		G	$1,000	5/19/2012	WCIL	Farmall, gas, good tires and paint
H	1946		G	$1,800	5/19/2012	NWMI	Farmall
H	1946		G	$925	6/22/2011	Online	*BigIron.com,* item in Colorado, Farmall, 5 speed, 3 pt., new battery, drawbar, runs
H	1946		G	$1,000	3/19/2011	SEWY	WF, gas
H	1947		G	$1,300	12/16/2013	ECIL	Farmall, NF, gas, 12V system, 15.5x38 rear tires, M&W fast gears, SN 244720
H	1947		G	$881	6/20/2012	Online	*BigIron.com,* item in Colorado, Farmall, 6' Maverick mower, manual, 4 cyl. gas, 540 PTO, tricycle front end, runs
H	1947		G	$1,351	5/9/2012	Online	*BigIron.com,* item in Nebraska, Farmall, gas, 540 PTO, new battery, belt pulley, new starter 2 years ago
H	1947		G	$1,100	9/9/2011	ECND	NF, belt pulley PTO
H	1947		G	$1,250	9/1/2011	WCMN	Farmall, PTO, 86" center to center front axle, 24" axle and 20" rear axle, rebuilt carburetor
H	1947		G	$4,000	8/24/2011	ECMN	American road grader conversion, model N.-6H, full fenders, new 13.6x38 rubber, 9' blade
H	1947		F	$900	2/21/2011	WCIL	Farmall, gas, new rear tires, International Harvester loader

I always have a ton of fun and I learn a bunch when I attend a Farm Journal Corn College event. During one of the breaks at a February 2014 Corn College event in Rochester, Minn., a gentleman came up to me, and we got to visiting. Toward the end of conversation he pulls out his cell phone and says, "Pete, I've got something I want to show you." There was a picture of a sweet 1954 Farmall Super H tractor that had been in his family since day one. As you can see below, a real honey.

But the story got better–much better. He had the actual cancelled check his grandfather wrote to purchase the tractor. How cool is it to see your grandfather's handwritten check? I asked if he could scan it and e-mail to me, and he did. I posted a fun note about this story to our Machinery Pete Facebook page including the tractor and the cancelled check from June 5, 1954, for $1,940.

PETE'S PICK

Just think how much money $1,940 felt like 60 years ago. As for these tractors today, as I sit and write this, so far in 2014 the average auction sale price on Super H models is $2,508.

International Harvester Company

Model	Year	Hours	Condition	Price	Date	Area	Comments
H	1947		G	$1,500	8/7/2010	SEWI	Farmall, nice, excellent rubber
H	1947		G	$1,950	2/20/2010	NCIL	Farmall, NF, fenders, restored, gas
H	1948		G	$2,000	3/12/2014	ECND	Farmall, loader
H	1948		F	$850	2/23/2013	ECMI	Farmall, gas, NF, PTO, 12V charging system
H	1948		G	$1,100	3/14/2012	ECND	Farmall, WF, 1 hyd., PTO, belt pulley, 15.5x38 tires
H	1948		G	$2,050	8/20/2011	SCMI	Farmall, NF, gas, OH
H	1948		G	$1,000	4/21/2011	WCMI	Farmall, gas, NF, 12V electric start, rear weights, good tires, recent OH
H	1948		G	$1,400	1/26/2011	NECO	SF, gas, hyd.
H	1948		G	$900	12/8/2010	NECO	SF, gas
H	1948		G	$1,050	8/28/2010	WCIL	Farmall, OD, new 13.6x38 rear tires
H	1948		G	$880	7/28/2010	Online	*PurpleWave.com,* item in Kansas, 33 hp 4 cyl. gas, 5F/1R, 540 PTO
H	1948		G	$1,225	6/11/2010	SEAB	Farmall, row crop, orig paint & rear tires, PTO, belt pulley, second owner
H	1949		G	$1,600	4/11/2014	ECND	Farmall, WF, PTO, Woods 306 belly mower
H	1949		G	$4,700	9/19/2013	SWIA	24 hp, 2WD
H	1949		G	$950	8/24/2013	WCMN	New paint
H	1949		G	$1,300	6/15/2013	WCMI	NF, 13.6x38 tires, loader, SN317420
H	1949		G	$900	7/25/2012	SEND	Farmall, NF, PTO, converted to 12V, new 12.4x38 tires
H	1949		F	$1,150	5/3/2012	WCSK	Farmall, PTO, belt pulley, not running
H	1949		G	$3,750	1/2/2010	NCIN	Farmall, PS, fenders
H	1950		G	$2,000	8/29/2013	NWIA	FFA restoration
H	1950		F	$1,500	5/5/2013	WCMN	Farmall, PTO, 1 hyd., good 12.4x38 rubber
H	1950		F	$800	7/11/2012	Online	*BigIron.com,* item in Nebraska, Farmall, row crop, 5F/1R, 152 cu. in., 4 cyl. gas, 540 PTO, step tool box
H	1950		F	$950	6/20/2012	SESD	Farmall, NF, good tin, runs nice, 12.9x38 tires, wheel weights
H	1950		G	$2,850	5/19/2012	SWMI	Farmall, WF, 13.6x38 new rear and front tires, fenders, restored in 2010
H	1950		G	$1,850	7/10/2010	SEIA	Farmall, 6V, new front tires, new starter
H	1951		G	$800	4/4/2013	Online	*IQBID.com,* NF, gas, PTO
H	1951		G	$1,200	11/16/2012	SWOH	Farmall, row crop, original
H	1951		G	$2,000	6/30/2012	NEIA	Farmall, OH, repainted
H	1951		F	$800	6/20/2012	SESD	Farmall
H	1951		F	$900	3/24/2012	SCMN	Farmall, gas, NF, 12.4x38 rear tires, 2nd owner, SN 368659XI
H	1951		F	$900	8/6/2011	NCIA	Farmall, straight arm loader
H	1951		F	$1,951	6/22/2011	NECO	Gas, WF, PTO converted to 12V
H	1951		G	$3,300	4/14/2011	SEND	Farmall, 2 hyd., Faul 3 pt. hitch
H	1952		G	$2,800	11/12/2011	WCIL	Farmall, one owner, runs
H	1952		G	$800	12/4/2010	SEWY	Double front, gas
H	1953		G	$1,250	3/2/2013	SEMN	All parts with it, good metal, needs restoration
H	1953		G	$1,600	12/15/2012	WCMI	Farmall, gas, NF, 12V, fenders, poor tires, SN 377909

International Harvester Company

Model	Year	Hours	Condition	Price	Date	Area	Comments
H	1953		F	$1,000	8/24/2011	Online	*BigIron.com,* item in South Dakota, 4 speed manual, 4 cyl. gas, 35 hp, 1 hyd., 540 PTO, muffler has been replaced, NF, seat pad has been replaced, no oil leaks, shedded
H	1953		E	$3,600	8/20/2011	NWOH	Farmall, fenders, M&W clutch
H	1954		G	$4,000	11/25/2011	ECIA	Farmall, NF, newer paint
H	2950		G	$1,000	8/10/2011	Online	*BigIron.com,* item in Nebraska, Farmall, unknown hours, 5 speed manual, gas, 24 hp, 540 PTO, NF, 3 pt., loader
H			G	$1,500	4/15/2014	SWSK	Farmall, 50x8 grain auger, built hyd. drive, new rear tires
H			F	$1,000	4/11/2014	ECND	Farmall, NF, PTO, Woods L306 belly mower, does not run
H			G	$1,900	3/15/2014	ECMD	Farmall
H			G	$1,000	2/22/2014	SCNE	Farmall
H			G	$1,100	2/22/2014	ECMI	Farmall, gas, NF, PTO, 12.4x38 tires
H			G	$1,400	2/22/2014	SCNE	Restored
H			G	$1,300	1/4/2014	WCNY	Farmall, 3 pt.
H			F	$900	12/30/2013	SEMN	
H			F	$800	12/26/2013	Online	*BigIron.com,* item in Nebraska, Farmall, 4 speed manual, 4 cyl. gas, 12.4x38 rear tires, 9.5x16 front tires, 540 PTO, side belt pulley drive, Kosch belly mount side, 7' sickle mower
H			G	$1,100	12/4/2013	WCSD	Farmall, WF
H			G	$900	9/12/2013	SEIA	NF, on steel, PTO
H			G	$1,200	9/12/2013	SEIA	Farmall, fenders, wheel weights, hand clutch
H			F	$900	9/7/2013	SEMN	Farmall, NF, Schwartz Loader, material bucket, manure bucket
H			F	$907	9/5/2013	ECWI	Farmall, WF, new rubber
H			G	$880	8/28/2013	Online	*PurpleWave.com,* item in Kansas, Farmall, 4 cyl. gas, manual, draw bar, 540 PTO, 13.6x38 tires
H			G	$850	8/24/2013	SEMN	12.4x38 tires
H			G	$1,200	8/24/2013	SEMI	Farmall, NF, fenders and lights
H			E	$3,700	8/24/2013	SEMI	Farmall, steel wheels
H			G	$800	8/15/2013	ECMN	NF, repainted
H			G	$908	8/6/2013	Online	*PurpleWave.com,* item in Kansas, Farmall, 4 cyl. gas, 4 speed, tricycle, 540 PTO, draw bar, after market 3 pt., 7' sickle bar mower
H			F	$800	7/25/2013	WCIL	Farmall, power steering, new 6V battery and cables, seems to run good
H			G	$1,200	6/8/2013	NEND	Farmall, factory WF, belly pump, recent OH, 12V system, PTO, running unit
H			G	$1,600	5/11/2013	NCOH	Farmall, repainted, runs
H			G	$1,175	5/4/2013	Online	*IQBID.com,* Farmall, 72" Woods mower, mid-mount, good rear tires
H			G	$1,000	4/10/2013	NETX	Farmall, SF, propane, new rear tires
H			G	$2,400	3/22/2013	NWMN	Farmall, late model, belt pulley, PTO, repainted, runs

International Harvester Company

Model	Year	Hours	Condition	Price	Date	Area	Comments
H			G	$1,200	2/6/2013	SESD	Farmall, new carburetor and rear tires
H			G	$1,000	11/7/2012	NEND	Farmall
H			G	$875	11/3/2012	SWMO	Farmall, good tires, makes a little noise in rear end
H			G	$950	11/3/2012	SWMI	Farmall, 4 cyl. gas, NF, drawbar, PTO, 11x38 rear tires
H			F	$800	9/29/2012	WCWI	Farmall, NF, gone through mechanically, runs great, needs paint and rear tires, metal is good
H			G	$1,400	9/15/2012	SCMN	Farmall, NF
H			G	$1,000	8/16/2012	Online	*IQBID.com*, item in Minnesota, Farmall, gas, NF, PTO, belt pulley, 11.2x38 tires
H			G	$2,200	8/14/2012	Online	*PurpleWave.com,* item in Kansas, Farmall, gas, manual, 540 PTO, drawbar, steel seat with cushion, 5.5x16 front tires, 11.2x38 rear tires, fully restored
H			G	$1,700	8/4/2012	ECMN	WF, fenders, 12V, gas, new battery box and battery
H			G	$1,300	7/25/2012	SEND	Farmall, WF, full lights
H			F	$950	6/21/2012	WCMI	Farmall, NF
H			F	$1,075	6/20/2012	SESD	Farmall, WF, 5th gear out
H			G	$1,100	6/9/2012	ECNE	WF, PTO, original, runs
H			F	$875	6/2/2012	SEMN	Good sheet metal
H			G	$1,540	5/9/2012	Online	*PurpleWave.com,* item in Kansas, Farmall, 4 cyl. gas, complete OH 3 years ago, manual, 5F/1R, spring seat, drawbar, 540 PTO, 1 rear hyd.
H			F	$1,050	4/28/2012	ECSD	Farmall, 13.6x38 tires
H			G	$1,400	3/24/2012	SWMI	Farmall, 4 cyl. gas, MF, drawbar, PTO, 11.2x38 rear tires
H			G	$1,700	3/24/2012	NEIN	Farmall, fenders, repainted, good tires, runs
H			G	$2,750	3/24/2012	NEIN	Repainted, new tires, runs
H			P	$800	2/25/2012	ECIA	Farmall, needs carburetor work
H			G	$2,100	2/4/2012	ECTX	Farmall, tricycle front end, 3 pt.
H			G	$875	1/28/2012	ECMO	Farmall
H			G	$825	1/18/2012	Online	*BigIron.com,* item in Nebraska, Farmall, 4 cyl. gas, 540 PTO, 6V system, spoke rear wheels
H			G	$950	12/22/2011	Online	*IQBID.com,* Farmall, 12V, 540 PTO, new rears, 5.5x16 rubber
H			G	$904	12/13/2011	Online	*BidNow.US,* Farmall, loader, front blade, PTO, umbrella, not run in years
H			G	$1,900	12/9/2011	NENE	New rubber, Woods L306 belly mower
H			G	$1,300	12/3/2011	NEMO	Farmall, short line WF, 13.6x38 tires, 540 PTO, older restoration
H			G	$1,050	12/1/2011	NEIN	NF, 12.4x38 rear tires
H			G	$1,601	11/23/2011	Online	*BigIron.com,* item in Nebraska, Farmall, 11.2x38 rear tires, 5.5x16SL front tires
H			G	$957	11/8/2011	Online	*BidNow.US,* Farmall, NF, converted to 12V, 12.4x38 tires, new clutch

TRACTORS

International Harvester Company

Model	Year	Hours	Condition	Price	Date	Area	Comments
H			G	$1,000	10/29/2011	ECMN	Farmall
H			G	$1,300	10/29/2011	ECMN	Farmall, WF
H			G	$2,000	9/17/2011	WCIL	Farmall, gas, loader, fenders
H			G	$853	9/14/2011	Online	*PurpleWave.com,* item in Kansas, 4 cyl., 5 speed, 3 pt., 6V system
H			F	$850	9/1/2011	Online	*IQBID.com,* NF, fenders, non-runner
H			G	$2,200	8/29/2011	WCWI	Farmall, scraper on front, NF, gas
H			F	$825	8/20/2011	NEKS	Farmall, NF, 1 new rear rubber 11.2x38
H			G	$2,250	7/30/2011	ECMO	
H			G	$1,175	6/18/2011	NEIA	Farmall
H			G	$1,201	6/14/2011	Online	*IQBID.com,* 72" Woods mower, PTO, NF, 12V conversion, 12.4x38 rear tires
H			G	$1,100	4/15/2011	SWMB	Farmall
H			G	$1,025	4/2/2011	ECMN	NF
H			G	$1,900	12/15/2010	SEMI	Farmall, 1941 model, new 13.6x38 tires
H			F	$1,200	12/11/2010	SCMN	Farmall, 6' Woods belly mower
H			E	$1,400	10/23/2010	NCMD	Farmall, restored
H			G	$1,500	10/23/2010	SCPA	Farmall
H			G	$1,300	10/2/2010	SWWI	Farmall, SF
H			G	$1,675	7/17/2010	SCON	Canadian sale, Farmall
H			F	$835	6/23/2010	Online	*BigIron.com,* item in Colorado, Farmall, PTO, motor free, damaged grill, electric start, new rear tires
H			G	$1,400	6/23/2010	SEND	Farmall, gas, WF, good rubber and tin
H			F	$800	6/5/2010	SEMN	WF
H			F	$950	5/26/2010	ECSD	Motor stuck
H			F	$1,000	5/26/2010	ECSD	
H			G	$1,200	5/8/2010	SEIA	Farmall
H			F	$900	5/5/2010	SEIA	Farmall
H			G	$1,300	5/1/2010	SENE	Farmall
H			G	$2,950	5/1/2010	SENE	Farmall
H			G	$1,050	4/10/2010	ECON	Farmall
H			G	$1,650	4/10/2010	NCTN	Farmall
H			G	$1,500	3/18/2010	WCMN	Farmall, WF, 1 hyd.
H			G	$1,700	2/13/2010	SWIA	Farmall
H			F	$800	1/30/2010	NETX	Super H for parts
HV			G	$6,750	3/23/2013	NEIN	High crop, repainted, fenders, new tires, runs
HV			G	$9,900	10/22/2011	NECO	Farmall
HV			G	$9,900	10/22/2011	NECO	Farmall
HV			P	$1,500	9/3/2010	NEIN	Farmall, high crop, dead row, may not run or drive, as is
HV			G	$6,000	6/19/2010	SWIL	Farmall, high crop, runs, original, lights, fenders, lights, nice drops and new seals
Hydro 70	1975	5,000	G	$6,900	7/16/2010	SCIA	Diesel, open station, WF, 3 pt.
Hydro 86	1978		G	$8,000	7/16/2011	NEKS	High crop, diesel, SN 8294, restored, new hydro, front end rebuilt, factory double seat, no 3 pt., 540 PTO, no hyd., new 16.9x38 Firestone tires

International Harvester Company

Model	Year	Hours	Condition	Price	Date	Area	Comments
Hydro 100	1974		G	$7,000	12/30/2010	ECMN	Open station, 2 hyd., dual PTO, 466 block, flat top fenders, repainted, 2,305 on OH
Hydro 100	1974	5,417	G	$10,000	11/20/2010	NWIA	New paint
Hydro 100	1975		G	$11,500	2/5/2014	SESD	Cab, rare
Hydro 100			G	$6,750	12/19/2013	SCNY	Cab
Hydro 100			G	$8,500	3/23/2013	NEIN	Repainted, dual hyd. and PTO, 3 pt., fenders, runs
Hydro 100			G	$4,700	3/21/2012	ECMN	Dual high lift loader
Hydro 100			G	$5,500	3/5/2010	NENE	Cab, 3 pt., PTO
Hydro 186	1977	7,445	G	$9,500	6/13/2012	Online	*BigIron.com,* item in Colorado, 2 hyd., 540/1,000 PTO, air, 3 pt., quick attach, 2450 loader, 8' Westendorf bucket
Hydro 186	1978	4,485	G	$16,500	1/25/2011	NCIL	Soft cab, 3 hyd., dual PTO, 7' bucket International Harvester 2350 loader,
M	1939		G	$1,825	5/26/2012	ECPA	Farmall, gas, 13.6x38 tires, drawbar, 540 PTO, fenders, NF
M	1939		G	$800	8/25/2011	ECND	Farmall, SF, PTO, belt pulley, 13.6x38 tires, loose
M	1939		F	$1,500	8/6/2011	NCIA	Farmall, fenders
M	1939		G	$800	8/28/2010	WCIL	Farmall, creeper gear, 14.9x38 rear tires
M	1940		G	$1,760	10/16/2013	Online	*PurpleWave.com,* item in Kansas, 4 cyl. gas, 4 speed, drawbar, 1 hyd.
M	1940		G	$1,050	8/25/2011	ECND	Factory WF, PTO, 15.5x38 rib tire, Farmhand loader, runs
M	1940		G	$2,000	5/25/2011	NECO	Gas, double front, set as pulling tractor
M	1940		G	$1,500	3/26/2011	NECO	DF, gas, for pulling, 18.4x38 rear tires
M	1941		G	$900	12/11/2013	Online	*BigIron.com,* item in Nebraska, Farmall, 5 speed, 4 cyl. gas, 13.6x38 rear tires, 6.5x16SL front tires, 2 pt.
M	1941		F	$770	10/10/2012	Online	*PurpleWave.com,* item in Kansas, engine turns over, will not run, 540 PTO, hyd.
M	1941		G	$2,000	3/28/2012	ECND	Farmall, newly painted
M	1941		G	$975	8/13/2011	WCIL	Farmall, 13.6x38 rear tires, 1 hyd., PTO
M	1941		G	$1,000	8/3/2011	ECND	Farmall, PTO, hyd., 6x16 fronts, 13.6x38 rears, new battery
M	1942		G	$1,100	11/10/2012	WCIL	Farmall, NF, gas
M	1942		G	$1,425	7/10/2010	SEIA	Farmall, new rubber
M	1943		F	$1,000	1/26/2011	NECO	Double front, gas, 3 pt., Du-Al loader
M	1944		G	$1,025	8/24/2013	WCMN	New paint restoration
M	1944		G	$1,200	7/30/2011	WCIL	Farmall, belt driven generator
M	1944		F	$1,400	9/22/2010	NECO	WF, gas, F11 loader
M	1944		G	$1,000	8/24/2010	NEMO	Farmall, 540 PTO and 2 hyd.
M	1945		G	$1,500	3/21/2014	ECIA	Farmall
M	1945		G	$1,600	8/11/2011	WCMN	NF, 1 hyd., PTO, 6' Art's Way belly mower
M	1945		G	$1,400	3/30/2010	ECND	Farmall, WF, 1 hyd., PTO, rear weights

International Harvester Company

Model	Year	Hours	Condition	Price	Date	Area	Comments
M	1946		G	$900	3/30/2013	NWIL	Farmall, runs, drives, makes noise in fourth gear
M	1946		G	$1,200	3/26/2011	NECO	Gas, SF
M	1947		G	$1,401	7/11/2012	Online	*BigIron.com,* item in Nebraska, 6' loader, 5 speed, 4 cyl. gas, 540 PTO, tricycle front end, original WF
M	1947		G	$1,500	6/20/2012	SESD	Farmall, gas, rebuilt to Super MTA, 15.5x38 Firestone tires, deep tread, owned since 1969
M	1947		G	$900	9/9/2011	ECND	NF, PTO, rear weights, original, runs
M	1947		G	$2,050	2/5/2011	SEMI	Farmall, new tires, new 3 pt. drawbar, new 12V electrical system w/ lights, SN 128448X1
M	1947		G	$1,800	12/4/2010	SEWY	WF, gas
M	1947		F	$950	7/10/2010	SEIA	Farmall, loader, snowblade, power steering
M	1948		P	$875	12/18/2013	Online	*BigIron.com,* item in Nebraska, 5F/1R, 4 cyl. gas, 33 drawbar, 36 PTO hp, 1 hyd., dual, 540 PTO, rear wheel weights
M	1948		G	$3,600	4/18/2013	SWSK	Farmall, fully restored, 36 PTO hp
M	1948		G	$3,250	2/9/2013	SENE	Farmall, NF, new tires
M	1948		G	$2,200	6/20/2012	Online	*BigIron.com,* item in South Dakota, Du-Al 250 loader, 5F/1R, 4 cyl. gas, WF, 12V system
M	1948		G	$1,400	2/1/2012	SEND	Farmhand F19 loader
M	1948		G	$1,250	5/1/2010	NCOH	Farmall, good original condition, 2 speed, new battery
M	1949		G	$1,400	9/12/2013	SEIA	540 PTO, restored in 2011
M	1949		G	$900	8/24/2013	WCMN	NF, McCormick mounted 2R corn picker
M	1949		G	$1,400	5/25/2013	NWMO	2R Massey Harris corn picker, runs
M	1949		F	$875	7/24/2012	NCIA	Farmall, 12V
M	1949		E	$2,300	6/13/2012	SWOH	Farmall, gas, good rubber
M	1949		F	$935	11/3/2011	Online	*PurpleWave.com,* item in Kansas
M	1949		F	$1,300	8/6/2011	NCIA	Farmall, fenders, live hyd., 2 speed
M	1949		G	$1,650	2/20/2010	NCIL	Farmall, gas, NF, good original
M	1949		F	$1,450	1/2/2010	NWOH	Farmall, not running, row crop
M	1950		G	$1,200	9/14/2013	SEMI	Farmall, NF, gas
M	1950		G	$925	4/24/2013	Online	BigIron.com, item in Nebraska, 5F/1R, 248 cu. in. 4 cyl. gas
M	1950		G	$1,000	2/23/2013	ECMI	Farmall, gas, NF, hyd., PTO, 12V
M	1950		F	$1,050	10/24/2012	NECO	SF, PTO, 1 hyd., axle mounted duals
M	1950		G	$3,000	9/14/2011	Online	*BigIron.com,* item in Nebraska, Farmall, Farmhand loader, 5 speed, 4 cyl. gas, 33 drawbar, 12V, engine heater, 8' bucket
M	1950		G	$3,400	8/24/2011	ECMN	Factory WF, PTO, fenders
M	1950		G	$1,400	3/26/2011	SEWI	Farmall, hillside hitch, 1 set rear weights, strong engine, built for pulling
M	1950		G	$1,000	8/26/2010	ECIL	Farmall
M	1951		F	$800	2/22/2014	SCNE	Schwartz WF, F10 loader, grapple
M	1951		F	$900	12/19/2013	WCMN	Farmall, live power
M	1951		G	$1,450	3/7/2013	ECIA	WF, loader, 3 pt. hitch, 12V

International Harvester Company

Model	Year	Hours	Condition	Price	Date	Area	Comments
M	1951		G	$1,200	10/25/2012	SEMN	Farmall, SN 278246, like new 13.6-38 tires, clam shell fenders
M	1951		G	$1,100	9/19/2012	Online	*BigIron.com,* item in Nebraska, 2WD, 4 cyl. gas, 1 hyd., 540 PTO, WF
M	1951		G	$1,400	8/13/2012	ECIL	Farmall, row crop, 60 hours on complete engine OH, new clutch
M	1951		G	$1,700	3/22/2012	ECMN	Farmall, WF, 12V system, fenders new, 13.6x38 rears
M	1951		G	$1,000	8/24/2011	Online	*BigIron.com,* item in South Dakota, 4 speed manual, 4 cyl. gas, 50 hp, tin work is straight, no dents, Du-Al loader, 10' hay basket, 5' bucket, grapple
M	1951		G	$2,900	7/16/2011	NEKS	Farmall, gas, SN 280594, restored, NF, Behlen PS, wheel weights, 1 hyd., new Titan 13.6x38 tires
M	1951		G	$800	7/13/2011	Online	*BigIron.com,* item in Kansas, Farmall, 5 speed, 1 hyd., 540 PTO, not stuck
M	1951		G	$875	6/22/2011	Online	*BigIron.com,* item in Nebraska, 5F/1R, 4 cyl. gas, 540 PTO, hyd. power steering, 12V system, 2 sets of wheel weights per wheel, drawbar
M	1951		F	$2,100	4/27/2011	NECO	Gas, WF, John Deere 158 loader, 8' bucket
M	1951		G	$3,000	9/25/2010	ECIA	Farmall
M	1951		G	$1,600	7/17/2010	SEIA	Farmall, 2nd owner, clean
M	1951		F	$1,500	1/2/2010	NWOH	Farmall, not running, row crop, Cozy cab, 3 pt., 1 hyd., original, New Idea loader
M	1952		G	$1,400	2/22/2014	WCNE	WF, 3 pt., gas
M	1952		G	$2,500	7/9/2013	Online	*IQBID.com,* Farmall, factory WF, new tires and paint with stickers in 2007
M	1952		G	$1,950	5/26/2012	ECPA	Farmall, gas, 14.9x38 tires, drawbar, PTO, 1 set rear weights, side pulley
M	1952		F	$850	3/30/2010	ECND	Farmall, WF, PTO
M	1953		G	$3,100	4/8/2013	SESK	2WD, built-in hyd., 6V, belt pulley, 12.4/11x38 rear tires
M	1953		G	$1,500	6/23/2010	Online	*BigIron.com,* item in Nebraska, Farmall, 4F/1R, 4 cyl. gas, 13.6x38 rear tires, 6.5x16 front tires, 540 PTO, WF, not stuck, live hyd., 12V system
M	1953		F	$900	3/23/2010	SEND	Farmall, WF, power steering, Schwartz front end, live hyd., PTO
M			G	$1,000	4/3/2014	NEIN	Farmall
M			G	$1,750	4/3/2014	NEIN	Farmall
M			G	$2,100	4/1/2014	WCMN	Farmall, NF, rear weights, PTO, single hyd., cast iron rims
M			G	$1,400	3/22/2014	SWMI	53 hp, new tires, hyd., less than 25 hours on new engine, completely restored
M			G	$2,500	3/15/2014	ECMD	Farmall
M			G	$980	3/5/2014	Online	*BigIron.com,* item in Nebraska, 5 speed, 12.4x38 rear tires, 6x16 front tires, gas, 1 hyd., 12V, Schwartz WF

International Harvester Company

Model	Year	Hours	Condition	Price	Date	Area	Comments
M			G	$1,200	2/22/2014	SCNE	Farmall, SF
M			G	$975	2/12/2014	ECWI	2WD, gas, NFE, OS, 2 wheel mounted rake, rusty paint
M			G	$1,200	12/30/2013	SEMN	Farmall, picker
M			G	$1,350	12/30/2013	SEMN	Farmall
M			G	$900	12/5/2013	SCIA	Farmall, new rubber
M			G	$1,450	12/5/2013	SCIA	Farmall
M			G	$1,550	12/4/2013	ECIN	Farmall
M			G	$1,100	11/30/2013	SWIA	Farmall
M			G	$1,900	11/20/2013	NWNE	Farmall, 8' FAA loader, NF, duals
M			G	$1,100	10/28/2013	NWWI	Farmall, Firestone tires, head recently replaced, converted to 12V
M			G	$1,650	10/16/2013	Online	*PurpleWave.com,* item in Kansas, Farmall, 4 cyl. gas, 5 speed, Farmhand loader, 540 PTO, 12' hay basket, NF
M			G	$1,760	10/16/2013	Online	*PurpleWave.com,* item in Kansas, 4 cyl. gas, 5 speed, Farmhand loader, 540 PTO
M			G	$900	9/12/2013	SEIA	Farmall, NF
M			G	$1,600	9/12/2013	SEIA	NF, PTO
M			G	$3,465	8/26/2013	NWWI	Farmall, rear hyd. hook ups
M			G	$850	8/24/2013	NWIL	Farmall, gas
M			E	$3,000	8/24/2013	SEMI	Farmall, factory WF
M			G	$850	8/15/2013	ECMN	Farmall, NF
M			G	$1,000	8/14/2013	WCMN	Farmall, 12V, lights, good rubber, NF
M			G	$1,500	8/8/2013	WCMN	Farmall, NF, fenders, single hyd., PTO, 6V, weights
M			G	$2,300	6/22/2013	SEWA	Farmall, NF, 4 cyl., gas, direct start, rear PTO, bucket add on, SN FBK151180
M			G	$1,100	6/1/2013	SEMN	Farmall, gas, new battery
M			G	$1,100	5/11/2013	NCOH	Farmall, repainted, runs
M			G	$850	4/26/2013	SWKY	Farmall
M			G	$1,100	4/24/2013	Online	*BigIron.com,* item in Nebraska, Farmhand F10, hydro, grapple, 8' wide
M			G	$1,700	4/13/2013	SCMI	Farmall, restored, NF, rear weights, belt pulley, 1 hyd., 12V electric start, SN 34733
M			F	$800	4/10/2013	NETX	Farmall, gas, loader
M			G	$1,400	4/6/2013	NCOH	Farmall, restored
M			G	$2,300	3/23/2013	NEIN	Farmall, PTO, fenders, new 13.6x38 rear tires, runs
M			G	$1,300	3/14/2013	NENE	Farmall, Schwartz WF, LP, 15.5x38 rear tires
M			G	$2,400	3/14/2013	ECWI	Farmall, super tin, paint, runner, 12V, everything works, parade ready
M			G	$1,200	3/7/2013	ECIA	Parade ready
M			G	$1,200	3/7/2013	SEIA	540 PTO, repainted less than a year ago, NF, new battery
M			G	$1,025	2/23/2013	SENE	Farmall, NF, 13.6x28 tires
M			G	$2,300	2/22/2013	NWIN	Farmall, diesel, original, factory fenders, runs

International Harvester Company

Model	Year	Hours	Condition	Price	Date	Area	Comments
M			G	$1,950	2/16/2013	NEIA	Farmall
M			G	$1,300	2/6/2013	SESD	Farmall
M			G	$1,600	2/6/2013	SESD	Gas, WF, PS, good runner
M			G	$2,850	12/10/2012	ECIL	Farmall, NF, 9 speed, rear weights, 1 owner
M			P	$1,150	12/6/2012	SEIA	Farmall, does not run
M			P	$6,400	12/6/2012	SEIA	Farmall, does not run
M			P	$7,000	12/6/2012	SEIA	Farmall, does not run
M			G	$1,000	11/17/2012	SWMN	Farmall, NF
M			G	$800	11/3/2012	SWMO	Farmall, starts, runs, good tires, good paint
M			G	$900	11/3/2012	SWMI	Farmall, Star Hoist loader, 4 cyl. gas, WF, drawbar, PTO, 13.6x38 rear tires
M			G	$1,000	11/3/2012	SWMO	Farmall, very nice, good tires, runs well
M			G	$1,050	11/3/2012	SWMO	Farmall, starts, runs, new tires on rear
M			G	$1,000	9/15/2012	SCMN	NF, repainted
M			G	$1,300	9/15/2012	SCMN	WF, live hyd., power steering
M			G	$1,100	8/30/2012	SEMN	Farmall
M			G	$950	8/21/2012	WCIL	Farmall
M			G	$1,000	8/21/2012	WCIL	Farmall
M			G	$2,200	8/21/2012	WCIL	Farmall
M			G	$1,950	8/14/2012	Online	*IQBID.com*, item in Minnesota, NF, gas, 540 PTO
M			G	$1,200	8/8/2012	Online	*IQBID.com,* item in North Dakota, loader, with new radiator in the box
M			F	$800	7/28/2012	SCNE	Farmall, WF, American loader
M			G	$1,100	7/28/2012	NWSC	Farmall
M			F	$850	6/14/2012	SEND	Farmall, NF, PTO, rusted
M			G	$1,750	6/9/2012	ECNE	Factory WF, new rear tires, PTO, runs
M			G	$1,250	6/2/2012	SEMN	Farmall, WF, fenders
M			G	$1,600	6/2/2012	SEMN	Farmall, NF, 13.9x38 tires, 12V, new radiator, good sheet metal, runs
M			G	$2,860	5/30/2012	Online	*PurpleWave.com,* item in Missouri, Farmall, IHC 4 cyl. gas, manual, 540 PTO, rear wheel weights, recently replaced paint, decals, rear tires, & seat
M			F	$950	5/19/2012	NWMI	Farmall
M			G	$1,900	3/24/2012	NEIN	Farmall, power steering, original, fenders, like new tires, runs
M			G	$1,100	2/18/2012	ECIL	Farmall
M			G	$1,850	2/4/2012	ECTX	Farmall, tricycle
M			G	$1,350	2/2/2012	NEIN	NF, 12x36 rear tires, 6 rear wheel weights
M			G	$1,650	1/31/2012	NEIN	Farmall, loader, 3 pt., power steering
M			G	$1,650	12/7/2011	Online	*PurpleWave.com,* item in Kansas, Farmall, 4 cyl. gas, 5 speed, spring ride seat, Du-Al loader 6' bucket, drawbar, 540 PTO
M			G	$950	12/1/2011	SEMN	Farmall, NF
M			G	$2,400	12/1/2011	NEIN	
M			G	$2,750	11/12/2011	WCMI	Farmall, NF, PTO, 14.9x38 rear tires, hyd.
M			P	$850	10/29/2011	ECMN	Farmall

International Harvester Company

Model	Year	Hours	Condition	Price	Date	Area	Comments
M			F	$900	10/29/2011	SEMN	Farmall, good sheet metal, does not run
M			G	$1,200	10/29/2011	ECMN	Farmall loader
M			G	$2,500	10/27/2011	NWND	Farmall, WF, PTO, power steering, 12V system, Koyker loader, bucket, grapple, PTO pump
M			F	$800	9/16/2011	ECND	Farmall, WF, PTO
M			G	$1,500	9/14/2011	Online	*BigIron.com,* item in Colorado, 4 cyl. gas, ran when parked, 540 PTO, rear hitch
M			G	$1,250	8/27/2011	WCIA	Farmall
M			G	$1,500	8/27/2011	WCIA	Farmall, power steering
M			G	$1,275	8/6/2011	NEIA	Farmall, good metal and paint, runs, no fenders
M			G	$1,300	7/13/2011	Online	*BigIron.com*, item in Nebraska, Farmall, 5F/1R, 4 cyl., I head gas, 33 drawbar, 42 PTO, 47 belt hp, 540 PTO, live hyd., M&W throttle control
M			G	$1,400	6/17/2011	SWMN	Farmall, New Idea hyd. loader, low hours on engine
M			G	$855	5/25/2011	Online	*BigIron.com,* item in Kansas, 540 PTO, 1 hyd. system, homemade battery box, Farmhand F10 loader and forage fork attach, homemade wire winder on belt pulley
M			G	$1,200	5/7/2011	SESK	Farmall, 2WD, gas, PTO, 3 pt., custom built 3 pt. post hole auger, 12V system
M			G	$875	4/13/2011	Online	*BigIron.com,* item in Nebraska, gas 4 cyl., 12V system, new battery, Schwartz WF, missing hook and front grill tin work, needs new manifold, drawbar, 540 PTO
M			G	$2,200	4/11/2011	Online	*AuctionTime.com*
M			G	$4,200	3/19/2011	SEIA	Farmall
M			G	$1,200	3/18/2011	SWIL	Farmall, 540 PTO, drawbar, rebuilt carburetor, new points, cap and rotor
M			P	$850	3/15/2011	ECNE	2R Massey Harris corn picker
M			G	$1,550	12/1/2010	WCIL	Farmall, NF, 13.6x38 rear tires and 6x16 front tires, Short Line 3 pt., nice straight and purchased new
M			G	$1,400	11/22/2010	NCOH	Farmall, gas, row crop
M			G	$1,300	11/20/2010	SCKY	Farmall
M			G	$1,400	9/11/2010	ECIA	Farmall
M			G	$1,100	8/24/2010	NEMO	Farmall, NF, 1 hyd., 540 PTO
M			G	$2,300	7/17/2010	SCON	Canadian sale, Farmall
M			G	$975	7/10/2010	SEIA	Farmall, live hyd., original
M			G	$1,100	6/23/2010	Online	*BigIron.com,* item in Nebraska, Farmall, 5 speed, 4 cyl. gas, 540 PTO, M&W live clutch attachment, tires are cracked
M			G	$1,625	6/23/2010	Online	*BigIron.com,* item in Nebraska, Farmall, 4 cyl. gas, 540 PTO, 1 dual hyd., 12V system, Behlen power steering
M			G	$1,010	6/14/2010	Online	*BigIron.com,* item in Iowa, Farmall, 5F/1R, 4 cyl. gas, 12V

International Harvester Company

Model	Year	Hours	Condition	Price	Date	Area	Comments
M			G	$1,351	6/14/2010	Online	*BigIron.com,* item in Nebraska, Farmall, 5 speed, 4 cyl. gas, 1 hyd., 540 PTO, hyd. lift loader, 6'8"W
M			G	$1,000	6/11/2010	SEAB	Farmall, row crop, orig paint & rear tires, PTO, belt pulley, second owner
M			G	$900	6/5/2010	WCMO	Farmall
M			G	$1,600	6/5/2010	ECMN	Farmall, loader, power steering
M			G	$900	5/26/2010	ECSD	Farmall, gas
M			G	$1,600	5/26/2010	ECSD	
M			G	$1,900	5/22/2010	SEMN	Farmall, new paint, new rubber
M			G	$1,400	5/5/2010	SEIA	Farmall
M			G	$2,000	5/1/2010	SENE	Farmall
M			G	$1,900	3/16/2010	SEND	Farmall, WF, Du-Al loader, grapple, power steering
M			G	$1,200	3/10/2010	ECND	Farmall, NF, PTO, belt pulley, new radiator
M			G	$950	2/13/2010	SWIA	Farmall
M			G	$1,800	2/13/2010	SWIA	Farmall
MD	1947		G	$1,900	1/26/2011	NECO	WF, diesel, 3 pt.
MD	1950		G	$1,900	8/22/2012	Online	*BigIron.com,* item in Colorado, Farmall, sliding gear 5F/1R, International Harvester vertical I-head diesel, 35 hp, 1 hyd., single axle, 540 PTO, new battery
MD	1951		G	$5,700	6/30/2012	NEIA	Farmall, complete OH, NF
MD	1951		G	$3,600	4/15/2011	NEND	Farmall, WF, PTO, hyd., single owner
MD			E	$2,550	9/21/2013	SEMN	Farmall, like new tires
MD			G	$1,075	7/28/2012	SCNE	Farmall, SF
MD			G	$1,100	6/9/2012	ECNE	PTO, hyd., not running
MD			G	$2,500	5/19/2012	NWMI	Farmall
MD			G	$2,300	10/22/2011	NECO	Farmall, WF, fenders
MD			G	$2,300	10/22/2011	NECO	Farmall, WF, fenders
MD			G	$950	3/15/2011	ECNE	NF
MD			G	$4,300	11/13/2010	NCIA	Farmall, diesel, fenders
MD			G	$1,800	6/23/2010	Online	*BigIron.com,* item in Nebraska, Farmall, PTO, starts on gas and runs on diesel, ran when parked
MTA			G	$2,100	7/31/2013	ECND	Gas, TA, PTO, hyd. loader, 18.4x38 rears
MTA			G	$7,250	6/9/2012	ECNE	Gas, new tires, fast hitch, power steering, runs, repainted
MV			G	$3,300	9/4/2010	NEIN	Farmall
O4			G	$1,000	5/19/2012	NWMI	McCormick, full skirt
O4			G	$7,100	10/22/2011	NECO	Full dress
OS4			G	$1,300	10/22/2011	NECO	
OS4			G	$1,300	10/22/2011	NECO	
OS6	1950		G	$12,000	8/7/2010	SEWI	Farmall, orchard, original fenders
Regular	1927		G	$3,100	6/30/2012	NEIA	Farmall, on steel
Regular	1928		G	$1,200	8/25/2011	ECND	Farmall, open steering, belt pulley, on full steel, flat spoke, loose
Regular	1930		G	$1,750	6/30/2012	NEIA	Farmall, cultivator
Regular			F	$800	2/22/2014	SCNE	New rubber, restored, no tag

International Harvester Company

Model	Year	Condition	Price	Date	Area	Comments
Regular		G	$1,300	2/22/2014	SCNE	Farmall, steel wheels with extensions, repaint, no tag
Super A	1948	G	$2,400	9/1/2011	WCMN	Farmall, PTO, new 11.2x24 rubber, older restoration
Super A	1950	G	$1,400	11/10/2012	NCNC	Farmall, runs
Super A	1952	G	$1,900	4/7/2012	NWMI	Farmall, gas, WF, new 11.2x24 tires
Super A	1953	G	$1,500	6/15/2013	WCMI	Farmall, WF, power lift, rear belt pulley, wheel weights, 12.4x24 tires, SN351535
Super A		G	$2,500	6/6/2013	ECAB	Farmall, PTO, 3 pt.
Super A		G	$2,100	9/15/2012	SCMN	Farmall industrial, square axle WF
Super A		F	$875	6/20/2012	SESD	Farmall
Super A		G	$2,750	3/24/2012	NEIN	Farmall, repainted, runs well
Super A		G	$2,000	2/4/2012	ECSC	Farmall, cultivator
Super A		F	$2,100	2/4/2012	ECSC	
Super A		G	$3,400	2/4/2012	NENC	4 speed, 4 cyl., cultivators, fast hitch
Super A		F	$1,050	11/12/2011	WCMI	Farmall, WF, PTO, 9.5x24 rear tires, not restored
Super A		G	$3,100	11/12/2011	WCMI	Farmall, PTO, WF, 11.2x24 rear tires
Super A		F	$1,600	10/29/2011	SEMN	Farmall, Woods belly mower, does not run
Super A		G	$4,600	10/29/2011	NEAR	Farmall
Super A		G	$3,350	6/18/2011	NEIA	Farmall
Super A		G	$2,000	5/13/2011	ECMS	Farmall, plows
Super A		G	$2,900	6/16/2010	SEND	Farmall, WF, belly mower
Super A		G	$2,300	6/11/2010	SEAB	Farmall, gas, PTO, hyd., belt pulley, restored
Super A		G	$2,000	5/26/2010	ECSD	
Super A		G	$1,800	4/3/2010	NENC	Farmall
Super AV	1951	G	$4,000	3/15/2014	ECMD	Farmall, cultivators, fresh paint, works, runs well, 50% tires, SN 322621
Super AV	1951	G	$5,000	7/16/2011	NEKS	Farmall, high crop, gas, SN 300293, restoration started, engine OH, 540 PTO, 1 hyd., new Titan 9.5x36 tires
Super AV	1952	G	$3,200	9/1/2011	WCMN	Farmall, older paint job
Super C	1948	F	$1,200	12/15/2010	SEMI	Farmall, hyd. 2 pt., rear sickle mower
Super C	1951	G	$1,950	6/8/2013	NEIA	Farmall, restored, new rubber
Super C	1951	G	$908	11/28/2012	Online	*PurpleWave.com,* item in Missouri, Farmall, 4 cyl. gas, manual, spring suspension seat, 3 pt., drawbar, 540 PTO
Super C	1951	F	$1,500	11/29/2011	WCMN	Farmall, NF, gas, 11.2x36 tires, PTO, live hyd., SN 107807
Super C	1952	G	$2,250	9/18/2013	ECMT	Farmall, fully restored, NF, 11.2x36 tires, SN 147413, good runner
Super C	1952	F	$1,650	11/29/2011	WCMN	Farmall, NF, gas, 11.2x36 tires, PTO, live hyd., SN 132990
Super C	1952	F	$1,200	11/12/2011	SEIA	Farmall, NF
Super C	1952	G	$2,051	9/14/2011	Online	*BigIron.com,* item in Nebraska, 4F/1R, 4 cyl. gas, 540 PTO, drawbar, front and rear lights, rear tires are weather checked
Super C	1952	G	$1,050	6/22/2011	NECO	Gas, SF, 3 pt., bolt-on cultivator
Super C	1953	E	$11,000	3/15/2014	ECMD	Farmall, rebuilt engine with overbore kit, new clutch, new bearings in transmission and rear end, NF, fast hitch w/ correct leveling and adjustment arms, 12V conversion w/ MSD ignition

International Harvester Company

Model	Year	Condition	Price	Date	Area	Comments
Super C	1953	F	$3,100	2/8/2014	NECO	Farmall, 4 cyl. gas, SF, front cultivator attached
Super C	1953	G	$2,100	9/21/2013	WCMI	Farmall, gas, PTO, electric start, NF, drawbar, 11.2x36 rear tires, wheel weights, restored
Super C	1953	F	$1,200	8/6/2011	NCIA	Farmall, belly mower
Super C	1953	G	$3,200	7/16/2011	NEKS	Farmall, gas, SN 185464, restored, NF, wheel weights, 2 pt., fenders, new Goodyear 12.4x36 tires
Super C	1953	G	$3,500	7/16/2011	NEKS	Farmall, gas, SN 180861, restored, engine OH, NF, 12V, fenders, new Titan 11.2x36 tires
Super C	1953	G	$1,600	12/11/2010	NEMI	Farmall, WF, fast hitch, mounted cultivator
Super C	1953	F	$800	6/23/2010	Online	*BigIron.com,* item in Utah, runs, manual 4 speed, 4 cyl. gas, 35-40 hp, 1 hyd., single axle, rear PTO, hyd. 3 pt.
Super C	1954	G	$1,850	8/24/2013	WCMN	Sunmaster 6' belly mower, new paint
Super C	1965	G	$2,550	2/20/2010	NCIL	Farmall, NF, fenders, restored, gas
Super C		G	$1,600	9/12/2013	SEIA	Farmall, new front tires, PTO, belt pulley, NF
Super C		G	$850	8/29/2013	NWIA	Farmall, NF, water pump, 11.2x36 rear tires, new front tires, new battery
Super C		G	$3,500	8/24/2013	SEMI	Farmall, NF, fast hitch, F/A grader blade
Super C		G	$1,100	4/10/2013	NETX	Farmall, tricycle, gas
Super C		F	$1,200	3/29/2013	SCMT	Farmall, single axle, 11.2x36 tires, PTO, front mount 2-wheel rake
Super C		F	$2,000	3/29/2013	SCMT	Farmall, WF, 11.2-36 tires, PTO, fast hitch
Super C		G	$4,200	3/23/2013	NEPA	Farmall, cultivator
Super C		G	$1,350	12/6/2012	SEIA	WF, 540 PTO
Super C		G	$1,000	11/24/2012	SEMN	Farmall, 2 bottom plow
Super C		G	$1,900	9/15/2012	SCMN	Farmall, mounted 5' sickle mower, NF, fenders
Super C		G	$2,700	9/15/2012	SCMN	Farmall, fast hitch
Super C		F	$1,200	6/20/2012	SESD	Farmall, NF
Super C		G	$4,000	6/16/2012	WCSD	Farmall
Super C		P	$800	6/9/2012	ECNE	Factory WF, rear pulley, PTO, hyd. raise, not running
Super C		G	$1,000	6/9/2012	ECNE	SF, PTO, original, runs
Super C		G	$2,300	6/9/2012	ECNE	WF, PTO, repainted, runs but clutch has problems
Super C		G	$1,150	3/24/2012	SWMI	Farmall, 4 cyl. gas, WF, drawbar, PTO, 12.4x36 rear tires
Super C		G	$1,700	3/24/2012	NEIN	Repainted, fenders, PTO, runs
Super C		G	$2,850	11/12/2011	WCMI	Farmall, PTO, fast hitch, 10x36 rear tires, NF
Super C		G	$2,650	6/18/2011	NEIA	Farmall
Super C		G	$2,900	4/1/2011	ECND	Farmall
Super C		G	$1,400	3/17/2011	ECMN	Farmall, NF, good tires
Super C		G	$1,900	3/16/2011	ECSD	Farmall, tricycle NF, PTO, recent recondition
Super C		P	$1,500	3/5/2011	SEMN	540 PTO, WF, fast hitch, front and rear weights, not running
Super C		G	$3,900	9/11/2010	SEIA	Farmall
Super C		F	$1,400	8/14/2010	SEMN	Farmall
Super C		G	$3,000	8/7/2010	SEWI	Farmall
Super C		F	$1,400	5/26/2010	ECSD	WF, runs
Super C		F	$1,950	5/26/2010	ECSD	
Super C		G	$2,600	5/1/2010	SENE	Farmall

International Harvester Company

Model	Year	Condition	Price	Date	Area	Comments
Super H	1953	F	$800	4/4/2014	SESD	
Super H	1953	G	$2,800	2/8/2014	NWIL	Farmall, good tires
Super H	1953	G	$3,500	9/18/2013	ECMT	Farmall, WF, PTO, excellent rubber
Super H	1953	G	$1,150	12/6/2012	Online	*IQBID.com,* Farmall
Super H	1953	G	$1,150	12/6/2012	SEIA	Farmall
Super H	1953	E	$3,250	8/20/2011	NWOH	Farmall, fenders, belt pulley
Super H	1953	G	$3,250	8/20/2011	NWOH	Farmall, fenders, M&W clutch
Super H	1953	G	$1,600	7/30/2011	ECMO	
Super H	1953	G	$3,400	7/16/2011	NEKS	Farmall, gas, SN 11997, restored, NF, belt pulley, fenders, Firestone 11.2x38 tires
Super H	1953	G	$6,000	3/26/2011	SEWI	Farmall
Super H	1953	G	$1,750	3/15/2011	WCIL	Farmall, 540 PTO, NF
Super H	1953	F	$1,600	5/26/2010	ECSD	
Super H	1954	E	$7,000	3/15/2014	ECMD	Farmall, stage 2 hyd., NF, fresh paint, 70% tires, 12V conversion, runs great, SN 125283
Super H	1954	G	$3,500	9/21/2013	WCMI	Farmall, gas, PTO, electric start, belt pulley, NF, 12.4x38 rear tires with weights, restored
Super H	1954	G	$4,000	6/30/2012	NEIA	Farmall, factory live hyd.
Super H	1954	G	$3,150	6/9/2012	ECNE	WF, PTO, runs, repainted
Super H	1954	G	$4,750	5/26/2012	ECPA	Farmall, gas, 12.4x38 tires, drawbar, ,fenders 540 PTO, rear tool box, 1 set rear weights
Super H	1954	G	$5,900	5/26/2012	ECPA	Farmall, gas, TA, 13.6x38 tires, drawbar, 540 PTO, fenders, live hyd.
Super H	1954	G	$5,100	8/24/2011	ECMN	Factory WF, PTO, fenders
Super H	1954	G	$5,450	3/20/2010	NEIA	Farmall
Super H		F	$1,050	8/30/2013	NCIA	Farmall, NF
Super H		G	$1,400	9/15/2012	SCMN	NF
Super H		G	$1,600	9/15/2012	SCMN	Farmall, Schwartz WF
Super H		G	$2,100	9/15/2012	SCMN	NF, repainted
Super H		G	$2,400	9/15/2012	SCMN	Farmall, repainted
Super H		G	$2,800	9/15/2012	SCMN	NF, repainted
Super H		G	$3,000	9/15/2012	SCMN	Farmall, NF, new rubber, repainted
Super H		G	$2,700	8/4/2012	ECMN	NF, good tin
Super H		G	$3,200	6/16/2012	WCSD	Farmall, 9' belly mower
Super H		P	$950	6/9/2012	ECNE	Hyd., PTO, runs, carburetor plugged
Super H		G	$2,800	6/9/2012	ECNE	Factory WF, PTO, hyd., runs
Super H		G	$6,000	6/9/2012	ECNE	WF, new tires, PTO, runs, repainted
Super H		G	$4,600	3/24/2012	NEIN	Farmall, PTO, runs
Super H		G	$1,700	3/20/2012	WCIL	Farmall
Super H		G	$1,100	12/28/2011	Online	*PurpleWave.com,* item in Kansas
Super H		F	$850	12/1/2011	NEIN	Farmall
Super H		G	$3,050	11/12/2011	WCMI	Farmall, PTO, 14.9x38 rear tires, NF, hyd.
Super H		G	$4,050	11/12/2011	WCMI	Farmall, PTO, 14.9x38 rear tires, NF, hyd.
Super H		G	$2,250	8/29/2011	WCWI	Farmall, loader, NF, gas
Super H		G	$3,200	11/20/2010	NEIA	Farmall, new tires, original
Super H		G	$4,100	11/20/2010	NEIA	Farmall, live hyd., good tires, original
Super HV	1953	G	$26,000	8/7/2010	SEWI	Farmall, high crop, 1 of 70 made
Super M	1952	G	$1,601	4/24/2013	Online	*BigIron.com,* item in Kansas, loader, 5 speed, 4 cyl.

International Harvester Company

Model	Year	Condition	Price	Date	Area	Comments
Super M	1952	G	$2,321	2/15/2012	Online	4 cyl. gas, 1 hyd., 540 PTO, WF, power steering, 3 pt., drawbar, chains, cement weights
Super M	1952	G	$3,750	8/24/2011	ECMN	Comfort cab, Schwartz 1600 quick attach loader, 8' bucket, new lift cyl., wheel weights, older restoration with International Harvester 560 WF
Super M	1952	G	$2,600	8/6/2011	SWMN	Farmall
Super M	1952	G	$3,250	4/9/2011	WCNE	WF, gas, F11 loader
Super M	1953	G	$3,000	3/15/2014	ECMD	Farmall, NF, 80% rubber, fresh paint, 12V conversion, standard hyd., standard swing drawbar, runs great, gas, SN 508050 (Louisville)
Super M	1953	G	$2,300	12/13/2013	NCMO	Farmall, NF, older restoration
Super M	1953	G	$1,300	12/4/2013	ECIN	Farmall
Super M	1953	G	$4,400	9/21/2013	WCMI	Farmall, gas, PTO, electric start, 1 hyd., NF, 14.9x38 rear tires with weights, restored
Super M	1953	G	$2,650	3/2/2013	WCIN	Farmall, NF, live hyd. pump, power steering, fenders, lights, belt pulley, aux. hyd. valve battery box between your feet, has been converted to 12V, engine has been OH
Super M	1953	G	$1,825	6/13/2012	Online	*BigIron.com,* item in Nebraska, gas, 540 PTO, Schwartz WF, battery 1 year old
Super M	1953	G	$1,750	12/7/2011	NCIA	Farmall
Super M	1953	E	$3,650	8/20/2011	NWOH	Farmall, fenders, NF, battery under seat
Super M	1953	G	$950	8/10/2011	Online	*BigIron.com,* item in Iowa, Farmall, 540 PTO, Charlynn steering
Super M	1953	G	$4,100	7/16/2011	NEKS	Farmall, gas, SN 43643, restored, Schwartz WF, Saginaw 3 pt., Behlen PS, 1 hyd., Titan 15.5x38 tires
Super M	1953	G	$2,500	6/22/2011	Online	*BigIron.com,* item in Nebraska, Farmall, NF, 5 speed, 4 cyl. diesel, 2 hyd.,540 PTO, 12V, 3 pt., 1 rear wheel weight, original tin, starts and runs
Super M	1953	G	$1,250	7/10/2010	SEIA	Farmall, 12V, live hyd. original
Super M	1953	G	$1,500	7/10/2010	SEIA	Farmall, older restoration
Super M	1953	G	$3,000	2/20/2010	NCIL	Farmall, NF, fenders, restored, good paint, gas
Super M	1953	G	$4,600	1/2/2010	NWOH	Farmall, row crop, new front tires, belt pulley, restored, very nice
Super M	1954	G	$4,000	3/15/2014	ECMD	Farmall, stage 2 live hyd., NF, 70% rubber, standard swing drawbar, runs great, gas, SN F-46020
Super M	1954	G	$7,700	5/26/2012	ECPA	Farmall, gas, TA, 15.5x38 tires, drawbar, 540 PTO, fenders
Super M	1954	G	$3,300	7/10/2010	SEIA	Farmall, 3 pt., 12V, hyd. fenders, older restoration
Super M		G	$2,700	2/8/2014	NECO	Gas, loader, manure bucket, 3 pt., WF, PTO, good rubber, hyd. pump is on PTO shaft, some welding on loader
Super M		G	$1,100	12/4/2013	ECND	WF
Super M		F	$1,800	11/30/2013	WCIL	Farmall, NF, 400 engine, electronic ignition
Super M		G	$1,300	9/18/2013	WCMI	Electric start, 12V, gas, NF, 15.5x38 rear tires, tires are loaded with chloride, draw bar, PTO, 1 hyd.

International Harvester Company

Model	Year	Condition	Price	Date	Area	Comments
Super M		G	$950	9/12/2013	SEIA	
Super M		F	$1,150	9/12/2013	NCIA	Farmall, 12V system, straight arm loader and 2 buckets
Super M		G	$2,035	8/28/2013	Online	*PurpleWave.com,* item in Missouri, Farmall, 4 cyl. gas, 5' bucket, 1 hyd., drawbar, 3 pt., rear wheel weights
Super M		G	$3,750	8/8/2013	WCMN	Farmall, NF, PTO, power steering
Super M		G	$2,600	3/16/2013	NEIL	Farmall
Super M		G	$3,150	3/16/2013	NEIL	Farmall, power steering, nice
Super M		G	$1,450	3/2/2013	ECMN	Farmall, NF, good tin, 13.6x38 tires, wheel weights
Super M		F	$2,800	2/16/2013	NEIA	Farmall, gone through
Super M		G	$3,100	2/6/2013	NCIL	Farmall, new rubber, set up for antique tractor pulling, 70 hp
Super M		G	$1,350	1/9/2013	Online	*BigIron.com,* item in Nebraska, Farmall, 13.6x38 rear tires, 6x16 front tires, 12V system, alternator, lights work, power steering, 2 rear wheel weights
Super M		G	$2,300	1/9/2013	Online	*BigIron.com,* item in Nebraska, Farmall, NF, gas, 13.6x38 rear tires, single hyd., 540 PTO, regular drawbar, Cornhusker, 3 pt., Murphy system, power steering, no weights
Super M		G	$2,450	12/10/2012	ECIL	Farmall, NF, 3 sets of rear wheel weights, one owner
Super M		F	$2,250	12/7/2012	NCIN	Farmall, NF, fenders, Behlen PS, New Idea loader
Super M		G	$1,625	12/5/2012	Online	*BigIron.com,* item in Nebraska, Farmall, 4 cyl. gas, rear tires 13.6x38, front tires 6x16, 1 hyd., 540 PTO, drawbar, rear tool box, SN F-8297J
Super M		G	$1,600	11/24/2012	SEMN	NF, fenders, 13.6x38
Super M		G	$1,550	9/15/2012	SCMN	NF, power steering, live hyd.
Super M		G	$1,600	9/15/2012	SCMN	Schwartz WF, repainted
Super M		G	$2,700	9/15/2012	SCMN	Farmall, factory WF
Super M		G	$1,500	8/30/2012	SEMN	
Super M		P	$1,025	6/20/2012	SESD	Farmall, Dakon loader, NF
Super M		G	$2,400	6/20/2012	SESD	Farmall, gas, repainted
Super M		F	$1,200	6/9/2012	ECNE	Aftermarket WF, PTO, hyd., not running
Super M		G	$1,500	6/9/2012	ECNE	Aftermarket WF, PTO, hyd., runs
Super M		G	$3,900	6/9/2012	ECNE	Gas, PTO, hyd., aftermarket WF, runs
Super M		G	$2,400	3/24/2012	NEIN	Farmall, hyd., fenders, repainted, late one, runs
Super M		G	$1,950	2/25/2012	WCMI	Farmall, NF, gas, PTO, 13x38 rear tires
Super M		G	$1,250	2/4/2012	ECTX	Farmall, tricycle
Super M		G	$2,800	11/26/2011	NCOH	Farmall, short line 3 pt., clean, original
Super M		G	$3,000	11/12/2011	WCMI	Farmall, NF, PTO, hyd., 14.9x38 rear tires
Super M		G	$6,750	11/12/2011	WCMI	Farmall, WF, PTO, 1 hyd., live power
Super M		G	$1,601	9/14/2011	Online	*BigIron.com,* item in Colorado, super M, 4 cyl. gas, 540 PTO, new left rear tire, 4' bucket, 3 pt.
Super M		G	$4,000	9/14/2011	Online	*BigIron.com,* item in Colorado, Farmall, 4 cyl. gas, runs, hyd. loader, PTO hyd. pump, TA
Super M		G	$1,150	7/30/2011	ECMO	Farmall

International Harvester Company

Model	Year	Condition	Price	Date	Area	Comments
Super M		F	$2,600	5/11/2011	Online	*BigIron.com,* Farmall, 2 hyds, 540 PTO, wire from starter melted
Super M		F	$1,750	12/17/2010	WCIL	Farmall
Super M		G	$2,600	12/4/2010	SEMN	Farmall, new rubber, live hyd., dual hyd., runs well
Super M		G	$3,400	9/18/2010	ECMO	New tires, PS, fenders, weights
Super M		G	$2,000	8/24/2010	NEMO	Farmall, WF, 540 PTO, single hyd.
Super M		F	$2,800	6/12/2010	NENE	Farmall, WF, 12V, new carb.
Super M		F	$1,300	3/31/2010	ECND	Farmall, live hyd., 12V, new clutch
Super M		G	$2,400	1/30/2010	NETX	
Super MD	1952	G	$19,000	8/6/2011	SEWI	Farmall, 1 of 89 built, starts on gas, switch to diesel
Super MD	1953	G	$4,500	6/30/2012	NEIA	Farmall, NF
Super MD	1958	G	$18,600	5/26/2012	ECPA	Farmall, diesel, TA, 15.5x38 tires, 2 pt., 540 PTO, 1 set rear weights, fenders, live PTO, SN 76148
Super MD		G	$4,250	3/24/2012	NEIN	Restored, fenders, power steering, PTO, hyd., new tires, runs
Super MD		G	$7,500	9/4/2010	NEIN	
Super MDTA	1954	G	$10,800	8/24/2011	ECMN	WF, PTO, fenders, new 15.5x38 rubber
Super MTA	1954	E	$8,400	3/15/2014	ECMD	Farmall, gas, NF, stage 2 hyd., standard swing drawbar, fresh paint, tires 90%, runs great, TA good, SN 74851
Super MTA	1954	E	$9,300	1/29/2014	Online	*eBay.com*, item in South Carolina, Farmall, diesel, WF, new tires front and rear, power steering, 2 way hyd., good brakes, fenders, TA
Super MTA	1954	G	$3,850	12/4/2013	ECIN	
Super MTA	1954	G	$3,500	6/15/2013	WCMI	Farmall, NF, PS, 15.5x38 tires, SN 78688
Super MTA	1954	E	$8,000	6/8/2013	NEIA	Farmall, NF, parade ready, OH, International Harvester umbrella
Super MTA	1954	E	$8,200	1/12/2013	NCIL	Farmall, 2003 fully restored, 1 owner
Super MTA	1954	G	$15,500	9/15/2012	SCMN	WF, power steering
Super MTA	1954	G	$4,700	9/13/2012	SEIA	WF, full restore 2 years ago
Super MTA	1954	G	$5,300	6/30/2012	NEIA	Farmall, diesel, NF
Super MTA	1954	G	$3,675	2/1/2012	SEND	WF, loader
Super MTA	1954	G	$5,800	8/6/2011	SWMN	Farmall
Super MTA	1954	F	$2,900	7/16/2011	NEKS	Farmall, gas, SN 61144, restoration started, Behlen power steering, new Firestone 13.6x38 tires
Super MTA	1954	G	$4,500	6/29/2011	NEND	Farmall, WF, PTO, hyd., good 14.9x38 tires, Du-Al 325 loader, working TA, straight, solid unit
Super MTA	1954	G	$6,500	3/19/2011	ECIL	Farmall, restored, new tires
Super MTA	1954	G	$3,200	8/28/2010	WCIL	Farmall, live PTO hyd. and power steering, 15.5x38 tires
Super MTA	1954	E	$51,000	8/7/2010	SEWI	Rare diesel high crop, only 64 high crops made, < 20 were diesel
Super MTA	1954	G	$5,250	7/10/2010	SEIA	WF, fenders, belt pulley
Super MTA	1954	G	$4,500	3/20/2010	NWIA	Farmall
Super MTA		G	$2,000	12/4/2013	ECND	WF, power steering
Super MTA		G	$3,250	8/15/2013	ECMN	Farmall, NF, 1 hyd.

International Harvester Company

Model	Year	Condition	Price	Date	Area	Comments
Super MTA		G	$3,200	7/10/2013	Online	*BigIron.com,* item in Nebraska, 5 speed, 4 cyl. gas, 540 PTO
Super MTA		G	$5,000	3/23/2013	NEIN	Gas, WF, weights, repainted, new tires, PS, runs
Super MTA		G	$5,500	2/16/2013	NEIA	Farmall, clean
Super MTA		G	$8,500	2/6/2013	Online	Item in Illinois, Farmall, NF, new battery, battery box, clutch, TA, seat, 13.6x38, new rubber, body shop paint, sharp, SN 71892
Super MTA		G	$5,250	11/13/2012	NCIA	
Super MTA		G	$3,400	9/15/2012	SCMN	Farmall, WF
Super MTA		G	$5,600	9/15/2012	SCMN	Factory WF, repainted
Super MTA		G	$3,100	7/14/2012	NWIA	Farmall, gas, power steering, NF
Super MTA		G	$5,000	7/14/2012	NWIA	Farmall, gas, good TA, new paint, PS, NF
Super MTA		F	$2,300	6/20/2012	SESD	Farmall, after market Nordem WF
Super MTA		G	$2,000	6/9/2012	ECNE	After market WF, rough, PTO, hyd., not running
Super MTA		G	$3,100	6/9/2012	ECNE	Fast hitch, PTO, hyd., after market WF, two set rear weights, not running, power steering
Super MTA		G	$3,300	6/9/2012	ECNE	Gas, PTO, power steering, runs, leaks water
Super MTA		G	$3,400	6/9/2012	ECNE	Power steering, PTO, original, runs
Super MTA		G	$4,000	6/9/2012	ECNE	Gas, after market WF, power steering, hyd., PTO, one set rear weights, repainted, runs
Super MTA		G	$4,250	6/9/2012	ECNE	Gas, PTO, older repaint, runs
Super MTA		G	$4,700	6/9/2012	ECNE	Diesel, PTO, hyd., original, runs, radiator leaks
Super MTA		F	$3,100	5/19/2012	NWMI	Farmall
Super MTA		G	$4,500	3/24/2012	NEIN	Nice original, power steering, fenders, PTO, hyd., weights, runs
Super MTA		G	$5,800	3/13/2012	NEWI	Farmall, great runner, looker and driver
Super MTA		G	$8,400	10/22/2011	NECO	Farmall, diesel, WF, fenders, fast hitch
Super MTA		F	$2,000	7/28/2011	NESD	Farmall, NF, 1 hyd., PTO
Super MTA		G	$2,800	5/25/2011	Online	*BigIron.com,* item in Nebraska, Farmall, gas, 1 hyd., 540 PTO, WF, hyd. steering, drawbar
Super MTA		G	$4,300	11/13/2010	NCIA	Farmall, power steering
Super MTA		G	$4,800	7/18/2010	SEMN	Farmall, gas, older loader
Super W4	1953	G	$2,950	2/20/2010	NCIL	Farmall, original, good rubber, gas
Super W4		G	$4,100	3/22/2013	NWMN	PTO, runs
Super W6	1953	G	$3,150	9/21/2013	WCMI	Gas, PTO, electric start, 1 hyd., belt pulley, 16.9x30 rear tires with weights, restored
Super W6	1953	G	$4,200	8/24/2011	ECMN	Live hyd., PTO, new 16.9x30 rubber
Super W6	1954	F	$2,700	9/1/2011	WCMN	Farmall, TA, PTO, 1 hyd., 12V, belt pulley with good TA, unrestored
Super W6		G	$1,100	7/17/2013	SESK	2WD, Deutz-Allis loader, 5' bucket
Super W6		P	$850	6/9/2012	ECNE	PTO, hyd., one bad tire, clutch problems
Super W6		F	$2,100	5/26/2010	ECSD	Runs
Super WD6	1952	G	$2,100	6/22/2011	Online	*BigIron.com,* item in Kansas, diesel, 2 hyd., 540 PTO, runs, swing hitch
Super WD9	1954	G	$5,500	9/21/2013	WCMI	Starts on gas, runs on diesel, PTO, 1 hyd., 1 belt pulley, 18.4x34 rear tires with weights, restored

International Harvester Company

Model	Year	Hours	Condition	Price	Date	Area	Comments
W30	1939		G	$3,900	6/30/2012	NEIA	McCormick, on steel
W4	1950		F	$1,595	3/27/2013	Online	*PurpleWave.com,* item in Kansas, International Harvester 2.5L, 4 cyl. gas, 26 hp, engine has a miss, manual
W4	1950		G	$3,750	8/24/2011	ECMN	PTO, wheel weights, new 14.9x26 rubber
W4	1951		F	$900	2/5/2014	SESD	Not running
W4	1951		G	$4,300	6/30/2012	NEIA	McCormick, good paint, runs
W4	1953		G	$4,800	8/24/2011	ECMN	PTO, new 14.9x26 rubber
W4			G	$2,000	9/22/2012	NEOR	WF
W4			P	$900	6/9/2012	ECNE	PTO, belt pulley, runs
W4			G	$1,700	4/12/2011	SEAB	Standard, gas
W4			F	$2,200	3/2/2011	ECND	Standard , fenders
W4			G	$2,500	9/4/2010	NEIN	All-fuel
W4			G	$3,300	9/4/2010	NEIN	
W4			G	$2,100	8/14/2010	SEMN	McCormick
W4			G	$5,250	8/7/2010	SEWI	Farmall, WF, standard, excellent mechanical condition, new tires
W4			G	$2,500	5/26/2010	ECSD	Repainted
W400	1955	2,859	G	$2,700	6/6/2011	SWSK	2WD, 50 PTO hp, gas, 1 hyd., PTO, 16.9x30 rear
W400	1957		G	$4,200	5/26/2012	ECPA	Gas, 18.4x30 tires, military pintle hitch, 540 PTO, belt pulley
W450	1957		G	$5,000	5/26/2012	ECPA	Diesel, TA, 18.4x30 tires, drawbar, 540 PTO, fenders, tool box
W6	1947		G	$1,980	3/27/2013	Online	*PurpleWave.com,* item in Kansas, International Harvester 4 cyl. gas, 37 hp, manual, spring seat, 21 gal. fuel tank
W6	1949		G	$2,400	6/30/2012	NEIA	McCormick, good paint, runs
W6	1949		G	$1,250	2/1/2012	SEND	
W6	1953		G	$3,600	8/24/2011	ECMN	PTO, disc brakes, new 16.9x30 rubber
W6			G	$2,900	2/22/2014	SCNE	Farmall, standard gas, restored
W6			G	$1,200	7/17/2013	SESK	2WD
W6			G	$3,200	2/6/2013	Online	Item in Illinois, standard, new rubber, front and rear, new: battery, battery box, seat, body shop paint, SN 14808
W6			F	$800	3/24/2012	SWMI	Standard, gas, drawbar, PTO, 18.9x30 rear tires, WF
W6			G	$1,100	5/7/2011	SWMB	
W6			G	$1,500	1/30/2010	NETX	
W9	1945		G	$4,100	8/24/2011	ECMN	PTO, 12V, new 16.9x34 rubber
W9	1949		G	$1,750	9/9/2011	ECND	PTO, belt pulley
W9	1952		G	$5,500	8/7/2010	SEWI	Farmall
W9			F	$880	4/25/2012	Online	*PurpleWave.com*, item in Kansas, 4 cyl. gas, drawbar, 540 PTO, rear wheel weights, 7.5x18 front tires, 16.9x34 rear tires
W9			G	$4,250	9/4/2010	NEIN	
W9			G	$3,500	5/1/2010	SENE	Farmall
WD6			F	$1,450	8/14/2010	SEMN	

International Harvester Company

Model	Year	Hours	Condition	Price	Date	Area	Comments
WD9	1949		G	$5,750	6/30/2012	NEIA	McCormick, good paint, runs
WD9	1954		G	$13,750	4/9/2011	SWSK	2WD diesel, 57 drawbar hp, new rear tires, 540 PTO, 1 hyd.
WD9			G	$1,900	6/22/2013	SEWA	4 cyl., diesel , direct start, rear PTO, right side belt drive, SN WDCB66652
WD9			G	$5,000	9/4/2010	NEIN	Nice, original, International Harvester Trojan blade
WD9			G	$2,200	6/5/2010	WCMO	Farmall

John Deere

Model	Year	Hours	Condition	Price	Date	Area	Comments
40	1953		G	$3,700	8/24/2011	ECMN	NF, 3 pt., PTO, front. weights
40	1953		F	$2,800	8/6/2011	NCIA	Fenders, tricycle
40	1953		G	$3,500	9/4/2010	SEVA	Gas, 2 cyl., standard
40	1953		G	$2,300	7/10/2010	ECOK	Tricycle
40	1954		G	$7,250	11/9/2013	SWON	High crop, WF, 3 pt., PTO, partial cultivators, 1 of 60 made
40	1954		G	$2,900	8/11/2010	ECMN	Factory WF
40			G	$2,500	4/1/2014	WCMN	WF, PTO, 3 pt., new carburetor
40			G	$1,350	9/12/2013	SEIA	NF, 3 pt., 540 PTO, clam shell fenders, no tag
40			G	$2,035	9/5/2013	ECWI	WF, 3 pt., new rear tires, fenders
40			G	$4,250	8/3/2013	ECMN	Gas, WF, new 11.2x24 tires, 3 pt.
40			G	$2,000	6/15/2013	WCMI	Mid 1950s, NF, 3 pt., 10x34 tires, clam fenders
40			G	$3,100	4/2/2013	ECIA	WF, 2 pt., 540 PTO, electric start, clam shell fenders
40			G	$1,750	12/19/2012	ECWI	3 pt., side mount mower
40			G	$900	8/1/2012	NEOK	
40			F	$1,200	3/20/2012	WCIL	NF
40			G	$2,500	10/22/2011	NECO	
40			G	$7,800	10/22/2011	NECO	
40			G	$1,980	8/31/2011	Online	*PurpleWave.com,* item in Oklahoma, cab only
40			G	$6,400	9/18/2010	ECMO	SF, restored
40			G	$2,200	9/4/2010	SEVA	2R
40			G	$2,200	9/4/2010	SEVA	2R
40			G	$3,500	9/4/2010	SEVA	Standard, 2 cyl., gas
40			G	$8,000	9/4/2010	NEIN	High crop
40			G	$1,450	7/17/2010	NEMT	
40			F	$1,750	7/17/2010	NEMT	Stuck
40			G	$2,850	7/17/2010	NEMT	
40			G	$2,950	5/26/2010	ECSD	WF
40			G	$3,100	1/30/2010	NETX	Spin out wheels, new rubber
40C			G	$5,100	7/17/2010	NEMT	No tag
40S	1953		G	$4,200	8/24/2011	ECMN	3 pt., PTO, new 11.2x24 rubber
40S			G	$3,200	3/23/2013	NEIN	3 pt., repainted, runs
40S			G	$4,200	3/23/2013	NEIN	Repainted, front weights, power set wheels, full cultivators, runs
40S			G	$2,750	3/24/2012	NEIN	Original, 3 pt., PTO, not running

John Deere

Model	Year	Hours	Condition	Price	Date	Area	Comments
40S			G	$3,500	3/24/2012	NEIN	Older repaint, straight, 3 pt., PTO, runs
40S			G	$4,000	10/22/2011	NECO	New rear tires
40S			F	$2,400	9/1/2011	WCMN	Dozer
40S			G	$1,700	7/17/2010	NEMT	
40T			G	$4,500	6/15/2013	WCOH	3 pt., fenders, front and rear weights, new tires, restored, runs
40T			G	$1,750	3/23/2013	NEIN	New tires, 3 pt., average, runs
40T			G	$2,700	3/23/2013	NEIN	WF, 3 pt., fenders, repainted, runs
40T			G	$3,400	6/9/2012	ECNE	PTO, 3 pt., fenders, front weights, very straight, runs
40T			G	$3,000	10/22/2011	NECO	WF
40T			G	$2,400	8/14/2010	WCMN	Good tires, 3 pt., belt pulley, NF, original
40T			G	$2,300	6/5/2010	WCMO	WF
40U	1953		G	$2,300	3/20/2012	WCIL	Factory 3 pt., 1 factory weight on front, original
40U			G	$3,135	10/22/2013	Online	*HansenandYoung.com,* 3 pt., PTO, starts, runs, drives
40U			G	$2,300	9/22/2012	NEOR	3 pt.
40U			G	$3,250	10/12/2011	NWOH	3 pt., PTO, orchard muffler
40W	1954		G	$4,200	8/24/2011	ECMN	Adj. WF, 3 pt., PTO
50	1953		G	$1,600	2/22/2014	SCNE	NF, runs, straight
50	1953		G	$1,650	11/9/2013	SWON	SF wheel, 3 pt. lift
50	1953	9,430	G	$1,351	5/22/2013	Online	*BigIron.com,* item in Nebraska, 6 speed, John Deere 2 cyl. gas, 27 hp
50	1953		G	$5,000	8/24/2011	ECMN	PTO, fenders, new 13.6x38 rubber

I've shot a lot of video for our Machinery Pete YouTube channel the past five years. The most emotional video came on a cold raw March 16, 2013, sale in Leland, Ill. This was my third trip down to cover the annual Leland Lions Club auction, which is a community-wide celebration featuring a mile-and-a-half long line of equipment for sale. I was focused on one item–the restored 1970 John Deere 2020 tractor with No. 48 loader selling to benefit a 25-year-old Somonauk, Ill., man with terminal cancer, Tom Belinski. Tom is an employee of the local John Deere dealership group AHW.

Tom's fellow employees at AHW got together to buy the John Deere 2020 and restore it. They did an amazing job. The tractor and loader sold for $20,000–a new record sale price. The buyer was James Witvoet from St. Anne, Ill. James happens to be in the auction business with his dad, Jim. Seeing the small town folks in northeast Illinois pull together to help one of their own was a beautiful, powerful and inspiring thing to witness. One year later Tom was doing okay in his cancer battle. Our thoughts and prayers are with you Tom.

PETE'S PICK

TRACTORS

John Deere

Model	Year	Hours	Condition	Price	Date	Area	Comments
50	1953		G	$1,800	7/10/2010	ECOK	
50	1954		G	$3,700	9/6/2012	Online	*IQBID.com,* item in Minnesota, NF, older restoration
50	1954		G	$3,200	7/14/2012	SWMN	Power steering, 12.4x38 rear tires, farmhand loader
50	1954		G	$2,800	4/7/2012	NWMI	PS, Roll-O-Matic, NF, new 11.2x38 tires, 1 hyd., drawbar hitch
50	1954		F	$1,600	8/6/2011	WCIL	Gas, NF, 13.4x38 rear tires
50	1954		F	$2,800	8/6/2011	NCIA	
50	1954		G	$3,000	3/23/2011	ECMN	Restored, all repainted
50	1954		G	$4,600	7/24/2010	WCIA	3 pt., power steering
50	1954		G	$2,000	7/10/2010	SEIA	Older restoration
50	1954		F	$3,302	6/23/2010	Online	*BigIron.com,* item in Iowa, 6 speed, gas, 12.4x38 rear tires, 5.50x16 new front tires, factory power steering
50	1954		G	$3,250	5/1/2010	NCOH	Live PTO, live hyd., PS, Roll-O-Matic, nice
50	1955		G	$3,800	8/10/2013	NCIA	SN 5025700
50	1955		G	$3,000	11/13/2010	NCIA	PS, one owner
50	1956		G	$1,000	3/22/2014	SWMI	Gas, NF, PTO
50	1956		G	$3,800	6/1/2013	SEMN	13.6x38 rubber, NF, all fuel
50	1956		G	$4,000	9/1/2011	WCMN	Gas, NF, PTO, 12.4x38 rubber, all new tires, restored
50			G	$4,250	4/1/2014	WCMN	NF, PS, PTO, John Deere hyd. Powr Trol
50			G	$950	1/17/2014	SEOK	Cultivator
50			G	$1,347	10/22/2013	Online	*HansenandYoung.com,* WF, Powr Trol, new rear tires, starts, runs, drives
50			G	$2,365	10/22/2013	Online	*HansenandYoung.com,* like-new rear tires, clam shell fenders, Powr Trol, PTO, starts, runs, drives
50			G	$1,350	9/12/2013	SEIA	NF, 3 pt., 540 PTO, like new 13.6x38 rears
50			G	$3,500	8/3/2013	ECMN	Gas, NF, new 12.4x38 tires, no fenders
50			G	$5,000	8/3/2013	ECMN	Gas, NF, new 12.4x38 tires, PS fenders
50			G	$2,600	6/22/2013	SESC	
50			G	$11,000	6/15/2013	WCOH	3 pt., fenders, attach, PS, new tires, restored, runs
50			G	$3,000	5/11/2013	NCOH	Repainted, runs
50			G	$4,200	5/11/2013	NCOH	Repainted, runs
50			G	$3,750	3/23/2013	NEIN	Repainted, fenders, runs
50			G	$6,000	3/23/2013	NEIN	Repainted, SF, new tires, runs
50			G	$2,100	11/24/2012	WCIL	
50			G	$4,900	11/17/2012	SWMN	Factory WF, power steering, like new 12.4x38 rubber, very sharp
50			G	$850	11/3/2012	SWMO	All original, starts, runs well
50			G	$3,750	9/22/2012	NEOR	Standard
50			G	$2,300	9/15/2012	SCMN	NF, power steering, electrical start
50			G	$1,451	8/8/2012	Online	*BigIron.com,* item in Nebraska, manual, gas, 540 PTO, belt pulley, power steering, 3 pt.
50			G	$1,600	7/21/2012	ECIA	Original, runs

John Deere

Model	Year	Hours	Condition	Price	Date	Area	Comments
50			G	$2,700	7/21/2012	ECIA	New tires, nice original
50		3,030	G	$2,900	7/21/2012	ECIA	45 loader, nice original
50			G	$3,000	3/24/2012	NEIN	Fenders, restored, runs
50			F	$3,750	3/20/2012	WCIL	
50			G	$2,000	10/22/2011	NECO	
50			G	$27,000	10/22/2011	NECO	High crop conversion, power steering
50			G	$3,000	7/16/2011	SCMN	
50		3,168	G	$2,800	4/19/2011	NEMN	
50			G	$2,800	12/21/2010	ECMI	Gas
50			F	$4,500	11/13/2010	NWIL	Gas, SF, 12x42 tires, long axle
50			G	$4,000	9/18/2010	ECMO	WF, clam shell, down draft exhaust, restored
50			G	$5,200	9/4/2010	NEIN	
50			P	$1,100	9/3/2010	NEIN	SF, dead row, needs work and may not run or drive, as is
50			G	$2,750	8/7/2010	SCMN	NF, 3 pt., newer 12.4x38 tires, PTO, John Deere 45 trip loader, 2nd owner, SN 5008116
50			G	$2,600	7/31/2010	NWIL	NF, like new rubber on back
50			G	$3,750	7/17/2010	NEMT	
50			F	$875	6/23/2010	Online	*BigIron.com,* item in Colorado, gas, tires are poor, complete, motor status unknown
50			G	$2,650	5/26/2010	ECSD	WF, Du-Al 325 loader
50			F	$1,800	5/8/2010	NETN	Roll-O-Matic, 1 hyd., 3 pt.
50			G	$1,750	1/30/2010	NETX	
60	1952		G	$900	8/16/2012	Online	*IQBID.com,* item in Minnesota, NF, gas, needs manifold
60	1952		G	$1,700	5/23/2012	Online	*BigIron.com,* item in Nebraska, collectible,7' front loader, power steering, 2 hyd., 540 PTO, WF, 2 pt. shaft rear hyd., electric start
60	1952		F	$1,150	6/23/2010	Online	*BigIron.com,* item in Nebraska, 2 cyl. gas, 1 hyd., 540 PTO, Roll-A-Matic front end, 2 Pt.
60	1953		G	$16,250	11/9/2013	SWON	High crop, power steering, WF, PTO
60	1953		P	$850	8/24/2013	SEIA	Rusted, hasn't run in a while, SN 6018030
60	1953		P	$1,500	12/3/2010	WCIL	Rough
60	1953		F	$1,300	11/4/2010	NEKS	NF, gas, 13.6x38 rear tires, 1 hyd., 540 PTO
60	1953		G	$800	9/22/2010	NECO	WF, gas, 3 pt., Du-Al loader
60	1953		G	$2,300	7/10/2010	SEIA	Recent OH, new radiator, rubber, older restoration
60	1953		F	$2,600	6/23/2010	Online	*BigIron.com,* item in Nebraska, gas, approx. 36.4 hp, 1 live hyd., live PTO, rear tires 13.6x38, front tires 16", rear tires new, front tires new, operators manual, new paint, new seat
60	1953		G	$2,300	6/5/2010	ECMI	3 pt., WF
60	1954		G	$4,900	4/20/2013	WCSK	Hyd., belt pulley, 18.4x30 rear tires new
60	1954		F	$1,600	6/20/2012	SESD	WF, fenders, good tin, loose, stored inside, not run in 10 years

John Deere

Model	Year	Hours	Condition	Price	Date	Area	Comments
60	1954		F	$1,600	11/9/2011	Online	*BigIron.com,* item in Nebraska, 6 speed, gas, 540 PTO, WF, 2 cyl., side belt pulley, power steering, 1 hyd., no 3 pt.
60	1954	4,836	G	$4,400	8/24/2011	ECMN	Standard, PTO, low seat, side steps
60	1954		G	$5,000	8/24/2011	ECMN	WF, PTO, clam shell fenders
60	1954		G	$5,600	11/13/2010	NWIL	Low seat standard, new tires, completely restored, all new tires, gas
60	1954		F	$1,350	11/4/2010	NEKS	Roll-O-Matic NF, gas, 13.6x38 rear tires, 1 hyd., live power, 540 PTO
60	1954		F	$2,000	11/4/2010	NEKS	NF, 13.6x38 rear tires, 6.5x16 front tires, 1 hyd., pump valve, 540 PTO, Du-Al loader, 5 ft. bucket, bale spear
60	1954		F	$775	6/23/2010	Online	*BigIron.com,* item in Nebraska, 37 hp, tires 13.6x38, 1 hyd., 540 PTO, live power, power steering, John Deere custom Powr Trol hyd.
60	1954	3,238	F	$3,000	6/23/2010	Online	*BigIron.com,* item in Nebraska, 6 speed, 2 cyl. LP, 1 hyd., restored, new tires
60	1954		G	$1,100	3/1/2010	NEKS	Gas, poor rubber, NF, Behlen power steering
60	1955		G	$4,500	1/28/2012	ECMO	
60	1955		G	$3,200	10/7/2011	NWSD	Gas, NF, new rear tires
60	1955		E	$6,500	9/15/2011	ECIA	Restored, SN 6011621
60	1955	4,836	G	$8,250	8/24/2011	ECMN	PTO, high seat, side steps
60	1955		E	$13,000	8/6/2011	SEWI	Factory front and tach., power steering, new tires, professional restoration 3 hours on OH, starts and runs
60	1955		F	$1,200	6/25/2011	ECIA	SN 6049674, non running, original
60	1955		G	$2,600	6/22/2011	NECO	Gas, SF, 3 pt.
60	1955		G	$2,400	5/25/2011	NECO	WF, gas, 3 pt.
60	1955		G	$2,500	4/16/2011	ECMI	Gas, aftermarket 3 pt., power steering, NF, good tires
60	1955		G	$1,250	9/22/2010	NECO	SF, LP, 3 pt.
60	1955		G	$2,500	7/10/2010	ECOK	Late model
60	1955		G	$3,250	5/1/2010	NCOH	Live PTO, live hyd., PS, Roll-O-Matic, 3 pt., nice
60	1955		G	$4,300	1/2/2010	NWOH	Gas, row crop, 3 pt., new front tires, power steering, 1 hyd., Roll-A-Matic front, newer restoration
60	1956		G	$3,350	12/3/2010	WCIL	3 pt. conversion
60	1962		G	$2,705	9/10/2013	ECND	WF, 1 hyd., PTO, Powr Trol, rock shaft, electric start, needs radiator core
60			G	$2,000	4/1/2014	WCMN	NF, power steering, PTO, 1 hyd.
60			G	$4,700	2/22/2014	SENE	
60			G	$2,860	12/17/2013	ECWI	Restored, clam shell fenders, aftermarket WF, new paint
60			G	$7,700	12/17/2013	ECWI	Wheatland, restored, adj. WF, PS, PTO, new Firestone rears, new paint, hyd.
60			G	$1,600	12/11/2013	Online	*BigIron.com,* item in Nebraska, 6 speed 1 reverse, 2 cyl. gas, 13.6x30 rear tires, 6x16 front tires, 1 hyd., 540 PTO, converted to 12V, PS, Powr Trol

John Deere

Model	Year	Hours	Condition	Price	Date	Area	Comments
60			G	$1,800	12/5/2013	SEMN	
60			G	$1,457	10/22/2013	Online	*HansenandYoung.com,* power steering, starts, runs, drives
60			G	$1,050	9/12/2013	SEIA	NF, PS, 3 pt., no third link, 15.5x38, new battery
60			G	$1,500	9/12/2013	SEIA	540 PTO, NF, PS, 1 hyd., 13.6x38 rears
60			G	$2,700	9/12/2013	SEIA	NF, power steering, 540 PTO, 1 hyd.
60			G	$3,600	8/27/2013	NCWI	Gas, NF, repaint, like new rear rubber, SN 6028551
60			G	$4,400	8/3/2013	ECMN	Gas, NF, 13.6x38 tires, PS 801, 3 pt., fenders
60			G	$1,500	6/8/2013	NEND	Factory WF, PTO, live hyd.
60			G	$1,500	5/11/2013	NCOH	Repainted, fenders, runs
60			G	$2,000	5/11/2013	NCOH	Older repaint, fenders, runs
60			G	$5,100	4/24/2013	Online	*BigIron.com,* item in Nebraska, propane
60			G	$2,600	3/23/2013	NEIN	PTO, hyd., PS, power block, repainted, runs
60			G	$3,800	3/23/2013	NEIN	Low seat standard, repainted, hyd., PTO, runs
60			G	$7,500	3/23/2013	NEIN	High seat standard, original, new tires, power steering, attach, runs
60			G	$8,500	3/22/2013	NWMN	Repainted, fenders, power steering, new tires, rear weights, runs
60			G	$1,500	3/20/2013	SWMI	NF, gas, 3 pt.
60			G	$2,000	2/6/2013	SESD	Running order
60			G	$2,700	2/6/2013	SESD	John Deere factory, 3 pt., running order
60			G	$1,250	11/24/2012	WCIL	
60			G	$1,500	11/24/2012	SEMN	Roll-O-Matic front, 12.4x38 rubber
60			G	$1,100	11/9/2012	NEAR	2 cyl. LP gas, NF, 3 pt., 540 PTO, 13.6x38 rears
60			G	$1,200	11/3/2012	SWMO	Nice mechanically, 3 pt
60			G	$1,600	9/14/2012	ECMN	1 cyl. John Deere engine, drawbar, PTO, NF, 72" loader, hyd., tires 70%
60			G	$1,400	6/9/2012	ECNE	PTO, hyd., original, runs
60			G	$4,700	3/24/2012	NEIN	Low seat, standard, repainted, PTO, hyd., weights, runs
60			G	$4,900	3/24/2012	NEIN	WF, 3 pt., repaint, fenders, runs
60			G	$7,500	3/24/2012	NEIN	High seat, standard, older repaint, PTO, hyd., power steering, runs
60			G	$9,500	3/24/2012	NEIN	High seat, standard, restored, adj. WF, factory 3 pt., power steering, runs
60			F	$1,800	3/20/2012	WCIL	
60			F	$2,600	3/20/2012	WCIL	
60			E	$4,000	3/10/2012	ECIN	Restored, gas
60			F	$1,300	1/21/2012	NEMS	WF, power steering
60			G	$3,000	12/1/2011	NEIN	
60			G	$1,850	10/30/2011	ECMN	NF
60			G	$3,000	10/22/2011	NECO	WF, 3 pt.
60			G	$5,500	10/22/2011	NECO	Low seat, standard
60			G	$9,750	10/22/2011	NECO	Orchard
60			G	$24,500	10/22/2011	NECO	High crop

John Deere

Model	Year	Hours	Condition	Price	Date	Area	Comments
60			G	$1,300	9/14/2011	Online	*BigIron.com,* item in Colorado, tricycle, 6 speed, 2 cyl. gas, 1 hyd., 540 PTO, 3 pt., custom Powr Trol, electric start
60			G	$2,050	9/14/2011	Online	*BigIron.com,* item in Colorado, 2 cyl. gas, 540 PTO, power steering, 3 pt., 4 hyd., 6 speed, power steering, hitch BAR, fenders
60			G	$1,375	8/16/2011	Online	*BidNow.us,* NF, 7x16 fronts, 13.6x38 rears
60			G	$1,050	8/13/2011	WCIL	540 PTO, 13.6x38 tires
60			G	$950	8/11/2011	WCMN	NF, gas, live PTO, Roll-O-Matic power steering
60			G	$5,000	7/30/2011	ECMO	
60			G	$5,400	6/25/2011	ECIA	Power steering, restored
60			G	$2,500	4/13/2011	Online	*BigIron.com,* item in Wyoming, 6 speed, 2 cyl. gas, 540 PTO, 2 pt., block heater, Farmhand F11 8' loader, PTO pump, 3 spool valve
60			G	$1,600	3/15/2011	WCIL	Power steering, 540 PTO, nice
60			G	$2,275	2/25/2011	ECIL	Row crop, 13.6x38 tires, gear drive
60			F	$2,000	11/13/2010	NWIL	LP, NF, 800 series hitch
60			G	$12,500	10/23/2010	SCPA	Orchard
60			G	$29,000	9/18/2010	ECMO	PS, high crop, restored, 1 of 62 built
60			G	$1,400	9/11/2010	SEIA	
60			G	$15,000	9/4/2010	NEIN	Orchard
60			P	$1,100	9/3/2010	NEIN	SF, dead row, needs work and may not run or drive, as is
60			P	$2,100	9/3/2010	NEIN	Loader, dead row, needs work and may not run or drive, as is
60			G	$1,250	8/11/2010	ECMN	PTO
60			F	$1,550	8/9/2010	ECIL	Row crop, stuck, power steering, fenders, owners donating all proceeds from sale to the Coles County Farm Bureau Foundation
60			G	$1,300	8/7/2010	SCMN	NF, Roll-O-Matic, power steering, PTO, 13.6x38 tires, SN 6010690
60			F	$3,100	7/17/2010	NEMT	LP, stuck
60			F	$7,250	7/17/2010	NEMT	Orchard, full tin, stuck
60			G	$11,100	7/17/2010	NEMT	Standard on steel with extensions
60			F	$13,000	7/17/2010	NEMT	Orchard, full tin work, stuck
60			F	$1,005	6/23/2010	Online	*BigIron.com,* item in Colorado, 2 cyl. gas, rear tires 12.4x38, front tires 7.5x16, power steering, hyd., jack shaft, motor status unknown, tires are poor, square front end
60			F	$1,005	6/23/2010	Online	*BigIron.com,* item in Colorado, 2 cyl., gas, power steering, hyd., jack shaft, tires poor, square front end
60			G	$1,105	6/23/2010	Online	*BigIron.com,* item in Oklahoma, 6F/1R, 2 cyl. gas, 15.5x38 rear tires, 6x16 front, 1 hyd., 540 PTO, tires all hold air, new carburetor
60			G	$1,650	6/23/2010	SEIA	2, cyl. gas, NF, 13.6x38 tires
60			F	$1,200	6/5/2010	SEMN	NF

John Deere

Model	Year	Hours	Condition	Price	Date	Area	Comments
60			G	$2,250	6/5/2010	ECMN	NF, power steering
60			G	$2,800	6/5/2010	ECMN	WF, good runner
60			F	$1,100	3/5/2010	NCMO	Front blade and heat houser
60			G	$1,900	1/30/2010	NETX	
62	1937		E	$36,000	8/6/2011	SEWI	This was the 9th Model 62 produced, orginally owned by brother of designer, total restoration after barn fire, all bolts removed
70	1953		G	$2,600	1/25/2012	Online	*BigIron.com,* item in Nebraska, 6F/1R, 2 cyl. gas, 45 drawbar, 58 belt pulley hp, 1 hyd., 540 PTO, grill, magneto
70	1953		F	$2,250	8/6/2011	NCIA	Stuck
70	1953	2,873	G	$1,550	6/8/2011	Online	*BigIron.com,* item in Kansas, Du-Al loader, 6 speed, 2 cyl. propane, 45 hp, 1 hyd., 540 PTO, runs, needs battery and propane to start, 5' bucket
70	1954		F	$2,100	6/20/2012	SESD	Gas, NF, Roll-O-Matic, PTO, PS, loose, 14.9x38 rubber, wheel weights, nice tin, kept inside, not run in 10 years
70	1954		F	$2,300	10/7/2011	NWSD	Original, gas, NF, 3 pt.
70	1954		G	$5,400	6/25/2011	ECIA	Gas, SN 7012774, restored
70	1954	500	G	$3,000	9/17/2010	ECMN	2WD, gas, power steering, 48 hp, 6 speed, Schwartz WF, PTO, live power
70	1954		G	$2,300	7/10/2010	SEIA	New tires, older restoration
70	1955		G	$1,750	6/15/2013	WCMI	NF, PS, 3 pt., clam fenders, 15.5x38 tires, Powr Trol, SN7032847
70	1955		G	$6,800	8/24/2011	ECMN	Standard, PTO, side steps, new 16.9x30 rubber
70	1955		G	$7,400	8/24/2011	ECMN	Standard, PTO, clam shell fenders
70	1955		G	$6,500	6/25/2011	ECIA	Gas, SN 7023427, WF, new tires, power steering
70	1955		F	$1,600	4/27/2011	NECO	Diesel, Roll-O-Matic double front, won't start
70	1955		P	$1,000	11/13/2010	NWIL	Standard, rough, not running, gas, for parts
70	1955		G	$2,700	11/13/2010	NWIL	Standard, power steering, diesel, WF, fenders
70	1955		G	$2,500	9/22/2010	NECO	WF, LP, 3 pt.
70	1955		G	$1,400	6/23/2010	Online	*BigIron.com,* item in Nebraska, John Deere square front end, 3 pt. does not sell with
70	1955		G	$1,700	6/16/2010	SEND	Diesel, Pony motor, rock shaft, PTO
70	1955		G	$7,000	5/29/2010	NCIL	Standard, new rubber
70	1956		G	$2,150	8/22/2012	Online	*BigIron.com,* item in Oklahoma, 2WD, 6 speed, John Deere LP, 1 hyd., 540 PTO, 3 pt., 540 live PTO, fenders, WF, power steering
70	1956		F	$1,650	6/20/2012	SESD	WF, PS, factory tach., 15.5x38 tires, runs
70	1956	5,414	G	$4,550	6/22/2011	Online	*BigIron.com,* item in Nebraska, LP, 3x2, 6 speed w/ reverse, 2 cyl., 540 PTO, 12V system, power steering, Roll-O-Matic walking front pedestal steer axle, rear step

TRACTORS

John Deere

Model	Year	Hours	Condition	Price	Date	Area	Comments
70	1956	2,064	G	$7,000	6/22/2011	Online	*BigIron.com,* item in Nebraska, LP, Hi/Lo, 1 hyd., 540 PTO, runs, owner's manual, power steering, WF, square axle, 6V system, 3 pt., 1 set of weights
70	1956		G	$2,500	8/28/2010	WCIL	Gas, NF, 13.6x38 rear tires, 1 hyd., chains, Stainhoist loader
70	1956		G	$2,600	8/7/2010	SEWI	Diesel, power steering, new rubber
70	1959		F	$850	8/25/2012	NWIL	Gas, not running, styled
70			G	$2,700	4/1/2014	WCMN	NF, power steering, John Deere custom Powr Trol, 1 hyd., PTO
70		2,807	G	$5,005	12/17/2013	ECWI	Diesel, restored, clam shell fenders, Pony start, 14.9x38 tires
70			G	$1,900	12/5/2013	SEMN	Roll-O-Matic
70			G	$15,000	11/9/2013	SWON	High crop, all fuel, WF, PTO, believed to be 1 of 6 made
70			G	$1,237	10/22/2013	Online	*HansenandYoung.com*
70			G	$3,080	10/22/2013	Online	*HansenandYoung.com,* 3 pt., starts, runs, drives
70			G	$4,900	8/3/2013	ECMN	Gas, NF, 13.6x38 tires, PS 3 pt., fenders
70			G	$2,000	7/31/2013	ECND	WF, electric start, rock shaft, PTO, Farmhand F11 hyd. loader, PTO pump
70			G	$5,500	7/31/2013	ECND	Standard
70			G	$13,250	6/15/2013	WCOH	Standard, PTO, hyd., weights, new tires, restored, runs
70			G	$3,000	5/11/2013	NCOH	Older repaint, factory 3 pt., runs
70			G	$3,100	3/23/2013	NEIN	LP, repainted, runs
70			G	$5,800	3/23/2013	NEIN	Gas, standard, power steering, original, 26" rubber, runs
70			G	$5,000	3/22/2013	NWMN	Gas, standard, nice original, runs
70			F	$3,600	1/9/2013	Online	*IQBID.com,* 2 cyl. gas, 1 hyd., PTO, power steering, 15.5x38 tires, engine turns over, has not been run in several years, not restored, SN 7040643
70			G	$2,500	11/24/2012	WCIL	
70			G	$4,200	10/20/2012	ECIL	
70			G	$3,200	9/15/2012	SCMN	WF, 14.9x38 tires, 80% rubber, 3 pt., no third link
70			G	$4,900	3/24/2012	NEIN	Diesel, standard, repainted, runs good
70			G	$1,600	3/20/2012	WCIL	
70			F	$2,900	3/20/2012	WCIL	
70			E	$9,500	3/20/2012	WCIL	Gas, expo quality
70			E	$6,000	3/10/2012	ECIN	Restored, gas, expo quality
70			G	$2,700	10/22/2011	NECO	LP, 3 pt., square tube WF
70			G	$3,100	10/22/2011	NECO	Gas, John Deere 227 picker
70			G	$3,800	10/22/2011	NECO	Diesel, standard, adj. front axle, 3 pt.
70			G	$7,000	10/22/2011	NECO	Gas, adj. standard front, power steering, 3 pt.
70			G	$28,000	10/22/2011	NECO	Diesel high crop
70			G	$2,600	9/14/2011	Online	*BigIron.com,* item in Colorado, 2 cyl. gas, 540 PTO, 3 pt., leak at PTO, new paint, tires look new
70			G	$5,900	9/18/2010	ECMO	LP, WF, clam shells, new tires, restored

John Deere

Model	Year	Hours	Condition	Price	Date	Area	Comments
70			G	$4,000	9/11/2010	NCIL	Diesel, standard, Pony motor, PS
70			G	$4,900	9/11/2010	NCIL	Diesel, standard, Pony motor, PS, good rubber
70			G	$5,000	9/11/2010	NCIL	Diesel, Pony motor, PS
70			F	$1,500	9/9/2010	NWWI	Diesel, NF
70			G	$6,000	9/4/2010	NEIN	LP
70			G	$7,000	9/4/2010	NEIN	Standard, diesel
70			G	$28,000	9/4/2010	NEIN	High crop
70			P	$5,000	9/3/2010	NEIN	All fuel, 1 hyd., dead row, needs work and may not run or drive, as is
70			G	$7,400	8/14/2010	WCMN	Standard, power steering adj. WF, nice rubber, inside weights, 3 pt., 800 hitch
70			G	$1,600	8/11/2010	ECMN	NF, Farmhand loader, original, unrestored, 1 owner, manuals
70			F	$2,800	8/7/2010	SEWI	2R corn picker
70			G	$3,100	7/17/2010	NEMT	
70			G	$4,200	7/17/2010	NEMT	Standard
70			G	$1,900	6/17/2010	SEIA	Diesel
70			G	$1,600	6/11/2010	SEAB	PTO, hyd., gas
70			G	$1,400	5/26/2010	ECSD	Standard, nice tin, runs
70			G	$4,900	5/26/2010	ECSD	LP
70			F	$800	1/30/2010	NETX	LP, fairly complete
70			F	$2,100	1/30/2010	NETX	LP, square WF, 3 pt.
70			G	$4,400	1/30/2010	NETX	WF, new tires
80	1955	6,784	G	$14,000	4/1/2014	WCMN	Standard, WF, power steering, PTO, new tires, 1 hyd.
80	1955		F	$2,300	8/6/2011	NCIA	
80	1955		G	$14,000	8/6/2011	SEWI	Pony motor excellent, complete restoration, hyd. work, PTO good, all lights work
80	1955		G	$9,000	7/24/2010	WCIA	Diesel, recent major OH and new rubber
80	1956		G	$13,700	9/21/2013	SEMN	Professionally restored, 2 hyd., like new 18.4x34 tires
80	1956		G	$6,600	10/7/2011	NWSD	Standard, diesel
80	1956		E	$12,750	8/24/2011	ECMN	Standard, power steering, hyd., PTO, Pony start
80	1956		G	$7,750	6/25/2011	ECIA	SN 8001508, PTO, hyd., Pony runs good, repainted
80	1956		G	$9,000	10/23/2010	SCPA	
80			G	$14,500	8/3/2013	ECMN	Standard diesel, new 18.4x34 tires, Pony start, dual hyd.
80			G	$13,000	6/15/2013	WCOH	PTO, dual hyd., new tires, restored, runs
80			G	$7,400	3/24/2012	NEIN	Diesel, cab, nice original, runs
80			G	$7,800	10/22/2011	NECO	Diesel, PTO
80			P	$4,250	10/2/2010	SESK	Gas, Pup start, diesel, for parts
80			G	$12,000	9/11/2010	NCIL	Diesel, Pony motor, PS, new tires
80			G	$7,600	9/4/2010	NEIN	
80			G	$8,100	8/14/2010	WCMN	Power steering, PTO, new rear rubber, 2 hyd., good Pony motor, WF
80			F	$8,700	7/17/2010	NEMT	

John Deere

Model	Year	Hours	Condition	Price	Date	Area	Comments
80			G	$14,000	5/29/2010	NCIL	Diesel standard, old restore, Pony start
300	1971	1,800	G	$1,700	4/6/2012	NEIA	300 industrial (1020 ag version) 3 cyl., gas, 3 pt., live PTO, 1,800 actual hours, was a DNR tractor, serviced every 50 hours
302	1966	1,850	G	$5,100	9/21/2013	SWIA	WF, gas, M&W pistons, 12V system converted to alternator, new battery, heat plug, 15.5x38 tires, fender mount radio
320	1957		G	$17,500	6/25/2011	ECIA	Southern Special, SN 322379, 3 pt., new tires, restored
320			G	$13,000	3/24/2012	NEIN	Southern special, restored, PTO, 3 pt., dual hyd., slant steer, Touch-O-Matic, runs
320			G	$12,000	3/20/2012	WCIL	
320			G	$19,000	10/22/2011	NECO	Duplicate tag, set up in V configuration
320			G	$9,750	9/4/2010	NEIN	
320			G	$20,000	9/4/2010	NEIN	Southern, special
320			P	$3,750	9/3/2010	NEIN	Standard, dead row, needs work and may not run or drive, as is
320			G	$6,000	8/14/2010	WCMN	Standard, new rubber, WF, 3 pt., restored
320S	1957		E	$12,000	8/24/2011	ECMN	3 pt., PTO, new 11.2x24 rubber
320S			G	$10,250	8/3/2013	ECMN	Gas, WF, new 11.2x24 tires, 3 pt.
320S			G	$7,000	3/23/2013	NEIN	Front weights, older repaint, 3 pt., runs
320S			G	$6,000	3/22/2013	NWMN	Older repaint, 3 pt., runs
320U	1958		G	$5,500	11/13/2010	NWIL	Slant steer, 1 of 199 built, gas, good tires
320U			G	$7,000	3/23/2013	NEIN	Repainted, rear weights, 3 pt., runs
320U			G	$7,100	10/22/2011	NECO	New tires
320U			G	$7,100	10/22/2011	NECO	New tires
320U			G	$5,000	7/17/2010	NEMT	Mower
320U			G	$7,000	7/17/2010	NEMT	Slant dash
330	1959		G	$23,000	9/21/2013	WCMI	Gas, 3 pt., PTO, 1 hyd., electric start, 11.2x24 rear tires, restored
330	1959		E	$26,000	6/28/2013	NEMO	Factory 3 pt., 12.4x24 rubber, SN 330640
330	1960		E	$31,000	8/3/2013	ECMN	330S, gas, WF, 10x24 tires, 3 pt., SN 330941
330			G	$14,000	7/21/2012	ECIA	Original, 3 pt., rear weights, runs
330			G	$15,000	10/22/2011	NECO	
330			G	$39,000	10/22/2011	NECO	Set up in V configuration
330			G	$14,500	7/17/2010	NEMT	No tag
330S	1959		G	$22,500	3/20/2012	WCIL	Total restoration, paper of authenticity from John Deere, SN 330225
330S	1960		G	$18,000	11/9/2013	SWON	WF, original top link, 3 pt., PTO, factory front weight
330S			G	$18,500	3/23/2013	NEIN	Repainted, front/rear weights, 3 pt., dual Touch-O-Matic runs
330S			G	$21,000	3/24/2012	NEIN	Front/rear weights, restored, 3 pt., PTO, dual Touch-O-Matic, runs
330S			G	$22,000	3/24/2012	NEIN	3 pt., dual Touch-O-Matic, restored, runs

John Deere

Model	Year	Hours	Condition	Price	Date	Area	Comments
330S			G	$20,250	9/4/2010	NEIN	
330U			G	$23,000	9/4/2010	NEIN	
420	1956		G	$4,000	6/20/2012	SESD	3 pt., WF
420	1957		G	$3,000	5/28/2012	ECMO	Tricycle, 3 pt., older restoration
420	1957		G	$6,000	8/24/2011	ECMN	5 speed, rear hyd. valves, 3 pt., PTO, fenders
420	1958	2,562	F	$2,400	9/1/2011	WCMN	SF, 3 pt., PTO, new block, rebuilt engine, new seat and steering wheel, fenders, long axles, original unrestored
420	1958	1,357	3	$3,500	9/22/2010	NECO	WF, gas, 3 pt., restored
420			G	$4,250	12/4/2013	ECIN	
420			G	$4,500	10/3/2013	NCIN	WF, cultivators
420			G	$1,500	9/12/2013	SEIA	3 pt., 540 PTO live power, 2 hyd., NF
420			G	$2,300	8/14/2013	WCMN	3 pt., 14.9x26 tires
420			G	$5,250	2/7/2013	NEIN	WF, cultivators
420			G	$4,900	3/24/2012	SWMI	Standard, 3 pt., PTO, gas, fresh paint, new rubber, WF, 14.9x24 tires
420			G	$7,750	3/20/2012	WCIL	
420			G	$15,000	10/22/2011	NECO	Straight steer
420			G	$7,500	10/23/2010	SCPA	Standard
420			G	$7,750	9/4/2010	NEIN	All fuel
420			G	$9,750	9/4/2010	NEIN	High crop
420			G	$10,000	9/4/2010	NEIN	High crop
420			G	$5,500	8/14/2010	WCMN	Standard, slant steer, 5 speed, 3 pt., PTO, restored
420			G	$2,600	7/17/2010	NEMT	
420			G	$1,800	3/27/2010	SWIA	Slant dash
420			G	$4,250	1/30/2010	NETX	
420C			G	$6,600	9/4/2010	NEIN	
420H	1957		G	$11,500	9/1/2011	WCMN	High crop, 2nd generation, 2 pt., Touch-O-Matic hyd. control, 6V, restored
420S			G	$3,500	5/11/2013	NCOH	Older repaint, 3 pt., runs
420S			G	$10,500	3/23/2013	NEIN	Restored, reverser, 3 pt., new tires, runs
420S			G	$4,100	3/22/2013	NWMN	Repainted, 3 pt., PTO, runs
420S			G	$4,200	7/21/2012	ECIA	Repainted, front weights, runs
420S			G	$3,600	10/22/2011	NECO	Repainted
420S			G	$4,800	9/18/2010	ECMO	Repainted
420T	1957		G	$5,300	3/24/2012	NEIN	PTO, 3 pt., fenders, factory WF, runs
420T	1958		G	$6,200	8/24/2011	ECMN	5 speed, hyd., 3 pt., PTO, slant steer, clam shell fenders, new 11.2x34 rubber
420T	1958		F	$4,000	11/13/2010	WCIL	LP, stuck, NF, new tires
420T	1958		G	$4,000	11/13/2010	NWIL	NF, good tires
420T			G	$2,600	3/23/2013	NEIN	Original, 4 speed, fenders, hyd., 3 pt., runs
420T			G	$3,250	2/6/2013	SESD	Fenders, 3 pt.
420T			G	$3,900	3/24/2012	NEIN	Fenders, front/rear weights, restored, runs
420T			G	$4,500	3/24/2012	NEIN	All fuel, original, rare, runs
420T			G	$8,000	3/24/2012	NEIN	WF, repainted, 3 pt., PTO, runs
420T			G	$2,000	10/22/2011	NECO	Slant steer
420T			G	$4,750	10/22/2011	NECO	Reverser, hyd.

John Deere

Model	Year	Hours	Condition	Price	Date	Area	Comments
420T		3,065	G	$2,100	4/11/2011	Online	*AuctionTime.com,* 2WD
420T			G	$4,500	9/18/2010	ECMO	Repainted
420T			F	$2,200	7/17/2010	NEMT	Stuck
420T			G	$2,250	7/17/2010	NEMT	
420T			F	$3,800	7/17/2010	NEMT	Stuck
420U			G	$6,500	8/3/2013	ECMN	Gas, WF, new 13.6x28 tires, 3 pt.
420U			F	$900	11/20/2010	ECFL	Project tractor, motor rebuilt
420U			G	$9,000	9/4/2010	NEIN	All fuel
420U			G	$3,500	7/17/2010	NEMT	
420U			G	$2,650	5/26/2010	ECSD	Mower
420W	1956		G	$4,400	6/25/2011	ECIA	SN 106696, fenders, power set wheels, 3 pt., PTO, 5 speed, repainted
420W	1956		F	$2,050	11/13/2010	NWIL	Hyd., original, WF, 3 pt., gas
420W	1957		G	$3,400	10/12/2011	NWOH	SN 101374, WF, 3 pt., PTO, older paint
420W	1958		G	$3,100	6/25/2011	ECIA	SN 133997, 5 speed, fenders, power set wheels
430	1958		G	$4,000	9/21/2013	WCMI	Gas, 3 pt., PTO, electric start, 13.6x28 rear tires, restored
430	1958		G	$8,000	6/28/2013	NEMO	WF, factory 3 pt., 13.6x28 rubber, SN 141516
430	1958		G	$4,600	6/15/2013	WCMI	WF, 3 pt., 13.6x28 tires, front-end loader, SN 141049
430	1959		G	$6,500	9/12/2013	SEIA	Standard, parade ready, 3 pt.
430	1959		E	$5,200	6/8/2013	NEIA	WF, 3 pt., parade ready
430	1959		G	$4,200	1/2/2010	NWOH	Gas, 3 pt., PS, 540 PTO, older repaint
430			G	$3,500	3/23/2013	NEIN	LG, diesel, deck, 3 pt., power steering, runs
430			G	$9,000	3/23/2013	NEIN	Repainted, 3 pt., new tires, hyd., factory power steering, runs
430			G	$22,000	3/24/2012	NEIN	High crop, repainted, new tires, 1 of 183 built, runs
430			G	$9,200	3/20/2012	WCIL	
430			G	$14,500	10/22/2011	NECO	Duplicate tag, power steering, 3 pt.
430			G	$7,500	3/26/2011	SEWI	
430			G	$4,600	8/14/2010	WCMN	3 pt., PTO
430			G	$2,500	6/23/2010	Online	*BigIron.com,* item in Oklahoma, 5 speed, John Deere gas, rear tires 14.9x28, front tires 6.5x16, PTO, 3 Pt., new battery
430S	1959		G	$7,600	11/9/2013	SWON	WF, 3 pt., PTO
430T	1959		E	$10,000	2/22/2014	NEIN	NF, spin outs, front and rear weights, 3 pt. with top link, PTO
430W	1959		G	$7,600	8/24/2011	ECMN	5 speed, hyd., 3 pt., PTO, fenders, new 13.6x38 rubber
435	1959		G	$10,600	2/22/2014	NEIN	Diesel, swept back, WF, slant steer, clam shell fenders, deluxe seat, 13.6x28 tires new, rear weights, 3 pt., top link, PTO
435	1959		E	$10,600	2/22/2014	NEIN	Gas, swept back WF, slant steer, clam shell fenders, deluxe seat, rear weights, 3 pt., top link, PTO, auctioneer said he'll buy seat for winning bidder

John Deere

Model	Year	Hours	Condition	Price	Date	Area	Comments
435	1959		G	$9,000	11/9/2013	SWON	GM diesel, WF, 3 pt., PTO, power steering, noise in 2nd gear
435	1959		G	$5,500	9/21/2013	WCMI	Diesel, 3 pt., PTO, 14.9x28 rear tires, restored
435	1959		F	$2,500	11/20/2010	ECFL	Diesel, runs, needs TLC, GM diesel
435	1959		G	$8,300	8/7/2010	SEWI	Rare 2 cyl. diesel, new front, good rears, WF
435	1960		E	$11,000	3/20/2012	WCIL	Diesel, rare swept back front axle, power steering, spinout rear wheels, deluxe seat, loaded with options, older restoration, SN 438659
435			G	$13,000	3/23/2013	NEIN	Diesel, heavy fenders, float ride seat, repainted, new tires, runs
435			G	$4,900	7/21/2012	ECIA	Fenders, 3 pt., runs
435			G	$12,000	3/24/2012	NEIN	3 pt., PTO, fenders, restored, runs
435			G	$3,400	1/31/2012	NEIN	Diesel
435			G	$4,500	10/22/2011	NECO	Diesel, block welded
435			G	$6,250	10/22/2011	NECO	Diesel, 38" rears
435			G	$6,250	10/22/2011	NECO	Diesel, 38" rears
435			G	$7,300	9/4/2010	NEIN	Power steering, float ride seat, loader
435			G	$8,750	9/4/2010	NEIN	DM diesel, spin out rims
435			P	$3,000	9/3/2010	NEIN	GM diesel, dead row, needs work and may not run or drive, as is
435			F	$6,000	7/17/2010	NEMT	Stuck
435			G	$15,000	7/17/2010	NEMT	
435			G	$6,300	1/30/2010	NETX	
520	1956	3,353	E	$7,000	10/10/2013	SCSK	Gas, 34.3 drawbar HP, 38.6 PTO hp, belt pulley, power steering, 540 PTO, 3 pt., 1 hyd., 12.4x36 tires
520	1956		F	$1,950	8/20/2011	NEMN	WF, power steering, 3 pt., no linkage, good rubber, SN 5200665
520	1957		G	$4,500	9/21/2013	SEMN	PS, live power
520	1957		E	$5,050	5/11/2013	ECIA	NF, power steering, live power, HD Roll-O-Matic, parade condition, 13.9x36 Titan tires
520	1957		F	$3,600	8/4/2012	WCWI	Gas, NF
520	1957		F	$3,000	6/20/2012	SESD	WF
520	1957		G	$8,000	8/24/2011	ECMN	WF, 2 hyd., 3 pt., PTO, power steering, clam shell fenders
520	1957		G	$4,600	8/6/2011	NCIA	Power steering
520	1957		G	$3,700	6/25/2011	ECIA	SN 5204170, new tires, repainted
520	1957		G	$9,000	6/25/2011	ECIA	LP, SN 5206917, 3 pt., fenders, WF, restored
520	1957		P	$4,000	4/1/2011	Online	*AuctionTime.com,* item in Wisconsin, factory propane, new rubber, 3 pt., non running
520	1957		G	$4,500	5/29/2010	NCIL	Gas, NF, all original
520	1958		G	$3,800	8/8/2013	WCMN	Gas, NF, Roll-O-Matic, 1 hyd., single Powr Trol, fenders, 13.9x36 tires, SN 5232174, restored
520	1958	3,049	G	$5,200	8/7/2013	Online	*IQBID.com,* factory WF, gas, 1 hyd., 3 pt., top link, quick hitch, PTO, 90% rear tires, unrestored

TRACTORS

John Deere

Model	Year	Hours	Condition	Price	Date	Area	Comments
520	1958		G	$7,250	2/6/2013	SESD	NF, PS, 3 pt., totally restored, new tires, new paint and OH
520	1958		G	$8,400	9/6/2012	Online	*IQBID.com,* item in Minnesota, complete restoration
520	1958		G	$6,000	11/13/2010	NWIL	LP, WF, 3 pt., black dash
520	1958		F	$3,500	7/10/2010	SEIA	Older restoration
520			G	$2,585	12/17/2013	ECWI	PTO, hyd.
520		4,209	G	$2,915	10/22/2013	Online	*HansenandYoung.com,* starts, runs, drives
520			G	$2,100	9/12/2013	SEIA	NF, like new rear tires, factory 3 pt., 1 hyd., 540 PTO
520			G	$3,750	8/24/2013	SEMN	NF, PS, 12.4x36
520			G	$6,000	8/3/2013	ECMN	Gas, NF, 12.4x36 tires
520			G	$3,300	12/5/2012	Online	*AuctionTime.com*
520			F	$2,800	11/30/2012	WCMN	NF, PS, hyd. PTO
520			G	$1,500	11/3/2012	SWMO	Starts, runs, 3 pt., power steering, all original
520			G	$5,200	9/15/2012	SCMN	NF, electric. start, repainted
520			G	$2,750	3/24/2012	NEIN	LP, original, new tires, runs
520			G	$8,500	3/20/2012	WCIL	
520			G	$5,000	10/22/2011	NECO	Gas, 3 pt., dual hyd., square tube WF
520			G	$33,000	10/22/2011	NECO	Gas, converted to high crop
520			G	$2,750	3/17/2011	ECMN	NF, Roll-O-Matic
520			G	$2,750	3/17/2011	ECMN	Roll-O-Matic, 13.9x36 tires
520			G	$6,000	9/18/2010	ECMO	3 pt., new tires, repainted
520			F	$2,800	9/11/2010	NCIL	Gas, PS, SF, good rubber, cut off axle left side
520			G	$14,500	9/4/2010	NEIN	
520			G	$4,400	8/14/2010	WCMN	NF, repainted
520			G	$1,900	8/11/2010	ECMN	NF
520		6,309	G	$3,000	8/7/2010	SCMN	NF, Roll-O-Matic, power steering,3 pt., PTO, 11.2x38 tires, SN 5200518
520			G	$2,400	7/17/2010	NEMT	WF
520			G	$5,100	7/17/2010	NEMT	3 pt.
520			G	$3,000	6/17/2010	SEIA	Power steering, aftermarket 3 pt.
520			G	$3,400	6/17/2010	SEIA	Power steering
520			G	$4,250	1/30/2010	NETX	Clam shell fenders, runs, like-new tires
530	1958		G	$6,000	9/21/2013	WCMI	Gas, PTO, 1 hyd., electric start, NF, power steering, 13.6x36 rear tires, restored
530	1958		E	$19,500	8/24/2011	ECMN	Hyd., PTO power steering, side steps, rock shaft, new 14.9x30 rubber
530	1958		G	$12,500	5/29/2010	NCIL	WF, gas, complete restore
530	1959		E	$15,250	2/22/2014	NEIN	Gas, WF, power steering, front and rear weights, fenders, 1 hyd., 3 pt., top link, PTO
530	1959	2,671	E	$14,000	2/8/2014	SENE	3 pt., NF
530	1959		G	$9,500	11/9/2013	SWON	WF, power steering, 3 pt., PTO, flat top fenders
530	1959		G	$5,750	6/28/2013	NEMO	NF, power steering, 3 pt., 12.4x36 rubber, SN 5304958

John Deere

Model	Year	Hours	Condition	Price	Date	Area	Comments
530	1959		E	$8,200	6/8/2013	NEIA	NF, flat top fenders, 3 pt., parade ready
530	1959		G	$4,250	12/12/2011	NEMO	NF, 2 cyl., factory 3 pt. 13.9x36 tires, straight and original
530	1959		E	$9,600	8/24/2011	ECMN	WF, hyd., 3 pt., PTO, power steering, flat top fenders
530	1959		E	$13,000	8/24/2011	ECMN	Hyd., PTO, power steering, side steps, new 16.9x30 rubber
530	1959		G	$3,900	8/6/2011	NCIA	
530	1959		G	$14,500	6/18/2011	SWMN	Custom built high crop, SN 5307105, new tires, repainted
530	1960		E	$8,400	8/10/2013	NCIA	Gas, NF, SN 5308443
530	1960		G	$7,700	1/13/2012	NCIA	NF, 3 pt.
530	1960		E	$22,000	1/24/2010	SCAZ	Sold for $20,000 + 10% buyer's commision, reconditioned by a 53-year-old John Deere dealership Frank Implement Company in Scottsbluff, Neb. to factory specs
530			G	$5,000	3/22/2014	ECSD	Gas, WF
530			G	$7,700	8/24/2013	NWIL	NF, good rubber, restored
530			G	$6,100	8/3/2013	ECMN	Gas, NF, new 13.6x38 tires
530			G	$4,200	3/23/2013	NEIN	Original, runs
530			G	$6,000	9/15/2012	SCMN	Factory WF, new front rubber
530			G	$5,300	7/21/2012	ECIA	Original, runs
530			G	$6,900	7/21/2012	ECIA	WF, 3 pt., fenders, rear weights, older repaint, runs
530			G	$14,750	7/21/2012	ECIA	Second owner, OH, nice
530			G	$5,000	3/24/2012	NEIN	Repainted, PTO, hyd., runs
530			G	$7,000	3/24/2012	NEIN	Nice original, 3 pt., PTO, hyd., new tires, runs
530		3,992	G	$9,000	3/24/2012	NEIN	Excellent original, 3 pt., new rear tires, deluxe fenders, runs
530			G	$7,500	3/20/2012	WCIL	Wrong decals but nice
530			G	$5,400	10/22/2011	NECO	3 pt.
530			G	$27,000	10/22/2011	NECO	Gas, converted to high crop
530			G	$11,100	7/16/2011	SCMN	Weights and cyl.
530		7,256	G	$7,500	1/28/2011	WCOH	Row crop, 12.4x36 tires
530			G	$10,500	9/11/2010	NCIL	Gas, PS, 3 pt., dual head light fenders, SF, long adj. axles
530			G	$7,200	9/4/2010	NEIN	Loader
530			G	$9,000	9/4/2010	NEIN	
530			G	$11,000	9/4/2010	NEIN	LP, spin out rims
530			G	$5,700	8/14/2010	WCMN	1 hyd., PTO, NF
530			G	$7,100	8/14/2010	WCMN	Good rubber, nice paint, PTO, 1 hyd., rock shaft, NF
530			G	$6,000	7/17/2010	NEMT	3 pt.
530			F	$6,750	7/17/2010	NEMT	Stuck, WF, 3 pt.
530			G	$4,900	6/19/2010	SWIL	Running, restored, fenders, PTO, lights, power steering
620	1956		G	$2,100	1/29/2014	Online	*BigIron.com,* item in Arkansas, 6F/1R, 2 cyl., 12.4x36 rear tires, 6.5x36 front tires, 1 hyd., PS, 3 pt.

John Deere

Model	Year	Hours	Condition	Price	Date	Area	Comments
620	1956		E	$32,500	10/28/2013	SCKS	LP, standard, fully restored, power steering, SN 6205652, only 37 built
620	1956		G	$5,000	6/25/2013	SWSK	2WD, 48 PTO hp, power steering, 1 hyd., PTO, 7.50x18 front, 16.9x30 rear, 50+ hours since OH
620	1956		E	$9,700	8/24/2011	ECMN	Standard, hyd., PTO, power steering, side steps
620	1956		G	$3,700	4/17/2010	ECNE	3 pt.
620	1957		G	$9,000	11/9/2013	SWON	Orchard, full dress, PTO
620	1957		G	$3,200	8/15/2013	ECMN	NF, 1 hyd., hand clutch, 12.4x38 new tires front/back
620	1957		G	$6,000	1/11/2013	NWIN	WF, 3 pt.
620	1957		G	$3,200	11/30/2011	SEMN	NF, Roll-O-Matic, rock shaft
620	1957	3,007	G	$3,250	9/1/2011	WCMN	Gas, NF, 2 hyd., PTO, power steering, rebuilt carburetor, older restoration
620	1957		G	$7,200	8/24/2011	ECMN	WF, hyd., 3 pt., PTO, power steering, clam shell fenders, new 14.9x38 rubber
620	1957		G	$6,250	8/6/2011	NCIA	Power steering, restored
620	1957		G	$2,500	7/27/2011	ECND	Collector, NF, 1 hyd., PTO, 12V, new rear tires, new wiring, new manifold intake, new water pump, green dash
620	1957	3,800	G	$2,525	6/17/2011	SWMN	NF, PS, nice
620	1957	943	G	$4,250	2/19/2011	ECNE	Gas, WF, 3 pt.
620	1957		F	$2,000	1/1/2011	ECKS	3 pt.
620	1957		F	$2,700	12/3/2010	WCIL	
620	1957		F	$6,300	11/13/2010	NWIL	Rock shaft, original, power steering, WF, gas
620	1957	1,560	G	$2,126	6/23/2010	Online	*BigIron.com,* item in South Dakota, 6 speed, gas, rear tires 13.6x38, front tires 6x16, 2 hyd., NF, 3 pt.
620	1957		G	$8,500	5/29/2010	NCIL	Gas, standard, complete restore, new rubber
620	1957		G	$5,500	1/2/2010	NWOH	Gas, row crop, new front tires, power steering, fenders, 3 pt., Roll-A-Matic, 1 hyd., newer restoration
620	1958		G	$4,600	2/27/2014	NWNE	Gas, WF, 3 pt.
620	1958		F	$3,956	12/26/2013	Online	*BigIron.com,* item in Nebraska, 6 speed, 13.6x38 rear tires, 6x16 front tires, circulating block heater, PS, F10 Farmhand, forks included
620	1958		F	$3,600	11/7/2012	SCNE	NF, 3 pt., power steering, PTO
620	1958		F	$1,500	6/21/2012	WCMI	SN 6218370, new 15.5x38 rear tires, front tires 6x16 tri rib, original paint, step stool box on axle, new battery box, NF, faded
620	1958		G	$5,900	1/13/2012	NCIA	NF, 3 pt., PS
620	1958		E	$64,000	10/22/2011	NECO	High crop, gas, 3 pt., new rear tires
620	1958		G	$2,600	6/25/2011	ECIA	SN 6215227, after, market WF, 3 pt., original
620	1958		G	$4,250	6/25/2011	ECIA	SN 6218199, tin straight, runs good
620	1958		F	$2,500	7/10/2010	SEIA	3 pt., older restoration
620	1958		G	$2,700	7/10/2010	SEIA	Original, 3 pt.
620	1958		G	$4,300	7/10/2010	SEIA	3 pt. top link, 4 new rims/tires

John Deere

Model	Year	Hours	Condition	Price	Date	Area	Comments
620	1958		G	$5,000	3/6/2010	NEKS	NF, 3 pt., new tires, runs great, gas
620			G	$1,500	8/14/2013	WCMN	Du-Al loader, power steering, new 13.6x38 tires
620			G	$3,200	8/8/2013	WCMN	NF, power steering, 1 hyd., PTO, fenders, quick hitch
620			G	$4,750	8/3/2013	ECMN	Gas, NF, new 13.6x38 tires
620			G	$6,000	8/3/2013	ECMN	Gas, NF, new 13.6x38 tires
620			G	$23,000	3/22/2013	NWMN	Restored, rare, runs, all fuel
620			G	$2,500	11/30/2012	WCMN	NF, PS, hydro
620			F	$2,300	9/1/2012	SWIA	Factory WF, original, missing 3 pt., tires just fair shape, in its work clothes
620			G	$5,600	3/24/2012	NEIN	Standard, PTO, hyd., nice original, low production, runs
620			F	$2,350	3/20/2012	WCIL	
620			F	$2,800	3/20/2012	WCIL	
620			G	$8,500	3/20/2012	WCIL	
620			G	$4,400	3/13/2012	NEWI	Power steering, Roll-O-Matic, Powr Trol
620			F	$3,900	2/24/2012	WCMN	NF, Roll-O-Matic, power steering, 13.6x38 tires, good tin, a little plain overall
620			G	$3,500	10/22/2011	NECO	Gas, SF, 3 pt.
620			G	$6,500	10/22/2011	NECO	Gas, standard, rock shaft
620			G	$12,000	10/22/2011	NECO	Orchard, power steering, PTO
620		900	G	$2,860	9/14/2011	Online	*PurpleWave.com,* item in Kansas, John Deere 2 cyl. gas
620			F	$2,300	7/27/2011	Online	*BigIron.com,* item in Nebraska, 6F/1R, gas, hand clutch, power steering, seat needs repair, needs new back
620		3,372	P	$1,950	5/25/2011	Online	*BigIron.com,* item in Nebraska, 6 speed, gas, 1 hyd., 540 PTO, WF, does not run
620			G	$5,750	1/29/2011	ECMO	LP, WF
620			F	$2,600	12/17/2010	WCIL	15.5x38 tires, 540 PTO, NF
620			F	$2,600	10/2/2010	SCIN	NF, rusted hood
620			G	$4,500	9/18/2010	ECMO	LP, standard, 3 pt., adj. WF, restored, 1 of 37 built
620			G	$28,500	9/18/2010	ECMO	New tires, 3 pt.
620			F	$2,400	9/11/2010	NCIL	Gas, NF, PS, cut off axles, main crank shaft leaking oil
620			G	$8,300	9/11/2010	NCIL	Gas, standard, PS, good rubber, nice paint
620			G	$4,600	9/4/2010	NEIN	LP
620			P	$1,100	9/3/2010	NEIN	LP, SF, dead row, needs work and may not run or drive, as is
620			P	$6,600	9/3/2010	NEIN	All fuel, orchard, dead row, needs work and may not run or drive, as is
620			G	$2,900	8/14/2010	WCMN	Original, NF, like-new rubber, PTO, 1 hyd., 3 pt., top link
620			G	$3,550	8/14/2010	WCMN	Rock shaft, PTO, 1 hyd., NF
620		2,856	G	$4,300	8/7/2010	SCMN	NF, Roll-O-Matic, power steering, 15.5x38 tires, aftermarket 3 pt., PTO, custom Powr Trol, SN 6216103
620			G	$3,250	7/17/2010	NEMT	

John Deere

Model	Year	Hours	Condition	Price	Date	Area	Comments
630	1958		G	$7,000	11/9/2013	SWON	NF, power steering, 3 pt., PTO
630	1958		G	$7,000	11/9/2013	SWON	NF, power steering, 3 pt., PTO
630	1958		G	$3,750	10/29/2011	NCNC	Power steering, relined brakes, new PTO clutches, new alternator
630	1958		G	$7,500	5/29/2010	NCIL	Gas, NF, complete restore, has front weights
630	1959		G	$6,750	9/21/2013	WCMI	Gas, 3 pt., PTO, 1 hyd., electric start, power steering, 16.3x38 rear tires, restored
630	1959		G	$5,750	8/24/2013	SEMN	NF, good tin, Roll-O-Matic power steering
630	1959		G	$8,200	6/28/2013	NEMO	WF, factory 3 pt., power steering, flat top fenders, 13.6x38 rubber, SN 6304147
630	1959		G	$15,000	9/6/2012	Online	*IQBID.com,* item in Minnesota, standard, complete restoration
630	1959		G	$7,700	8/25/2012	NWIL	John Deere 45 loader, bucket, nice runner, gas, NF
630	1959		F	$2,750	6/20/2012	SESD	NF, Roll-O-Matic, rock shaft, PTO, PS, good tin, 15.5x38 tires, loose, stored inside, not run in 10 years
630	1959		F	$3,000	6/20/2012	SESD	Gas, power steering, 13.6x38 tires, shedded, not run in 2 years, motor stuck
630	1959		G	$2,400	10/28/2011	NETX	48 hp propane, NF, 13.6x38 tires, 1 rear hyd.
630	1959		E	$9,500	8/24/2011	ECMN	WF, hyd., 3 pt., PTO, power steering, flat top fenders
630	1959		E	$18,000	8/24/2011	ECMN	Standard, hyd., PTO, power steering, side steps
630	1959		G	$5,200	8/6/2011	NCIA	Power steering, restored
630	1959		G	$5,000	6/25/2011	ECIA	SN 6306177, WF, 3 pt., 2 hyd.
630	1959		G	$6,000	3/16/2011	ECSD	WF, 1 hyd., 3 pt., PTO, electric start, power steering, new Firestone rears, new fronts, recent restoration
630	1959	8,000	G	$4,600	6/23/2010	Online	*BigIron.com,* item in Nebraska, 6 speed, 2 cyl. gas, 60 hp, 1 hyd., 540 PTO, narrow front end Roll-O-Matic, 3 pt. lift, power steering
630	1960		E	$18,000	2/22/2014	NEIN	Gas, swept back, WF, standard, power steering, front and rear weights, 3 pt., top link, PTO
630	1960		G	$7,700	9/5/2013	SWMN	Factory WF, 3 pt., fenders, SN 6317025, 1 owner family
630	1960	2,836	F	$2,900	7/27/2013	NCIA	NF, original 13.6x38 tires, all original tin
630	1960	2,836	G	$2,900	6/27/2013	Online	*IQBID.com,* NF, original 13.6x38 tires, all original tin, SN SRV1173
630	1960		E	$9,000	6/8/2013	NEIA	NF, flat top fenders, 3 pt., parade ready
630	1960		E	$9,300	5/11/2013	ECIA	211 hours on recondition, original square WF, power steering, factory 3 pt., 14.9x38 Firestones, high speed 5th gear, deluxe style fenders, restored 2005, Nava Star poly paint with clear coat finish, buggy top

Model	Year	Hours	Condition	Price	Date	Area	Comments
630	1960		G	$5,100	6/9/2012	ECNE	Factory 3 pt., hyd., PTO, repainted, runs with a miss
630	1960		G	$5,700	6/9/2012	ECNE	3 pt., WF, PTO, repainted, runs
630	1960		G	$4,200	5/28/2012	ECMO	Schwartz front end, PS, 3 pt.
630	1960	4,065	G	$5,800	1/13/2012	NCIA	NF, 3 pt., PS
630	1960		F	$3,500	2/21/2011	WCIL	Gas, NF, power steering, John Deere loader
630	1960		G	$6,700	8/5/2010	NCIA	Gas, HD Schwartz WF, 3 pt., rear fenders
630	1960		G	$17,750	5/29/2010	NCIL	Standard gas, complete restore, new rubber, new float ride seat
630		4,774	G	$3,000	12/11/2013	Online	*BigIron.com,* item in Nebraska, 7' Wizard loader, 6 speed w/reverse, 2 cyl. gas, 15.5x38 rear tires, 9.5Lx15 front tires, 1 hyd., 540 PTO, 540 PTO pump to run loader, rear concrete wheel weights, PS, needs battery
630			G	$6,600	8/3/2013	ECMN	Gas, WF, new 13.6x38 tires
630			E	$12,500	3/23/2013	NEIN	Standard, runs, excellent original
630			G	$8,250	3/22/2013	NWMN	Standard, 3 pt., repainted, new tires, runs
630			G	$4,750	3/2/2013	ECMN	Gas, factory WF, rock shaft, square fenders, live PTO
630			G	$4,000	11/30/2012	WCMN	NF, PS, hydro, PTO, newer paint assembly, looking for missing hood
630			G	$6,100	9/15/2012	SCMN	Factory WF, new rubber
630			G	$5,000	7/21/2012	ECIA	3 pt., fenders, rear weights, loader, runs
630			G	$5,100	7/21/2012	ECIA	Repainted, deluxe fenders, new tires, runs
630			G	$6,100	6/2/2012	SEMN	Good rubber, runs great
630			G	$4,300	3/24/2012	NFIN	Repainted, SF, 3 pt., runs
630			G	$8,400	3/24/2012	NEIN	WF, 3 pt., fenders, restored, new tires, runs
630			G	$60,000	3/24/2012	NEIN	LP, standard, excellent original, very rare, 1 of 16 made, runs
630			G	$9,000	3/20/2012	WCIL	
630			G	$10,000	12/3/2011	ECNE	NF
630			G	$3,800	11/27/2011	ECIA	Consigned by neighbor
630			G	$4,700	10/22/2011	NECO	3 pt., SF wheel
630			G	$9,750	10/22/2011	NECO	Standard, gas, 3 piece front weights
630			G	$4,600	9/1/2011	WCMN	Gas, NF, power steering, new tires
630			G	$3,500	4/2/2011	ECMN	
630			G	$4,750	3/5/2011	SEMN	Gas, WF, new tach., 540 PTO, new radiator, new pistons/rings, new battery, rebuilt head, power steering 1 hyd.
630			G	$4,600	11/26/2010	WCOH	WF, round tube front
630			G	$7,000	11/20/2010	NCKY	Flat fenders, 3 pt., PS, restored, hyd. cyl., top link
630			G	$5,250	11/16/2010	ECNE	John Deere WF, 13.6x38 rear tires, 2 hyd., 540 PTO, factory 3 pt., live power, power steering
630			G	$10,100	9/18/2010	ECMO	WF, 3 pt., fenders

Model	Year	Hours	Condition	Price	Date	Area	Comments
630			G	$3,800	9/11/2010	NCIL	Gas, NF, PS, 3 pt., flat top fenders
630			E	$19,250	9/11/2010	NCIL	Gas, standard, NF, PS, fenders, nice paint
630			G	$10,250	9/4/2010	NEIN	3 pt., nice original, new rubber
630			P	$1,950	9/3/2010	NEIN	Dead row, needs work and may not run or drive, as is
630		3,287	G	$4,500	8/14/2010	WCMN	Original, NF, 3 pt., 1 hyd., PTO
630			G	$5,500	8/14/2010	WCMN	Rock shaft, PTO, 1 hyd., good rubber, new paint, NF
630			G	$8,750	8/7/2010	SEWI	LP
630			G	$14,000	7/17/2010	NEMT	Standard
630			G	$3,800	6/23/2010	SEIA	2, cyl. gas, NF, 13.6x38 tires, factory 3 pt.
630			G	$4,000	6/17/2010	SEIA	Power steering, factory 3 pt., original
630			G	$3,150	3/27/2010	SWIA	
630			F	$1,400	1/30/2010	NETX	For parts
630			G	$2,400	1/30/2010	NETX	3 pt., aftermarket WF
630			G	$7,200	1/30/2010	NETX	Flat top fenders, like new tires, runs
720	1956	900	G	$3,300	10/24/2012	NECO	WF, 3 pt., diesel, 1 hyd., Pony start
720	1956		G	$3,100	6/23/2010	Online	*BigIron.com,* item in Nebraska, 6 speed, 2 cyl. LP, 1 hyd., electric start, lights, power steering, live hyd., step, 540 PTO, hyd. power lift, strong puller
720	1956		G	$3,500	6/23/2010	Online	*BigIron.com,* item in Nebraska, diesel, 6F/1R, 2 cyl. diesel 4 cyl. Pup start motor, 1 hyd., 540 PTO, gas Pup starter, 6v starter, new seat
720	1956		G	$3,500	6/5/2010	ECMI	WF, new front rubber
720	1957		G	$6,000	4/3/2014	NEIN	WF, 3 pt.
720	1957		G	$6,250	12/19/2013	WCMN	Diesel, Pony start, WF, 3 pt., 540/1,000 PTO, restored
720	1957	2,600	G	$4,250	10/19/2013	WCIL	Diesel, Pony start, 3 pt.
720	1957		G	$3,750	9/13/2012	SEIA	Pony start, Wheatland WF, restored in 2004, 540 PTO, 1 hyd., power steering, clam shell fenders
720	1957	5,911	G	$3,533	8/22/2012	Online	*BigIron.com,* item in Kansas, 6F/1R, 2 cyl. gas, 1 hyd., Category II 3 pt. arms, top link is category I, power steering, WF, weights front/back
720	1957		F	$3,500	6/20/2012	SESD	NF
720	1957		G	$3,750	10/7/2011	NWSD	3 pt., PTO, hyd., WF
720	1957		E	$9,000	8/24/2011	ECMN	Standard, hyd., PTO, power steering, side steps
720	1957		G	$29,500	6/25/2011	ECIA	Diesel, Pony start, high crop, SN 7214095, new tires, struts, draw bar, repainted
720	1957		G	$2,100	4/11/2011	Online	*AuctionTime.com,* 2WD
720	1957		G	$3,100	4/11/2011	Online	*AuctionTime.com,* 2WD
720	1957		G	$4,200	2/1/2011	NEIN	Nice original
720	1957	1,546	E	$5,200	9/22/2010	NECO	WF, 3 pt., diesel, restored, Pony start
720	1958		E	$6,750	8/10/2013	NCIA	WF, SN 7225012
720	1958	6,171	G	$1,900	12/1/2012	SEWY	LP, SF, 3 pt.

John Deere

Model	Year	Hours	Condition	Price	Date	Area	Comments
720	1958		G	$7,000	9/22/2012	NEOR	Standard, gas, only 143 built, WF
720	1958		F	$5,500	6/20/2012	SESD	Square WF, PS, fenders, 3 pt., 1 hyd., carb rebuilt, radiator leaks, sometimes runs poor, rust in gas line, 15.5x38 tires
720	1958		G	$7,500	8/24/2011	ECMN	Hyd., 3 pt., PTO, power steering, Pony start, clam shell fenders
720	1958		E	$117,500	8/6/2011	SEWI	High crop, 1 of 9, this was shipped March 11, 1958, destination of Stockton, CA, electric start, power steering, 3 pt.
720	1958		G	$4,300	7/13/2011	Online	*BigIron.com,* item in Nebraska, custom Powr Trol, 540 PTO, John Deere Pony motor, runs and starts, new coil and rebuilt carburetor on Pony, 3 pt., no top link
720	1958		G	$2,600	6/25/2011	ECIA	LP, SN 7222817, black dash, older repaint
720	1958		G	$3,200	2/1/2011	NEIN	Pony, WF, front. weights, 3 pt., motor OH, older repaint
720	1958		F	$3,200	11/13/2010	NWIL	LP, WF, 3 pt., black dash, good tires
720	1958	4,721	G	$4,500	9/22/2010	NECO	WF, gas, not restored, F11 loader
720	1958		G	$2,750	6/11/2010	SEAB	Diesel, gas start
720	1959	2,236	G	$4,000	9/1/2011	WCMN	Gas, WF, PTO, power steering, rock shaft, fenders, original unrestored
720	1959	2,236	G	$4,000	9/1/2011	Online	*IQBID.com,* WF, gas, PTO, power steering, rock shaft, fenders, original unrestored
720			G	$6,500	4/3/2014	NEIN	NF, 3 pt.
720			E	$14,000	2/22/2014	NEIN	Diesel, square WF, power steering, front and rear weights, electric start, 3 pt., top link, PTO, very straight original
720			G	$4,750	12/4/2013	ECIN	
720			G	$5,500	12/4/2013	ECIN	
720			F	$4,200	8/24/2013	SEMN	Diesel, 3 pt., NF, PS, 13.6x38, stuck in 6th gear
720		2,959	G	$3,410	8/14/2013	Online	*PurpleWave.com,* item in Kansas, 2 cyl. 4 valve gas, 8 speed PS, John Deere 500 loader, 64" bucket
720			G	$5,000	8/3/2013	ECMN	Gas, NF, new 15.5x38 tires
720			G	$12,250	8/3/2013	ECMN	Electric start, diesel, NF, new 15.5x38 tires
720			G	$5,700	3/23/2013	NEIN	Gas, 3 pt., weights, repainted, new tires, runs
720			G	$2,600	2/12/2013	WCIL	
720			F	$3,400	11/30/2012	WCMN	Gas, NF, PS, hydro
720			F	$3,600	11/30/2012	WCMN	Gas, NF, PS, hydro, PTO
720			G	$3,800	11/13/2012	NCIA	Diesel, WF, 3 pt.
720			G	$3,250	9/15/2012	SCMN	Pony motor starter, NF, restored
720			G	$3,200	7/14/2012	SWMN	13.6x38 rear tires
720			G	$3,700	6/9/2012	ECNE	LP, square tube WF, factory 3 pt., fenders, runs but noisy transmission

TRACTORS

John Deere

Model	Year	Hours	Condition	Price	Date	Area	Comments
720			G	$3,800	3/24/2012	NEIN	LP, standard, hyd., original, runs
720			G	$5,900	3/24/2012	NEIN	Gas, square WF, 3 pt., fenders, restored, runs
720			G	$8,000	3/24/2012	NEIN	Diesel, Pony, square WF, 3 pt., fenders, dual hyd., quick coupler, rear wheel weights, 3 piece weight set, runs
720			E	$8,000	3/10/2012	ECIN	Restored, diesel, Pony motor, expo ready
720			G	$2,950	1/21/2012	NEMS	WF, power steering, one owner
720			G	$6,000	10/22/2011	NECO	Diesel, standard, new rear tires, dual hyd., adj. WF
720			G	$6,000	10/22/2011	NECO	Diesel, standard, new rear tires, dual hyd., adj. WF
720			G	$26,000	10/22/2011	NECO	Diesel high crop, Pony start, new tires
720			F	$4,100	6/22/2011	Online	*BigIron.com,* item in Nebraska, diesel, 2 cyl. diesel, 1 hyd., 540 PTO, converted to electric start, starter needs repair
720		7,037	G	$2,100	4/13/2011	Online	*BigIron.com,* item in Nebraska, runs, LP, 6 speed, 50 hp,1 hyd., 540 PTO, hyd. work, no third link or sway bars
720			G	$4,900	3/19/2011	ECIL	Gas, NF, factory 3 pt., 2 hyd.
720			G	$3,500	1/29/2011	ECMO	NF
720			G	$4,600	11/18/2010	WCKS	Wheatland, WF, diesel, 6 speed, 18.4x30 rear tires, 7.50x18 front tires, power steering, rear wheel weights, 540 PTO, custom Powr Trol, less than 200 hours on engine and trans.
720			G	$5,250	11/13/2010	NCIA	Pony start, square WF, motor is great, diesel
720			G	$4,250	9/18/2010	ECMO	3 pt.
720			P	$1,100	9/11/2010	NCIL	Diesel, electric start, PS, not running, rough
720			G	$6,400	9/11/2010	NCIL	Diesel, Pony motor, WF, PS, 3 pt.
720			G	$4,500	9/4/2010	NEIN	LP, SF
720			P	$6,000	9/3/2010	NEIN	All fuel, weights, 1 hyd., dead row, needs work and may not run or drive, as is
720			G	$4,200	8/14/2010	WCMN	Gas, NF, new tires, rock shaft, PTO, 1 hyd., 15.5x38 tires
720			G	$4,800	8/14/2010	WCMN	Standard, rock shaft, 1 hyd., PTO, WF, good rubber all around, power steering,
720			F	$5,100	8/14/2010	WCMN	Diesel, power steering, NF, PTO, repainted, some mechanical work, cab, air, heat
720			G	$9,700	8/14/2010	WCMN	WF, 1 hyd., PTO, new paint, gas standard, complete OH and restore, rock shaft, new rubber
720		6,106	G	$5,100	8/7/2010	SCMN	NF, Roll-O-Matic, power steering, factory 3 pt., new 15.5x38 tires, PTO, SN 7225318
720		7,326	G	$6,300	8/7/2010	SCMN	Diesel, John Deere WF, Pony start, power steering, factory 3 pt., John Deere Powr Trol, new 15.5x38 tires, PTO, SN 7217093

John Deere

Model	Year	Hours	Condition	Price	Date	Area	Comments
720			F	$3,100	7/17/2010	NEMT	Standard, diesel, stuck
720			G	$4,700	7/17/2010	NEMT	WF
720			G	$3,000	6/23/2010	SEIA	2 cyl. diesel Pony motor, factory SF, 15.5x38 tires, tear drop fenders, factory 3 pt.
720			P	$1,300	5/26/2010	ECSD	Diesel, not running
720			F	$1,300	5/26/2010	ECSD	Wheatland, Pony start, rare 3 pt. rock shaft option
720			F	$1,750	3/18/2010	WCMN	
720			F	$2,250	1/30/2010	NETX	LP, for parts, square WF, 3 pt.
730	1958		G	$9,500	11/9/2013	SWON	Diesel, Pony motor, WF, 3 pt., PTO, flat top fenders, factory weights
730	1958		G	$9,500	11/9/2013	SWON	Diesel, Pony motor, WF, 3 pt., PTO, flat top fenders, factory weights
730	1958		G	$6,100	5/19/2012	WCIL	Diesel, WF, power steering, good tires and paint
730	1958		G	$5,900	12/17/2011	WCMO	Diesel
730	1958		F	$4,000	11/12/2011	NEIA	Diesel, power steering, Pony start, NF, 3 pt.
730	1958	926	G	$5,800	5/11/2011	Online	*BigIron.com,* diesel, electric start, 3 pt., no third link, WF end
730	1958		E	$8,100	6/11/2010	SEAB	Electric start, power steering, hyd., PTO, fully rebuilt and restored, excellent paint
730	1959		G	$6,400	2/22/2014	SCNE	Pony WF, 3 pt., repaint, many new parts, runs excellent
730	1959		G	$3,500	11/9/2013	SWON	WF, 3 pt., PTO, flat top fenders, original
730	1959		G	$5,610	10/16/2013	Online	*PurpleWave.com,* item in Kansas, 6.2L,2 cyl. diesel, 6 speed, 3 pt., PTO
730	1959		G	$5,050	9/12/2013	SEIA	Gas, WF, 3 pt., 540 PTO, 15.5x38 tires
730	1959		G	$7,100	3/7/2013	ECIA	NF, power steering, 3 pt., 540 PTO
730	1959		G	$4,600	8/16/2012	Online	*IQBID.com,* item in Minnesota, WF, diesel, 540 PTO, open station, hand clutch, new 15.5x38 tires, 7.5x16 tires, 95% rubber, complete OH, restored
730	1959		G	$7,000	7/14/2012	SWMN	Factory 3 pt., electric start, 15.5x38 rear tires
730	1959		G	$5,900	12/22/2011	Online	*IQBID.com,* factory WF, diesel, electric start, 3 pt., fenders
730	1959		G	$7,500	12/7/2011	NCIA	Diesel, Pony motor, 3 pt., 15.5x38 tires
730	1959		G	$3,900	9/9/2011	ECND	Standard, Pony motor, power steering, 2 hyd., PTO, Powr Trol
730	1959		G	$4,100	9/1/2011	WCMN	Diesel, NF, 1 hyd., 3 pt., 540/1,000 PTO, power steering, electric start, Roll-O-Matic front, sway blocks, 12V, lights, new seat assembly
730	1959		G	$7,400	9/1/2011	WCMN	Gas, WF, 3 pt., 1 hyd., power steer, sway blocks, fenders, new front. tires
730	1959		G	$10,800	8/24/2011	ECMN	WF, hyd. 3 pt., PTO, electric start, power steering, flat top fenders
730	1959		E	$10,900	8/24/2011	ECMN	Standard, electric start, PTO, power steering, factory side steps, new 18.4x40 rubber

John Deere

Model	Year	Hours	Condition	Price	Date	Area	Comments
730	1959		G	$6,300	6/25/2011	ECIA	Diesel, electric start, SN 7316436, 3 pt., 2 hyd., fenders, older repaint
730	1959		G	$13,500	6/25/2011	ECIA	Gas, Standard, SN 7311926, new tires, low production, nice original
730	1959		F	$2,500	2/21/2011	NEMO	Diesel, WF (Norden axle, Mfg. by Russell Manufacturing Inc.), 540 PTO, 15.5x38 rear tires, power steering, 1 hyd.
730	1959		G	$11,500	2/1/2011	NEIN	Options, completely restored
730	1959	2,912	E	$5,750	9/22/2010	NECO	WF, diesel, 3 pt., restored, Pony start
730	1959	5	E	$13,000	9/22/2010	NECO	LP, Wheatland, 1 owner, totally restored
730	1959	4,200	G	$8,600	6/23/2010	Online	*BigIron.com,* item in Oklahoma, 6F/1R, 2 cyl. diesel, 1 hyd., 540 PTO
730	1959		F	$3,950	6/5/2010	SEMN	LP, NF, PS, Roll-O-Matic
730	1959		G	$10,750	5/29/2010	NCIL	Gas, standard, original paint, new float ride seat
730	1959	1,119	G	$9,100	2/20/2010	NCIL	Diesel, Pony start, factory 3 pt., NF
730	1959		E	$16,000	1/2/2010	NWOH	Gas, standard, factory 3 pt., 1 of 292 built, new front tires, power steering, 1 hyd., front weights, nicely restored
730	1960		G	$6,400	2/22/2014	SCNE	Pony start, WF, 3 pt., restored, starts, runs
730	1960		G	$7,500	2/22/2014	SCNE	Pony, WF, 3 pt., repaint, runs good
730	1960		E	$10,400	9/21/2013	SEMN	Standard, PS, like new 18.4x30 tires
730	1960		G	$12,250	9/6/2012	Online	*IQBID.com,* item in Minnesota, standard, original condition
730	1960		G	$8,300	8/25/2012	NWIL	Electric start, nice runner, older repaint, diesel, NF
730	1960	7,625	G	$9,000	8/21/2012	WCIL	Diesel, electric start, power steering, WF, 3 pt., older restoration, nice
730	1960		G	$4,000	7/14/2012	SWMN	Diesel, 15.5x38 tires, Pony motor
730	1960		G	$2,300	6/29/2012	NETX	59 hp, LP gas, WF, 14.9x38 tires, power steering, 3 pt., 1 rear hyd.
730	1960		G	$6,750	1/31/2012	NEIN	Electric start, 3 pt., restored
730	1960		G	$6,500	10/12/2011	NWOH	Gas, (new pistons, headwork, carb rebuild, starter, radiator), WF, fenders, 3 pt., PTO, repainted
730	1960		G	$4,400	8/11/2011	WCMN	WF, electric start, new battery box and front tires
730	1960		G	$6,500	5/29/2010	NCIL	Gas, 3 pt., new antique front rubber
730	1960		G	$12,500	5/29/2010	NCIL	Diesel standard, complete restore, new rubber, new float ride seat
730			G	$12,700	3/22/2014	WCMO	Diesel, tricycle, 24V, PS, fully restored, new rubber
730			G	$6,750	9/28/2013	SWMN	Diesel, WF, power steering, duals, 3 pt.
730			G	$6,000	8/24/2013	NWIL	Diesel, gas, NF, restored
730			G	$7,000	8/3/2013	ECMN	Gas, new 15.5x38 tires, 3 pt., fenders, dual hyd.
730			G	$11,000	8/3/2013	ECMN	Diesel, 15.5x38 tires, 3 pt., fenders
730			G	$8,400	5/11/2013	NCOH	Diesel, Pony start, repainted, new tires, deluxe fenders, 3 pt., dual hyd., runs
730			G	$9,750	3/23/2013	NEIN	Diesel, electric start, repainted, fenders, 3 pt., runs

John Deere

Model	Year	Hours	Condition	Price	Date	Area	Comments
730			G	$13,000	3/23/2013	NEIN	LP, standard, new tires, older repaint, runs
730			G	$16,000	3/23/2013	NEIN	Diesel, electric start, repainted, fenders, 3 pt., WF, weights, runs
730			G	$13,000	3/22/2013	NWMN	Diesel, high crop, Argentina, original, 3 pt., electric start, runs
730			G	$7,900	11/30/2012	WCMN	Diesel, WF, PS, fenders, hyd. PTO, power control, new paint restoration
730			G	$5,250	11/6/2012	ECOK	WF, 3 pt., PTO, rebuilt
730			G	$6,800	9/22/2012	NEOR	Row crop, high seat, 3 pt., PTO, new rubber, WF
730			G	$3,300	9/15/2012	SCMN	Electric start, not complete
730			G	$4,200	9/15/2012	SCMN	Factory WF, electrical start, fenders
730			G	$5,750	9/15/2012	SCMN	Electrical start, SF wheel, repainted
730			G	$7,000	9/15/2012	SCMN	Factory WF, electric. start, fenders
730			G	$2,850	8/22/2012	Online	*BigIron.com,* item in Oklahoma, 2WD, John Deere LP, 1 hyd., 540 PTO, NF, 3 pt., rear weights on outside, 540 live PTO, no fenders
730			G	$16,500	7/21/2012	ECIA	Restored, first 730 to leave factory
730			G	$5,100	6/16/2012	ECIN	3 pt., deluxe fenders, older repaint
730			P	$3,250	6/9/2012	ECNE	LP, WF, 3 pt., original, not running
730			G	$3,800	6/9/2012	ECNE	Gas, factory 3 pt., PTO, hyd., factory deluxe fenders, unrestored, runs
730			G	$6,750	3/24/2012	NEIN	Diesel, Pony start, fenders, 3 pt., 3 piece weight set, restored, runs
730			G	$7,300	3/24/2012	NEIN	Gas, repainted, new tires, deluxe fenders, 3 pt., WF, runs
730			G	$7,500	3/24/2012	NEIN	Diesel, standard, Pony start, nice original, runs
730			G	$9,400	3/24/2012	NEIN	Gas, square WF, deluxe fenders, 3 pt., rear weights, restored, runs
730			G	$11,000	3/24/2012	NEIN	Electric start, standard, restored, PTO, hyd., weights, runs
730			G	$13,500	3/24/2012	NEIN	Gas, standard, 3 pt., adj. front, PTO, hyd., repainted, runs
730			G	$14,000	3/24/2012	NEIN	LP, standard, nice original, new tires, PTO, hyd., runs
730			G	$14,500	3/24/2012	NEIN	WF, 3 pt., fenders, front weights, PTO, hyd., restored, runs
730			E	$15,000	3/24/2012	NEIN	Diesel, electric start, new tires, SQ WF, 4 piece weight set, deluxe fenders, dual hyd., complete 3 pt., quick hitch, buddy seat
730			G	$23,000	3/24/2012	NEIN	Diesel, electric start, PTO, 3 pt., weights, original, 1st 730 off assembly line w/documentation, runs
730			G	$30,000	3/24/2012	NEIN	Mounted picker, restored, runs, gas
730			G	$47,000	3/24/2012	NEIN	All fuel, standard, 1 of 28 made, adj. WF, 3 pt., PTO, dual hyd., new tires, runs
730			F	$5,100	3/20/2012	WCIL	
730			G	$8,700	3/20/2012	WCIL	Gas
730			G	$4,100	3/10/2012	NCOK	NF

TRACTORS

John Deere

Model	Year	Hours	Condition	Price	Date	Area	Comments
730			G	$3,800	11/19/2011	NCMO	Electric start
730			G	$4,300	11/19/2011	NCMO	Electric start
730			G	$4,000	10/22/2011	NECO	3 pt., deluxe fenders, WF, LP
730			G	$6,900	10/22/2011	NECO	Diesel, 3 pt., WF, electric start
730			G	$7,750	10/22/2011	NECO	Diesel, standard, 3 pt., 3 piece front weights
730			G	$8,000	10/22/2011	NECO	Gas, 3 pt., fenders, WF
730			G	$12,000	10/22/2011	NECO	Standard, LP, flat back, low production, adj. axle
730			G	$14,500	10/22/2011	NECO	Standard, diesel, 3 pt., new rear tires, 3 piece front weight set
730			G	$29,000	10/22/2011	NECO	Diesel high crop, Argentina, new tires, 3 piece front weight set
730			G	$45,000	10/22/2011	NECO	Diesel high crop, new rear tires
730			G	$9,000	9/17/2011	ECMN	
730			G	$3,550	8/24/2011	ECMN	Schwartz WF, good shape
730			G	$5,000	8/16/2011	Online	*BidNow.us,* WF, no weights
730			G	$15,000	8/6/2011	SEWI	
730			G	$6,250	3/26/2011	SEMN	Gas, WF, 3 pt., 15.5x38 rubber, power steering
730			F	$4,000	2/25/2011	ECIL	Not running, diesel
730			G	$6,250	11/13/2010	NCIA	Diesel
730			G	$7,900	9/18/2010	ECMO	WF, front. weights, deluxe fenders
730			G	$11,900	9/18/2010	ECMO	3 pt., Argentine, high crop, restored
730			G	$15,500	9/18/2010	ECMO	Electric start, 3 pt., Argentine, high crop, restored
730			G	$2,800	9/11/2010	NCIL	Gas, NF, PS
730			G	$6,000	9/11/2010	NCIL	Diesel, NF, PS, new rears
730			G	$8,300	9/4/2010	NEIN	Electric start
730			G	$9,000	9/4/2010	NEIN	Standard
730			G	$9,500	9/4/2010	NEIN	Gas, standard, 3 pt.
730			G	$10,500	9/4/2010	NEIN	Argentina high crop
730			G	$11,000	9/4/2010	NEIN	LP, standard, gas
730			G	$12,000	9/4/2010	NEIN	All fuel, flat back
730			G	$12,000	9/4/2010	NEIN	Diesel, WF
730			G	$13,000	9/4/2010	NEIN	Diesel, WF, front weights
730			G	$19,000	9/4/2010	NEIN	High crop, diesel, electric start
730			P	$9,250	9/3/2010	NEIN	Diesel, high crop, dead row, needs work and may not run or drive, as is
730			P	$12,000	9/3/2010	NEIN	All fuel, weights, dead row, needs work and may not run or drive, as is
730			G	$6,900	8/14/2010	WCMN	Roll-O-Matic, 1 hyd., PTO
730			G	$10,200	8/14/2010	WCMN	Electric start, completely OH, restored, rock shaft, 1 hyd., PTO, new tires all around
730			G	$12,000	8/14/2010	WCMN	Standard, original, outside wheel weights, PTO, 1 hyd., power steering
730			G	$7,000	8/7/2010	SEWI	Diesel, 3 pt., brand new rubber, power steering, top quality restoration
730			G	$8,700	7/17/2010	NEMT	WF, 3 pt.

John Deere

Model	Year	Hours	Condition	Price	Date	Area	Comments
730			G	$10,200	7/17/2010	NEMT	Standard diesel
730			G	$2,200	6/23/2010	SEIA	2, cyl. diesel, NF, fenders, 15.5x38 tires
730			G	$13,750	6/19/2010	SWIL	Old restoration/repaint, fenders, PTO, lights, hyd., deluxe seat, 3 pt., belt pulley
730			G	$14,750	6/19/2010	SWIL	Running, restored, rear wheel weights, fenders, PTO, lights, hyd.
730			G	$3,000	6/5/2010	WCMO	LP, WF, 1 hyd.
730			F	$1,250	1/30/2010	NETX	LP, for parts
730			G	$4,700	1/30/2010	NETX	Diesel, electric start
730			G	$6,700	1/30/2010	NETX	Diesel standard, electric start
730			G	$13,000	1/30/2010	NETX	LP, standard, rare, low production, very hard to find, runs
820	1957		G	$11,000	10/12/2013	NESD	Diesel, WF, power steering, Pony motor, black dash, SN 8202900
820	1957		E	$17,000	9/21/2013	SEMN	Professionally restored
820	1957		G	$4,500	8/24/2013	SWWI	Unrestored, diesel
820	1957		G	$3,000	6/18/2013	SCSK	2WD, Pup start, diesel, dual hyd., 540 PTO, 23.1x26 rubber
820	1957		G	$12,750	3/20/2012	WCIL	Diesel, power steering, float ride seat, no PTO, total restoration, 18.4x34 Firestone tires, SN 8202871
820	1957		E	$6,500	10/7/2011	NWSD	Restored, diesel, PTO, power steering, hyd., Pony motor runs, good rubber
820	1958		G	$5,600	10/7/2011	NWSD	Standard, diesel
820	1958		G	$6,600	8/24/2011	Online	*BigIron.com,* item in Iowa, unknown hours, 5 speed, 2 cyl. diesel, 2 hyd., 540 PTO, gas Pony motor, new gauges, new tires
820	1958	1,539	G	$8,600	5/11/2011	Online	*BigIron.com,* diesel, 1958 Pony start
820	1971		G	$3,200	6/29/2012	NETX	32 hp, diesel, 2WD, OROPS, 7F/1R, 13.6x28 tires
820	1973		G	$5,000	9/21/2013	WCMI	Diesel, 3 pt., PTO, 14.9x28 rear tires, loader, unrestored
820		8,200	E	$9,500	4/16/2014	ECAB	2WD, 31 PTO hp diesel, starter Pup, 18.4x34 rear, 3 rib front, 1 hyd.
820			G	$8,750	8/3/2013	ECMN	Standard diesel, PTO, new 18.4x34 tires
820			G	$5,100	5/29/2013	Online	*BigIron.com,* item in Nebraska, Wheatland standard, 7.7 L, 2 cyl. diesel
820			G	$6,250	3/23/2013	NEIN	Original, cab, runs
820		3,552	P	$1,800	4/7/2012	SCOK	
820			G	$5,750	3/24/2012	NEIN	Pony, 4 sets of rear weights, PTO, hyd., repainted, runs
820			G	$14,000	3/24/2012	NEIN	PTO, hyd., restored, runs
820			G	$4,900	1/31/2012	NEIN	Cyl. diesel, PTO, hyd., 3 sets of weights
820			G	$4,200	10/22/2011	NECO	Diesel, PTO
820			E	$11,000	4/2/2011	SEMN	Diesel, Pony start, new rubber, wheel weights, very straight
820			G	$11,000	9/18/2010	ECMO	

John Deere

Model	Year	Hours	Condition	Price	Date	Area	Comments
820			F	$3,750	9/11/2010	NCIL	Diesel, standard, steering stuck, bad Pony motor
820			P	$2,700	9/3/2010	NEIN	Dead row, needs work and may not run or drive, as is
820			G	$5,100	8/14/2010	WCMN	New Firestone 18.4x34 tires, outside weights, good Pony, WF
820			G	$6,100	8/7/2010	SCMN	Diesel, WF, Pony start, 1 hyd., PTO, 18.4Rx34 tires, SN 8206327
820			G	$5,400	7/17/2010	NEMT	
820			G	$3,300	6/5/2010	NETN	Diesel
820			G	$6,100	6/5/2010	WCMO	Diesel
820			G	$7,200	2/13/2010	SWIA	
830	1958		E	$14,700	8/24/2011	ECMN	Standard, Pony start, PTO, power steering, new 18.4x34 rubber
830	1958		G	$11,000	6/25/2011	ECIA	Diesel, electric start, SN 8300469, electric start, PTO, hydraulics, repainted
830	1959		G	$10,000	9/21/2013	WCMI	Diesel, 3 pt., 2 hyd., electric start, power steering, 18.4x34 rear tires, weights, restored
830	1959		G	$10,000	5/23/2012	Online	*BigIron.com,* item in South Dakota, 6 speed, 2 cyl. diesel, 1 hyd., 540 PTO, gas Pony motor just OH, factory John Deere cab, power steering
830	1959		G	$16,500	3/20/2012	WCIL	18.4x34 rear Firestone tires (new), 2 hyd., 540 PTO, older restoration, SN 8304843
830	1959		E	$20,000	8/6/2011	SEWI	2 cyl., electric start, shipped 7/2/59 to Medicine Lake, Mon., foot throttle control pedal
830	1959		G	$8,000	5/29/2010	NCIL	Diesel standard, all original, antique tires, low hours
830	1960		G	$20,000	11/9/2013	SWON	Diesel, electric start, WF
830	1960	4,991	E	$13,500	6/25/2011	ECIA	Diesel, Pony, SN 8306668, PTO, hyd., rear weights, excellent original
830	1960	4,500	G	$11,750	6/22/2011	Online	*BigIron.com,* item in Oklahoma, 6F/1R, 2 cyl. diesel, 2 hyd., 540 PTO, electric start, power steering, buggy top needs cover, shedded
830	1960		G	$9,000	5/14/2011	SWSK	Diesel, electric start, belt pulley, 2 hyd., 18.4x34 rear tires
830	1960		G	$18,500	5/29/2010	NCIL	Diesel, good running condition
830	1960		G	$20,000	5/29/2010	NCIL	Diesel, Rice special, complete restore
830	1974		G	$2,600	6/29/2012	NETX	35 hp diesel, 2WD, open station, 14.9x28 tires
830	1974	889	G	$3,800	2/1/2011	NEIN	
830			G	$11,000	8/3/2013	ECMN	Standard diesel, electric start, new 18.4x34 tires, dual hyd.
830		2,922	G	$24,750	4/10/2013	SWMN	Diesel, electric start, PTO, original tires, seat and paint
830			G	$10,000	3/23/2013	NEIN	Diesel, Pony, PTO, dual hyd., runs
830			G	$13,000	3/23/2013	NEIN	Electric start, repainted, PTO, dual hyd., runs
830			G	$16,000	3/23/2013	NEIN	Electric start, dual hyd., PTO, new tires, restored, diesel

John Deere

Model	Year	Hours	Condition	Price	Date	Area	Comments
830			G	$3,100	1/21/2013	NCIA	WF, 50 hp, 2WD
830			G	$10,200	11/30/2012	WCMN	Diesel, Wheatland, fenders, power steering hyd./PTO, new paint restoration
830			G	$7,000	8/22/2012	Online	*BigIron.com,* item in Oklahoma, 2WD, 6 speed, John Deere diesel, 1 hyd., 540 PTO, electric start, rear weights inside and out, swinging drawbar
830			G	$2,400	8/4/2012	NEAR	3 cyl. diesel, 3 pt., 540 PTO, 16.9x28 rears
830			G	$7,900	7/21/2012	ECIA	Pony start, rear weights, PTO, hyd., foot throttle, runs
830			G	$10,600	6/16/2012	ECIN	Electrical start, weights, PTO, hyd., nice original
830			G	$10,000	3/24/2012	NEIN	Diesel, electric start, 26" rear tires, older repaint, runs
830			G	$14,500	3/24/2012	NEIN	Diesel, electric start, PTO, hyd., restored, runs
830			G	$3,750	1/31/2012	NEIN	Diesel, 3 pt., PTO, hyd.
830			G	$2,600	1/28/2012	ECMO	Diesel
830		1,268	G	$3,600	10/27/2011	NETX	EROPS, 3 pt., diesel
830			G	$9,900	10/22/2011	NECO	Electric start, diesel, no PTO
830			G	$2,000	11/20/2010	NCLA	Hyd.
830			G	$3,300	11/18/2010	SEOK	
830			G	$7,500	9/11/2010	NCIL	Diesel, standard, Pony motor, new tires
830			G	$15,000	9/4/2010	NEIN	Electric, dual hyd.
830			F	$10,250	7/17/2010	NEMT	Stuck, industrial
830			G	$10,500	7/17/2010	NEMT	
830			G	$10,600	1/30/2010	NETX	Like new rear tires
950	1978	1,789	G	$2,800	8/20/2013	WCIL	Diesel, 72" belly mower
1010	1961		G	$3,400	6/18/2011	SWMN	SN 15174, front and rear weights, float ride seat, original
1010	1962		E	$9,000	9/15/2011	ECIA	Special, restored, WF
1010	1962		G	$6,750	6/18/2011	SWMN	RS, SN 24904, front weight, power, set rear wheels
1010	1962		G	$2,000	7/10/2010	SEIA	
1010	1962	1,468	G	$2,200	6/23/2010	Online	*BigIron.com,* item in Oklahoma, 5 speed, John Deere gas, 36 PTO hp, 30 drawbar hp
1010	1962		G	$1,250	4/9/2010	WCNE	3 pt., 1 hyd., 38 hp
1010	1962	5,500	G	$4,100	3/5/2010	NCMO	2WD, 3 pt., 1 hyd.
1010	1963		G	$5,500	6/18/2011	SWMN	Utility, SN 38255, hyd., fenders, new tires, repainted
1010	1964		G	$4,300	6/15/2013	WCMI	WF, 3 pt., 13.6x28 tires, front-end loader, SN51949
1010	1964		G	$3,700	8/11/2011	WCMN	Open station, WF, aftermarket 3 pt., PTO, front. aux. hyd., all hyd. loader, like new
1010	1964		F	$2,000	11/13/2010	NWIL	Gas, WF, 3 pt.
1010	1965		G	$3,800	6/18/2011	SWMN	1010 row crop, SN 53587, NF, sickle mower, original
1010	1965		G	$7,500	6/18/2011	SWMN	Utility, SN 56792, turf tires, 3 pt., float ride seat, repainted, yellow

John Deere

Model	Year	Hours	Condition	Price	Date	Area	Comments
1010	1965		G	$15,000	6/18/2011	SWMN	RS, gas, 3 pt., SN 55718, converted to high crop, repainted, new tires
1010	1965		G	$4,700	7/10/2010	SEIA	Diesel
1010			G	$3,100	11/9/2013	SWON	Standard, 41 bottom cultivators and side dresser, 5 speed
1010			G	$4,500	6/28/2013	NEMO	Special, WF, factory 3 pt., 12.4x24 rubber
1010			G	$4,000	2/6/2013	SESD	RS, WF, fenders, 3 pt.
1010			G	$3,900	10/24/2012	WCWI	13.6x28 tires
1010			G	$3,700	7/21/2012	ECIA	Power steering, runs, repainted
1010			G	$3,400	3/24/2012	NEIN	RS, 3 pt., PTO, original, runs
1010			G	$7,900	3/24/2012	NEIN	RS, completely restored, 3 pt., PTO, runs
1010			G	$13,750	3/24/2012	NEIN	Diesel, 3 pt., PTO, front and rear weights, runs
1010			G	$2,250	1/28/2012	SEAB	
1010			G	$3,750	10/22/2011	NECO	
1010			G	$1,800	6/8/2011	Online	*BigIron.com,* item in Missouri, sliding gear, gas, external PTO, 4 cyl. gas
1010		2,099	G	$4,425	3/9/2011	Online	*BigIron.com,* item in Colorado, John Deere 46A loader, 5 speed manual, 4 cyl. gas, OH in 2009, 1 hyd., 540 PTO, 3 pt., 5' bucket
1010			G	$2,100	2/25/2011	NENC	12.4x28 rear tires, 5.5x16 front tires, 540 PTO, gas
1010			F	$1,500	12/30/2010	ECMN	4 cyl., gas, 5 speed, adj. WF, fenders
1010			G	$3,000	9/4/2010	NEIN	
1010			G	$4,000	9/4/2010	NEIN	Crawler, blade
1010			G	$4,500	9/4/2010	NEIN	RS
1010			G	$14,000	9/4/2010	NEIN	Diesel
1010			G	$7,600	8/14/2010	WCMN	Completely restored, WF, 3 pt., PTO
1010			G	$2,800	7/10/2010	SEIA	
1010			G	$2,000	6/5/2010	WCMO	Utility, 1 hyd., WF fenders
1010			P	$1,900	5/26/2010	ECSD	Not running
1010		2,421	G	$1,600	5/7/2010	WCOH	5 speed, no 3 pt.
1010 RS	1962		G	$18,500	9/6/2012	Online	*IQBID.com,* item in Minnesota, complete restoration
1020	1965		G	$4,000	8/28/2010	SCTX	WF
1020	1966		G	$3,200	6/18/2011	SWMN	Gas, SN 35760, rear weights, 3 pt., old repaint, mix matched tires
1020	1967	4,000	G	$7,000	9/22/2012	WCMN	Gas, no cab, under frame muffler, WF, 3 pt., 1 hyd., good 13.9x36 tires, PTO, very nice metal
1020	1968		G	$4,000	9/21/2013	WCMI	Diesel, 3 pt., PTO, 1 hyd., electric start, underslung exhaust, 16.9x24 rear tires, restored
1020	1971	7,342	G	$4,800	8/20/2011	NEMN	Gas, WF, 3 pt., Hi/Lo 5 speed, PTO, 1 hyd., SN 127009T
1020	1972		F	$3,000	12/7/2011	NCIA	
1020	1973	8,647	G	$2,375	6/23/2010	Online	*BigIron.com,* item in Colorado, 16 speed manual, 3 cyl. gas, rear tires 16.9x24, front tires 7.5Lx15, 1 hyd., 540 PTO, 3 pt.

John Deere

Model	Year	Hours	Condition	Price	Date	Area	Comments
1020		2,797	G	$2,900	4/3/2014	NEIN	Gas, WF, 13.6x28, 1 hyd., top link
1020			G	$4,500	3/26/2014	ECMS	
1020			F	$3,600	2/4/2014	WCOK	3 cyl., 1 hyd.
1020		194	G	$2,731	12/4/2013	Online	*BigIron.com,* item in Nebraska, mower, 8F/4R, 3 cyl., 12.4x38 rear tires, 6.50x16SL front tires, gas, 6' mower
1020		2,391	G	$3,600	4/2/2013	ECIA	John Deere 4 cyl., 3 pt., 540 PTO
1020		2,089	G	$7,100	7/25/2012	Online	*BigIron.com,* item in Nebraska, gas, 540 PTO, 4 speed, Hi/Lo range, tool box, live PTO, no visible leaks/welds, John Deere 148 5' loader bucket
1020			G	$4,200	6/9/2012	ECNE	Gas, 3 pt., PTO, fenders, weights, runs, repainted
1020			G	$7,000	3/24/2012	NEIN	Hard-nose orchard, front weights, 3 pt., PTO, hyd., original, runs
1020			G	$2,000	2/18/2012	SWAR	
1020			G	$4,250	2/4/2012	ECSC	
1020		1,365	G	$2,900	2/2/2012	NEIN	2WD, 13.6x28 rear tires, WF, 1 hyd., gas
1020			G	$3,000	1/28/2012	ECMO	Gas
1020		1,567	G	$7,700	10/28/2011	NETX	John Deere 520 loader, 66" bucket and joystick, 2WD, open station, 14.9x28 tires
1020			G	$5,750	10/22/2011	NECO	Gas, 3 pt.
1020		329	G	$2,500	5/13/2011	ECMS	Front end loader, hay spear
1020			G	$4,600	4/2/2011	SEMN	Diesel, row crop, front weights, 3 pt., 12.4x36 tires
1020			E	$5,500	4/2/2011	SEMN	Diesel, front weights, 3 pt., very sharp, 13.6x28 tires
1020			G	$3,200	11/18/2010	SEOK	John Deere loader
1020			G	$3,750	11/18/2010	SEOK	John Deere 47 loader and boom
1020			G	$4,000	11/18/2010	SEOK	John Deere 47 loader
1020			F	$4,600	11/18/2010	SEOK	
1020			G	$9,000	9/9/2010	NWWI	
1020			G	$6,300	9/4/2010	NEIN	John Deere 47 loader, bucket and manure bucket
1020			G	$21,000	9/4/2010	NEIN	Orchard
1020			G	$4,200	7/17/2010	NEMT	
1020			G	$3,400	6/5/2010	NETN	John Deere 37 FR loader
1520	1969		G	$3,750	9/21/2013	WCMI	Gas, 3 pt., PTO, 1 hyd., electric start, 13.6x38 rear tires, restored
1520	1969		G	$6,000	6/18/2011	SWMN	Gas, down draft exhaust, SN 101023, new tires, 2 hyd., 3 pt., repainted
1520	1971	1,902	G	$4,500	2/1/2011	NEIN	Dual hyd., 3 pt.
1520	1973	3,553	F	$3,520	9/26/2012	Online	*PurpleWave.com,* item in Iowa, collar shift 8 speed., Hi/Lo, 14.9x28 rear tires
1520			G	$9,000	10/22/2011	NECO	Diesel, new rear and front tires
1520			G	$9,000	10/22/2011	NECO	Diesel, new rear and front tires
1520			G	$6,000	9/15/2011	ECIA	Restored
1520			G	$4,700	8/14/2010	WCMN	1 hyd., PTO, new paint, WF
1530	1975	2,120	E	$5,000	8/21/2012	WCIL	ROPS canopy, diesel, 3 pt., 15.5x38 tires, front and rear weights

TRACTORS

John Deere

Model	Year	Hours	Condition	Price	Date	Area	Comments
1530			G	$8,000	8/24/2013	SEMN	Diesel, open station, 3 pt., 540 PTO, 1 hyd., John Deere 145 loader
1530			G	$3,750	2/22/2013	SWKY	
1530			G	$2,800	1/19/2013	NEMS	
1530			F	$5,300	10/22/2011	ECTX	John Deere 145 loader, 2 hyd.
1530			G	$3,200	11/20/2010	NCLA	Diesel, 3 pt.
1530			G	$5,900	5/26/2010	ECSD	Loader
1830	1973		G	$10,500	4/10/2013	SWSK	2WD, John Deere 37 front-end loader, 66 PTO hp, 2 hyd., PTO, Groening 3 pt., 16.9x30 rear, 7.5x16.5L front
1830	1975		F	$6,600	4/8/2011	WCSK	2WD, 60 PTO hp, dual PTO, 2 hyd., 3 rib, cab
1830	1978	3,654	G	$4,000	4/18/2011	WCSK	2WD, John Deere 146 front end loader, 60 PTO hp, 3 pt., Cozy cab
2010	1960	4,478	G	$4,900	7/27/2011	ECND	Open station, synchro, 1 hyd., 3 pt., 540 PTO, Koyker K2 loader, 66" bucket
2010	1961		G	$7,000	9/28/2013	SESD	Diesel, synchro, 13.9x36 tires, John Deere 36 loader
2010	1961	1,880	G	$1,650	8/28/2013	Online	*PurpleWave.com,* item in Missouri, John Deere 4 cyl. gas, 3 pt., drawbar, rear hyd. hyd., John Deere 609 6' rotary mower, 78,14 front tires, 13.6x28 rear tires
2010	1961		G	$3,000	3/7/2013	ECIA	WF, 3 pt.
2010	1961		G	$5,000	3/7/2013	SEIA	Gas, WF, 3 pt.
2010	1961	2,234	G	$4,500	9/1/2011	WCMN	Gas, row crop, WF, synchro, 3 pt., PTO, 1 hyd.
2010	1961	2,234	G	$4,500	9/1/2011	Online	*IQBID.com,* row crop, WF, gas, synchro, 1 hyd., 3 pt., PTO, fenders
2010	1961	5,122	G	$4,700	7/12/2011	Online	*IQBID.com,* 1 hyd., 3 pt., PTO, block heater, straight tin, good paint
2010	1961		G	$6,100	6/18/2011	SWMN	Diesel, SN 14843, factory WF, power, set rear wheels, 3 pt., hyd., restored
2010	1961	3,030	G	$2,400	1/29/2011	ECMO	
2010	1962		G	$2,100	12/1/2010	ECND	Johnson Works loader
2010	1963		G	$2,100	9/13/2012	SEIA	NF, repainted, no hyd. pump
2010	1963		G	$4,900	6/18/2011	SWMN	LP, row crop, SN 37222, new tires, down draft exhaust, 3 pt., hyd., repainted
2010	1963	3,570	G	$2,900	6/16/2010	SEND	NF, Roll-O-Matic, open station, comfort cab, 1 hyd., 3 pt., PTO, fenders, 12.4x36 rear tires, John Deere 36 hyd. loader
2010	1963	3,570	G	$2,900	6/16/2010	SEND	NF, Roll-O-Matic, open station, comfort cab, 1 hyd., 3 pt., PTO, fenders, rock shaft, PTO
2010	1963		F	$2,250	2/20/2010	ECMI	NF, 3 pt., 1 hyd., gas, rough
2010	1964		G	$3,400	4/3/2013	NEND	Soft cab, gas, 540/1,000 PTO, 6' belly mower
2010	1965		F	$3,200	4/26/2011	SWMN	OH in 1990, gas, NF, no cab
2010	1965		F	$2,500	11/13/2010	NWIL	LP, WF, 3 pt.
2010	1966		G	$7,250	6/25/2011	ECIA	Diesel, high crop, SN 36608, new tires, 3 pt., repainted

John Deere

Model	Year	Hours	Condition	Price	Date	Area	Comments
2010		1,249	P	$1,700	4/3/2014	NEIN	NF, loader, 13.9x36, won't start, trip bucket
2010		3,073	G	$1,750	1/29/2014	Online	*BigIron.com,* item in Utah, synchro 8F/3R, 4 cyl. diesel, 14.9x28 rear tires, 215/70Rx15 front tires, 1 hyd., 540 PTO
2010			G	$1,500	12/4/2013	ECIN	
2010			G	$5,550	12/4/2013	Online	*BigIron.com,* item in Wyoming, loader, synco, gas, 13.9x36 rear tires, 7.5Lx15 front tires, 540 PTO hyd., 3 pt., Cozy cab
2010		3,831	G	$4,000	5/1/2013	Online	*BigIron.com,* item in Nebraska, loader, 540 PTO
2010			G	$1,700	2/22/2013	SWKY	Hyd. PTO, gas
2010			G	$4,250	2/6/2013	SESD	Motor OH
2010			G	$3,000	8/16/2012	Online	*IQBID.com,* item in Minnesota, 2WD, NF, diesel, 3 pt., PTO, no top link, 13.9x38 tires
2010			G	$2,050	8/4/2012	ECMN	Gas, 3 pt., 540 PTO, 1 hyd., 13.6x28 tires, 48 John Deere loader
2010			G	$1,600	8/1/2012	NEOK	
2010			G	$2,800	7/21/2012	ECIA	Industrial, loader, original, gas, runs
2010			G	$5,500	6/9/2012	ECNE	LP, row crop, fenders, new tires, hyd., PTO, 3 pt., repainted
2010		4,935	F	$3,400	5/8/2012	Online	*IQBID.com,* gas, 3 pt., 1 hyd., PTO
2010			G	$5,000	3/24/2012	NEIN	Diesel, high crop, repainted, new tires, runs
2010			F	$3,500	2/2/2012	NEIN	
2010			G	$2,100	1/31/2012	NEIN	Row crop, NF
2010			F	$4,500	8/21/2011	WCOH	WF, gas, John Deere 36A loader
2010			G	$825	6/22/2011	Online	*BigIron.com,* item in Nebraska, synchro, 540 PTO, for parts, does not run, WF, 4 cyl. gas, 3 pt., John Deere 86 loader, 5' bucket, 2 spool valve
2010			G	$10,500	6/18/2011	SWMN	Gas, high crop, no tag, repainted, new tires, 3 pt.
2010		1,225	G	$3,550	3/17/2011	ECMN	WF, gas
2010		4,448	G	$3,400	1/8/2011	ECMI	Gas, Freeman loader
2010		3,266	G	$2,500	12/4/2010	SEMN	Gas, WF, synchro, 3 pt., fenders, 1 hyd., power adj. wheels
2010			P	$3,250	9/23/2010	NCOH	Row crop, loader, clutch went out sale day
2010			G	$4,500	9/4/2010	NEIN	Diesel, high crop, 3 pt.
2010			P	$1,500	9/3/2010	NEIN	Diesel, high crop, dead row, needs work and may not run or drive, as is
2010			G	$3,100	8/14/2010	WCMN	All new rubber, spin outs, 3 pt., PTO, 1 hyd., NF
2010		6	G	$40,000	7/17/2010	NEMT	Diesel
2010			G	$800	6/5/2010	WCMO	Power set rims, 1 hyd.
2010			E	$2,100	6/5/2010	SEMN	Gas, industrial, canopy, hyd. loader, PTO, hyd., new
2010			G	$7,000	6/5/2010	ECMN	Gas, WF, loader, fluid in tires, runs well
2010			G	$5,500	5/15/2010	WCIN	Gas, loader, fresh paint, looked good, tires above average

John Deere

Model	Year	Hours	Condition	Price	Date	Area	Comments
2010			G	$3,500	5/6/2010	SWMN	Gas
2010R	1965	2,396	G	$3,500	11/9/2013	SWON	Power steering, 3 pt., PTO
2020	1966		G	$3,800	9/21/2013	WCMI	Gas, 3 pt., PTO, 1 hyd., electric start, 13.6x28 rear tires, restored
2020	1966		G	$4,600	1/28/2012	ECMO	Loader
2020	1966		G	$4,900	6/18/2011	SWMN	Gas, SN 28146, new tires, 2 hyd., 3 pt., repainted
2020	1966	5,092	F	$3,500	12/2/2010	ECWY	4 cyl. gas, 2 hyd., 540 PTO, 14.9x28 tires, wheel weights, mid-mount PTO, John Deere 47 loader
2020	1968		G	$16,250	4/6/2013	SWSK	2WD, John Deere 47 front-end loader, 54 hp, 4 cyl. gas, 3 pt., 540 PTO, dual hyd., 14.9x28 rear rubber, 5' bucket, joystick control
2020	1968	8,648	G	$4,850	8/3/2011	Online	*IQBID.com,* gas, hyd., 3 pt., PTO, new 16.9x28 rear tires, John Deere 47 hyd. loader
2020	1968	1,394	G	$5,720	5/12/2010	Online	*PurpleWave.com,* item in Kansas, 540 PTO, dual hubs
2020	1969	1,629	G	$4,290	8/14/2013	Online	*PurpleWave.com,* item in Kansas, John Deere 4 cyl. gas, manual, John Deere 47 loader, 3 pt.
2020	1970		E	$20,000	3/16/2013	NEIL	Restored, restored John Deere 48 loader, restored by employees at AHW (Deere dealership in Somonauk, IL) to sell at auction to benefit young 25-year-old co-worker with cancer
2020	1971	5,591	G	$5,100	8/21/2012	WCIL	1 dual action hyd. (factory), 3 single action hyd. ports, canopy, tool box, ROPS
2020		1,507	G	$4,270	3/5/2014	Online	*BigIron.com,* item in Nebraska, Hi/Lo 8F/4R, 4 cyl. gas, 2 hyd., drawbar, 3 pt., 540 PTO, wheel weights
2020		1,507	G	$4,270	3/5/2014	Online	*BigIron.com,* item in Nebraska, Hi/Lo 8F/4R, 4 cyl. gas, 45 hp, 2 hyd., drawbar, 3 pt., 540 PTO, weights
2020			G	$3,800	1/4/2014	WCNY	Fender, 1 hyd., 3 pt., PTO
2020			F	$2,200	10/3/2013	NCIN	Gas
2020			G	$3,000	10/3/2013	NCIN	
2020			P	$1,950	5/31/2013	NCOK	3 pt., PTO, needs work
2020			F	$4,950	2/9/2013	SWOH	Diesel, WF, John Deere 37 loader
2020			G	$1,900	10/24/2012	WCWI	Water in oil
2020			G	$6,750	5/12/2012	NWIL	WF, gas, Cozy cab, 2 hyd., 290 hours on tach., hour meter doesn't work but executor of the estate believes that hours low, but unknown, one owner, 3 pt., 8 speed Hi/Lo.
2020			G	$4,000	10/22/2011	NECO	Diesel
2020			G	$29,000	10/22/2011	NECO	Diesel, orchard, PTO
2020			G	$36,000	10/22/2011	NECO	Diesel, orchard, PTO
2020			G	$4,000	8/11/2011	WCMN	WF, 3 pt., PTO, original
2020		4,542	G	$24,000	6/18/2011	SWMN	Orchard/grove, diesel, no tag, full orchard sheet metal, repainted

John Deere

Model	Year	Hours	Condition	Price	Date	Area	Comments
2020			G	$5,700	4/1/2011	Online	*AuctionTime.com,* item in Indiana, John Deere 148 loader, 4 cyl. gas, Goodyear rear tires
2020			G	$6,500	9/4/2010	NEIN	Grove tractor
2020			G	$9,200	9/4/2010	NEIN	Gas, nice, original
2020			G	$5,400	7/17/2010	NEMT	
2020			G	$5,700	6/23/2010	NEWI	Gas, 3 pt., 16.9x28 tires 80%, John Deere all hyd. loader, 6' material bucket, off a small hobby farm
2020			G	$6,500	5/1/2010	ECIA	Diesel, John Deere 47 loader
2020			G	$5,800	3/20/2010	NWIL	Gas, WF, John Deere 48 loader, 1,000 hours on OH
2030	1974	2,368	G	$5,100	12/26/2013	Online	*BigIron.com,* item in Nebraska, 8 speed twin stick, 4 cyl. diesel, 15.5x38 rear tires, 7.50x10 front tires, 16 car tires, 540 PTO, 2 hyd. hyd., 3 pt. lift, WF, fenders, lights, block heater, cast wheels
2030	1974	7,184	G	$6,100	3/27/2013	Online	*BigIron.com,* item in Minnesota, collar shift Hi/Lo
2030	1974		G	$8,300	3/10/2012	NCOH	John Deere 45 loader
2030	1974		G	$7,500	12/7/2011	NCIA	Diesel, John Deere 145 loader
2030	1975	5,199	G	$3,500	3/15/2011	WCIL	540 PTO
2030	1975	4,288	G	$6,000	3/4/2011	NWIA	Diesel, WF, 3 pt., 2 hyd., 7 speed Hi/Lo., 16.9x28 rear rubber (all rubber like new), SN 219863T
2030	1975	1,891	G	$10,000	2/1/2011	NEIN	Dual hyd., 3 pt.
2030			G	$2,500	4/3/2014	NEIN	John Deere 148 loader, bucket, 2 hyd., no 3 pt. arms, diesel
2030			G	$6,400	3/8/2014	NWLA	John Deere 175 loader, hyd.
2030		2,401	G	$4,600	2/22/2014	SWAR	John Deere 48 loader
2030			G	$5,100	12/4/2013	ECIN	
2030		2,132	G	$6,250	10/3/2013	NCIN	WF, diesel
2030			G	$4,100	7/10/2013	Online	*BigIron.com,* item in Nebraska
2030			G	$5,000	6/22/2013	SEMN	16.9x30 tires, 3 pt. dual hyd., PTO, John Deere 146 hyd. loader
2030			G	$12,000	6/1/2013	SEMN	540 PTO, John Deere 145 loader
2030			G	$4,950	3/27/2013	Online	*PurpleWave.com,* item in Kansas, John Deere 4 cyl. diesel, manual, 540 PTO
2030		4,486	G	$4,500	3/2/2013	ECMN	John Deere 146 loader, 16.9x30 tires, 3 pt., 2 hyd., 540 PTO
2030			G	$5,000	3/2/2013	ECMN	John Deere loader, 16.9x28 tires, 3 pt., 540 PTO, rear wheel weights
2030			G	$5,000	2/22/2013	SWKY	8 speed, rack, pinion axle
2030		5,983	G	$4,400	12/13/2012	WCIA	Diesel, fenders, 16.9x28 tires, 60% rubber, John Deere 146 loader
2030			G	$8,000	12/8/2012	NWIL	Diesel, John Deere 146 loader, 3 pt., shows 930 hours, 90% rear tires
2030			G	$5,200	7/21/2012	ECIA	Diesel, repainted, fenders, runs
2030			G	$4,500	1/28/2012	ECMO	2 hyd., dual PTO, new batteries, rebuilt PTO
2030			G	$3,300	10/30/2011	ECMN	Gas, loader, 3 pt.

John Deere

Model	Year	Hours	Condition	Price	Date	Area	Comments
2030			G	$8,400	7/30/2011	ECMO	John Deere 145 loader
2030			G	$5,500	3/25/2011	ECWI	Gas, John Deere 145 loader, 1 hyd.
2030			P	$900	11/17/2010	ECMS	Salvage
2030			G	$8,300	10/16/2010	SWMO	
2030			G	$3,450	8/9/2010	WCMO	Tires 90%
2030			F	$6,000	3/6/2010	SEMN	John Deere 145 loader, hours unknown
2040	1976	294	G	$3,960	10/10/2012	Online	*PurpleWave.com,* item in Texas, 3 cyl. diesel, manual, hand and foot throttle
2040	1976	2,850	G	$6,000	7/30/2010	ECIA	Diesel, 14.9x28 tires
2130	1976	12,528	G	$5,000	7/18/2013	SCSK	2WD, John Deere 146 front-end loader, grapple, 66 PTO hp diesel, dual PTO, 2 hyd., 18.4x30 rear
2130	1976		G	$11,000	6/20/2011	ECSK	John Deere 146 loader, 66 PTO hp, 3 pt., 18.4x30 rear tires, quick attach bucket, SN 200158
2130	1977		G	$8,250	4/14/2014	SCSK	2WD, 66 PTO hp, Hi/Lo 8 speed, Hi/Lo, 2 hyd., 540/1,000 PTO, 3 pt., roll guard canopy, 10 front weights, 7.50x16 front, 15.5x38 rear
2130	1977		G	$8,000	3/14/2013	SESK	2WD, John Deere 146 front-end loader, Hi/Lo, dual PTO, 3 pt., 18.4x30 tires with fluid
2130	1977		F	$15,000	4/4/2011	SWSK	2WD, John Deere 146 front-end loader, 66 PTO hp, diesel, 6' bucket
2240	1976	3,400	G	$5,000	12/5/2013	NEIN	Loader
2240	1976		G	$3,600	3/20/2012	WCIL	
2240	1978	1,473	G	$8,910	6/8/2010	Online	*PurpleWave.com,* item in Kansas, tach. replaced, diesel, John Deere 145 front-end loader, 540 PTO
2440	1976		G	$3,900	12/5/2013	NEIN	
2440	1976		G	$5,500	2/23/2013	ECMI	3 pt., PTO, 1 hyd., 16.9x30 tires, loader attach
2440	1976		F	$5,000	4/12/2012	NEMI	Gas, John Deere 146 hyd. loader, 1 hyd., PTO
2440	1977	2,863	G	$7,000	3/7/2013	ECIA	3 pt., 1 hyd., mid-mount 1 hyd., John Deere 175 loader
2440	1978	8,162	G	$5,300	2/25/2012	WCMI	146 loader, WF, 3 pt., 484 PTO, new batteries
2440	1978		F	$3,300	11/4/2011	SEWA	2WD, roll bar, 3 pt., PTO, hyd., 21.5Lx16.1 rear tires, high hours
2510	1964	4,400	G	$6,200	4/11/2011	Online	*AuctionTime.com*, 2WD
2510	1966		E	$11,300	8/10/2013	NCIA	Diesel, WF, SN 001349
2510	1966	5,258	G	$4,500	7/14/2012	NWIA	Gas, NF, 3 pt., synchro
2510	1966	8,473	G	$13,500	7/14/2012	NWIA	Gas, WF, PS, 3 pt., new paint
2510	1966		G	$14,500	7/14/2012	NWIA	Diesel, PS, complete OH, 2 hyd., 3 pt., WF
2510	1966		G	$5,700	10/14/2011	WCMI	Gas, shedded, WF, John Deere loader and bucket
2510	1966	2,282	G	$4,600	7/30/2011	ECMO	Gas, new clutch, starter and battery
2510	1966		G	$11,250	6/18/2011	SWMN	Diesel, SN 2412, new tires, front weights, 2 hyd., synchro, repainted
2510	1966		G	$14,000	6/18/2011	SWMN	Gas, SN 8131, front weights, new tires, NF, PS

John Deere

Model	Year	Hours	Condition	Price	Date	Area	Comments
2510	1966	3,618	G	$4,800	4/9/2011	WCNE	WF, diesel, 3 pt., no cab
2510	1966		G	$3,400	9/8/2010	NWMN	Synchro, 4,775 hours on OH
2510	1967	3,807	G	$4,600	12/29/2012	WCMI	Diesel, WF, hyd.
2510	1967	5,250	G	$6,300	9/13/2012	Online	*IQBID.com,* item in Iowa, gas, John Deere 48 loader, rear weights, 540/1,000 PTO, 3 pt.
2510	1967		G	$11,500	3/31/2012	NEIA	Diesel, WF, 3 pt., 2 hyd., 1,000 hours on OH
2510	1967		F	$3,900	8/6/2011	NCIA	WF
2510	1967		F	$2,250	9/8/2010	NWMN	Synchro, 2 hyd., 3 pt., 80% rubber
2510	1968	1,400	G	$5,750	7/14/2012	NWIA	NF, 1 hyd., synchro, 3 pt., diff. lock
2510	1968	10,165	G	$4,600	3/15/2011	WCIL	Gas, synchro, WF, 540 PTO, John Deere 47 loader and bucket
2510			G	$6,000	4/4/2014	SEND	3 pt., PTO, dual 345 loader
2510			G	$5,000	3/26/2014	ECMS	
2510			G	$7,500	7/10/2013	NETX	SN T713R005441R
2510			G	$4,600	3/23/2013	NEIN	Diesel, PS, WF, 3 pt., fenders, runs
2510			G	$24,500	3/23/2013	NEIN	Diesel, high crop, new tires, restored, runs
2510			G	$11,900	3/2/2013	ECNJ	PS, diesel, OH, high hours, 2 hyd., straight
2510		6,034	G	$3,500	8/16/2012	Online	*IQBID.com,* item in Minnesota, WF, gas, 1 hyd., 3rd arm, top link, new 15.5x38 tires
2510		2,190	G	$5,450	7/21/2012	ECIA	Nice original
2510			G	$20,000	7/21/2012	ECIA	High crop, synchro, restored, 1 of 103 total built
2510		2,280	G	$5,000	6/2/2012	SEMN	3 pt.
2510			G	$6,000	3/24/2012	NEIN	Gas, synchro, dual hyd., PTO, original, runs
2510			G	$10,750	3/24/2012	NEIN	High crop, no tag, 3 pt., PTO, hyd., runs
2510			G	$19,000	3/24/2012	NEIN	Diesel, high crop, synchro, good tag, rare, 1 of 103 built, runs
2510		5,500	G	$3,100	3/21/2012	ECMN	WF
2510			G	$11,400	10/22/2011	NECO	Diesel, ROPS
2510			G	$19,000	10/22/2011	NECO	Diesel high crop, synchro, 3 pt. quick coupler
2510			G	$6,900	7/30/2011	ECMO	Unknown hours, new paint, redone front end, 3 pt., 1 hyd.
2510		2,244	G	$3,900	4/13/2011	Online	*BigIron.com,* item in Iowa, synchro, gas, 1 hyd., 540 PTO, 1,000 rpm, tin is straight, single owner
2510			G	$5,100	3/17/2011	ECMN	WF, 3 pt., 2 hyd., diff. lock, 540/1,000 PTO
2510			F	$3,500	11/18/2010	SEOK	
2510			G	$3,700	8/9/2010	WCMO	Tricycle front, gas, tires 75%
2510			F	$2,800	5/26/2010	ECSD	
2510			F	$4,800	5/26/2010	ECSD	WF
2510		4,860	G	$6,000	2/25/2010	NWIA	Gas, new battery, good original condition, paint faded
2510			G	$7,500	1/9/2010	ECIL	Gas, John Deere 46 loader, 8 speed synchro, 540/1,000 PTO, 2 hyd.

John Deere

Model	Year	Hours	Condition	Price	Date	Area	Comments
2520	1968		G	$11,500	5/29/2010	NCIL	Diesel, new rubber
2520	1969	5,375	E	$22,000	2/8/2014	SENE	Diesel, synchro, side console, 2 hyd., WF, starter weights plus 5, rear weights, new OH
2520	1969		G	$9,000	12/12/2013	IRON	
2520	1969	3,503	E	$20,000	8/11/2012	SEMN	Diesel, converted from gas, 500 hours on diesel, open station, synchro, side console, 3 pt., PTO, 2 hyd., second owner, 2 sold on this sale
2520	1969	4,305	G	$5,200	7/14/2012	NWIA	Gas, 30% rubber, synchro, NF
2520	1969	5,161	G	$9,750	7/14/2012	NWIA	WF, rear fenders, 2 hyd., 3 pt.
2520	1970		G	$7,000	8/10/2013	NCIA	Gas, WF, SN 021581
2520	1970	5,815	E	$20,500	8/11/2012	SEMN	Diesel, converted from gas, 500 hours on diesel, open station, synchro, side console, 3 pt., PTO, 2 hyd., second owner
2520	1970		G	$8,900	4/7/2012	NWMI	Diesel, side console, NF, hours unknown, synchro, 3 pt., PTO, front and rear weights
2520	1970		G	$10,000	6/18/2011	SWMN	Gas, SN 20663, synchro, new tires, console, front weights, repainted
2520	1971		G	$10,000	6/25/2011	ECIA	Diesel, SN 22308, WF, original
2520	1971		G	$74,750	6/18/2011	SWMN	High Crop, SN 22819, synchro, struts, 3 pt., fenders, new tires
2520	1971	1,921	G	$8,000	5/22/2010	WCIL	Gas, single NF, estate tractor, new tires and weights
2520	1972	8,689	G	$14,250	2/4/2014	NWNE	Diesel, WF, 3 pt., 2 hyd., no cab, synchro, 13.6x38 tires
2520	1972		G	$15,000	12/19/2013	WCMN	Row crop, WF, gas, PS, 1 hyd., factory 3 pt., PTO, flat top fenders, 15.5x38 tires at 80%, second owner, original, rare, 122 made total, 20 made in 1972
2520	1972	4,083	E	$19,000	9/22/2012	WCMN	Diesel, one owner, side console, diff. lock, John Deere WF, 2 hyd., synchro, excellent 15.5x38 tires, front side weights, fenders, very clean
2520	1972		G	$15,000	3/24/2012	NEIN	Diesel, synchro, repainted, new tires, front weights, dual hyd., 3 pt., PTO, runs
2520	1972		G	$23,250	1/6/2011	NENC	Diesel, PS, 1 of 356 diesel PS models, 1 hyd., side console, well cared for, original, buyer from Canada
2520			G	$10,000	3/23/2013	NEIN	Diesel, synchro, repainted, 3 pt., PTO, hyd., runs
2520			G	$19,000	3/23/2013	NEIN	Diesel, synchro, repainted, runs
2520			G	$60,000	3/23/2013	NEIN	Diesel, high crop, synchro, restored, runs
2520		5,046	E	$91,000	3/23/2013	NEIN	High Crop, 1 of only 8 made, gas, SN T731R18580R, high crop
2520			G	$4,700	3/22/2013	NWMN	Gas, NF, fenders, 3 pt., older repaint, runs
2520			G	$4,900	8/4/2012	ECMN	Gas, side console, new rear rubber, 2 hyd.
2520			G	$10,300	7/21/2012	ECIA	Diesel, repainted, dual hyd., front weights, runs

John Deere

Model	Year	Hours	Condition	Price	Date	Area	Comments
2520		3,965	G	$9,000	3/24/2012	NEIN	Gas, dual hyd., 3 pt., PTO, rear weights, original, runs
2520			G	$9,500	3/24/2012	NEIN	Synchro, diesel, PTO, 3 pt., dual hyd., runs
2520		5,237	G	$72,000	3/24/2012	NEIN	Gas, SF, 3 pt., PTO, fenders, original, runs
2520			G	$100,000	3/24/2012	NEIN	Gas, high crop, synchro, original, 1 of 7 built, runs
2520		4,565	G	$8,700	1/31/2012	NEIN	Synchro, weights, 3 pt., hyd. PTO
2520			G	$6,000	12/22/2011	Online	*IQBID.com,* 2WD, gas, cab, synchro, 2 hyd., 3 pt., 540/1,000 PTO, John Deere 47 loader
2520		3,962	G	$9,100	10/14/2011	WCMI	Gas, shedded, WF
2520		4,436	G	$10,500	4/19/2011	NEMN	
2520			G	$10,500	9/4/2010	NEIN	Diesel
2520			G	$14,000	9/4/2010	NEIN	Gas, PS
2520			G	$18,500	7/17/2010	NEMT	
2520		307	G	$12,250	4/10/2010	ECON	Loader, PTO, hydro., 4WD
2520		7,299	G	$8,100	4/1/2010	NCIN	Diesel, side console, 1 hyd., 15.5x38 tires 50%
2630	1972		G	$4,250	12/4/2013	ECND	65 hp, open station, 8 speed, 2 hyd., 3 pt., 540 PTO, John Deere 145 6' loader, 16.9x30 rear tires, 11Lx15 fronts, several new parts
2630	1972		G	$9,000	12/3/2013	NEMO	16.9x28 and 9.5Lx15 tires, 540 PTO, tear drop fenders, complete with Workmaster 800 loader and John Deere 7' material bucket, SN 1964781
2630	1974		F	$5,750	8/1/2012	NWMN	Showing 4,742 hours, John Deere 145 loader, no cab, SN 3499
2630	1974		G	$4,200	2/7/2012	WCOK	8 speed, dual hyd. diesel, 2 speed, approximately 15 hours on rebuild
2630	1974	662	G	$9,000	4/27/2011	NECO	WF, diesel, 3 pt., John Deere 148 loader, ROPS
2630	1974	6,210	G	$13,000	7/30/2010	ECIA	John Deere 145 loader, diesel, 16.9x28 tires
2630	1975		F	$9,000	12/28/2013	SEIA	2 hyd., John Deere 146 loader
2630	1975	4,832	G	$7,000	12/3/2011	NCIN	SN 226192, diesel, Hi/Lo, front and rear weights, 2 hyd.
2630	1975	5,016	G	$9,000	9/14/2011	Online	*BigIron.com,* item in Nebraska, John Deere 146 loader, 8 speed manual, 4 cyl., diesel, 2 hyd., 540 PTO, material bucket, LG round bale loader spear, collar shift, hyd. brakes, block heater
2630	1975	5,159	G	$5,750	3/15/2011	WCIL	Diesel, 21 hyd., 540 PTO, front weights, ROPS, canopy
2630	1975	3,962	F	$3,300	3/5/2010	NCMO	Diesel, 16.9x30 tires
2630		2,430	G	$6,000	4/1/2014	WCMN	2WD, WF, 3 front weights, 3 pt., PTO, 2 hyd., fenders
2630			G	$3,500	12/19/2013	SCNY	Fenders
2630			G	$5,000	12/12/2013	IRON	
2630		2,090	G	$5,600	8/24/2013	SEMN	Diesel, Allied 595 hyd. loader

TRACTORS

John Deere

Model	Year	Hours	Condition	Price	Date	Area	Comments
2630			G	$6,000	8/15/2013	ECMN	2WD, 2 hyd., 5' dirt bucket, 145 loader, full hyd., new seat, 18.4x34 tires, third arm
2630		3,439	G	$5,450	4/3/2013	Online	*BigIron.com,* item in Illinois, 4 speed Hi/Lo and torque converter, 16.9x28 rear tires, 9.5x15 front tires, diesel, drawbar, 3 pt., John Deere 146, needs brakes, left hyd. leaks, bucket and hay fork
2630			F	$2,900	3/17/2012	SEMN	3 pt., 2 hyd., PTO
2630			G	$7,000	10/30/2011	ECMN	3 pt., John Deere 146 loader
2630			G	$5,500	8/2/2011	ECNE	
2630			G	$4,350	4/21/2011	WCMI	2WD, diesel, hyd. loader, 1,000 hours on OH, 2 hyd., 3 pt., PTO
2630			G	$6,000	4/11/2011	NEIA	John Deere 146 loader
2630			G	$9,000	4/2/2011	SEMN	Diesel, 15.5x38 tires, wheel weights, 3 pt., 2 hyd., John Deere 175 loader and joystick
2630			G	$8,500	2/23/2011	WCVT	2WD, 4 cyl. diesel, 145 loader, hours unknown
2630			G	$5,400	1/29/2011	ECMO	John Deere 146 hyd. loader, diesel
2630			F	$5,800	8/9/2010	WCMO	Gear shift broken, loader
2630			G	$7,250	5/4/2010	WCOK	3 pt., PTO, dual hyd., 148 loader, hours not available
2640	1976	4,473	G	$8,500	2/12/2013	WCIL	16.9x30 rear tires, 540 PTO
2640	1977		G	$5,000	3/15/2011	WCIL	John Deere 145 loader, 540 PTO
2640	1978	1,673	G	$8,000	3/21/2013	ECIL	John Deere 146 loader
2840	1977	2,696	G	$7,150	12/7/2011	Online	*PurpleWave.com,* item in Oklahoma, 5.4L, 6 cyl. diesel, 80 PTO hp, partial PS, differential lock, 3 pt., drawbar
2840	1977		P	$4,100	8/20/2011	NEKS	Diesel, open station, roll bar, 18.4x38 rubber 50%, 2 hyd., SN 244294, engine #202953T, rebuilt starter, tach. needs work
2840	1977	3,142	G	$5,400	4/11/2011	Online	*AuctionTime.com*
2840	1978		F	$5,500	5/31/2013	NCOK	3 pt., PTO, 80 hp, bad rod journal on #6
2840	1978	3,200	G	$9,100	3/16/2013	NEIL	Diesel, WF, original, nice
2840	1978		G	$12,000	1/21/2013	NCIA	Hiniker 1300 cab, heat, radio, Westendorf TA26 84" loader, joystick, quick attach, 2WD, 85 hp
2840	1978	6,400	G	$5,800	3/5/2011	NWMO	
3010	1960	1,600	G	$5,800	3/22/2014	WCMO	Gas, fully restored, John Deere 46 front loader, NF, new rubber
3010	1961		E	$11,300	8/10/2013	NCIA	Diesel, WF, standard, SN 16743
3010	1961	5,833	G	$3,000	6/28/2013	SWIL	Gas, 8 speed synchro, 1 hyd., 540 PTO, 3 pt., 7.50x18 front, 13.6x36 rear
3010	1961		G	$3,100	5/25/2013	NWMO	3 pt., dual hyd., pancake and wheel weights, Roll-O-Matic front end, T18180, 194x30 rubber 30%
3010	1961		G	$3,300	4/30/2013	WCSK	2WD, Ezee-On front-end loader, 55 hp diesel, 540 PTO, 2 hyd., 18.4x30 rear
3010	1961		G	$4,250	4/4/2013	NWWA	8 speed synchro, 13.6x38, 7.5Lx15 3 pt., PTO, 2 hyd.

John Deere

Model	Year	Hours	Condition	Price	Date	Area	Comments
3010	1961		G	$4,300	11/16/2012	NCIA	Gas, factory WF, OH, 3 pt., 1 hyd., 13.6x38 tires
3010	1961	2,945	G	$4,620	9/12/2012	Online	*PurpleWave.com,* item in Missouri, John Deere 4 cyl. diesel, manual
3010	1961	4,777	G	$7,750	8/23/2012	SWMN	2WD, diesel, 4,777 hours showing, 3 pt., PTO, 2 hyd., 15.5x38 tires, new starter, second owner SN T15544
3010	1961	6,674	G	$6,250	7/14/2012	NWIA	LP Underhood, 3 pt., 1 hyd., very few made, new rear rubber
3010	1961	1,888	G	$5,750	6/14/2012	SEND	Diesel, gear drive, 1 hyd., 3 pt., converted 12V, factory front weights
3010	1961		G	$4,800	4/18/2012	SWSK	2WD, John Deere 46A front loader, 55 hp PTO, gas, synchro, 540 PTO, 2 hyd., 18.4x30 rear, 5' bucket
3010	1961		F	$4,300	3/7/2012	SEIA	ROPS, synchro., 2 hyd., 540 PTO, 3 pt., John Deere 4430 WF
3010	1961	2,053	G	$4,600	8/11/2011	WCMN	2 hyd., 540 PTO, rock box, cab, heat
3010	1961		G	$14,000	6/18/2011	SWMN	Gas, SN 6773, front weights, power set wheels, 3 pt.
3010	1961		G	$15,000	6/18/2011	SWMN	Diesel, SN 8871, synchro, 3 pt., hyd., power set rear wheels, front weights, restored
3010	1961		G	$2,750	12/30/2010	ECMN	NF, 1 hyd.
3010	1962		G	$6,250	12/19/2013	WCMN	WF, diesel, synchro, 1 hyd., 3 pt., PTO, fenders, new seat, 16.9x34 tires, 150 hours on major, approx. $8K in work orders in 2009, SN 24675
3010	1962		G	$3,650	8/20/2013	WCIL	Gas, synchro, 1 hyd., 540 PTO, 13.6x36 tires
3010	1962	4,780	G	$6,200	7/31/2013	ECND	Open station, 1 hyd., 3 pt., PTO, John Deere 46A hyd. loader
3010	1962	4,500	G	$3,000	2/7/2013	NEIN	15.5x38 T-rail duals @ 10%, 1 hyd., 2WD
3010	1962		G	$3,000	2/7/2013	NEIN	
3010	1962		G	$3,600	12/3/2012	WCIL	Gas, NF, Roll-O-Matic, 1 hyd., 15.5x38, 600 hours on major OH, sleeves, pistons, valves
3010	1962	270	G	$2,970	10/31/2012	Online	*PurpleWave.com,* item in Nebraska, John Deere 3.3L, 4 cyl. gas, 55 hp, partial synchro, power steering, hand/foot throttle, 3 pt., drawbar, 540 PTO, NF
3010	1962		G	$14,400	8/14/2012	SWMN	Diesel, open station, canopy, rock box, SN T28911
3010	1962		G	$2,600	6/13/2012	Online	*BigIron.com,* item in Kansas,loader, hr meter not working, 8F/3R, gas, 55 hp, 1 hyd., 540 PTO, recently painted, IHC loader
3010	1962	6,190	G	$1,105	6/22/2011	Online	*BigIron.com,* item in Nebraska, synchro, 4 cyl. gas, 1 hyd., 540 PTO, does not run, 3 pt., no third link
3010	1962	8,868	G	$2,200	6/22/2011	Online	*BigIron.com,* item in Oklahoma, #46 loader, standard, diesel, 1 hyd., 540 PTO, 5' bucket, 3 pt., third arm, new seat, recent paint

John Deere

Model	Year	Hours	Condition	Price	Date	Area	Comments
3010	1962	4,448	G	$3,200	12/2/2010	ECWY	Gas, synchro, 1 hyd., 3 pt., 13.9x36 tires
3010	1963		G	$8,400	4/11/2014	WCMN	Diesel, NF, new tires and new paint, 3 pt., 1 hyd.
3010	1963		G	$4,900	12/12/2013	ECNE	Roll-O-Matic front
3010	1963	6,827	G	$6,000	8/20/2013	WCIL	Diesel, synchro, 2 hyd., 540 PTO, 13.6x38 rear tires, under 300 hours on complete OH
3010	1963		G	$7,000	3/2/2013	SENE	Gas, HD WF off 5020, 4 hyd., synchro, 16.9x34, 325 Du-Al loader and 7' bucket
3010	1963	9,331	G	$4,700	2/7/2012	SEIA	WF, diesel, synchro, 3 pt., 1 hyd.
3010	1963	5,784	G	$3,500	1/28/2012	ECMO	Gas, 540 PTO, WF, 3 pt., 1 hyd., 16.9x38 tires
3010	1963		G	$8,500	6/18/2011	SWMN	LP, row crop, SN 41407, synchro, front weights, ROPS, 2 hyd., repainted
3010	1963		G	$12,000	6/18/2011	SWMN	Gas, standard, SN 42835, synchro, front and rear weights, nice original
3010	1963		G	$22,750	6/18/2011	SWMN	LP, standard, SN 38536, synchro, front weights, repainted
3010	1963	3,472	F	$2,750	3/26/2011	SEIL	Gas, NF
3010	1963		G	$4,000	12/8/2010	NEMI	WF, quick hitch, PTO, 2 hyd.
3010	1963		G	$3,600	11/13/2010	NWIL	Gas, WF, good tires
3010	1965	5,056	G	$3,005	12/28/2011	Online	*BigIron.com,* item in Nebraska, synchro, factory Roll-O-Matic front end, 3 pt., top link now showing, new radiator, new battery box, block heater
3010			G	$3,000	3/22/2014	SWMI	4 cyl. gas, WF, 3 pt., PTO, side mower attach, 15.5x38 rear tires
3010		1,761	G	$5,950	3/19/2014	Online	*BigIron.com,* item in Colorado, synchro, 6 cyl.
3010		2,403	G	$3,100	3/13/2014	SCID	Diesel, synchro, 2 hyd., 540 PTO, 3 pt., 14.9x38 rubber, Farmhand F11 hyd. loader, PTO pump, bale fork
3010		5,079	F	$2,715	12/18/2013	Online	*BigIron.com,* item in Utah, 8 speed synchro, 4 cyl. diesel, 18.4x30 rear tires, 236/75R16 front tires, 540 PTO, 2 hyd., missing top link
3010		3,954	G	$3,000	12/18/2013	Online	*BigIron.com,* 8 speed synchro, 3 cyl. gas, does run, carburetor needs cleaning
3010		9,302	G	$4,600	12/18/2013	Online	*BigIron.com,* 8 speed synchro, 4 cyl., 1 hyd., 3 pt., fenders
3010			G	$3,000	12/5/2013	SCIA	Gas, NF, fenders, 3 pt.
3010		454	G	$1,430	11/13/2013	Online	*PurpleWave.com,* item in Kansas, John Deere 4 cyl. gas, 59 hp, synchro, power steering
3010		4,542	F	$2,750	9/18/2013	ECMT	Diesel, 2 hyd., SN 301012T4426, 60% rubber, new starter and alternator
3010		200	G	$5,610	8/26/2013	NWWI	Diesel, WF, 3 pt. dual hyd., like new Firestone 16.9x38 tires, newer paint, starts, runs, drives
3010			G	$1,300	8/24/2013	SEMN	WF, gas, 3 pt. hyd., PTO, SN4935
3010			G	$5,300	8/24/2013	SEMI	Gas, WF, dual hyd.
3010		9,701	G	$2,750	8/20/2013	WCIL	Gas, NF, synchro, 1 hyd., 540 PTO
3010			G	$3,400	8/15/2013	ECMN	WF, 1 hyd., works

John Deere

Model	Year	Hours	Condition	Price	Date	Area	Comments
3010		1,393	G	$4,750	8/15/2013	ECMN	WF, no cab, 3 pt., loader
3010			G	$15,500	6/15/2013	WCOH	Diesel, fenders F&H weights, 3 pt., PTO, restored, runs
3010			G	$1,650	5/28/2013	NWWI	Gas, synchro, 3 pt., NF
3010			G	$3,905	5/28/2013	NWWI	Diesel, John Deere 48 all hyd. loader, quick attach, 1 hyd., 3 pt., WF, synchro
3010			F	$3,600	4/6/2013	NCOH	Gas
3010			F	$3,800	4/6/2013	NCOH	Gas, WF, hours unknown
3010			G	$2,900	3/7/2013	SEIA	Gas
3010			G	$2,950	3/2/2013	NCWI	Gas, 16.9x38S tires, WF, quick attach, cab, synchro, 2 hyd., hours unknown
3010			G	$3,300	3/2/2013	ECMN	Gas, 15.5x38 tires, 540 PTO, 3 pt., rock box, 1 hyd., synchro, new carburetor
3010			G	$2,750	2/12/2013	WCIL	
3010			G	$3,500	2/12/2013	WCIL	
3010		10,000	G	$4,950	2/9/2013	SWOH	Diesel, WF
3010			G	$9,700	12/8/2012	ECTX	Diesel, 15.5x38 rear tires, 9.5Lx15 front tires, fenders, canvas buggy shade, 1 hyd., 3 pt., 540 PTO, standard shift, John Deere 720 front loader, bucket
3010		1,419	G	$4,000	12/5/2012	Online	*BigIron.com,* item in South Dakota, synchro, 4 cyl. gas, 15.5x38 rear tires, 9.5Lx15 front tires, hyd., 540 PTO, 3 pt., John Deere 48 loader, SN IT35493
3010			G	$2,900	11/24/2012	SEMN	Gas, NF, 3 pt., hyd., PTO, 15.5x38
3010			G	$6,000	11/13/2012	NCIA	Diesel, canopy, 3 pt.
3010		1,245	G	$8,300	11/13/2012	NWTX	8 speed synchro, 15.5x38 rear tires, 9.5Lx15 front tires, John Deere 720 loader, shop built bale carrier, 1 hyd.
3010			G	$3,100	10/24/2012	WCWI	Woods 1027 loader, 13.9x36 tires
3010		2,155	G	$3,600	8/21/2012	WCIL	
3010			G	$2,950	6/13/2012	SWOH	Gas
3010			G	$3,700	5/9/2012	Online	*BigIron.com,* item in Nebraska, loader, 3 pt. mount pivot mover
3010		199	F	$2,250	5/8/2012	Online	*IQBID.com,* gas, 1 hyd., PTO, 15.5x38 tires, rock box (needs work), new clutch, battery box, rebuilt starter
3010		2,031	G	$5,000	3/24/2012	NEIN	Gas, excellent original, dual hyd., PTO, fenders, runs
3010			G	$5,300	3/24/2012	NEIN	Diesel, 3 pt., dual hyd., original, runs
3010			G	$7,250	3/24/2012	NEIN	Diesel, John Deere 148 loader, dual hyd., PTO, 5 sets rear wheel weights, nice original, runs
3010			G	$2,500	2/4/2012	NEAR	Gas, WF, synchro, 540 PTO
3010			G	$2,950	2/1/2012	SEND	3 pt., PTO
3010			G	$7,500	1/28/2012	ECMO	
3010			G	$4,250	10/30/2011	ECMN	Gas
3010			G	$7,600	10/22/2011	NECO	Diesel, standard
3010		2,069	G	$5,100	8/10/2011	Online	*BigIron.com,* item in Colorado, dual 340 loader, QR, diesel, 1 hyd., 540 PTO, 5' bucket, 12V system, 2"x1" drawbar, front bend on hood
3010			G	$3,000	7/30/2011	ECMO	Gas, NF, new attach, new seat

John Deere

Model	Year	Hours	Condition	Price	Date	Area	Comments
3010			G	$800	7/13/2011	Online	*BigIron.com,* item in Nebraska, cab only, all mounting brackets, all glass and rubber seals included
3010			G	$2,350	5/25/2011	Online	*BigIron.com,* item in Nebraska, synchro, 1 hyd., 540 PTO, NF, 3 pt., no batteries
3010		5,665	G	$5,200	5/25/2011	Online	*BigIron.com,* item in Nebraska, QR, gas, 540 PTO, 3 pt., top link, Schwartz front PTO hyd. pump, gas gauge does not work, Farmhand 8' loader bucket, quick attach
3010			G	$6,500	3/16/2011	NWIA	Gas, WF, 2 hyd., sheet metal OK, tires poor
3010			G	$6,000	11/13/2010	NCIA	WF, diesel
3010			G	$8,000	11/13/2010	NCIA	Diesel, less than 200 hours on OH
3010		366	G	$3,850	6/23/2010	Online	*BigIron.com,* item in Oklahoma, 8 speed, propane, 1 hyd., PTO, 3 pt., row crop tires on back
3010			G	$2,500	6/5/2010	NETN	
3010			G	$3,900	6/5/2010	NWIA	Gas
3010			F	$4,200	5/26/2010	ECSD	John Deere 47 loader
3010			G	$6,300	5/26/2010	ECSD	Diesel, Koker loader
3010			F	$5,750	5/15/2010	WCIN	Diesel, new tires front and back, outside appearance average condition
3010		6,622	G	$2,970	4/27/2010	Online	*PurpleWave.com,* item in Oklahoma, LP, 4 cyl., 3 pt., no third link, 1 hyd., 540 PTO
3010			G	$8,000	4/21/2010	SESK	Diesel
3010			G	$5,750	3/6/2010	SEMN	Diesel, 15.5x38 tires, 1 hyd., 3 pt., rear wheel weight, synchro, clean
3010			G	$2,600	1/30/2010	NETX	
3020	1963		G	$11,750	1/11/2013	ECIL	1,097 hours on OH, factory propane, SN 53649, WF, weights, John Deere 148 loader and 6' material bucket, joystick control
3020	1964		G	$2,300	12/10/2013	IRON	Gas, PS, hyd., no third arm, 15.5x38 single tires
3020	1964		E	$10,800	11/11/2013	ECMO	Gas, synchro, 1 hyd., tach. replaced, hours not known, John Deere 720 loader
3020	1964		G	$8,750	9/21/2013	WCMI	Diesel, 3 pt., PTO, electric start, PS, 2 hyd., 16.9x34 rear tires, restored
3020	1964	8,379	G	$9,250	7/16/2013	SESK	2WD, John Deere 148 front loader, 71 hp diesel, synchro, 2 hyd., dual PTO, 5' bucket, John Deere umbrella
3020	1964		G	$11,000	6/18/2013	SCSK	2WD, 70 PTO hp, diesel, PS, dual hyd., PTO, 18.4x30 rear, new tires front and back, 150 hours on motor OH
3020	1964		G	$6,750	2/23/2013	SENE	Diesel, WF, PS, 2 hyd., 16.9x38 tires
3020	1964		G	$9,750	8/23/2012	SWMN	2WD, diesel, hours unknown, 3 pt., 1 hyd., 16.9x34 tires, rock box, SN 30201TT53975
3020	1964	2,731	G	$11,900	8/16/2012	NCIA	Diesel, WF, synchro, 2 way valve and 1 single valve in rear, 540 PTO, side arm front weight bracket and 1 waffle weight quick coupler
3020	1964		G	$9,200	7/14/2012	NWIA	Diesel, PS, WF, rear fenders, 3 pt.

John Deere

Model	Year	Hours	Condition	Price	Date	Area	Comments
3020	1964	4,643	G	$6,000	3/22/2012	ECMN	Factory WF, 2 hyd., 3 pt., PTO, 60 series step kit, fenders, John Deere 148 loader
3020	1964	8,000	G	$6,400	2/7/2012	SEIA	Diesel, 3 pt., 1 hyd., PS, 15.5x38 tires, SN 63365
3020	1964		G	$6,000	1/28/2012	ECMO	PS, John Deere factory WF, dual hyd.
3020	1964	6,864	G	$3,410	9/14/2011	Online	*PurpleWave.com,* item in Kansas, 65 hp, PS, 3 pt., 540/1,000 PTO, 29 gal. fuel tank
3020	1964	5,230	G	$4,200	8/11/2011	WCMN	Cab, heat, 2 hyd., 3 pt., PTO, new shift forks, Westendorf loader
3020	1964		G	$10,500	6/18/2011	SWMN	LP, row crop, SN 53768, synchro, front weights, new tires, repainted
3020	1964	6,826	G	$7,000	2/19/2011	ECNE	Diesel, WF, 3 pt., open station
3020	1964		F	$5,900	12/10/2010	NWMO	16.9x34 tires, 1 hyd., recent OH, John Deere 148 loader
3020	1964	6,380	G	$6,500	12/1/2010	ECND	Gas, PS, cab, 1 hyd., 540/1,000 PTO, 3 pt., quick hitch, 16.9x38 rear tires, 10 hours on in-frame OH, electric ignition, new starter, new batteries
3020	1964		F	$6,000	6/9/2010	ECIA	WF, PS, GB loader
3020	1965	5,793	G	$5,000	6/27/2013	Online	*IQBID.com,* NF, 8 speed synchro, 12V, 2 hyd., 540/1,000 PTO, John Deere 148 loader, 5' bucket, drawbar, Goodyear 15.5x38 tires, SN T111R072190R
3020	1965		E	$18,000	4/27/2013	WCSK	Shedded, 2WD, diesel, 71 PTO hp, PS, 24V, 2 hyd., PTO, 18.4x34 rear, 3 rib front, SN P079667R
3020	1965	6,734	F	$6,000	4/19/2012	WCSK	2WD, Ezee-On front-end loader, 71 hp PTO, synchro, dual PTO, 2 hyd., 18.4x30 rear tires, front bucket
3020	1965		G	$4,750	4/12/2012	NEMI	Diesel, Year Round cab, PS, 1 hyd., 3 pt., PTO
3020	1965		G	$5,500	4/11/2012	SEAB	2WD, 71 PTO hp, 4 cyl. gas, PS, 2 hyd., PTO, 18.4x30 rear, 3 rib front
3020	1965	1,996	F	$4,300	3/22/2012	ECMN	WF, PS, 1 hyd., 3 pt., PTO, fenders
3020	1965	2,840	G	$5,000	3/14/2012	ECND	Open station, 1 hyd., 3 pt., PTO
3020	1965	3,570	G	$5,500	1/31/2012	NEIN	Excellent original
3020	1965	7,543	E	$20,000	6/18/2011	SWMN	Gas, Standard, SN 76657, synchro, Front and rear weights, dust shields, 2 hyd., nice original
3020	1965	1,940	G	$11,500	5/19/2011	ECMI	Diesel, WF, 2 hyd., 3 pt., bolt on duals, main rubber at 90%
3020	1965		G	$7,500	3/20/2010	SEIA	PS, WF, new tires year ago
3020	1965		G	$8,000	2/16/2010	ECNE	WF, diesel, synchro, Du-Al 325 axle mount loader, 7' bucket and 4-tine grapple fork, 15.5x38 rear tires, flotation 11L5x15 front tires, 540/1,000 PTO, cement rear wheel weights
3020	1966	5,500	G	$2,500	12/5/2013	SEMN	WF, gas
3020	1966	6,980	G	$3,080	8/28/2013	Online	*PurpleWave.com,* item in Nebraska, 3.7L, 227 cu. in. 4 cyl. gas, synchro, damaged spring suspension seat, WF, power steering, drawbar, 90" WB

John Deere

Model	Year	Hours	Condition	Price	Date	Area	Comments
3020	1966	5,265	G	$11,250	8/17/2012	SCMI	2 hyd., diesel, original, 16.9.28 rear tires
3020	1966	4,049	F	$6,200	7/14/2012	NWIA	LP, WF, 2 hyd., 3 pt., not repainted
3020	1966		G	$10,000	7/14/2012	NWIA	Diesel, SN T113P090367R,diesel, PS, WF, 2 hyd., 3 pt., new tires, new paint, 800 hours on OH
3020	1966		G	$3,250	6/29/2012	NETX	65 hp, 2WD, open station, synchro, 15.5x38 tires, 1 rear hyd., no reverse
3020	1966	1,124	G	$7,000	6/20/2012	SESD	Diesel, WF, 3 pt., 1 hyd., synchro, fenders, new 15.5x38 rubber, rebuilt starter, new filters, serviced, runs
3020	1966	5,657	G	$10,000	5/1/2012	SWSK	2WD, John Deere 148 front end loader, 71 hp PTO, 3 rib front
3020	1966		G	$4,700	1/28/2012	ECMO	Great Bend loader, PS
3020	1966		G	$12,500	8/18/2011	SEMN	PS, diesel, open station, full set of front weights, new style step, roll bar, 2 hyd., new 18.4x34 tires, SN T113PR094034R
3020	1966	7,000	G	$6,900	7/27/2011	Online	*BigIron.com,* item in Nebraska, 8 speed synchro, 4 cyl., 63 drawbar hp, 71 PTO hp, 2 hyd., 540/1,000 PTO, 3 pt., fenders, lights, cast rear wheels, differential lock, power steering
3020	1966	7,495	F	$3,300	4/6/2011	Online	*PurpleWave.com,* item in Oklahoma, 3.7L, LP, 70 hp, synchro, 8F gears, 3 pt., drawbar, 540/1,000 PTO, rear hyd. set, 7' Walden blade
3020	1966	7,922	F	$3,600	3/26/2011	NECO	WF, diesel, 3 pt., needs work
3020	1966		G	$4,000	3/15/2011	WCIL	Gas, 540 PTO
3020	1966		F	$5,300	11/13/2010	NWIL	LP, WF, 3 pt., 2 hyd.
3020	1966	3,882	G	$4,700	6/26/2010	NCIL	Gas, NF, PS, 1 hyd., 15.5x38 tires
3020	1966		F	$5,050	6/23/2010	Online	*BigIron.com,* item in Colorado, Farmhand 4233 loader, 5572 hours showing, 8 speed synchro, 4 cyl. John Deere diesel
3020	1966		G	$4,200	3/12/2010	SEIA	NF, gas
3020	1966		G	$4,500	3/6/2010	NEMO	Diesel, WF, no cab, 15.5x38 tires, 540 PTO, synchro, fenders, front weight pads
3020	1966	6,388	G	$5,200	3/1/2010	NEKS	Gas, 3 pt., WF, front weights, synchro, 500 hours on OH
3020	1967	4,200	E	$6,000	2/8/2014	NECO	6 cyl. gas, 1 hyd. set, PTO, 3 pt., good rubber, like new condition, new paint on hood
3020	1967	8,399	G	$4,000	12/5/2013	SEMN	Allied loader, WF, gas
3020	1967	2,822	G	$5,000	12/3/2013	NWNE	Synchro, WF, good rubber, 2 hyd., 3 pt., 64 hp
3020	1967		G	$3,600	9/19/2013	SWIA	60 hp, 2WD, gas, PS hours say 1,441, 540 PTO, 4 hyd.
3020	1967	7,400	G	$14,500	9/12/2013	SEIA	NF, 34" radials, new clutch, points, plugs, alternator, 700 hours on OH
3020	1967	7,347	G	$3,300	6/12/2013	Online	*BigIron.com,* item in Iowa, synchro 8F/2R, 3.7L, 4 cyl. liq. cooled

John Deere

Model	Year	Hours	Condition	Price	Date	Area	Comments
3020	1967	7,735	G	$5,600	6/12/2013	Online	*BigIron.com,* item in Nebraska
3020	1967		G	$5,750	3/28/2013	Online	*IQBID.com*
3020	1967		F	$5,700	3/21/2013	WCNE	Farmhand loader, 3 pt., 1 hyd., 8 speed PS, 15.5x38 rear rubber (35%), SN T113P073837R, FH pump
3020	1967	6,910	G	$10,100	2/21/2013	ECMI	Diesel, open station, 2 hyd., OH and clutch 1,400 hours use, new Firestone 15.5x38 tires, SN T113R109320R
3020	1967		G	$12,550	8/22/2012	Online	*BigIron.com,* item in Nebraska, diesel, new Crate motor less than 5 hours ago, rear weights, 3 pt., 540 PTO, 1 hyd.
3020	1967	11,836	G	$7,500	10/27/2011	NWND	Diesel, WF, 3 pt., 540/1,000 PTO, 2 hyd., 12V system, Farmhand F11 loader, grapple, good rubber
3020	1967	6,562	G	$4,250	9/28/2011	Online	*BigIron.com,* item in Nebraska, loader, synchro, 4 cyl. gas, 67 drawbar, 2 hyd., 1,000 PTO, 7' bucket, grapple
3020	1967	4,580	G	$10,250	9/2/2011	NCMO	Diesel, one owner, WF, front weights, 16.9x34 like new rubber, brand new front rubber, synchro, all new batteries, real good paint, always shedded
3020	1967		G	$4,500	7/30/2011	ECMO	New battery, with top link
3020	1967		G	$16,750	6/20/2011	ECSK	Diesel, 71 PTO hp, standard., 2 hyd., 540/1,000 PTO, 18.4x30 rear tires, 3 rib front tires, block heater, SN 105135R, shedded
3020	1967		G	$11,000	6/18/2011	SWMN	Gas, SN 102644, synchro, 3 pt., 2 hyd., new tires, front weights, down draft exhaust, repainted
3020	1967	6,615	G	$7,500	4/27/2011	NECO	WF, diesel, 3 pt., recent OH
3020	1967	3,147	G	$5,000	3/17/2011	ECMN	2 hyd., 3 pt., PTO
3020	1967		G	$8,500	3/16/2011	NWIA	Diesel, John Deere WF, 2 hyd., tires poor
3020	1967	6,671	G	$4,150	3/15/2011	WCIL	Gas, 540 PTO, synchro, ROPS, canopy
3020	1967	8,000	G	$5,250	3/5/2011	NWMO	
3020	1967		G	$8,100	2/1/2011	NEIN	PS
3020	1967	5,318	G	$7,200	6/23/2010	Online	*BigIron.com,* item in Iowa, row crop, synchro 8F/2R, 4 cyl., 227 cu. in., In-line gas, 70 hp
3020	1967	4,029	G	$5,000	3/5/2010	NCMO	Gas, synchro
3020	1967	3,922	G	$7,700	1/27/2010	Online	*PurpleWave.com,* item in Kansas, 540 PTO, 4 cyl. gas, 3 pt., rear axle weights
3020	1968	8,402	G	$8,750	12/19/2013	WCMN	Diesel, synchro, 1,200 hours on major OH, WF, fenders, 7.6x15 front tires, 15.5x38 rear tires
3020	1968	7,826	G	$7,200	2/26/2013	SEIA	Diesel, open station, synchro, 540/1,000 PTO, 3 pt., 2 hyd., 16.9x34 rear tires, 11Lx15 front tires, SN 118667
3020	1968	4,044	G	$3,700	2/7/2013	NEIN	2WD, 15.8x38 tires, 1 hyd.
3020	1968		G	$3,700	2/7/2013	NEIN	
3020	1968	9,806	G	$6,600	11/20/2012	NEND	Standard, diesel, open station, 2 hyd., 540/1,000 PTO, John Deere 148 loader brackets, rear weights
3020	1968	4,800	F	$3,500	6/20/2012	SESD	Diesel, row crop, 3 pt., NF

John Deere

Model	Year	Hours	Condition	Price	Date	Area	Comments
3020	1968	7,355	G	$5,900	5/19/2012	SWMI	Diesel, WF, 18.4x34 tires, 3 pt., square fenders, lights, dual 1 hyd. 540/1,000 PTO, synchro, John Deere 148 loader, hyd. bucket
3020	1968		G	$7,500	9/10/2011	ECIA	Diesel, NF, duals
3020	1968		G	$9,500	6/18/2011	SWMN	Diesel synchro, SN 114299, 2 hyd., older repaint
3020	1968		G	$11,000	6/18/2011	SWMN	Diesel, SN 113554, synchro, front weights, 3 pt., 2 hyd., repainted
3020	1968	2,538	G	$7,650	5/5/2011	ECNE	Diesel, WF, SQ fenders, 3 pt., double hyd., newer seat
3020	1968		G	$5,550	3/5/2011	NWMO	Gas, WF, 2 hyd., Westendorf TA25 loader
3020	1968		G	$5,600	12/10/2010	NWMO	3,613 hours on OH, PS, canopy, 2 hyd.
3020	1969	6,540	G	$4,500	3/15/2014	WCIL	Gas, 1 hyd., 540 PTO, 3 pt., 15.5x38 rear tires, front weights
3020	1969		G	$6,400	3/1/2014	SEPA	Side console, WF, dual hyd., dual PTO, 3 pt., synchro, good sheet metal except fenders, 15.5x38 rubber 10%, hole in 1 rim at valve stem
3020	1969		G	$8,000	11/30/2013	SWIA	OH and repainted in 2008, WF, gas, side console
3020	1969	8,900	G	$12,800	3/3/2013	ECNJ	PS, side console, repainted, straight, no diff. lock
3020	1969	2,488	G	$15,250	8/16/2012	Online	*IQBID.com,* item in Minnesota, 2WD, WF, diesel, open station, PS, 2 hyd., 3 pt., 540 PTO, side console, front weights
3020	1969		G	$30,250	7/21/2012	ECIA	High crop, console, synchro, completely restored, 1 of 48 built
3020	1969	5,128	G	$13,100	9/17/2011	NEIA	Diesel, NF, 3 pt., tool box, side console, fenders, rear weights, front weights, new 16.9x34 rear tires, SN 128622R, clean, 30 hours on OH
3020	1969	1,687	G	$5,850	6/22/2011	Online	*BigIron.com,* item in Nebraska, synchro, diesel, 2 hyd., 540/1,000 PTO, side console, 3 pt., missing third link, 3 rear wheel weights
3020	1969	2,424	G	$9,000	4/2/2011	ECMN	Synchro range, side console, 3 pt.
3020	1969		G	$8,900	1/6/2011	NENC	540 PTO, 1 hyd.
3020	1969	4,771	G	$8,200	12/8/2010	NECO	WF, diesel, front weights
3020	1969		F	$7,000	2/19/2010	WCIL	Gas, synchro, WF, 540/1,000 PTO, 2 hyd., 16.9x34 tires
3020	1970	7,272	G	$5,850	4/24/2013	Online	*BigIron.com,* item in South Dakota, 8 speed synchro, 4 cyl. diesel
3020	1970	6,694	E	$17,000	2/23/2013	SENE	Diesel, WF, synchro, 2 hyd., 15.5x38 tires
3020	1970	7,374	G	$12,500	8/18/2011	SEMN	PS, diesel, open station, new style step, 16.9x34 rubber 95%, 2 hyd., SN T113P133278R
3020	1970		G	$36,000	6/25/2011	ECIA	Gas, factory front wheel drive, SN 130604, PS, console
3020	1970		E	$38,500	6/18/2011	SWMN	Diesel, PS, console, SN 130659, front wheel drive, ROPS, front weights, 2 hyd., original
3020	1970	6,969	G	$10,525	5/11/2011	Online	*BigIron.com,* synchro, diesel, 540 PTO, 2 hyd., 8' Massey point blade

John Deere

Model	Year	Hours	Condition	Price	Date	Area	Comments
3020	1970		G	$12,000	4/11/2011	Online	*AuctionTime.com*
3020	1970		G	$5,150	2/1/2011	NEIN	Cab, synchro, dual hyd., console
3020	1970	4,405	G	$9,500	11/17/2010	WCMN	Gas, open station, side console, gear drive, 1 hyd., differential lock, 3 pt., PTO, factory front weights, 16.9x34 rear tires
3020	1970	2,000	G	$9,000	8/14/2010	NCIL	Gas, synchro, side console, 15.5x38 tires
3020	1971		G	$6,700	10/3/2013	NCIN	
3020	1971	5,404	G	$10,400	9/21/2013	SWOH	Canopy, weights
3020	1971		E	$18,300	8/10/2013	NCIA	Diesel, WF, console, SN 512263
3020	1971	6,990	G	$8,900	5/4/2013	WCSD	Gas, WF, 64 hp, 3 pt., 2 hyd., good rubber, SNT111R151419R, unmounted John Deere 148 quick attach loader, bucket/grapple
3020	1971		G	$10,750	11/10/2012	ECIA	Diesel, WF, complete OH 5 years ago and used very little since
3020	1971	6,125	E	$12,000	3/17/2012	WCOH	Side console
3020	1971		G	$8,500	2/24/2012	WCMN	Shows 3,995 hours, gas, John Deere WF and 3 pt., ROPS, comfort steps, synchro, front weights, fenders, sharp
3020	1971	4,509	G	$5,400	11/23/2011	Online	*BigIron.com,* item in Iowa, farm, 2WD, synchro, 4 cyl. gas, 2 hyd., 540/1,000 PTO, new front tires and wheels
3020	1971		G	$14,500	6/18/2011	SWMN	Diesel, console, synchro, SN 150918, ROPS, front weights, 2 hyd., repainted
3020	1971		E	$34,000	6/18/2011	SWMN	High Crop, Console, PS, SN151068, front weight, struts, repainted
3020	1971		G	$4,700	1/1/2011	ECKS	Gas, 60% tires
3020	1972	3,796	E	$18,000	8/8/2013	SESD	Diesel, synchro, 1 hyd., WF, original paint, Firestone 16.9x34 rear tires
3020	1972		G	$19,500	3/23/2013	NEIN	Diesel, PS, repainted, weights, dual hyd., 3 pt., fenders, runs
3020	1972		G	$23,000	3/24/2012	NEIN	Diesel, PS console, restored, front weights, ROPS, new tires, dual hyd., PTO, 3 pt., runs
3020	1972	6,410	G	$12,000	8/18/2011	SEMN	Side console, synchro, diesel, open station, 18.4x34 rubber 90%, new style step, SN 155920R
3020	1972		G	$3,500	1/1/2011	ECKS	Gas, tires 20%
3020			G	$2,600	3/15/2014	WCIL	Gas, side console, 18.4x34 tires, 1 hyd., 540/1,000 PTO, 3 pt., Dunham Lehr loader and 5' bucket
3020			G	$8,500	3/8/2014	NWWI	Diesel, side console, 2 hyd., 540/1,000 PTO, diff. lock and top link, owner paid <$7K for it years ago
3020		5,625	G	$5,400	2/22/2014	ECMI	Diesel, 2WD, WF, 3 pt., PTO, back blade, 2 hyd., 15.5Rx38 rear tires
3020			F	$3,500	1/4/2014	WCNY	Diesel, problem
3020		4,031	G	$3,700	12/18/2013	Online	*BigIron.com,* 8 speed synchro, 6 cyl. diesel, no top link, 540/1,000 PTO, 2 hyd.
3020			G	$4,500	12/4/2013	ECIN	
3020		3,125	G	$4,250	10/3/2013	NCIN	Schwartz WF, synchro, 1 hyd.

John Deere

Model	Year	Hours	Condition	Price	Date	Area	Comments
3020			G	$2,025	9/12/2013	SEIA	Unknown hours, 3 pt., no third link, 540/1,000 PTO, 1 hyd., gas, NF, synchro, 15.5x38 tires
3020			G	$3,500	9/12/2013	SEIA	Gas, 3 pt., 540 PTO, 1 hyd., 14.9x38 rears
3020			G	$5,610	9/5/2013	ECWI	Dual hyd., dual PTO, gas, WF, 16.9x38 tires
3020			G	$2,400	8/29/2013	NWIA	NF, diesel, PS, 2 hyd., 3 pt., PTO, fenders
3020			G	$3,400	8/29/2013	NWIA	NF, gas, PS, 2 hyd., 3 pt., 540/1,000 PTO, fenders, new battery, 15.5x38 rear tires
3020			G	$5,100	8/24/2013	SEMN	Gas, 3 pt., hyd. PTO, 15.5x38, SN130383R
3020			G	$7,250	8/14/2013	WCMN	2 hyd., 15.5x38 tires, SN 124620R
3020			G	$3,000	7/10/2013	NETX	Open PS, SN 127445R
3020		4,747	G	$6,000	4/24/2013	Online	*BigIron.com,* item in South Dakota, 8 speed synchro, 4 cyl. gas
3020			F	$2,400	3/30/2013	NWIL	Synchro, NF, runs, drives, hyd. system does not work
3020			G	$2,900	3/30/2013	SCMN	Gas, factory WF
3020			G	$3,250	3/30/2013	SCMN	Synchro, double hyd., factory WF
3020		5,364	G	$5,200	3/30/2013	NWIL	Gas, 2 hyd., synchro
3020			G	$7,750	3/30/2013	SCMN	Synchro, rock box, Year Round cab
3020			G	$4,785	3/27/2013	NWWI	Gas, side console, dual hyd., 3 pt., WF, 16.9x38 rear tires
3020			G	$6,800	3/23/2013	NEIN	Diesel, PS, dual hyd., 3 pt. weights, runs
3020			G	$7,400	3/23/2013	NEIN	Gas, WF, quick coupler, front/rear weights, dual hyd., runs
3020			G	$11,000	3/23/2013	NEIN	Gas, console, nice, original, 3 pt., runs
3020			G	$14,500	3/23/2013	NEIN	PS, diesel, John Deere 158 loader, weights, dual hyd., 3 pt., runs
3020			G	$5,000	3/2/2013	ECMN	Synchro, 3 pt.
3020		7,922	G	$3,400	2/7/2013	SEAR	Diesel, single range synchro
3020			G	$3,900	11/24/2012	SEMN	WF, gas, John Deere 46A hyd. loader, 3 pt. hyd. PTO
3020			G	$6,750	11/7/2012	SCNE	Diesel, WF, 1 hyd., 15.5x38 tires
3020			G	$4,500	10/24/2012	WCWI	Factory WF
3020		1,761	G	$5,200	10/13/2012	NCCO	Diesel, Great Bend loader
3020			G	$6,200	9/13/2012	SEIA	Synchro, new tires, recent OH, Westendorf loader
3020			G	$4,750	8/16/2012	Online	*IQBID.com,* item in Minnesota, WF, gas, PS, 3 pt., PTO, no top link, 16.9x34 tires
3020		1,845	G	$6,500	8/16/2012	Online	*IQBID.com,* item in Minnesota, diesel, PS, 1 hyd., 3 pt., dual PTO, no top link, 16.9x34 tires
3020		3,748	G	$2,800	8/4/2012	ECMN	Gas, NF, 16.9x34 tires, 3 pt., 540/1,000 PTO, 2 hyd., wheel weights
3020		2,269	E	$13,400	7/21/2012	SEPA	Diesel, NF, side console, actual hours, bought by dealer, owner was a real estate broker whose father-in-law used this as his baby to mow
3020			G	$1,969	6/20/2012	ECIL	WF, 16.9x38 radials, front weights, recent OH, 1 hyd., synchro

John Deere

Model	Year	Hours	Condition	Price	Date	Area	Comments
3020		4,211	G	$5,350	6/20/2012	ECIL	Gas, 15.5x32 and 9.5x15 tires, fenders, top link, 1 PTO, 1 hyd.
3020			G	$7,750	6/9/2012	ECNE	Diesel, PS, WF, ROPS, 3 pt., PTO, hyd., runs
3020		4,768	G	$3,900	6/2/2012	SEMN	Gas, WF, 3 pt., 1 hyd., 15.5x38 tires, 90% tires
3020			G	$6,500	6/2/2012	SEMN	NF, duals, synchro, new clutch
3020			G	$8,500	6/2/2012	SEMN	WF, 540/1,000, 1 hyd.
3020		8,680	G	$5,000	5/23/2012	Online	*BigIron.com,* item in Wyoming, synchro, 6 cyl., 1 hyd., 540/1,000 PTO, 3 pt., third link, cracked windows, new batteries
3020		3,341	G	$5,900	5/9/2012	Online	*BigIron.com,* item in Kansas, 6 cyl. diesel, 65 hp, 15.5x38 rear tires, 9.5x15 front tires, 1 hyd., 540/1,000 PTO
3020		4,908	G	$4,200	3/24/2012	NEIN	Gas, front weights, excellent rubber, 3 pt., runs
3020			G	$7,000	3/24/2012	NEIN	Diesel, synchro, 3 pt., hyd., runs
3020			G	$9,100	3/24/2012	NEIN	Console, synchro, dual hyd., excellent original, runs
3020			G	$11,250	3/24/2012	NEIN	Console, synchro, repainted, runs
3020			G	$31,000	3/24/2012	NEIN	PS, diesel, console, rare front wheel assist, runs
3020		2,222	G	$3,900	2/2/2012	NEIN	Diesel, hours questionable, WF, 15.5x38 rear tires, 1 set hyd.
3020		8,701	G	$4,200	1/31/2012	NEIN	WF, synchro, gas, 3 pt., PTO, fenders
3020			G	$9,250	1/31/2012	NEIN	Console, repainted, turf tires
3020			G	$37,000	1/28/2012	ECMO	Loader, recent OH
3020			E	$6,252	12/6/2011	Online	*BidNow.us,* gas, PS, 15.5x38 rear tires, 2 hyd., 3 pt., PTO
3020			F	$2,600	11/22/2011	WCIL	NF, gas, unknown hours
3020			G	$4,900	10/28/2011	NETX	65 hp, propane, open station, PS, WF, 16.9x34 tires, 1 rear hyd.
3020			G	$12,000	10/22/2011	NECO	Diesel high crop, synchro, rock shaft
3020			G	$37,000	10/22/2011	NECO	Diesel, orchard, PTO, no 3 pt.
3020			G	$45,000	10/22/2011	NECO	Diesel, orchard, 3 pt.
3020			G	$45,000	10/22/2011	NECO	Diesel, orchard, 3 pt.
3020		4,812	G	$10,000	10/15/2011	Online	*IQBID.com,* 2WD, diesel, non-factory cab, heat, 2 hyd., 3 pt., PTO, synchro, recent OH on motor, rear fenders, new WF, Koyker 385 loader
3020			G	$9,600	9/17/2011	SEMN	Diesel, synchro, side console, SN tag unreadable, had to be a late model 3020 to have a side console, owner said he had it 19 years, it ground one load of feed every week for 19 years, Vaughn M97 loader (loader seen very light duty)
3020			G	$3,000	8/24/2011	ECMN	PS, NF, good rubber, 1 hyd., PTO, 3 pt.
3020			F	$2,000	8/21/2011	WCOH	NF, gas, John Deere 46 loader, transmission out
3020		3,419	G	$12,100	8/13/2011	WCIL	Diesel, WF, 3 pt., synchro, original, good paint and tires

John Deere

TRACTORS

Model	Year	Hours	Condition	Price	Date	Area	Comments
3020			G	$5,700	7/30/2011	ECMO	Diesel, new clutch and oil change with new filters, cab, air, heat
3020		4,264	G	$5,550	4/13/2011	Online	*BigIron.com,* item in Nebraska, diesel, set of weights, add on pan, fuel gauge does not work
3020		6,852	F	$3,900	4/2/2011	ECMN	Gas, needs work
3020		2,424	G	$9,000	4/2/2011	ECMN	Diesel, synchro, side console, 3 pt.
3020			G	$3,000	3/23/2011	ECMN	WF, new cart, 38" tires
3020			G	$3,000	3/19/2011	SEIA	Gas, NF, new rear tires, new alternator, new batteries, new kit in carburetor
3020			G	$3,900	3/19/2011	ECIA	NF, new rear tires
3020			G	$5,500	3/19/2011	ECIA	PS, Westendorf loader
3020			G	$5,000	3/5/2011	SEMN	WF, gas, 540/1,000 PTO, 3 pt., 2 hyd., synchro, unknown hours
3020			G	$3,100	1/29/2011	ECMO	Gas
3020			G	$7,500	1/29/2011	ECMO	John Deere 148 loader
3020			G	$5,250	1/1/2011	ECKS	PS
3020			G	$6,100	12/11/2010	SCMN	Synchro, 2 hyd., WF, new rubber, diesel, 15.5x38 tires
3020			G	$2,600	11/18/2010	SEOK	
3020			G	$6,750	11/18/2010	SEOK	John Deere 48 loader
3020			G	$14,500	11/13/2010	NCIA	Diesel
3020			G	$4,300	9/4/2010	NEIN	Gas, PS
3020			G	$8,250	9/4/2010	NEIN	Diesel, PS
3020			G	$19,000	9/4/2010	NEIN	Standard, diesel
3020		6,283	G	$5,600	9/2/2010	Online	*IronPlanet.com,* item in Minnesota
3020			G	$4,200	8/14/2010	WCMN	Gas, synchro, 1 hyd., 3 pt., 540/1,000 PTO, WF
3020			G	$7,100	8/11/2010	ECMN	WF, PS, 3 pt., PTO, one owner, 48 loader
3020			G	$8,500	8/11/2010	ECMN	WF, synchro, 3 pt., PTO
3020			G	$10,750	8/11/2010	ECMN	Side console, WF, 2 hyd., 3 pt., PTO, restored
3020			G	$10,100	8/7/2010	SCMN	Diesel, side console, diff. lock, 3 pt., 2 hyd., new style step, PTO, rock box, 18.4Rx34 tires, SN 131603R
3020			G	$6,700	6/5/2010	SEIA	Diesel
3020			F	$3,000	5/26/2010	ECSD	Dual 300 loader
3020			G	$4,550	5/26/2010	ECSD	3 pt.
3020			G	$6,500	5/26/2010	ECSD	WF, John Deere 48 loader
3020			G	$4,100	4/10/2010	ECIA	Gas, WF, console
3020			G	$5,700	3/20/2010	NWIL	Gas, NF, 1,200 hours on OH
3020			G	$24,600	3/1/2010	ECWI	Hyd. FWA, online government auction
3020			G	$4,500	2/11/2010	NENC	Diesel, PS, side console, fender
3020			G	$7,300	1/21/2010	SCMI	Diesel, WF, synchro, 38" rubber
3130	1976	822	G	$4,200	2/22/2014	ECMI	Diesel, WF, 3 pt., PTO, 2 hyd., canopy, 2WD, 18.4x34 rear tires
4000	1969	6,000	G	$17,500	11/17/2012	NWMO	Diesel, SN 218395R, WF, 18.4x34 rear tires, wheel weights, synchro, no cab, excellent new appearance, 2 sold on this sale
4000	1969	4,348	G	$12,000	7/14/2012	NWIA	Diesel, 2 hyd., 3 pt., side console, NF, rear fenders

John Deere

Model	Year	Hours	Condition	Price	Date	Area	Comments
4000	1969		G	$41,000	6/25/2011	ECIA	Diesel, SN 211422, synchro, WF, original, first John Deere 4000 built
4000	1969		F	$7,100	2/17/2011	WCNE	WF, diesel, 3 pt., cab, John Deere 158 loader, grapple
4000	1970	8,009	G	$11,255	7/13/2011	Online	*BigIron.com,* item in Nebraska, synchro, 6 cyl. diesel, 1,000 PTO, Westendorf All-Matic 42 loader, 5' bucket, 3-tine grapple, twin cyl., WF, 8 inside wheel weights
4000	1970		G	$17,000	6/18/2011	SWMN	Diesel SN 229775, synchro, down draft exhaust, front and rear weights, repainted
4000	1970	7,299	G	$8,000	2/19/2011	ECNE	WF, diesel, 3 pt., open station
4000	1970	6,900	G	$11,500	2/1/2011	NEIN	Synchro, weights, one owner, restored
4000	1970		G	$8,600	11/13/2010	NCIA	2,073 hours on OH, original paint
4000	1971		G	$7,000	9/21/2013	WCMI	Gas, 3 pt., PTO, 1 hyd., electric start, 16.9x38 rear tires, restored
4000	1971	8,301	G	$15,000	8/8/2013	SESD	Diesel, synchro, 2 hyd., WF, 3 pt., John Deere 55 series ISO coupler, hyd. boxes, original paint
4000	1971	5,562	G	$35,000	12/18/2012	NEIA	Diesel, PS, WF, ROPS, 18.4Rx38 rear tires, 11x16 front tires, 2 hyd., rear weights, quick hitch, rare, SN 257681
4000	1971	5,929	G	$7,800	10/24/2012	NECO	Diesel, WF, 3 pt., cab
4000	1971	7,082	G	$8,900	3/22/2012	ECMN	Factory WF, diesel, synchro, 1 hyd., 3 pt., PTO, top link, console, fenders
4000	1971	10,600	G	$9,500	12/22/2011	Online	*IQBID.com,* 1 hyd., 3 pt. differential lock, side console, LG shifter, new clutch and seals, OH
4000	1971		F	$19,500	2/20/2011	SCPA	PS, diesel, side console, WF, 2 hyd., mechanically sound, needs some sheet metal repair
4000	1972		F	$23,000	3/20/2014	ECWI	Diesel, PS, factory 2 hyd., 38" rear tires, need hood help, strong on the throttle, SN 269477, sold on same auction with twin sister SN John Deere 4000 ($25,000, had diff. lock)
4000	1972		F	$25,500	3/20/2014	ECWI	Diesel, PS, factory 2 hyd., 38" rear tires, front slab weights, diff. lock, need hood help, strong on the throttle, SN 269478, sold on same auction with twin sister SN John Deere 4000 ($23,000, no diff. lock)
4000	1972	8,970	G	$9,000	2/4/2014	NWNE	Diesel, WF, 3 pt., no cab, synchro, 2 hyd.
4000	1972	5,400	E	$36,000	11/2/2013	ECIA	Restored, like new, PS
4000	1972		G	$8,500	3/24/2012	NEIN	Diesel, dual hyd., 3 pt., PTO, original, runs
4000	1972		G	$27,000	6/25/2011	ECIA	Diesel, PS, SN 267404, ROPS, 2 hyd., original
4000	1972		G	$15,000	6/18/2011	SWMN	Gas, SN 265891, synchro, front weights, new tires, 2 hyd., repainted
4000	1972		G	$20,000	6/18/2011	SWMN	Diesel, console, standard, SN 262755, 2 hyd., front weight, new tires, synchro, repainted

John Deere

Model	Year	Hours	Condition	Price	Date	Area	Comments
4000			G	$24,000	3/23/2013	NEIN	Diesel, PS, repainted, new tires, 3 pt., fenders, runs
4000		5,700	G	$13,900	12/8/2012	NWIL	Diesel, WF, 3 pt., fenders, weights, 90% rear rubber tires
4000		6,000	G	$13,000	11/17/2012	NWMO	Diesel, synchro, no cab, excellent new appearance
4000		6,385	G	$10,400	6/20/2012	ECIL	1 hyd., 18.4x34 and 10x16 tires, 4 front weights, top link, 1 PTO
4000			G	$7,000	3/24/2012	NEIN	Diesel, console, repainted, WF, fenders, triple hyd., 3 pt., PTO, runs
4000		6,211	E	$14,000	3/24/2012	NEIN	Gas, dual hyd., PTO 3 pt., excellent original, runs
4000			G	$6,000	2/18/2012	SCTX	
4000			G	$11,000	4/19/2011	NEMN	
4000			G	$17,500	1/29/2011	ECMO	PS, 2 post, 2,owner
4000			G	$9,000	12/30/2010	ECMN	WF, 3 pt., PTO
4000			G	$9,500	9/4/2010	NEIN	Diesel
4000			G	$13,000	9/4/2010	NEIN	Diesel, standard
4000		2,553	G	$8,255	6/23/2010	Online	*BigIron.com,* item in Nebraska, synchro, rebuilt injector pump, rebuilt starter, new batteries, new fuel pump
4010	1961	3,200	G	$8,500	2/22/2014	SCNE	Synchro, John Deere 58 loader
4010	1961	908	G	$4,600	2/5/2014	SESD	Synchro, 2 hyd., 3 pt., front slat weights, fenders
4010	1961		G	$3,800	12/12/2013	ECNE	WF
4010	1961		G	$6,200	7/3/2013	Online	*BigIron.com,* item in Kansas, unknown hours showing, 8 speed synchro, 6 cyl.
4010	1961	12,648	G	$9,500	6/18/2013	SCSK	2WD, John Deere 148 front-end loader, 80 PTO hp, 2 hyd., 540 PTO, 18.4x34 rear, 5' bucket, manure tines
4010	1961		G	$2,800	6/7/2013	NESD	NF, 3 pt., diesel, turbo, Westendorf loader and pallet fork attach
4010	1961	7,115	G	$5,250	6/7/2013	ECAB	2WD, John Deere 48 front-end loader, 3 hyd., air, heater, radio
4010	1961	517	G	$5,010	4/17/2013	Online	*BigIron.com,* item in Iowa, synchro, John Deere 6.2L, diesel, 80 hp, 1 hyd., 3 pt., NI trip bucket loader, OH 800-900 hours ago, 540/1,000 PTO WF, 3' loader
4010	1961	2,643	G	$5,750	3/7/2013	SEIA	WF, synchro, gas, 2 hyd., 3 pt., top link, fenders, 14.9x38 tires, OH
4010	1961		G	$4,300	8/22/2012	Online	*BigIron.com,* item in Nebraska, diesel, 2 hyd., PTO, 18.4x34 rear tires, 7.5Lx15 front tires
4010	1961		G	$6,750	6/21/2012	ECND	Diesel, row crop, 3 pt., quick hitch, PTO, 2 hyd., Farmhand F258 quick attach loader and bucket, 13.6x38 rear tires
4010	1961		F	$4,250	4/28/2012	ECSD	Diesel, factory WF
4010	1961		F	$5,100	3/22/2012	NCMI	Diesel, motor rebuilt to 4020 specs, 1 hyd., 3 pt., clutch weak
4010	1961		G	$7,800	3/10/2012	NWMO	WF, synchro, 2 hyd., 16.9x34 tires 75%, front pancake weights, new battery, clean

John Deere

Model	Year	Hours	Condition	Price	Date	Area	Comments
4010	1961		P	$5,900	12/29/2011	WCIL	Rough, open station, WF, turbo, duals, John Deere 48 loader
4010	1961		G	$3,900	8/6/2011	WCIL	WF, Koyker hyd. loader, 7' bucket, 3 pt., 1 hyd., diesel
4010	1961		G	$4,900	8/6/2011	NCIA	Diesel, WF
4010	1961	1,447	F	$2,750	6/22/2011	NECO	Gas, WF, 3 pt., cab
4010	1961	6,104	G	$3,750	6/22/2011	NECO	LP, WF, 3 pt.
4010	1961		G	$10,500	6/18/2011	SWMN	LP, standard, SN 8886, synchro, new tires, front weights, repainted
4010	1961		G	$11,300	6/18/2011	SWMN	Diesel, standard, SN 7474, synchro, front weights, restored
4010	1961		G	$15,750	6/18/2011	SWMN	Gas, standard, SN 8374, synchro, new tires, repainted
4010	1961	8,000	G	$6,600	3/23/2011	Online	*BigIron.com,* diesel, synchro, 540 PTO, 2 hyd., 3 pt., external block heater
4010	1961	9,009	G	$6,100	2/1/2011	NEIN	Diesel, turbo, cab, dual hyd., synchro
4010	1961	5,298	G	$3,500	9/22/2010	NECO	WF, diesel, 3 pt., F11 loader
4010	1961		G	$3,900	5/8/2010	NETN	No cad, diesel, 2 hyd., 3 pt.
4010	1961	6,455	F	$4,000	5/4/2010	WCOK	3 pt., PTO, dual hyd.
4010	1962		E	$17,000	8/10/2013	NCIA	WF, diesel, standard, SN 20933
4010	1962		G	$7,250	11/29/2012	ECIL	Diesel, new tach. with 273 hours, 2 hyd., 16.9x34 rear tires, rear wheel weights, aux. fuel tank, SN 21T21952
4010	1962	3,387	G	$11,750	11/24/2012	SEMN	Diesel, fenders, WF, 34" radials
4010	1962	8,000	G	$9,200	9/19/2012	Online	*BigIron.com,* item in Nebraska, 2WD, 48 hours of use since restoration, 2 hyd., diesel, 84 PTO hp
4010	1962		G	$4,500	2/25/2012	WCMI	Loader tractor, diesel, 3 pt., PTO, 1 hyd., new batteries, 15.5x38 rear tires
4010	1962		F	$4,300	8/27/2011	NEIA	Open station, gas, synchro, 2 hyd., one owner, 200 hours on head, clutch and rear end repairs, fenders, weights, fully hyd. loader, no 3 pt. arms, paint on the sheet metal is very poor
4010	1962		G	$3,800	8/24/2011	Online	*BigIron.com,* item in Nebraska, Wheatland, synchro, 6 cyl. diesel, 2 hyd., 540 PTO, does not run, swinging drawbar, wheel weights, John Deere 148 6' loader
4010	1962	6,681	G	$4,070	6/29/2011	Online	*PurpleWave.com,* item in Kansas, 6 cyl. diesel, 3 pt., 540 PTO, drawbar, hyd. set
4010	1962		G	$2,710	6/22/2011	Online	*BigIron.com,* item in Nebraska, synchro, 6 cyl. diesel, duals, 540 PTO, 3 pt., wheel weights
4010	1962		F	$3,400	6/22/2011	Online	*BigIron.com,* item in Nebraska, Wheatland, synchro, 6 cyl. diesel, 2 hyd., 540 PTO, does not run, swinging drawbar, 6' loader
4010	1962	5,915	G	$4,000	6/22/2011	NECO	Diesel, WF, 3 pt., cab
4010	1962		F	$3,400	4/20/2011	NWMI	Diesel, open station, synchro, 2 hyd., 3 pt., PTO, 18.4x34 tires, approx. 1,000 hours on OH
4010	1962	557	G	$9,250	4/9/2011	WCNE	WF, diesel, 3 pt., cab, John Deere 148 loader and big square grapple

John Deere

Model	Year	Hours	Condition	Price	Date	Area	Comments
4010	1962	557	G	$6,800	3/26/2011	NECO	WF, cab, diesel, 3 pt., John Deere 148 loader
4010	1962	7,000	G	$4,150	3/5/2011	NWMO	
4010	1962	3,396	F	$3,500	12/2/2010	ECWY	Synchro, diesel, WF, open station, 3 pt., 540 PTO, 18.4x38 tires, single weights
4010	1962		G	$3,600	9/11/2010	ECIA	
4010	1962	1,200	G	$4,250	6/17/2010	SWND	100 hp, 2 hyd., no cab, Farmhand F11 loader, 3 tine bale fork and bucket, fresh trans. OH
4010	1962		G	$9,100	3/13/2010	ECNE	Synchro, 2 hyd., NF, 3 pt.
4010	1963	2,659	G	$5,100	3/4/2014	ECND	Open station, 1 hyd., 3 pt., OH, front weights
4010	1963		G	$6,500	3/1/2014	SEPA	1 hyd., diesel, John Deere 48 loader, 3 pt., synchro, runs well, good sheet metal, dull paint, 16.9x34 rubber 50%
4010	1963		G	$3,000	12/4/2013	ECIN	
4010	1963	9,812	G	$7,000	10/22/2013	WCSK	2WD, 80 PTO hp, synchro, 2 hyd., 18.4x34 rear, 3 rib front, 540 PTO, open station
4010	1963		G	$6,500	7/31/2013	ECND	Open station, 2 hyd., 3 pt., PTO, factory front and rear weights
4010	1963		E	$10,000	4/27/2013	WCSK	Shedded, 2WD, diesel, 84 PTO hp, 4020 sleeves and pistons, standard., 24V, 1 hyd., PTO, 18.4x34 rear, 3 rib front, SN 52468
4010	1963	8,000	G	$9,250	9/29/2012	SWIN	Turbo diesel, factory wide adj. front axle, extra long rear axle, 3 pt., PTO, 12V, 2 hyd., synchro, 18.4x34 rubber, front weights, new style M&W turbo, Watson SS muffler, one owner, <500 hours on OH, SN 59280
4010	1963		F	$5,200	3/7/2012	SEIA	ROPS, canopy, synchro, 2 hyd., 540 PTO, front and rear weights, 42020 updated engine and new clutch
4010	1963	4,967	G	$9,000	11/22/2011	WCIL	Bush Hog 2846 loader, 16.9x38 tires, 2 hyd.
4010	1963		G	$5,000	7/20/2011	NEND	Standard, 3 hyd., cornhusker 3 pt., PTO, fenders, wheel weights
4010	1963		G	$14,000	6/18/2011	SWMN	Diesel high crop SN 52752, struts, 3 pt., repainted
4010	1963	3,246	G	$3,200	5/25/2011	NECO	LP, Wheatland, dual 300 loader
4010	1963		G	$4,300	11/13/2010	NWIL	LP, WF, 2 hyd., nice original, good tires
4010	1963	6,665	G	$6,200	11/12/2010	ECIL	Diesel, hyd. loader, WF, 3 pt., 2 hyd., new tires, OH 1,000 hours ago
4010	1963		G	$7,700	7/30/2010	ECIA	Diesel, WF, 2 hyd., 18.4x34 tires
4010	1963		G	$4,840	5/26/2010	Online	*PurpleWave.com,* item in Kansas, John Deere 380 cu. in. 6 cyl. diesel, 80 hp, 540 PTO
4010	1963		F	$6,750	4/9/2010	NECO	Gas, 2 hyd., 3 pt., PTO, loader, 8' bucket, bale spear
4010	1963		F	$7,260	2/24/2010	Online	*PurpleWave.com,* item in Kansas, OH in 2008, 520 hours on OH, drawbar, 540 PTO, 12V electric SYS, Westendorf WL457 loader, 8' bucket

John Deere

Model	Year	Hours	Condition	Price	Date	Area	Comments
4010	1963	8,578	F	$3,500	2/20/2010	ECMI	NF, 3 pt., 1 hyd., rough
4010	1964	6,224	G	$4,200	3/15/2011	WCIL	Diesel, 2 hyd., 540 PTO
4010	1964	6,223	G	$4,200	12/17/2010	WCIL	18.4x34 tires, 2 hyd., 540 PTO
4010	1972		G	$8,250	1/1/2011	ECKS	10% tires
4010			G	$7,000	4/3/2014	NEIN	Synchro
4010			G	$4,100	3/22/2014	ECSD	Diesel, WF, 3 pt.
4010		1,256	G	$4,900	3/5/2014	Online	*BigIron.com,* item in Wyoming, diesel, 80 hp, 2 hyd., 3 pt., drawbar, 540 PTO, Egging cab
4010		6,216	G	$6,150	3/5/2014	Online	*BigIron.com,* item in Nebraska, synchro, 6 cyl. diesel, 1 hyd., 3 pt., drawbar, Wheatland rear fenders, WF, rear inside wheel weights
4010			G	$3,600	2/15/2014	SWAR	KD loader
4010		7,591	G	$3,000	1/4/2014	WCNY	Gas, fender
4010			G	$2,000	12/19/2013	SCNY	Diesel, cab
4010		2,604	G	$2,550	12/18/2013	Online	*BigIron.com,* 8 speed synchro, 6 cyl. diesel, 540/1,000 PTO, 2 hyd.
4010		1,055	G	$3,415	12/18/2013	Online	*BigIron.com,* 8 speed synchro, 6 cyl. diesel
4010		1,338	G	$4,700	12/18/2013	Online	*BigIron.com,* 2 function spool valve, 8 speed synchro, PTO, 3 pt., John Deere 46A loader
4010			G	$2,750	12/4/2013	ECIN	Loader
4010		7,754	G	$4,601	12/4/2013	Online	*BigIron.com,* item in Nebraska, synchro, 18.4x34 rear tires, 7.5x18 front tires, diesel, 2 hyd., 3 pt., John Deere 158 loader, 540 PTO
4010		1,098	G	$3,250	10/3/2013	NCIN	Tractor/loader, synchro, 1 hyd.
4010			G	$3,541	9/10/2013	ECND	QR, 2 hyd., 540 PTO, blown motor
4010			G	$4,000	9/6/2013	ECSD	3 pt., PTO, synchro, diesel, John Deere 148 loader, SN 2T31133
4010			G	$4,950	5/8/2013	Online	*IQBID.com,* snowblower, PTO does not work
4010			F	$2,700	4/10/2013	Online	*BigIron.com,* item in Colorado, 6 cyl. propane, 8' blade, 18.4x34 rear tires, 7.5x18 front tires, 1 hyd., 540 PTO, rust
4010			G	$3,600	4/10/2013	NETX	Open, PS
4010			G	$8,200	3/30/2013	NWIL	Diesel, NF, new Roll-O-Matic, 370 hours on complete OH, rebuilt injector pump, hyd. pump and power steering pump, 15.5x38 70%, new front tires, 2 hyd.
4010			G	$3,200	3/28/2013	SCMN	LP, WF, John Deere WF, 3 pt.
4010			G	$6,600	3/28/2013	SCMN	Diesel, Schwartz WF, 12V, 2 hyd., John Deere 4020 sleeves and pistons
4010			G	$4,900	3/23/2013	NCOH	Gas, WF, 1,750 hours on OH
4010			G	$5,250	3/23/2013	NEIN	Diesel, standard, original, runs
4010			G	$15,750	3/22/2013	NWMN	Repowered with Detroit motor, NF, 3 pt., original, runs
4010			G	$3,500	12/19/2012	ECWI	Gas
4010		1,149	G	$3,550	12/5/2012	Online	*BigIron.com,* item in South Dakota, 6 cyl. diesel, rear tires 18x30, front tires 7.5x18, 1 hyd., SN 22T,881

John Deere

Model	Year	Hours	Condition	Price	Date	Area	Comments
4010			G	$7,400	9/13/2012	SEIA	WF, 2 hyd.
4010		5,478	G	$4,500	8/16/2012	Online	*IQBID.com,* item in Minnesota, WF, gas, cab, synchro, 2 hyd., 3 pt., PTO, top link, 18.4x34 tires, 80% rubber
4010			G	$3,700	7/27/2012	SWKY	
4010		7,593	F	$2,450	6/20/2012	ECIL	15.5x38 rear, 4 rear weights, 10x16 front, ROPS, 1 hyd., 1 PTO
4010		5,783	G	$6,750	2/25/2012	WCMI	WF, Year Round cab, 18x4x38 tires, snap on duals
4010		7,055	F	$5,700	2/6/2012	ECIL	Diesel, NF, front weights
4010			G	$8,500	1/31/2012	NEIN	Diesel, repaint, dual hyd., 3 pt.,top link, new 11Lx15 front and 18.4x38 rear tires
4010			G	$4,250	12/1/2011	SEMN	Diesel, WF, 3 pt.
4010			G	$9,500	9/24/2011	WCSD	Diesel, 2 hyd., 3 pt., John Deere 58 loader
4010			G	$4,250	9/16/2011	ECND	Diesel, 3 pt., excellent tires, clean
4010			F	$1,950	9/14/2011	Online	*BigIron.com*, item in Colorado, parts engine and rear end
4010			G	$4,500	8/31/2011	SEMN	
4010			G	$6,100	8/19/2011	NWIL	Diesel, recent OH, WF, good paint
4010			G	$8,500	8/16/2011	SCMN	Diesel, rock box, synchro, 2 hyd.
4010		11,031	G	$6,300	7/26/2011	ECND	Hiniker cab with cooler, 3 pt., 540/1,000 PTO, 2 hyd., duals, dual 320 loader with bucket
4010			G	$5,500	7/9/2011	ECND	3 pt., excellent tires, clean
4010			G	$4,000	5/7/2011	SESK	2WD, PTO, dual hyd., 12V starter and alternator, sleeve, pistons, mains and rod bearings done fall of 2010
4010		8,100	G	$6,250	4/14/2011	NCND	Diesel, loader, 540 PTO
4010		5,466	G	$10,200	4/9/2011	SCMN	WF, 2 hyd., 3 pt., cab
4010		1,679	G	$2,585	4/6/2011	Online	*PurpleWave.com,* item in Oklahoma, 6 cyl. diesel, 80 hp, synchro, 8F gears, drawbar, John Deere mid-mount 1 hyd., joystick
4010			G	$7,700	4/2/2011	ECMN	Diesel, synchro, 2 hyd., 3 pt.
4010		4,300	G	$7,800	2/25/2011	ECIL	Row crop, diesel, 15.5x38 tires, weights
4010			G	$8,000	12/17/2010	WCIL	Diesel, John Deere 148 loader, 540 PTO, 1 hyd.
4010			F	$2,100	11/18/2010	SEOK	LP
4010			G	$3,600	11/18/2010	SEOK	LP, John Deere loader, forks, no bucket
4010		5,658	G	$3,250	9/11/2010	SEIA	12V
4010			G	$10,500	9/4/2010	NEIN	Diesel, high crop, synchro
4010			G	$20,000	9/4/2010	NEIN	Cut away, diesel, synchro
4010			G	$5,000	8/11/2010	ECMN	WF, synchro, 2 hyd., 3 pt., PTO
4010			G	$5,600	6/23/2010	Online	*BigIron.com,* item in Colorado, Ezee-On 125 loader, 7' Bucket, rear tires 18.4x34, front tires 10x16 poor, propane, starts and runs
4010			G	$3,400	6/5/2010	WCMO	Diesel, synchro, running, WF
4010			F	$6,000	6/5/2010	SEMN	Canopy, 3 pt., PTO, hyd.
4010			G	$8,164	4/12/2010	NEMI	Diesel, new paint, 12V starting system, 2 hyd., 3 pt., PTO, price includes 6% buyer's premium

John Deere

Model	Year	Hours	Condition	Price	Date	Area	Comments
4010			G	$2,500	4/3/2010	ECTN	
4010			G	$3,800	3/31/2010	ECND	2 hyd., 3 pt., PTO
4010			G	$4,300	3/31/2010	ECND	Cozy cab, 2 hyd., 3 pt., PTO
4010			F	$2,700	3/13/2010	WCIL	WF, 18.4x34 tires
4010		2,360	G	$4,500	3/5/2010	NENE	Synchro, 1 hyd., 2 spool hyd., no 3 pt. arms
4010			G	$3,200	2/26/2010	SEMN	Diesel, 3 pt., dual hyd., PTO, new 18.4x34S tires
4020	1964		F	$5,250	2/4/2014	WCOK	3 pt., PTO, synchro
4020	1964	3,597	G	$6,000	9/6/2013	ECSD	WF, PS, diesel, 3 pt., PTO, Schwartz 1500 loader, SN 21T67741
4020	1964	2,800	G	$14,000	8/8/2013	ECIN	PS, shows 2,800 hours, nice
4020	1964		G	$7,500	6/13/2013	SEAB	2WD, John Deere 158 front-end loader, 95 PTO hp, diesel, 8F/2R synchro, 2 hyd., dual PTO, 18.4x34 rear, 7' bucket
4020	1964		G	$2,500	2/23/2013	ECMI	Gas, NF, Roll-O-Matic, 3 pt., PTO, 1 hyd., 18.4x34 rear tires
4020	1964	260	G	$8,800	2/19/2013	NWWI	Diesel, WF, 3 pt., 2 hyd., synchro, 18.4x34 rear tires
4020	1964	5,315	G	$11,000	1/18/2013	WCOH	PS, 2 hyd., 16.9x34 tires, SN 73067
4020	1964	7,831	F	$4,600	12/1/2012	SEWY	WF, diesel, cab, older GB loader, 3 pt.
4020	1964		G	$6,500	6/27/2012	NEND	Cab, 3 pt., 540/1,000 PTO, hyd., 2 new matched rear tires, John Deere 158 QT loader, bucket
4020	1964		F	$3,000	4/13/2012	WCMI	Open station, synchro, 2 hyd., diesel, 18.4x34 tires
4020	1964	9,141	G	$6,750	4/11/2012	SEAB	2WD, John Deere 48 front-end loader, 95 PTO hp, standard, 2 hyd., PTO, 3 rib front, bucket
4020	1964		G	$4,500	1/28/2012	ECMO	Synchro, 2 hyd., dual PTO
4020	1964		G	$8,500	9/19/2011	NCIL	PS, climate air cab, saddle tanks
4020	1964		G	$9,000	9/10/2011	ECIA	Diesel, cab, PS, front stack weights and rear wheel weights, duals
4020	1964		G	$5,750	8/11/2011	WCMN	95 hp, 1 hyd., 3 pt., PTO, loader
4020	1964	3,000	G	$2,900	7/30/2011	ECMO	
4020	1964	3,891	F	$2,510	6/22/2011	Online	*BigIron.com,* item in Nebraska, synchro, 6 cyl. diesel, 1 hyd., 540/1,000 PTO, does not run, swinging drawbar, wheel weights
4020	1964		E	$16,000	6/18/2011	SWMN	LP, standard, SN 81753, new tires, PS, repainted
4020	1964		F	$5,000	5/5/2011	SCKS	Diesel, 2 hyd., 3 pt., Kent High loader
4020	1964	4,946	G	$12,500	5/4/2011	WCSK	2WD, John Deere 158 front-end loader, 95 PTO hp, synchro, 2 hyd., dual PTO, 4 rib front, excellent cab, 7' bucket
4020	1964		F	$5,800	3/26/2011	NCKS	One owner, standard., PTO, 3 pt., hyd.
4020	1964	5,193	G	$10,000	3/1/2011	SCNE	Diesel, PS, 18.4x34 rear tires, 7.5Lx15 Front Tires, 2 hyd., 3 pt., John Deere quick hitch, new batteries, oil and filters, SN 77696
4020	1964	371	G	$6,000	5/4/2010	WCOK	Diesel, 3 pt., PTO, loader
4020	1964	9,310	G	$7,500	3/24/2010	ECWA	Synchro, 3 pt., PTO, 2 hyd., 15.5Rx38 tires, front weights

John Deere

Model	Year	Hours	Condition	Price	Date	Area	Comments
4020	1964		G	$6,900	2/27/2010	WCOH	PS
4020	1965	8,365	G	$4,000	3/15/2014	WCIL	LP, 1 hyd., 540 PTO, 3 pt., 18.4x34 rear tires, front/rear weights
4020	1965	6,051	G	$5,200	12/10/2013	IRON	Diesel, 2 hyd., no 3 pt., 18x34 tires
4020	1965		G	$8,500	12/10/2013	NWIA	Diesel, factory WF, synchro, 18.4x34 tires, 2 hyd., 2 new batteries
4020	1965	6,809	G	$7,700	12/3/2013	NWNE	Diesel, 3 pt., Year Round cab, 2 hyd., good rubber, 86 hp
4020	1965	5,313	F	$9,500	10/10/2013	SCSK	2WD, GB800 front-end loader, cab, 95 PTO hp, diesel, synchro, 540/1,000 PTO, dual hyd., 18.4x34 tires, 7.5x18 front, bucket
4020	1965		F	$9,500	10/10/2013	SCSK	Great Bend 800 Workmaster loader, cab, 95 PTO hp, diesel, synchro, 540/1,000 PTO, 2 hyd., 18.4x34 tires, 7.5x18 front, bucket, 5,313 hours showing (not original meter), SN T223R105114R
4020	1965	3,800	G	$15,100	9/21/2013	NCOH	Open station
4020	1965		G	$10,500	8/14/2013	WCMN	2 hyd., 18.4x34 tires, diesel, fenders, WF, 3 pt., PTO, 1,000/540
4020	1965	5,912	F	$6,101	7/9/2013	Online	*IQBID.com,* WF, synchro, 2 hyd., PTO, new batteries
4020	1965		G	$5,100	4/30/2013	WCSK	2WD, 95 PTO hp diesel, 8 speed PS, dual PTO, 2 hyd., 18.4x34 rear
4020	1965	6,383	G	$5,005	3/27/2013	NWWI	Gas, synchro, electricronic ignition, Zenith carburetor, new tires within 500 hours, alternator, water pump, radiator
4020	1965	9,343	G	$8,700	2/21/2013	ECMI	Diesel, one owner, quick attach, cab, heat, synchro, 18.4x34 tires, 1 hyd., 3 pt., PTO, SN T213R101058R
4020	1965		G	$14,000	12/27/2012	NCIA	Diesel, John Deere 720 loader and grapple, 2 buckets, synchro, 18.4x38 tires, 2 hyd., 3 pt., 540/1,000 PTO, SN T213R097922R
4020	1965		G	$9,700	12/3/2012	WCIL	Diesel, WF, synchro, 2 hyd., 60 series step, ROPS, pair rear weights, 18.4x34 and 10x16 tires
4020	1965		G	$15,800	11/24/2012	SEMN	$16K spent on OH, 28 hours on new tach. and OH, diesel, OROPS, fenders, WF, new front tires, near-new rear
4020	1965	7,200	G	$12,250	8/17/2012	SCMI	Diesel, 2 hyd., front and rear weights
4020	1965		G	$7,000	7/11/2012	Online	*BigIron.com,* item in Nebraska, 18.4x34 rear tires, 10x16SL front tires
4020	1965		G	$7,000	12/10/2011	WCMO	900 hours on OH, PS, 1 hyd.
4020	1965		G	$6,000	12/7/2011	NCIA	Diesel, synchro
4020	1965	4,455	G	$9,600	8/31/2011	WCMN	WF, diesel, synchro, 3 pt., 2 hyd., 12V, fenders, quick hitch, PTO, 18.4x34 tires
4020	1965	1,158	G	$9,100	4/27/2011	Online	*BigIron.com,* item in Nebraska, Farmhand XL940 quick attach loader, PS, diesel, 540/1,000 PTO, hr meter not working, 12V, 3 pt., tin bucket and grapple fork, 8' bucket
4020	1965		G	$4,500	2/28/2011	SCMI	Diesel, WF, PTO, dual hyd., cab, no doors or glass, synchro, 3 pt.

John Deere

Model	Year	Hours	Condition	Price	Date	Area	Comments
4020	1965	7,797	F	$3,700	12/7/2010	SCNE	Great Bend 800 loader, propane, 2 hyd., bucket
4020	1965		F	$8,200	11/19/2010	SENE	Diesel, ROPS canopy, WF, 18.4x34 tires
4020	1965		F	$3,500	11/13/2010	NWIL	LP, 2 hyd., WF, 3 pt., original, WF
4020	1965	3,556	F	$7,700	6/23/2010	Online	*BigIron.com,* item in Nebraska, PS, 6 cyl. LP gas, rear tires 18.4x34, front tires 9.5Lx15, 1 hyd., adj. WF, 3 pt., PTO, engine heater, new starter
4020	1965	5,096	G	$6,160	4/28/2010	Online	*PurpleWave.com,* item in Missouri, 6 cyl. 95 hp diesel, 540/1,000 PTO, 3 pt., 1 hyd.
4020	1966	8,455	G	$8,250	2/22/2014	NEIN	Cab, 1 hyd., 3 pt., PTO, weights
4020	1966	6,170	P	$3,800	8/20/2013	WCIL	Diesel, 2 hyd., 540 PTO, 18.4x34 tires, aftermarket WF, rough
4020	1966		G	$11,000	8/10/2013	NCIA	Diesel, WF, PS, SN 144895
4020	1966	9,041	G	$3,500	7/25/2013	WCSK	2WD, 95 PTO hp, 2 hyd., 540 PTO, 18.4x34 rear
4020	1966	7,424	E	$18,500	4/27/2013	WCSK	2WD, diesel, 95 PTO hp, PS, 24V, 2 hyd., 18.4x34 rear, 10x15 4 rib front, SN 144166R, 2nd owner, shedded
4020	1966	5,836	G	$7,500	4/9/2013	Online	*IQBID.com,* WF
4020	1966		G	$11,900	3/9/2013	NCOH	Diesel, Allied 595 loader, 2,493 hours on 2nd tach., 2 hyd., 18.4x34 rubber 80%, SN 5NT213R136985R
4020	1966		G	$6,300	2/23/2013	ECMI	Diesel, 3 pt., PTO, dual hyd., WF, 18.4x34 tires
4020	1966		G	$8,100	12/6/2012	Onllne	*IQBID.com,* SN T213R129532R
4020	1966		G	$8,100	12/6/2012	SEIA	Synchro, ROPS, 2 hyd., 540/1,000 PTO, 3 pt., clamp on duals, shows 777 hours but unknown
4020	1966		G	$6,500	9/6/2012	Online	*IQBID.com,* item in Minnesota, row crop, WF, original condition
4020	1966	2,111	G	$5,200	8/22/2012	Online	*BigIron.com,* item in Nebraska, 35' Sudenga auger, PS, diesel, 2 hyd., 540 PTO, wide intake, rear wheel weights
4020	1966	8,866	G	$4,800	5/23/2012	Online	*BigIron.com,* item in Wyoming, synchro, 6 cyl. diesel, 2 hyd., 540/1,000 PTO, 3 pt., third link, 8' hyd. lift blade, open station, ROPS, new batteries
4020	1966	8,733	G	$9,500	1/13/2012	NCIA	WF, PS, excellent cab
4020	1966		G	$9,900	12/10/2011	SEMN	Synchro, has 4320 John Deere engine, 2 hyd., 3 pt., SN T212R133351R
4020	1966	5,167	F	$3,200	11/22/2011	WCIL	Synchro, 2 hyd., SN SNT212R138820R
4020	1966		G	$9,000	9/16/2011	ECND	Cab, PS, PTO, 2 hours on complete OH
4020	1966		G	$10,000	9/10/2011	ECIA	Diesel, synchro, WF, cab, 3 pt., front stack weights and rear wheel weights
4020	1966	4,725	G	$8,500	8/31/2011	WCMN	OH, diesel, PS, 2 hyd., 18.4x34 tires
4020	1966	9,717	G	$14,500	8/18/2011	SEMN	PS, diesel, open station, totally restored, new style step, new rubber, SN 1213P126568R
4020	1966	3,749	G	$10,500	6/30/2011	ECMO	Diesel, one owner, synchro, near new 18.4x34 rear tires and 10x16SL front tires, 540/1,000 PTO, front weights, SN T213R 131491R

John Deere

TRACTORS

Model	Year	Hours	Condition	Price	Date	Area	Comments
4020	1966	4,369	G	$5,450	6/22/2011	Online	*BigIron.com,* item in Iowa, gas, 2 hyd., carburetor has been serviced, 3 pt.
4020	1966	6,053	G	$11,000	6/20/2011	ECSK	Diesel, John Deere 46A loader, 95 PTO hp, PS, 2 hyd., 540/1,000 PTO, 18.4x34 rear tires, 4 rib front, 5' bucket, SN 121344R
4020	1966		P	$2,500	6/18/2011	SWMN	LP, standard, SN 135679, synchro, 3 pt., 2 hyd., not running, rough
4020	1966	2,418	G	$6,000	4/27/2011	NECO	Diesel, WF, 3 pt., cab, GB900 loader
4020	1966		G	$5,200	4/16/2011	ECMI	Synchro, diesel, 18.4x34 tires, 1 hyd.
4020	1966	6,400	G	$10,750	4/16/2011	NWOH	Diesel, synchro, dent in hood, tach. replaced, 700 hours on new tach., found old tach. on sale day, it read 5,700 hours, good 15.5x38 tires, 1 hyd., front weight, one owner, SN 213R128564R
4020	1966	5,999	G	$4,180	4/6/2011	Online	*PurpleWave.com,* item in Oklahoma, 6 cyl., LP, 90 hp, synchro, encl cab
4020	1966		G	$8,000	3/19/2011	ECIA	
4020	1966		G	$8,750	2/21/2011	NEMO	Diesel, synchro, 18.4x34 rear tires like new and 11x16 front tires, ROPS, canopy, front and rear weights, 1 hyd., 540/1,000 PTO
4020	1966		F	$5,700	11/20/2010	SCKS	Synchro, 3 pt., PTO, loader, John Deere 709 rotary mower
4020	1966		G	$4,700	11/13/2010	NWIL	LP, standard, PTO, bareback, long axle
4020	1966	5,687	G	$4,800	9/8/2010	NWMN	Diesel, PS, 2 hyd., 3 pt., PTO
4020	1966		G	$8,000	8/28/2010	WCIL	Diesel, WF, 2 hyd., 18.4x34 rear tires excellent, front weights, M&W turbo
4020	1966		F	$8,000	2/19/2010	WCIL	LP, WF, 540/1,000 PTO, 2 hyd., 18.4x34 and 7.5x16 tires, 83 hours on new tach.
4020	1966		F	$5,500	2/11/2010	NENC	Diesel, synchro, fender, new paint, good tires
4020	1966		G	$9,250	2/4/2010	NCNE	PS, Kramer built loader and bucket
4020	1967		G	$9,700	3/1/2014	ECMO	1 hyd., good tires, straight
4020	1967		G	$13,000	2/22/2014	SCNE	PS, 3 pt., 2 hyd.
4020	1967	1,578	G	$13,250	2/22/2014	ECIL	Family owned, mostly original, family maintained no. of hours were correct/ original but question on the attach if it was original, auctioneer addressed to bidders on sale day
4020	1967		G	$12,250	1/30/2014	ECIL	Diesel, PS, WF, 3 pt., 1,800 hours on OH, new 18.4x34 tires
4020	1967		G	$4,950	12/10/2013	Online	*IQBID.com,* WF, open station
4020	1967	10,000	G	$9,000	11/26/2013	SEIA	Synchro, 2 hyd., 540/1,000 PTO, diesel, 16.9x38 tires
4020	1967	10,223	G	$8,500	11/25/2013	SCIA	WF, 2 hyd.
4020	1967	6,738	G	$8,250	10/16/2013	Online	*PurpleWave.com,* item in Kansas, John Deere 6 cyl. diesel, PS, diff. lock
4020	1967	9,091	G	$4,100	8/20/2013	WCIL	2 hyd., both PTO, synchro, diesel
4020	1967	8,696	G	$9,750	4/20/2013	WCSK	2WD, John Deere 148 5' front end loader, 95 PTO hp, diesel, synchro, dual PTO, 2 hyd., 18.4x34 rear tires, 3 rib front

John Deere

Model	Year	Hours	Condition	Price	Date	Area	Comments
4020	1967	5,611	G	$9,150	3/27/2013	Online	*BigIron.com,* item in Colorado, 6 cyl. diesel
4020	1967	4,630	G	$9,650	3/27/2013	Online	*BigIron.com,* item in Colorado, 6.6L, 6 cyl.
4020	1967		F	$5,250	3/14/2013	WCNE	Synchro range, 3 pt., PTO, 2 hyd., hours unknown
4020	1967	9,073	G	$6,000	1/29/2013	WCIL	Gas, 18.4x34 rear, front aux. gas tank, 2 hyd., front weights, standard shift, SN T211R121564R
4020	1967		G	$19,000	12/8/2012	SWIA	WF, 2 hyd., 12V, 168 hours on OH, has been restored, very nice
4020	1967		G	$12,700	11/16/2012	NCIA	Diesel, OH, synchro, Year Round cab, front tank, 2 hyd., quick coupler, factory WF
4020	1967	8,795	G	$11,500	8/28/2012	WCIL	Diesel, open station, WF, 2 hyd., 3 pt., John Deere 158 loader, 7' bucket
4020	1967	12,083	F	$4,000	6/20/2012	SESD	Diesel, Year Round cab
4020	1967		G	$4,000	5/19/2012	WCIL	Gas, 6,155 hours, PS, 3 pt., WF
4020	1967		G	$6,750	4/20/2012	WCSK	Blade, 95 PTO hp, 8 speed standard, dual PTO, 2 hyd., 18.4x34 rear tires
4020	1967	6,983	G	$6,100	3/22/2012	ECMN	Factory WF, turbo, PS, 1 hyd., 3 pt., PTO
4020	1967		G	$6,100	3/20/2012	WCIL	
4020	1967		E	$8,000	3/10/2012	ECIN	Restored, WF, 2 hyd., good tires
4020	1967		G	$6,700	2/25/2012	WCMI	Loader, diesel, 3 pt., PTO, WF, 18.4x34 tires
4020	1967		G	$10,250	12/10/2011	SEMN	PS, Hiniker cab, 18.4x34 tires, 2 hyd., 3 pt., rock box, SN T213P171374R
4020	1967		F	$6,400	11/30/2011	SEMN	Gas, synchro, 18.4x34 tires, yellow cab
4020	1967		F	$7,250	11/22/2011	WCIL	WF, diesel, SN 157359
4020	1967	9,780	G	$7,400	11/9/2011	Online	*BigIron.com,* item in Nebraska, 2WD, sync range, diesel, 1 hyd., 540/1,000 PTO, 1500 lb. rear wheel weights
4020	1967		F	$2,025	8/27/2011	WCIL	Open station, needs restoration, gas, WF
4020	1967	9,251	G	$9,000	8/27/2011	WCOH	Synchro, axle duals with hubs
4020	1967	7,646	F	$4,500	8/20/2011	NEKS	Propane, WF, snychro, new radiator, 16.9x34 rubber 65%, 1 hyd., SN SNT212R125565R
4020	1967	9,800	G	$9,500	8/19/2011	NWIL	Diesel, WF, 18.4x34 tires, 8 speed PS, SN 166924, 2 hyd.
4020	1967	1,986	G	$9,250	8/18/2011	SEMN	Diesel, open station, synchro, new style step, 18.4x34 rubber 60%, 2 hyd., SN 152632R
4020	1967	3,728	G	$9,750	8/18/2011	SEMN	Diesel, open station, synchro, 18.4x34 rubber 70%, 2 hyd., new style step, SN 173287R
4020	1967	7,652	G	$7,800	8/13/2011	WCIL	Diesel, PS, 18.4x34 and 10x16 tires, John Deere 48 loader
4020	1967		G	$6,400	6/18/2011	SWMN	Diesel, synchro, SN 148464, 3 pt., 1 hyd., original
4020	1967		G	$12,750	6/18/2011	SWMN	Diesel standard SN 160767, front weights, dust shields, 2 hyd., synchro, repainted

John Deere

Model	Year	Hours	Condition	Price	Date	Area	Comments
4020	1967	4,100	G	$5,800	6/6/2011	NCIA	One owner original hours, consigned by 92-year-old local farmer, seat in poor condition but very nice overall condition
4020	1967	9,304	P	$2,200	3/19/2011	SEWY	Diesel, WF, 3 pt., ROPS, needs work
4020	1967		F	$9,000	2/19/2011	WCWI	PS, average shape
4020	1967	4,586	G	$7,750	2/1/2011	NEIN	
4020	1967	7,650	G	$8,500	12/16/2010	NCMI	Diesel, PS, M&W turbo kit, 900 hours on major OH, 2 hyd., 16.9x34 tires
4020	1967	6,572	G	$3,350	12/8/2010	NECO	WF, gas, 3 pt.
4020	1967		G	$15,200	12/1/2010	SCNE	Koyker K5 loader, 3 sets rear weights, joystick control
4020	1967		G	$6,500	9/11/2010	ECIA	
4020	1967	6,448	G	$7,000	6/17/2010	SEIA	Diesel, synchro
4020	1967	4,829	G	$7,200	6/17/2010	SEIA	Diesel, PS, front and rear weights
4020	1967		P	$3,950	5/26/2010	ECSD	Weak clutch
4020	1967	4,619	G	$6,500	5/4/2010	WCOK	PS, power steering, 3 pt., PTO, inside wheel weights
4020	1967		G	$11,000	3/6/2010	NEKS	4,742 hours since major OH, rollbar, canopy, diesel
4020	1967		G	$6,700	2/25/2010	SEND	Diesel, synchro, Year Round cab, 2 hyd., 3 pt., quick hitch, PTO
4020	1967		F	$9,750	2/11/2010	NENE	WF, no cab, Westendorf loader
4020	1968		E	$13,500	11/2/2013	ECIA	New trans, PTO seals and load shaft seals, new batteries and cable, good tires

In our www.machinerypete.com "auction results" database we have 1,710 auction prices on John Deere 4020 tractors from the past 18 years. What are my favorites? Well, there was the all-time record high 1969 model 4020, a restored front-wheel assist model that sold for $50,000 at a June 18, 2011, collector auction for Bill DeYeager in southwest Minnesota. Then there was the one-owner, always-shedded 1972 4020 with 566 actual hours that sold at a June 9, 2001, farm auction in north-central Nebraska for $29,000. The buyer was from Ohio. He told me on his drive home he was stopped twice before leaving Nebraska and asked if he wanted to sell. Wonder what that 1972 model with 566 hours would sell for today? It's probably a lot more than $29,000.

PETE'S PICK

More recently, I enjoyed seeing the original, one-owner, 1972 4020 diesel with 4,175 hours sold for $30,000 (pictured) on a Feb. 22, 2014, consignment auction in northeast Indiana. Bidding opened at $20,000. Bids flew, boom, boom, boom. Auctioneer said first one to $30,000 gets it. Yes sir.

John Deere

Model	Year	Hours	Condition	Price	Date	Area	Comments
4020	1968	3,989	G	$8,690	9/11/2013	Online	*PurpleWave.com,* item in Kansas, John Deere 6 cyl. diesel, John Deere 153 loader, 540/1,000 PTO
4020	1968	2,904	G	$14,000	8/14/2013	WCMN	PS, ROPS, roof, 16.9x38 rubber 80%, recent rebuilt engine, 540/1,000 PTO, 2 hyd., 3 pt., SN 109141R
4020	1968	1,128	G	$5,000	5/8/2013	Online	*BigIron.com,* item in Iowa, synchro, 8F
4020	1968	10,097	G	$7,705	5/8/2013	Online	*BigIron.com,* item in Iowa, synchro, 8F/2R
4020	1968	8,700	G	$12,000	4/2/2013	ECIA	Open station, synchro, 2 hyd., 3 pt., 540 PTO, 12V conversion, 4430 front axle, OH, new clutch
4020	1968	5,762	G	$5,500	2/12/2013	WCIL	
4020	1968		G	$11,000	2/6/2013	SESD	Diesel, repainted
4020	1968		G	$5,750	12/14/2012	SWKY	
4020	1968	3,632	G	$10,800	12/12/2012	NCIL	Gas, 1\one owner, synchro, fenders, SN 184873R
4020	1968		G	$7,900	12/1/2012	NCOH	Diesel, WF, good rubber
4020	1968	7,890	G	$12,500	11/24/2012	SEMN	Diesel, OROPS, fenders, WF, 2 hyd., 34" radial tires
4020	1968		F	$8,360	10/10/2012	Online	*PurpleWave.com,* item in Kansas, 6 cyl. diesel, manual., spring ride seat, Great Bend 900 loader
4020	1968	9,199	G	$5,500	8/22/2012	Online	*BigIron.com,* item in South Dakota, synchro, 6 cyl. gas, 2 hyd., 540/1,000 PTO, 12V system, 3 pt., Hiniker cab
4020	1968		F	$5,000	7/24/2012	NCIA	Gas, Hiniker cab, John Deere WF, 2 hyd., synchro, electronic ignition, 16.9x34 axle duals
4020	1968	4,090	G	$9,100	5/9/2012	Online	*BigIron.com,* item in Nebraska, Buhler 7' loader, 8 speed synchro, 404 cu. in. diesel, 95 hp, 2 hyd.
4020	1968	1,068	G	$6,900	3/14/2012	ECND	2 hyd., 3 pt., quick hitch, dual 3000 loader, loader controls
4020	1968		G	$4,650	2/1/2012	SEND	Diesel, PS, 3 pt., PTO
4020	1968	6,000	G	$8,600	1/31/2012	NEIN	Excellent
4020	1968		G	$5,500	11/30/2011	ECND	Row crop, 2 hyd., 3 pt.
4020	1968		G	$7,800	8/23/2011	NCIA	Cab, WF, 2 hyd., synchro, 3 pt., 18.4x34 tires
4020	1968	9,757	G	$8,300	8/6/2011	WCOK	Fully weighted, 3 pt., 1 hyd., snap on duals
4020	1968		G	$8,600	7/30/2011	ECMO	
4020	1968	3,925	G	$12,500	6/30/2011	ECMO	One owner, diesel, synchro, 18.4x34 rear tires and 10x16SL front tires, 540/1,000 PTO, front weights, SN T213R 177306R
4020	1968		G	$12,500	2/19/2011	NCWI	Console synchro, 3 pt., 2 hyd., 600 hours on OH, new injector pump, clamp on duals John Deere 148 loader, Shur Lok quick attach material bucket, joystick controls
4020	1968	4,115	G	$14,500	1/11/2011	WCIL	WF, synchro, like new tires, 2 hyd., 3 pt.
4020	1968	5,500	F	$7,750	12/16/2010	NCIA	Kind of rough, PS
4020	1968	9,684	F	$4,300	12/8/2010	NECO	WF, diesel, 3 pt., cab, duals

John Deere

Model	Year	Hours	Condition	Price	Date	Area	Comments
4020	1968	5,200	E	$16,750	11/13/2010	NCIA	Diesel, WF, 18.4x38, 5,200 one owner hours, original paint, John Deere 58 loader, 4020 mounts, canopy
4020	1968		G	$7,600	10/23/2010	ECMO	Near new tires, new paint
4020	1968		G	$5,900	9/11/2010	SEIA	Turbo out of 7700 combine, used this spring in field
4020	1968		G	$10,900	9/11/2010	ECIA	Turbo, ROPS, aux. fuel tank, WF, 3 pt., new tires
4020	1968		G	$5,500	8/11/2010	ECMN	WF, 3 pt., synchro, PTO, cab, heat, recent OH
4020	1968		G	$7,500	8/11/2010	ECMN	WF, open station, PS, 2 hyd., 3 pt., dual PTO, converted to 12V
4020	1968	8,189	G	$7,500	3/11/2010	WCMN	Diesel, synchro, 2 hyd., 3 pt., PTO, 18.4x34 tires
4020	1968	4,090	F	$4,400	3/5/2010	NCMO	Gas, synchro
4020	1969		G	$13,500	3/1/2014	SEPA	Side console, 800 hours on complete OH, new paint, synchro, dual hyd., dual PTO, 3 pt., John Deere ROPS roof, 18.4Rx34 rubber 25%, 1 tire has cuts in lugs
4020	1969	7,776	G	$17,000	9/21/2013	SEMN	Diesel, WF, side console, 2 hyd., front weights, 18.4x34 tires
4020	1969		G	$8,800	9/6/2013	NEIA	Cab, dual console hyd., WF, 3 pt.
4020	1969	5,544	G	$4,200	8/20/2013	WCIL	Gas, side console, synchro, 1 hyd., 540 PTO, front weights, 18.4x34 tires
4020	1969	6,756	G	$14,000	7/31/2013	ECND	Side console, 2 hyd., 3 pt., QH, 540/1,000 PTO
4020	1969	7,486	G	$9,000	3/14/2013	WCNE	Side console, synchro, 3 pt., PTO, 2 hyd.
4020	1969	7,249	G	$18,250	1/11/2013	ECIL	Diesel, console, SN 216863, fender, WF, 2 hyd., recent clutch, water pump, injectors, injector pump and repairs
4020	1969		G	$15,900	12/10/2012	ECIL	
4020	1969		G	$16,000	12/10/2012	ECIL	PS, second owner, differential lock, turbo, WF
4020	1969	8,420	G	$17,000	12/1/2012	NCMO	Diesel, PS, console
4020	1969	6,151	G	$8,500	4/14/2012	NENC	2WD, open station, synchro range, WF end, 6 short chest weights, 2 hyd., 540 PTO, side console, top link
4020	1969	8,545	G	$5,100	3/31/2012	SWSK	95 hp, 2WD, 8F/2R synchro, 18.4x34 singles rear, 2 hyd., brackets for John Deere 146 loader
4020	1969		G	$8,850	3/20/2012	WCIL	Loader
4020	1969	7,912	G	$9,110	2/1/2012	SEND	Diesel, side console, loader
4020	1969		G	$10,750	1/28/2012	ECMO	Console
4020	1969		F	$8,500	1/26/2012	ECIN	WF
4020	1969		G	$8,750	12/7/2011	NCIA	Diesel, synchro, 18.4x34 tires
4020	1969		G	$13,900	12/3/2011	NCIA	Diesel, console, 2 hyd., 3 pt., PTO, factory WF
4020	1969		P	$4,025	8/6/2011	NCIA	Rough, stuck, diesel, console, WF
4020	1969		E	$19,750	8/2/2011	ECNE	Side console, synchro
4020	1969		E	$38,000	6/18/2011	SWMN	Standard console synchro, SN 217130, front weights, fenders, new tires

John Deere

Model	Year	Hours	Condition	Price	Date	Area	Comments
4020	1969		E	$50,000	6/18/2011	SWMN	Diesel, PS, console, SN 220862, front wheel drive, new tires, ROPS, front weights, 3 hyd., repainted
4020	1969	10,337	G	$4,500	4/26/2011	SWMN	OH twice, gas, no cab, WF, front end weights
4020	1969	7,152	G	$17,500	4/13/2011	Online	*BigIron.com,* item in Nebraska, splitter valve, self leveling loader, spear, just repainted, less than 400 hours on complete OH
4020	1969	8,049	G	$5,200	4/7/2011	WCMI	Diesel, one owner, Year round cab, side console, 18.4x34 tires, 2 hyd., M&W turbo
4020	1969	9,600	G	$11,000	12/30/2010	ECMN	WF, open station, side console, synchro, hay spear, front. weights
4020	1969		G	$7,100	12/11/2010	NEMI	Diesel, side console, 2 hyd., synchro, axle duals
4020	1969	11,447	F	$6,300	12/7/2010	SCNE	Farmhand 258 loader, cab, synchro, 2 hyd., grapple AND bucket, loader valve
4020	1969	7,303	G	$9,500	3/24/2010	ECWA	PS, 3 pt., PTO, 2 hyd., 14.9Rx38 tires
4020	1969	4,980	G	$16,500	2/20/2010	NCIL	Diesel, WF, 3 pt., 2 hyd., new paint and tires, one owner
4020	1969		G	$6,800	2/11/2010	NENE	WF, no cab, standard 3 pt., synchro
4020	1970	4,119	G	$8,000	3/15/2014	WCIL	Diesel, synchro, 2 hyd., 540/1,000 PTO, 3 pt., 18.4x34 tires, 4 pad weights and starter weights
4020	1970	6,717	G	$17,000	3/4/2014	ECND	Factory cab, 2 hyd., 3 pt., quick hitch, 540/1,000 PTO, diff. lock
4020	1970		F	$8,250	2/15/2014	ECMO	Diesel, synchro, side console, ROPS, 18.4x34 rear tires, 11Lx15SL front tires, 540/1,000 PTO, SN T213R227652R
4020	1970	7,525	G	$9,900	1/15/2014	Online	*BigIron.com,* item in Utah, 8 speed PS, 6 cyl. diesel
4020	1970	7,400	G	$13,600	9/28/2013	NEIA	Diesel, Lundeen cab, WF, 3 pt., new 18.4x34 rears, new injectors
4020	1970	5,800	G	$16,000	9/28/2013	NEIA	Diesel, open station, WF, 3 pt., new 18.4x34 rears, original paint
4020	1970		G	$14,500	9/12/2013	SEIA	Synchro, Cozy cab, power steering, 3 pt., 540 PTO, 1 hyd.
4020	1970	6,785	G	$7,500	2/6/2013	SESD	Gas, WF, side console, 2 hyd., 3 pt., 16.9x38, nice
4020	1970		G	$7,300	10/18/2012	WCMI	Side console, synchro, 2 hyd.
4020	1970		G	$12,000	7/14/2012	NWIA	Diesel, QT cab, side console, 3 pt., 827 hours on engine OH
4020	1970	1,686	G	$9,100	6/13/2012	Online	*BigIron.com,* item in Wyoming, PS, 6 cyl. diesel, 15.5x38 duals, 2 hyd., 540/1,000 PTO, SF, 3 pt., third link, side console, new batteries
4020	1970	7,290	G	$11,250	3/3/2012	SEMN	Side console, 18.4x34 tires, 3pt., 2 hyd., 540/1,000 PTO, synchro, SN T213R236389R
4020	1970	6,000	G	$7,000	1/31/2012	NEIN	Synchro
4020	1970	7,300	G	$8,100	12/22/2011	Online	*IQBID.com,* synchro, ROPS, 2 hyd., side console

TRACTORS

John Deere

Model	Year	Hours	Condition	Price	Date	Area	Comments
4020	1970	5,600	G	$12,750	12/14/2011	WCMN	Diesel, roll bar canopy, side console, PTO, nice 18.4-38 tires
4020	1970	1,411	G	$8,580	8/31/2011	Online	*PurpleWave*.com, item in Texas, 6.6L, 6 cyl., 95 PTO hp, synchro, John Deere 158 loader, 540/1,000 PTO
4020	1970		G	$8,000	7/30/2011	ECMO	
4020	1970	5,739	G	$8,601	6/8/2011	Online	*BigIron.com,* item in Iowa, diesel, 2 hyd., 540/1,000 PTO, side console hyd., 2 hyd., cab DR available
4020	1970	5,700	F	$26,100	6/3/2011	SEIA	Hyd. power front assist, rough, diesel, PS, side console, 2 hyd., 3 pt., parking brake not working, tin work had been off prior to the sale
4020	1970		G	$10,750	3/16/2011	NWIA	Gas, looked nice, tires shot in back, John Deere WF, 2 hyd., good sheet metal, runs nice
4020	1970	8,766	G	$15,100	2/25/2011	ECIL	Diesel, console, WF, 50 hours on rebuilt engine, new 18.4x34 tires
4020	1970		G	$10,500	12/30/2010	ECMN	WF, PS, side console
4020	1970		G	$14,400	12/17/2010	WCIL	Diesel, synchro, 18.4x34 tires, 11Lx15 front tires, 540/1,000 PTO, SN 234196R, nice, John Deere 720 loader, 6' bucket
4020	1970	4,055	E	$17,000	12/15/2010	SEMI	One owner, unrestored, PS, WF, side console, 1 hyd., 18.4x34 tires
4020	1970	9,500	G	$8,250	11/13/2010	NCIA	Side console, 2 hyd., Hiniker cab
4020	1970	6,881	G	$11,750	10/25/2010	WCNE	Diesel, WF, fenders, 3 pt., 2 hyd., PTO, side console, synchro, nice straight
4020	1970		E	$16,800	8/28/2010	WCIL	Diesel, WF, 2 hyd., 18.4x34 rear tires new, front and rear weights, new paint, sharp
4020	1970	5,762	E	$26,000	8/14/2010	NCIL	WF, diesel, PS, side console, 18.3x34 tires, one owner, original
4020	1970		G	$11,000	7/30/2010	NCNE	2 hyd., PS, mounted front, easy clean sweeper, bunk cleaner
4020	1970	8,423	G	$10,000	4/17/2010	ECNE	NF, 1 hyd., side controls, front weights
4020	1970		F	$5,500	4/9/2010	NECO	Cab, diesel, 2 hyd., John Deere 158 loader and 9' bucket, bale spear
4020	1970	6,209	G	$16,100	3/13/2010	ECNE	Synchro, 2 hyd.
4020	1970		E	$27,500	3/6/2010	NCOK	Sold with John Deere 725 loader, 2nd owner, always shedded, turbo PS, 3 pt., 2 hyd., roll guard canopy, 18.4x34 tires, fully weighted, quick coupler, joystick, 72" bucket, bale spike
4020	1970		G	$8,100	2/26/2010	SEMN	3 pt., PTO hyd.
4020	1970	5,930	G	$9,750	1/6/2010	ECIL	Diesel, console, fender, no cab, 18.4x34 tires, quick hitch, weights
4020	1971		G	$8,750	3/1/2014	SEPA	Side console, synchro, WF, 1 hyd., dual PTO, 3 pt., runs well, good sheet metal, dull paint, 16.9x38 rubber 15%
4020	1971		G	$2,500	9/25/2013	SEMN	Gas, 3 pt., PTO
4020	1971		G	$15,750	9/21/2013	WCMI	Diesel, 3 pt., PTO, 1 hyd., electric start, 18.4x38 rear tires, weights, restored
4020	1971		G	$20,000	1/11/2013	NWIN	Diesel, WF, 3 pt., console, PS, 2 hyd., front weights, 18.4x38 tires

John Deere

Model	Year	Hours	Condition	Price	Date	Area	Comments
4020	1971	8,774	F	$10,050	11/30/2012	SWIA	Diesel, synchro, side hyd. controlS, 3 pt., 2 hyd., rear wheel weights, WF, John Deere 148 loader, forklift attachment
4020	1971	7,977	G	$15,100	11/8/2012	ECNE	Diesel, synchro, 3 pt., 2 hyd., 16.9x38 rear tires, side hyd. controls, John Deere 48 loader, bucket, rear wheel weights
4020	1971	3,064	E	$25,000	8/17/2012	SCMI	Like new, diesel, front and rear weights, 2 hyd.
4020	1971	2,523	G	$14,000	7/14/2012	NWIA	Diesel, WF, rear fenders, side console, 3 pt., 2 hyd.
4020	1971		G	$18,000	4/7/2012	NWMI	Diesel, side console, 2 hyd., 3 pt., PTO, front and rear weights
4020	1971		F	$4,800	2/24/2012	NETX	ROPS canopy, PS, 18.4x34 tires, 2 hyd.
4020	1971	213	G	$10,750	2/2/2012	NEIN	Diesel, side console, new paint
4020	1971	6,000	G	$20,050	11/15/2011	Online	*IQBID.com,* high crop, diesel, 2 hyd., 3 pt., PTO, roll bar, new tires, fully restored
4020	1971		G	$14,000	6/18/2011	SWMN	Diesel, console, synchro, SN 258995, high crop, front weights, struts, repainted
4020	1971	9,868	F	$5,700	4/14/2011	WCMI	Diesel, dual hyd., PTO, 18.4x38 rear tires
4020	1971	14,000	G	$9,500	2/19/2011	ECNE	Diesel, front weights and cab
4020	1971	2,987	E	$22,250	11/13/2010	NCIA	Console, WF, 2 hyd., 2,987 hours, very nice original
4020	1971	5,470	E	$15,250	3/20/2010	NWIA	WF, synchro, 3 pt., 2 hyd., sharp
4020	1972	4,175	E	$30,000	2/22/2014	NEIN	Diesel, side console, 2 hyd., 3 pt., PTO, one owner, original
4020	1972	6,650	G	$11,500	6/20/2013	ECSK	2WD, John Deere 148 front-end loader, 91 hp PTO, 6.6L, 6 cyl. diesel, synchro, 2 hyd., dual PTO, 6' bucket, John Deere factory cab, air, 18.4x34 duals, joystick
4020	1972	3,064	E	$25,000	8/17/2012	SCMI	Like new, diesel, front and rear weights, 2 hyd.
4020	1972	6,755	G	$16,750	4/25/2012	Online	*BigIron.com,* item in Nebraska, Farmhand loader, 8 speed synchro, 95 hp, 2 hyd., 540/1,000 PTO, grapple and joystick loader control, 3 pt.
4020	1972	3,660	E	$28,000	3/24/2012	SEOH	Open station, diesel, WF, side console, 480/85Rx34 tires, second owner (bought it with 500 hours on it), 4 bidders in on it up past mid $20k's on the auction
4020	1972	7,558	G	$13,700	1/19/2012	ECIL	SN 263268, diesel, WF, John Deere cab, air, synchro, 18.4x34, 2 hyd.
4020	1972	4,601	G	$12,500	7/30/2011	ECMO	
4020	1972	8,344	G	$12,600	4/11/2011	Online	*AuctionTime.com*
4020	1972		G	$14,500	3/5/2011	ECIA	Factory cab, nice original
4020	1972	6,900	G	$18,000	2/5/2011	NCKS	Synchro
4020	1972		G	$10,000	2/1/2011	NEIN	Completely restored
4020	1972		G	$15,800	3/23/2010	SEND	
4020			G	$4,900	4/3/2014	NEIN	1 hyd., synchro, rough
4020			G	$1,900	3/26/2014	ECMS	Tricycle front, 2WD, 6 cyl., propane
4020			G	$7,600	2/22/2014	SCNE	Synchro, 2 hyd., 3 pt., Farmhand F11 black stripe loader, 8' bucket

TRACTORS

John Deere

Model	Year	Hours	Condition	Price	Date	Area	Comments
4020			G	$6,500	2/5/2014	SESD	PS
4020			G	$7,100	2/5/2014	SESD	
4020		1,268	G	$6,450	1/4/2014	ECOH	Diesel, hard to put into gear
4020		7,568	G	$8,700	1/4/2014	ECOH	Diesel, cab, original, good tires
4020			G	$2,250	12/19/2013	SCNY	Gas
4020			G	$8,500	12/19/2013	WCMN	Diesel, synchro, 2 hyd., 3 pt., 540/1,000 PTO, new paint
4020		7,538	G	$4,200	12/18/2013	Online	*BigIron.com,* 8 PS, 6 cyl. diesel, 540 PTO, 2 hyd.
4020		6,576	G	$5,200	12/18/2013	Online	*BigIron.com,* 8 speed PS, 6 cyl. diesel, 540/1,000 PTO, 2 hyd.
4020		8,495	G	$6,500	12/18/2013	Online	*BigIron.com,* 8 speed PS, 6 cyl. diesel
4020			G	$5,000	12/5/2013	NEIN	Diesel, WF, no tag, 2 hyd., top link, synchro
4020			G	$2,500	12/4/2013	ECIN	
4020			G	$12,000	10/9/2013	NWND	John Deere 148 loader, 3 pt., open station
4020		7,109	G	$9,100	9/21/2013	SEMN	Gas, WF, side console, 2 hyd., front weights, canopy roll guard, like new 18.4x34 tires
4020		499	G	$10,010	9/10/2013	Online	*PurpleWave.com,* item in Kansas, John Deere 6 cyl. diesel, PS, spring suspension seat, 3 pt., drawbar, aux. outlet, sun shades
4020			G	$3,500	9/6/2013	ECSD	PS, 3 pt., PTO, John Deere 148 loader, SN T213P112500R
4020			G	$5,200	8/24/2013	SEMN	Diesel, Wheatland PTO, hyd., 18.4x34 tires, SN 147177R
4020		3,219	G	$5,750	8/24/2013	SEMN	3 pt., hyd., PTO, 18.4x38 tires, SN 72209
4020		2,575	G	$4,700	8/22/2013	SEMN	1 hyd., diesel, SN 218164
4020		6,778	G	$8,000	8/22/2013	SEMN	2 hyd., diesel
4020			F	$4,800	7/27/2013	WCIL	1970s, propane, loader, SN T212R154S02R
4020			G	$9,500	6/22/2013	SEMN	Side console, 3 pt., hyd., PTO
4020		8,196	G	$4,400	6/19/2013	Online	*BigIron.com,* item in Colorado, 8F/2R synchro, 6 cyl. diesel
4020		5,019	G	$5,278	6/19/2013	Online	*BigIron.com,* item in Colorado, 8F/2R synchro
4020			G	$5,300	6/10/2013	Online	*IQBID.com,* synchro, 2 hyd., 540/1,000 PTO, Big M loader, bucket
4020		681	G	$8,800	5/28/2013	NWWI	Side console, synchro, 2 hyd., 3 pt., WF, rebuilt engine, cab, 18.4x34 rear tires
4020		8,951	G	$4,066	5/22/2013	Online	*BigIron.com,* item in Nebraska, synchro
4020		8,168	G	$6,100	5/22/2013	Online	*BigIron.com,* item in Nebraska, synchro
4020		8,032	G	$7,100	5/22/2013	Online	*BigIron.com,* item in Nebraska
4020		4,441	G	$4,201	5/8/2013	Online	*BigIron.com,* item in Colorado, 8 speed synchro, 6 cyl. normal aspirated engine
4020		6,717	G	$3,100	5/1/2013	Online	*BigIron.com,* item in Wyoming, 2 hyd.
4020		6,500	G	$5,100	5/1/2013	Online	*BigIron.com,* item in Nebraska, synchro, 2 hyd.
4020			G	$8,030	4/23/2013	Online	*HansenandYoung.com,* loader
4020		6,794	G	$7,880	4/17/2013	Online	*BigIron.com,* item in Nebraska, loader, 8 speed, John Deere 6 cyl. diesel

John Deere

Model	Year	Hours	Condition	Price	Date	Area	Comments
4020			G	$11,000	4/10/2013	NETX	Diesel, open
4020			G	$7,900	3/30/2013	NWWI	Diesel, PS, Westendorf TA26 hyd. loader, 3 pt. dual hyd., PTO, 18.4x34
4020			G	$8,250	3/30/2013	SCMN	Synchro, Year Round cab, 2 hyd.
4020		9,657	G	$8,225	3/27/2013	Online	*BigIron.com,* item in Nebraska, synchro
4020			G	$6,000	3/23/2013	NEIN	Diesel, standard, big rubber, original, runs
4020			G	$6,750	3/23/2013	NEIN	Gas, console, original, runs
4020			G	$7,000	3/23/2013	NEIN	Gas, repainted, front/rear weights, synchro, dual hyd., 3 pt., runs
4020		4,605	G	$7,900	3/23/2013	NEIN	Diesel, synchro, weights, cab, dual hyd., 3 pt., original, runs
4020		4,874	G	$8,500	3/23/2013	NEIN	Diesel, PS, original, weights, ROPS, 3 pt., quick coupler, runs
4020			G	$12,000	3/23/2013	NEIN	Diesel, synchro, console, dual hyd., 3 pt., fenders
4020			G	$16,000	3/23/2013	NEIN	Diesel, PS, console, repainted, weights, 3 pt., fenders, runs
4020			G	$19,500	3/23/2013	NEIN	PS, 4WD, original, runs
4020			G	$7,750	3/22/2013	WCMI	Diesel, 3 pt., PTO, 1 hyd., WF, newer 18.4x34 rears
4020		9,068	G	$6,000	3/8/2013	SWMN	2WD, diesel, synchro, 2 hyd., 3 pt., PTO, step kit, rock box, 18.4x34 tires
4020		805	G	$8,900	3/7/2013	SEIA	2 hyd., 3 pt., PTO, side console, includes cab, 18.4x34 tires
4020		5,678	G	$7,100	3/2/2013	ECMN	2 hyd.
4020			G	$9,900	2/16/2013	NEIA	Early model (1965 or 1966), diesel, WF, 3 pt., PS
4020		2,000	F	$6,300	2/9/2013	SWOH	WF, hours listed since major OH, runs
4020			G	$4,000	2/7/2013	SEAR	Diesel, straight shift, PTO, 700 hours on new motor
4020		3,865	F	$4,200	2/7/2013	SEAR	Diesel, PS, PTO, runs, drives, transmission slips
4020			G	$7,500	1/19/2013	NEMS	Loader
4020			G	$5,500	12/6/2012	SEIA	2 hyd., 540/1,000 PTO, 3 pt., John Deere 46A loader
4020			G	$5,500	12/6/2012	Online	*IQBID.com,* 2 hyd., 540/1,000 PTO, SN T213H100173R
4020		6,950	G	$9,200	12/5/2012	Online	*BigIron.com,* item in Nebraska, Du-Al 340 loader, PS 8F/4R, 6 cyl. gas, 18.4x34 rear tires, 9.5Lx15 front, 1 hyd., 540 PTO, 7' bucket, grapple, 540 PTO pump, 3 pt., drawbar, SN 4020 21T76123
4020		8,823	E	$24,000	10/25/2012	SCWI	Diesel, PS, side console, late model, WF, very nice, one owner, 6 bidders still in at $15K
4020			G	$2,400	10/24/2012	WCWI	
4020			G	$8,000	10/24/2012	WCWI	John Deere 158 loader, 18.4Rx38 tires, PS
4020			G	$8,000	10/20/2012	ECIL	WF, dual hyd., front and rear weights and aux. fuel tank
4020		1,446	G	$11,000	9/22/2012	NCCO	Cozy cab

TRACTORS

John Deere

Model	Year	Hours	Condition	Price	Date	Area	Comments
4020			G	$16,750	9/15/2012	SCMN	Side console hyd., factory WF, synchro, diff. lock, repainted
4020			G	$8,000	9/12/2012	Online	*IQBID.com,* item in North Dakota, PS, 4 hyd., 3 pt., 540/1,000 PTO, cab, 14.9x38 rears, 245/75R16 fronts, Du-Al 1291 loader, 5 hours on new OH
4020			G	$6,000	8/22/2012	ECMN	3 pt., PTO, 8 speed PS, 2 hyd., canopy and fenders
4020			G	$3,500	8/16/2012	Online	*IQBID.com,* item in Minnesota, WF, PS, factory LP, 1 hyd., 3 pt., PTO, no top link, 18.4x38 tires
4020		3,072	G	$4,200	8/16/2012	Online	*IQBID.com,* item in Minnesota, WF, diesel, 1 hyd., 3 pt., dual PTO, synchro, fenders, 16.9x38 tires 95%
4020		8,241	G	$15,000	8/16/2012	Online	*IQBID.com,* item in Minnesota, WF, diesel, PS, side console, 3 pt., dual PTO, top link, 18.4x38 tires
4020		4,407	G	$3,600	8/4/2012	NEAR	6 cyl. diesel, 3 pt., 540/1,000 PTO, dual hyd., roll bar, 18.4x34 rears
4020			G	$4,600	8/4/2012	NEAR	6 cyl. diesel, PS, canopy, 3 pt., 540 PTO, mid-mount PTO, dual hyd., 18.4x34 rears
4020		7,617	G	$5,400	8/4/2012	NEAR	3 pt., 6 cyl. diesel, 540 PTO, canopy
4020		7,500	G	$8,600	8/1/2012	NEOK	Diesel, loader, new clutch, battery, starter injection redone
4020		7,283	G	$5,900	6/20/2012	ECIL	John Deere 7' loader, 15.5x38 rear tires, 2 rear weights, gas, top link, 1 hyd., 1 PTO, 10x16F
4020			G	$5,500	6/9/2012	ECNE	Diesel, high crop, 3 pt., PTO, hyd., synchro, runs
4020			G	$8,500	6/2/2012	SEMN	Open station, synchro, 3 pt., 2 hyd.
4020			G	$9,000	6/2/2012	SEMN	Open station, synchro, 3 pt., 2 hyd.
4020		9,398	G	$7,000	5/8/2012	Online	*IQBID.com,* PS, 3 hyd., John Deere 158 loader, 8' bucket, 3 year on OH, 16.9x38 rear tires
4020			G	$4,500	3/24/2012	SWMI	Diesel, synchro, 540/1,000 PTO, 3 pt., 1 hyd., 18.4x34 tires
4020			G	$4,800	3/24/2012	NEIN	Diesel, standard, synchro, repainted, fenders, rear weights, PTO, hyd., runs
4020			G	$8,600	3/24/2012	NEIN	Diesel, synchro, original, front weights, dual hyd., 3 pt., PTO, runs
4020			G	$10,000	3/24/2012	NEIN	Diesel, console, synchro, repainted, runs
4020			G	$11,250	3/24/2012	NEIN	Console, synchro, front weights, restored, runs
4020		3,247	E	$11,800	3/24/2012	NEIN	Diesel, PS, dual hyd., quick coupler, front weights, runs
4020			G	$14,500	3/24/2012	NEIN	Pulling tractor, unreadable, 30.5x32 cut pulling tires, runs, receipts
4020			G	$21,000	3/24/2012	NEIN	Diesel, synchro, dual hyd., PTO, 3 pt., ROPS, restored, runs
4020			G	$22,000	3/24/2012	NEIN	HFWD, console, PS, hyd., PTO, 3 pt., runs
4020			F	$5,600	3/8/2012	NCTX	John Deere 48 loader, rusted bucket, cab, WF
4020			F	$6,800	3/3/2012	SEMN	John Deere 48 loader, 3 pt., synchro, 540/1,000 PTO, 2 hyd.

John Deere

Model	Year	Hours	Condition	Price	Date	Area	Comments
4020		2,350	G	$4,200	2/25/2012	WCMI	Gas, WF, 3 pt., PTO, 2 front weights, 18.4x34 rear tires
4020			G	$9,700	2/4/2012	ECSC	
4020			G	$6,000	2/2/2012	NEIN	2WD, 18.4x34 rear tires, diesel, 1 set hyd., 540/1,000 PTO
4020		4,021	G	$7,500	2/2/2012	NEIN	WF, diesel, side step, 18.4x38, 2 hyd., 1 pair rear wheel weights, front weight, 540/1,000 PTO
4020			G	$3,100	1/28/2012	SEAB	
4020			G	$8,000	1/28/2012	SEAB	
4020			F	$3,750	12/14/2011	WCMN	Synchro, 2 hyd., 3 pt., PTO
4020			G	$7,800	12/10/2011	ECKS	Tires 50%, no console
4020			G	$5,500	12/1/2011	NEIN	18.4x34 rear tires, 1 hyd.
4020			G	$6,000	12/1/2011	SEMN	Diesel, WF, 3 pt.
4020			G	$4,000	10/28/2011	NETX	Propane
4020			G	$20,000	10/22/2011	NECO	Diesel, console, synchro, rock shaft
4020			F	$4,700	9/17/2011	WCIL	Diesel
4020		2,201	G	$10,250	9/14/2011	Online	*BigIron.com,* item in Colorado, weights, 540/1,000 PTO, 4 hyd., 3 pt., Leon 707 lift, 7' bucket, Year Round cab, runs
4020			G	$9,300	8/31/2011	ECMN	
4020			P	$4,600	8/19/2011	NWIL	Diesel, WF, 2 hyd.
4020			G	$11,000	8/11/2011	WCMN	WF, side console, PS, 2 hyd., 3 pt., PTO
4020			G	$4,900	7/30/2011	ECMO	Loader, gas
4020			G	$5,500	7/30/2011	ECMO	John Deere 46 loader, diesel, new battery and radiator
4020			G	$7,200	7/30/2011	ECMO	Bush Hog loader
4020			G	$9,000	7/30/2011	ECMO	John Deere 48 loader
4020			F	$4,250	6/17/2011	WCSK	Front-end loader, dual, PTO, cab, 8 speed, PS 9300
4020		4,455	G	$6,750	6/11/2011	ECMN	Diesel, synchro, QT, dual rear hyd., 3 pt., converted to 12V
4020		5,862	G	$9,500	5/19/2011	SWMT	Diesel, PS, 3 pt., PTO, John Deere 148 loader, 16.9x34 tires, cab, 95 hp
4020			G	$4,000	5/13/2011	ECMS	Diesel
4020		394	G	$7,950	5/11/2011	Online	*BigIron.com,* 58 loader, 2 hyd., 540/1,000 PTO, loader welded
4020			G	$4,500	5/4/2011	ECSK	2WD, diesel, synchro, dual hyd., 2 speed, PTO, open station
4020		7,670	G	$14,000	4/26/2011	ECSK	2WD, John Deere 148 front-end loader, 95 PTO hp diesel, Cozy cab with cooler, 2 hyd., dual PTO, rear duals, 4 rib front, bucket, bale spike, shop built dozer blade
4020		9,877	G	$4,110	4/13/2011	Online	*BigIron.com,* item in Wyoming, synchro, 6 cyl. diesel, 2 hyd., 540/1,000 PTO, 3 pt., 2 inside rear wheels weights
4020		5,979	G	$5,126	4/13/2011	Online	*BigIron.com,* item in Kansas, 8' dozer blade, propane, 2 hyd., 540 PTO, one owner, 3 pt., rear weights, dents in tin work
4020			G	$7,400	3/18/2011	SWIL	Diesel, console, synchro, 2 hyd., 3 pt.
4020		6,934	G	$6,300	3/15/2011	WCIL	Diesel, new tires, 2 hyd., 540/1,000 PTO, synchro, front weights

John Deere

Model	Year	Hours	Condition	Price	Date	Area	Comments
4020			G	$3,750	3/5/2011	SEMN	Diesel, 3 pt., 1 hyd., 540/1,000 PTO
4020			G	$6,200	3/5/2011	SEMN	Diesel, 1 hyd., 3 pt., synchro
4020			G	$4,100	1/29/2011	ECMO	Gas
4020			G	$5,100	1/29/2011	ECMO	WF, synchro
4020			G	$5,900	1/29/2011	ECMO	Gas
4020		6,207	G	$10,800	1/28/2011	WCOH	Diesel
4020			G	$6,150	1/1/2011	ECKS	Tires 90%
4020			G	$11,500	12/21/2010	ECMI	Synchro
4020			G	$7,400	12/4/2010	SEMN	Diesel, synchro, very clean
4020			G	$12,750	12/4/2010	SEMN	Diesel, synchro, side console, very clean
4020			F	$7,750	12/2/2010	ECWY	Diesel, John Deere 148 loader
4020			G	$11,000	12/2/2010	ECWY	Koyker loader, gas, 3 pt., no cab
4020			G	$3,400	11/18/2010	SEOK	
4020			G	$3,850	11/18/2010	SEOK	
4020			G	$15,800	11/18/2010	SEOK	John Deere 158 loader
4020			G	$3,500	11/13/2010	WCIL	LP, cab, good tires, no 3 pt.
4020		5,500	G	$4,800	11/13/2010	WCIL	LP, 2 hyd., WF, good tires
4020			E	$19,000	11/13/2010	NCIA	MFWD
4020			G	$5,750	11/6/2010	SWLA	Walden dozer blade in front, 7' Bush Hog IN rear
4020			G	$9,100	11/2/2010	ECOK	3 pt., PTO, 1 hyd., ROPS, new canopy
4020		6,744	G	$6,200	9/4/2010	SEVA	6 cyl., diesel, synchro, solid
4020			G	$7,000	9/4/2010	NEIN	
4020			G	$8,000	9/4/2010	NEIN	Dual hyd.
4020			G	$8,100	9/4/2010	NEIN	Gas, synchro
4020			G	$11,000	9/4/2010	NEIN	Front and rear weights, top link, dual hyd.
4020			G	$11,500	9/4/2010	NEIN	High crop, diesel, PS
4020			G	$13,000	9/4/2010	NEIN	Diesel, PS, side console
4020			G	$27,500	9/4/2010	NEIN	Front wheel assist, restored, new rubber
4020			P	$1,700	9/3/2010	NEIN	High crop kit, dead row, needs work and may not run or drive, as is
4020			G	$13,000	8/14/2010	SEMN	Side console, synchro, rock box, open station, 18.4x34 tires
4020			G	$8,000	8/11/2010	ECMN	Side console, 3 pt., PTO
4020		8,478	G	$8,400	8/7/2010	SCMN	Diesel, cab, side console, 3 pt., PTO, 2 hyd., new 18.4x38 tires, 10x16 front tires, new style step, front weights, SN 255090R
4020			G	$13,000	7/17/2010	NEMT	Diesel, loader
4020			G	$10,000	6/26/2010	NCMD	Cab
4020			G	$19,000	6/19/2010	SWIL	Running, restored, lights, deluxe seat, power steering, used by John Deere for The Precision Farming ad campaign
4020		7,780	F	$6,700	6/12/2010	NENE	Cab, PS, not used in 20+ years
4020			F	$3,300	6/5/2010	SEMN	WF, 46A hyd. loader
4020			F	$3,600	6/5/2010	SEMN	Gas, 3 pt., hyd., PTO
4020			F	$6,000	6/5/2010	SEMN	Diesel, PS, cab, 3 pt., dual hyd., PTO
4020			G	$8,250	6/5/2010	NWIA	Diesel, John Deere LDR
4020			G	$6,800	5/26/2010	ECSD	

John Deere

Model	Year	Hours	Condition	Price	Date	Area	Comments
4020			G	$10,100	4/8/2010	SEAB	Cab, diesel, PS, PTO, dual hyd., John Deere 158 front-end loader, grapple
4020		6,130	G	$8,250	4/1/2010	NCIN	2 hyd., top link, 3 pair front weights, 1 pair rear weights, diesel, side console
4020			F	$4,700	3/30/2010	WCKY	Dozer blade
4020			G	$9,000	3/20/2010	SEIA	New paint, synchro, diesel
4020		7,460	G	$6,050	3/10/2010	Online	*PurpleWave.com,* item in Texas, 540 PTO, 6 cyl. diesel, 2 hyd., ROPS, 72" bucket
4020			G	$5,000	3/5/2010	NCMO	Synchro
4020			G	$9,000	3/5/2010	SEWA	PS, 3 pt., PTO, John Deere 158 loader
4020			G	$13,000	2/13/2010	SWIA	
4020			F	$4,000	2/11/2010	NENC	Gas, ran good, new paint
4020			G	$13,750	2/11/2010	NENE	WF, synchro, 18.4x34 rear tires, 10x16 front tires, HD rims, 3 pt.
4030	1973	548	G	$14,250	4/10/2013	Online	*BigIron.com,* item in Kansas, QR, 329 diesel, 80 hp, dual hyd., total OH at 67 hours, new fuel supply pump
4030	1973	13,000	G	$6,750	2/19/2013	SCMN	One owner, diesel, cab, air, heat, 3 pt., 540/1,000 PTO, 2 hyd., QR, 18.4Rx34 tires 70%, 80 hp, new engine put in at approx 10,000 hours
4030	1973	4,297	F	$10,750	11/24/2012	SEMN	Cab, air, heat, QR, 2 hyd., new Firestone 16.9x38 tires
4030	1973	4,391	G	$18,000	9/22/2012	WCMN	John Deere 148 loader and 6' material bucket and 5' manure bucket, no cab, diesel, WF, 3 pt., 2 hyd., QR, 18.4x34 tires, 540/1,000 PTO
4030	1973		G	$7,750	3/31/2012	SWSK	2WD, 80 hp, QR, 3 hyd., 18.4x34 rear, hr meter not working
4030	1973	3,392	E	$20,000	10/14/2011	WCMI	Cab, QR, shedded, diesel
4030	1973	7,500	G	$10,300	4/1/2011	NCMN	Sound Guard cab, QR, 3 pt., 18.4x34 rubber, band duals
4030	1973	7,380	E	$17,000	11/20/2010	SCMN	Diesel, factory cab, air, factory WF, QR, 2 hyd., 3 pt., rock box, 16.9x34 tires, plastic seat, SN 9956R
4030	1973		G	$13,250	11/4/2010	NEKS	Cab, diesel, QR, 15.5x38 rear tires, 11Lx15 tires, 2 hyd., 540 PTO, 3 pt., air
4030	1973	5,637	G	$13,500	11/4/2010	NEKS	Cab, diesel, QR, 16.9x34 rear tires, 9.5Lx15 front tires, 2 hyd., 540/1,000 PTO, 3 pt., air
4030	1974	7,271	G	$7,000	4/4/2013	NWWA	8 speed synchro with creeper, 14.9Rx46 and 9x20 tires, 3 pt., PTO, 2 hyd.
4030	1974	1,193	F	$9,800	5/13/2011	NWTX	John Deere 158 loader, 2 hyd., 3 pt., PTO, 18.4Rx34 tires, SN 4030H008814R
4030	1974	5,761	G	$10,100	12/9/2010	NEMO	ROPS, 15.5x38 and 9.5Lx15SL tires, QR, 2 hyd., 540/1,000 PTO
4030	1974	7,499	G	$12,900	11/4/2010	NEKS	Cab, diesel, synchro, 18.4x34 rear tires, 10x16 front tires, 2 hyd., 540/1,000 PTO, 3 pt., air
4030	1975		G	$15,000	10/12/2013	NCMN	Cab, air, heat, QR, 3 pt., 540/1,000 PTO, 2 hyd. rebuilt injection pump in 2013, low hours on recent eng major

TRACTORS

John Deere

Model	Year	Hours	Condition	Price	Date	Area	Comments
4030	1975	6,251	G	$14,850	9/25/2013	Online	*PurpleWave.com,* item in Kansas, 6 cyl. diesel, 80 hp, QR PS, air, heat, tilt steering, 3 pt., 540/1,000 PTO, drawbar
4030	1975		F	$8,000	4/21/2012	SCMB	John Deere 158 loader, diesel, Sound Guard cab, 3 pt., 2 hyd., dual PTO, QR has been OH, 18.4x34 clamp on duals
4030	1975	7,472	G	$7,600	1/28/2012	SEVA	2WD, 4 post, synchro, shifts good, 540/1,000 PTO, 15.5x38 rear tires, 11Lx15SL, 1 hyd., 2nd owner, SN 010537R
4030	1975	4,746	G	$11,000	10/14/2011	WCMI	Diesel, shedded, ROPS canopy, QR, front weights
4030	1975	6,791	G	$12,100	9/14/2011	Online	*PurpleWave.com,* item in Kansas, John Deere 6 cyl., 80 hp, QR PS, Allied 594 loader
4030	1975	2,657	E	$18,500	3/5/2010	SCON	Canada sale and $$, cab, air, John Deere 720 loader, almost new 18.4x34 radial tires, 2nd owner
4030	1976		G	$14,500	8/10/2013	NCIA	WF, SN 013727
4030	1976	7,782	G	$16,700	8/25/2012	NEIA	Sound Guard cab, air, heat, 3 pt., OH, QR, rock box
4030	1976	6,500	G	$12,500	12/3/2011	NCIA	Open station, 2 hyd., 3 pt., PTO, OH at 4,800 hours, parade ready
4030	1976		G	$13,200	1/21/2011	NEMO	Open station, QR, 2 hyd.
4030	1976	6,685	G	$13,250	11/4/2010	NEKS	Cab, diesel, QR, 15x34 rear tires, 11Lx15 front tires, 2 hyd., 540/1,000 PTO, 3 pt., air
4030	1977		F	$13,000	12/28/2013	SEIA	Fully equipped cab, QR, 2 hyd., front suitcase weights
4030	1977	3,233	G	$18,700	8/31/2011	Online	*PurpleWave.com,* item in Missouri, 6 cyl., ROPS, spring ride seat, John Deere 158 loader, 540/1,000 PTO
4030			G	$4,100	3/26/2014	ECMS	QR shift
4030		3,775	G	$6,000	3/22/2014	SEMN	Roll guard, cab
4030			G	$4,600	1/4/2014	WCNY	Diesel, canopy, 1 hyd., 3 pt., PTO
4030		8,132	G	$10,100	12/18/2013	Online	*BigIron.com,* 16 speed QR, 6 cyl. diesel, 2 hyd., 540/1,000 PTO
4030		6,600	G	$13,600	9/21/2013	WCMO	Original, cab, QR
4030			G	$16,000	3/23/2013	NEIN	4 post ROPS, synchro, original, dual hyd., runs
4030			G	$11,400	7/27/2012	SWKY	
4030		2,380	G	$19,000	7/14/2012	NEKS	Diesel, Cab, air, 3 pt., 2 hyd., QR, rough cab interior, rear rubber 20%
4030			G	$14,000	11/26/2011	NEIA	Synchro, NF, open station, M&W turbo, 3 pt., Goodyear 18.4x36 rear tires
4030		6,124	G	$7,500	3/5/2011	NWMO	
4030		2,854	F	$6,100	2/25/2011	NENC	15.5x38R1 rear tires, 10x16SL, diff. lock, open station, 1 hyd., side shaft 1,000 PTO, 540 straight PTO, all new tires last spring
4030			G	$4,800	1/29/2011	ECMO	Diesel, dual hyd., QR, open station, top link
4030			G	$8,400	11/18/2010	SEOK	
4030			G	$10,000	11/18/2010	SEOK	John Deere loader

John Deere

Model	Year	Hours	Condition	Price	Date	Area	Comments
4030			G	$12,000	8/14/2010	WCMN	2 hyd., PTO, open station, synchro, WF, new seat
4030			G	$9,600	5/26/2010	ECSD	Miller loader
4040	1978	6,825	G	$19,500	2/5/2014	SESD	Cab, air, heat, QR, John Deere 148 loader, 18.4x34 rubber, 3 hyd., 3 pt. Ride-N-Drive
4040	1978	2,540	G	$20,000	2/15/2012	IRON	QR 16F/4R, 6 cyl., diesel, 95 hp, 3 hyd., 540 PTO, 95 hp, heat, air
4040	1978	4,821	G	$19,750	12/3/2011	NWOH	Cab, air, 8 speed., 2 hyd.
4040	1978	1,368	E	$33,000	9/2/2011	NCMO	Diesel, one owner, cab, air, heat, 2 way hyd., 18.4x34 rubber, front weights, all new batteries, like-new paint, always shedded
4110	1964		G	$5,700	2/22/2014	NEIN	Dual rear wheels, fenders, hyd., 1 of a kind, with fenders, mower and misc parts
4230	1973		G	$10,500	4/1/2014	WCMN	QR, dual hyd., 3 pt., diff. lock, 540/1,000 PTO
4230	1973		G	$11,250	8/24/2013	NWIL	18.4x34 rears, dual hyd., QR
4230	1973		G	$8,900	6/19/2013	Online	*BigIron.com,* item in Nebraska, QR, 16F/6R, 404 cu. in.
4230	1973	15,419	F	$10,000	4/19/2013	SEAB	2WD, John Deere 158 front-end loader, 100 PTO hp, QR, 3 hyd., 3 rib front, 20.8x38 rear, 6' bucket and grapple
4230	1973	10,874	G	$8,000	4/4/2013	NWWA	QR, 14.9Rx46 and 7.5x18 tires, 3 pt., PTO, 2 hyd.
4230	1973		G	$11,500	11/7/2012	SCNE	QR, 18.4xx38 duals
4230	1973	8,812	G	$9,100	8/4/2012	WCWI	2WD, cab
4230	1973	7,894	G	$23,250	7/11/2012	Online	*BigIron.com,* item in Nebraska, loader and grapple, QR, 404 cu. in. diesel, 2 hyd., 540 and small shaft 1,000 PTO, new cab kit, new paint job, heat and air
4230	1973	2,544	F	$5,900	5/9/2012	Online	*BigIron.com,* item in Missouri, synchro, 6 cyl. diesel, 100 hp, 2 hyd., 540/1,000 PTO, paint faded, scratches
4230	1973	8,155	G	$8,500	3/31/2012	SWSK	2WD, 100 PTO hp, QR, 3 hyd., PTO, singles
4230	1973	8,481	G	$13,500	2/25/2012	NETX	Cab, air, new 18.4x38 rear tires, new 11x16 front tires, 540/1,000 PTO, QR, 2 hyd., independent valve, hay fork, SN 010825R
4230	1973		G	$13,500	6/18/2011	SWMN	High crop, SN 5414, synchro, struts, new tires, repainted
4230	1973	2,301	G	$11,000	3/26/2011	NECO	WF, cab, front and rear weights
4230	1973	8,215	G	$9,500	1/29/2011	ECMO	Open station, synchro
4230	1973	1,017	G	$12,100	12/10/2010	NWMO	2WD, 18.4x38, QR, 2 hyd., new paint
4230	1973		G	$14,250	11/30/2010	WCMN	Cab, QR, 2 hyd., 3 pt., 540/1,000 PTO, rock box, 18.4x38 tires
4230	1973	6,901	G	$18,000	11/19/2010	ECMN	Sound Guard cab, dual hyd., 540/1,000 PTO
4230	1973	1,805	G	$11,550	4/28/2010	Online	*PurpleWave.com,* item in Kansas, 6 cyl. diesel, QR 16 speed, suspension seat, work lights, 3 pt., 2 hyd., 6 front weights

John Deere

Model	Year	Hours	Condition	Price	Date	Area	Comments
4230	1974		G	$12,000	4/11/2014	SWSK	2WD, John Deere 148 front-end loader, 100 hp PTO, QR, 540/1,000 PTO, 2 hyd., 18.4x38 rear, 4 rib front
4230	1974	3,565	E	$24,500	11/16/2013	SEMN	QR, 18.4x38 tires 90%, band duals, 540 PTO, 3 pt., quick hitch, 2 hyd., very clean, SN 019270R
4230	1974	16,148	F	$11,000	6/7/2013	ECAB	2WD, John Deere 148 front-end loader, 100 PTO hp, QR, dual PTO, 2 hyd., 18.4x38 rear, 4 rib front, 6' bucket, 5,000 hours on OH
4230	1974	6,094	G	$18,700	9/17/2011	NEIA	Westendorf WL 42 loader, 84" bucket and bale spear, self,leveling, diesel, WF, like new 18.4x34 rubber, 2 hyd., QR, rear chains
4230	1974	7,200	G	$13,250	8/13/2011	WCIL	New tires, rebuilt hyd. pump, QR, 2 hyd., 540/1,000 PTO, front weights
4230	1974		G	$11,000	6/17/2011	SWMN	QR, 18.4x38 rubber, cab, air, nice
4230	1974	6,215	G	$15,500	6/8/2011	SWSK	2WD, John Deere 158 front-end loader, 100 PTO hp, QR, dual hyd., snap on duals, joystick, separate control for grapple
4230	1974		G	$11,500	2/1/2011	NEIN	Front and rear weights, QR
4230	1974	5,171	E	$17,000	12/15/2010	SEMI	One owner, QR, 18.4x34 cast hubs, clamp duals, 3 hyd.
4230	1974	9,138	G	$9,000	12/8/2010	NECO	WF, diesel, John Deere 148 loader
4230	1974	7,214	F	$7,000	12/6/2010	NEMO	18.4x34 and 10x16 tires, synchro, 2 hyd., dual PTO, weights, cab, rebuilt 4 years ago
4230	1974		G	$12,500	10/2/2010	ECMI	Cab, 2 hyd., WF
4230	1975		G	$14,000	3/15/2014	NCOR	Cab
4230	1975	6,528	G	$16,750	12/4/2013	ECIN	Cab, air, heat, QR
4230	1975	9,281	G	$9,750	7/10/2013	NETX	16.9x38 tires, cab, air, PS, SN 4230P026241R
4230	1975		G	$6,750	3/20/2013	NCOK	86 hp
4230	1975	6,828	G	$12,000	2/6/2013	NEIL	Cab, air, heat, QR, 2 hyd., 18.4x34 rear tires, SN 027194R
4230	1975	7,900	G	$9,900	6/20/2012	ECIL	Cab, air, QR
4230	1975	12,482	G	$13,000	6/21/2011	WCSK	2WD, Leon 700 7' front-end loader, 100 PTO hp, QR, dual PTO, 2 hyd., bale spear
4230	1975	5,200	G	$17,000	12/4/2010	SEMI	Cab, air, QR
4230	1975	6,429	G	$9,250	8/26/2010	SCNE	PS, 18.4x38 duals
4230	1975	3,784	G	$12,000	7/30/2010	NCNE	2 hyd., PS, 3 pt., John Deere 158 loader
4230	1975	5,578	G	$16,900	1/9/2010	ECIL	One owner, QR
4230	1976	9,500	G	$8,350	12/3/2012	WCIL	Cab, 18.4x34, QR, 2 hyd., OH at 7K hours
4230	1976	8,848	G	$17,000	11/24/2012	SEMN	Cab, air, heat, QR, 2 hyd., new 480/80Rx38 rear tires
4230	1976	8,564	G	$16,000	4/16/2012	SCSK	2WD, 100 hp PTO, QR, 3 pt. rock shaft, dual PTO, 2 hyd., 20.8x34 rear tires new, 4 rib front tires
4230	1976	8,442	F	$12,750	2/7/2012	SEIA	QR, 3 pt., 2 hyd.
4230	1976	3,400	G	$20,000	8/27/2011	WCOH	Cab, PS, original, one owner
4230	1976	9,765	G	$10,600	8/23/2011	NCIA	Cab, synchro, 3 hyd., motor OH, 18.4x34 tires

John Deere

Model	Year	Hours	Condition	Price	Date	Area	Comments
4230	1976	1,801	G	$23,500	6/30/2011	ECMO	One owner, fully equipped cab, QR, 18.4x34 and 10x16 tires, 2 hyd., 540/1,000 PTO, one-owner, SN 034776R, purchased new in 1977
4230	1976	10,057	G	$16,000	4/21/2011	WCSK	2WD, Ezee-On 100 loader, 100 PTO hp, QR, 2 hyd., 4 rib front, bucket, 2-tine bale fork, manure fork
4230	1976	4,895	G	$8,500	3/19/2011	SEWY	Diesel, WF, 3 pt., Farmhand GL520 loader
4230	1976		G	$12,100	2/1/2011	NEIN	Full front weights, QR
4230	1976		P	$10,000	12/23/2010	NCKS	Very rough, dual 3100 loader, QR, 3 hyd., 3 pt., PTO, hours unknown?
4230	1976	6,001	G	$11,900	12/6/2010	NEMO	18.4x35 and 11x15 tires, QR, 2 hyd., dual PTO, cab
4230	1976	7,950	F	$4,600	11/29/2010	ECIA	ROPS
4230	1977	7,288	G	$20,000	12/10/2011	SEMN	PS, new style step, 18.4x38 tires, extension fuel tank, 2 hyd., 3 pt., SN P039041R
4230	1977	7,301	G	$15,000	6/6/2011	SWSK	2WD, 100 PTO hp, QR, dual PTO, 2 hyd., 3 rib front
4230	1977	5,524	G	$20,250	4/9/2011	WCNY	Repainted, Sound Guard cab, QR, 2 hyd., 1,573 hours on rebuilt engine, very late SN
4230	1977	2,678	G	$16,000	3/1/2011	SCNE	QR, 18.4x38 rear tires, 11Lx15 front tires, 3 hyd., 3 pt., quick hitch, 2 sets of 50 lb. rear wheel weights, loader, joystick loader controls, new batteries, oil and filters in December 2010
4230	1977	8,000	F	$8,200	12/8/2010	NEMI	16.9x38 duals, 8 speed auto, quick hitch
4230	1977	10,101	G	$9,500	12/2/2010	ECWY	Cab, air, QR, 15.5x38 tires
4230		2,000	G	$6,000	4/3/2014	NEIN	2WD, canopy, 1 hyd., 540/1,000, 18.4x34 tires, PS
4230		8,065	G	$6,750	3/22/2014	SWMI	6 cyl. diesel, WF, 2 hyd., 3 pt., PTO, 18.4x38 rear tires, 200 hours on engine rebuild
4230		10,022	G	$12,000	3/13/2014	SCID	16 speed QR, 3 hyd., 540/1,000 PTO, 3 pt., 12.4Rx46 rubber, WF
4230			G	$9,200	2/5/2014	SESD	Cab, air, heat, QR
4230			G	$11,750	2/5/2014	SESD	Cab, air, heat, QR
4230			G	$6,000	12/19/2013	SCNY	QR, canopy
4230		3,083	P	$8,600	12/4/2013	Online	*BigIron.com,* item in Kansas, 8 speed PS, 18.4x38 rear tires, 11x16 front tires, diesel, does not run
4230		11,400	G	$7,000	8/24/2013	NWIL	500 hours on OH, 18.4x34 rears, QR dual hyd., long axles
4230			G	$9,000	8/24/2013	SEMN	Cab, QR, 3 pt., dual hyd., PTO, 18.4x38 tires, SN 013836R
4230			G	$10,250	6/22/2013	SESC	Front bucket
4230			G	$12,750	6/22/2013	SEMN	18.4x34 tires, 3 pt. dual hyd., PTO, SN 003689R
4230		10,860	G	$11,350	4/10/2013	Online	*BigIron.com,* item in Kansas, QR, 18.4x34 rear tires, 11Lx15 front tires, diesel, dual hyd., OH at 7,000 hours, rear wheel weights, 3 pt., seat is bad
4230			G	$13,000	3/30/2013	ECTX	Cab, air

John Deere

Model	Year	Hours	Condition	Price	Date	Area	Comments
4230			G	$13,000	3/23/2013	NEIN	QR, dual hyd., 3 pt., hours unknown, runs
4230			G	$10,250	3/22/2013	NWMN	Open station, PS, original, 3 pt., dual hyd., runs
4230			G	$12,000	3/22/2013	NWMN	Open station, PS, 3 pt., dual hyd., original, runs
4230		3,400	G	$10,250	3/16/2013	NEIL	Diesel, M&W turbo
4230			G	$6,700	3/2/2013	NETN	Cab
4230		9,060	G	$8,400	2/23/2013	NCIL	3 pt., 2 hyd., new rear tires
4230			G	$11,000	2/6/2013	SESD	TWA, cab, air, heat, QR, 3 hyd., 3 pt., new injectors, pistons, and sleeves abt 5 years ago, 18.4x38 tires
4230			G	$13,400	1/19/2013	NEMS	Loader
4230			G	$8,500	12/8/2012	ECTX	Cab, air, QR, 18.4x34 rear tires, 10x16 front tires, 3 hyd., 540/1,000 PTO, K&D Loadmaster loader, bucket
4230		6,300	G	$10,000	11/13/2012	NCIA	
4230			G	$12,100	11/13/2012	NCIA	148 loader
4230			G	$13,700	11/13/2012	NCIA	148 loader
4230			G	$13,200	5/8/2012	Online	*IQBID.com,* QR, cab, air, heat, 3 hyd., 3 pt., PTO, John Deere 158 loader, 8' bucket, grapple, 18.4x38 tires, 10x16SL front tires
4230		4,891	G	$13,250	3/8/2012	NCTX	WF, diesel, cab, air, good rubber
4230		8,900	G	$10,500	2/2/2012	NEIN	Cab, air, heat, 18.4x34 rear tires, bolt on dual hubs, 2 hyd.
4230			G	$5,900	1/28/2012	SEAB	John Deere 725 front loader
4230			G	$7,250	1/27/2012	SEAL	
4230		5,000	G	$9,800	12/3/2011	NCOH	Cab, air, heat, T-rail duals
4230		3,680	G	$16,250	12/1/2011	SEMN	Synchro range
4230			G	$15,750	8/24/2011	ECMN	158 John Deere loader
4230		1,953	G	$10,750	6/3/2011	ECMN	Cab, heat, 3 pt., drawbar, rear hyd.
4230		5,614	G	$16,250	5/11/2011	Online	*BigIron.com,* item in Nebraska, John Deere 148 loader, 6 speed synchro, 6 cyl. diesel, 2 hyd., 8' bucket, cab, air, heat, 540/1,000 interchangeable PTO
4230			G	$8,500	5/7/2011	SESK	2WD, 2 speed PTO, dual hyd., cab, air, heat, QR
4230		4,515	G	$15,000	4/19/2011	NEMN	
4230			G	$12,500	12/16/2010	NWIA	QR, John Deere 58 loader, cab, 18.4x34 tires
4230		7,950	G	$11,500	12/2/2010	ECWY	PS, 2 hyd., 16.9x38 tires, GB 440 loader, 7' bucket
4230		6,053	F	$5,000	11/20/2010	SEIA	Synchro, 16.9x38 rear
4230			G	$11,800	11/18/2010	SEOK	John Deere 148 loader
4230			G	$21,500	9/4/2010	NEIN	Low profile, PS, very rare
4230			G	$4,750	8/13/2010	Online	*IronPlanet.com,* item in Utah
4230			G	$14,750	8/9/2010	WCMO	Cab, new engine
4230			G	$9,000	4/10/2010	ECIA	WF, cab, 3 pt.
4230			F	$7,800	3/5/2010	NCMO	QR, cab, air, heat, 2 hyd., 3 pt.
4240	1978	3,452	E	$32,000	8/28/2012	WCMN	2WD, QR, cab, air, heat, 2 hyd., aux. hyd. and radar for John Deere air planter, block heater
4240	1978	8,600	G	$22,000	12/28/2011	NEMO	2WD, cab, 110 hp, QR

John Deere

Model	Year	Hours	Condition	Price	Date	Area	Comments
4240	1978		G	$17,500	8/13/2011	SWMN	
4320	1970	11,527	G	$14,000	9/9/2010	SWMI	Open station, side console
4320	1971	5,114	G	$12,250	3/15/2014	WCIL	Synchro
4320	1971		E	$6,200	6/20/2013	ECSK	2WD, John Deere 46A front-end loader, 115 hp PTO, 6.6L, 6 cyl. turbo diesel, 2 hyd., synchro, dual PTO, dual rubber, factory heat and air
4320	1971	7,348	G	$12,850	5/15/2013	Online	*BigIron.com,* item in Nebraska, synchro, John Deere diesel
4320	1971	3,137	G	$10,000	3/7/2013	ECIA	WF, open station, 540/1,000 PTO, 3 pt.
4320	1971		G	$13,000	2/22/2013	SWKY	Diesel
4320	1971	8,096	G	$11,200	1/16/2013	Online	*AuctionTime.com,* item in Illinois, 116 hp, 2WD, SN T613R008409R
4320	1971	2,541	G	$7,700	8/11/2012	NWIL	Diesel, WF, no cab, rear weights
4320	1971	9,543	G	$6,050	5/23/2012	Online	*BigIron.com,* item in Wyoming, 8 speed, 6 cyl. diesel, 2 hyd., 540/1,000 PTO, 3 pt., third link, new batteries, reconditioned starter
4320	1971		F	$6,000	3/7/2012	SEIA	ROPS and canopy, synchro, 2 hyd., 540/1,000 PTO, new engine and needs clutch work
4320	1971	7,177	G	$8,400	3/7/2012	SEIA	Open station, synchro, 2 hyd., 540/1,000 PTO, 3 pt., front and rear weights
4320	1971		F	$8,000	12/7/2011	NCIA	Cab
4320	1971		G	$11,000	11/30/2011	SEMN	18.4x34 tires
4320	1971		G	$7,000	7/30/2011	ECMO	
4320	1971		G	$26,000	6/18/2011	SWMN	SN 15567, front weights, 2 hyd., rear weights, front wheel drive, repainted
4320	1971	7,218	G	$9,750	3/26/2011	NECO	Diesel, WF, cab, 3 pt., FH258 loader
4320	1971		G	$12,250	1/29/2011	ECMO	Canopy, restored
4320	1971	7,600	G	$7,500	1/26/2011	NECO	Cab, diesel, 3 pt., FH-F236 loader
4320	1971	1,101	F	$4,500	12/4/2010	SEWY	WF, diesel, cab
4320	1971	8,700	G	$7,900	6/9/2010	ECIA	Synchro, open station, diesel
4320	1971	7,900	G	$8,900	5/26/2010	ECSD	
4320	1971		G	$9,300	5/26/2010	ECSD	
4320	1971	1,555	E	$15,500	3/20/2010	NWIA	WF, synchro, 3 pt., 2 hyd., 166 hours on complete OH spring of 2006, sharp
4320	1971	5,438	G	$11,500	3/19/2010	SEIA	Diesel, cab, original, 540/1,000 PTO, 2 hyd., 18.4x34 tires
4320	1972	6,830	G	$16,000	4/11/2014	WCMN	Synchro range, New Alliance 18.4x38 tires, 3 pt., 2 hyd., 540/1,000 PTO, Year Round cab, one owner
4320	1972	6,253	G	$13,000	2/4/2014	NWNE	Diesel, cab, WF, synchro, 3 pt., 2 hyd., snap on duals, rear weights
4320	1972	12,500	F	$11,750	11/30/2013	SWIA	
4320	1972	7,000	E	$31,250	11/2/2013	ECIA	Restored, new tires all around, canopy, side step, new battery and cable
4320	1972	6,800	E	$38,000	11/2/2013	ECIA	Restored, Standard, open station, Like New
4320	1972	8,200	G	$15,000	3/23/2013	ECIA	Open station, 400 hours on John Deere OH, 200 hours on new rear tires, no weights

John Deere

Model	Year	Hours	Condition	Price	Date	Area	Comments
4320	1972	5,590	E	$16,300	3/1/2013	ECPA	WF, diesel, canopy, synchro, side console, 2 hyd., 18.4x38 tires
4320	1972	2,659	G	$13,000	11/30/2012	SCMT	Synchro, dual PTO, 2 hyd., 116 hp, 460/85Rx38 tires 90%, FH F258 loader, 5' bucket, grapple, stand
4320	1972	9,911	G	$14,000	8/28/2012	WCMN	2WD, 3 pt., 2 hyd., PTO, rock box, OH at 9,000 hours, 4430 final drive gear, bought in 1981 at 3,200 hours
4320	1972		G	$13,000	7/14/2012	SWMN	18.4x34 rears, 2 hyd., rock box
4320	1972	407	G	$8,400	7/11/2012	Online	*BigIron.com,* item in Nebraska, loader, 8 speed synchro, 404 cu. in. diesel, 540/1,000 PTO, cab, heat and air, block heater
4320	1972	3,805	G	$11,750	3/23/2012	WCNE	Cab, ROPS, side console hyd., Cat II quick hitch, 3 pt., 2 hyd., PTO, 18.4x38 tires 40%, synchro, John Deere 158 loader, 7' bucket
4320	1972		F	$9,250	2/6/2012	ECIL	Cab, duals, front weights, 3 pt.
4320	1972	8,030	G	$8,750	12/14/2011	WCMN	2WD, synchro, 2 hyd., 18.4x34 tires
4320	1972	8,887	G	$7,706	9/28/2011	Online	*BigIron.com,* item in Nebraska, synchro, diesel, 115 hp, 2 hyd., 540/1,000 PTO, cab, AM/FM radio, dent in hood, aux. lights
4320	1972	2,700	G	$12,750	11/13/2010	NCIA	Factory open station

I keep harping on what I call "the new collector tractor," which are models from the mid 1960s to mid 1970s in either very nice original or restored condition. Well, Saturday Nov. 2, 2013, pretty much offered all the proof you'd ever need on this trend. I spent the day covering the Mecum "Gone Farmin'" collector auction in Davenport, Iowa. It was an amazing collection of tractors that rolled across the staging area right in front of me. While there in Davenport, I got a message on our Machinery Pete Facebook page…"Pete, did you hear about the John Deere 4320 sold today on farm auction in Springville, Iowa?" It was a real beauty; the 1972 model with 7,000 hours, restored with canopy, new tires all around and new battery and cable sold for $31,250–a new record.

PETE'S PICK

The record lasted for less than an hour.

Back at the Mecum auction in Davenport, a pristine restored 1972 John Deere 4320 with 6,800 hours, open station rolled onto the sale stage. It went for $38,000. Two record high sale prices in one day at two different auctions on a 40+ year-old tractor model. Wow.

John Deere

Model	Year	Hours	Condition	Price	Date	Area	Comments
4320	1972	2,249	G	$9,501	6/14/2010	Online	*BigIron.com,* item in Nebraska, 6 cyl. diesel, 116 hp, cab, heat and air, synchro,range
4320	1972	8,000	G	$8,100	3/5/2010	NCMO	2WD, 114 hp, synchro, 20.8x38 tires
4320	1972		F	$14,250	2/19/2010	WCIL	Diesel, WF, synchro, 540/1,000 PTO, 2 hyd., 8.4Rx38 and 10x16 tires, 81 hours on new attach
4320	1973	4,884	G	$16,000	8/8/2013	NCIN	
4320			G	$9,000	3/22/2014	SWGA	
4320		643	E	$18,000	3/15/2014	NCNC	MFWD, 40 hp, 4 cyl., standard, shuttle differential lock, 540 shift on the go PTO, set dual hyd., 1 hyd., folding 2 post roll guard, canopy, hyd. hook up and joystick control for loader
4320		9,988	G	$8,701	1/29/2014	Online	*BigIron.com,* item in Nebraska, 8 speed synchro, diesel, 18.4x38 rear tires, axle duals, 10x16 front tires, 540/1,000 PTO, WF, 3 hyd., cab, no weights or bracket
4320		9,537	G	$8,400	12/18/2013	Online	*BigIron.com,* 8 speed synchro, 6 cyl. John Deere engine, 3 pt., drawbar
4320			G	$5,500	6/22/2013	SESC	2WD
4320			G	$10,000	6/22/2013	SEMN	WF, 3 pt., dual hyd., PTO
4320			G	$9,500	3/22/2013	NWMN	Dual hyd., PTO, 3 pt., runs
4320		8,772	G	$4,700	2/7/2013	SEAR	Diesel, straight shift, PTO, front loader
4320		9,088	G	$5,750	2/7/2013	SEAR	Diesel, standard shift, PTO, OROPS
4320			G	$7,000	12/12/2012	SESD	
4320			G	$3,900	11/9/2012	NEAR	6 cyl. diesel, synchro, 18.4x38 rears, dual hyd., loader
4320		8,900	G	$6,700	9/14/2012	NCVA	Diesel, cab, air, like-new Firestone 18.4x34 rear rubber 95%, this is from local Clarke County farmer downsizing, owned by same farm for 20+ years, 2nd owner
4320		9,693	G	$9,500	8/16/2012	Online	*IQBID.com,* item in Minnesota, diesel, WF, cab, 3 pt., dual PTO, no top link, 18.4x38 tires, 95% rubber
4320			G	$4,500	7/28/2012	SCTX	Standard, 3 pt., diesel, 115 hp, canopy/brush guard, brush tires on rear, 200 hours on newly OH
4320		4,996	G	$7,000	6/20/2012	ECIL	10x16 and 18.4x38 tires, ROPS, cab, 2 hyd., 1 PTO, no top link
4320		6,017	G	$6,050	4/25/2012	Online	*PurpleWave.com,* item in Kansas, John Deere 6 cyl., 540/1,000 PTO
4320			G	$9,300	3/24/2012	NEIN	Original, dual hyd., 3 pt., PTO, runs
4320			G	$17,500	3/24/2012	NEIN	HFWD, original, fenders, 3 pt., PTO, dual hyd., runs
4320			G	$8,700	3/22/2012	ECMN	Synchro, 2 hyd., 3 pt., PTO
4320		8,952	G	$8,900	3/17/2012	SEMN	Cab, side console, 3 pt., 2 hyd., PTO
4320			G	$8,500	1/31/2012	NEIN	Cab, low hours, original
4320			G	$6,500	1/28/2012	SEAB	
4320		7,600	G	$11,000	12/1/2011	SEMN	Year Round cab, air
4320			G	$9,500	4/14/2011	NCND	John Deere 148 loader, grapple, factory 3 pt.

John Deere

Model	Year	Hours	Condition	Price	Date	Area	Comments
4320			E	$17,500	4/1/2011	ECND	Factory roll guard cab, 2 pioneer hyd., extremely nice
4320		8,809	G	$8,700	3/23/2011	Online	*BigIron.com,* 8 speed sync range, John Deere diesel, 2 hyd., 540 PTO, 3 pt.
4320			G	$9,750	3/19/2011	NCPA	
4320			G	$8,500	9/11/2010	ECIA	3 pt., 2 hyd., synchro
4320			G	$16,000	9/4/2010	NEIN	Rear weights, dual hyd., top link
4320		7,300	G	$5,000	6/10/2010	SEND	Diesel, 2 hyd., 3 pt., factory air and John Deere roll guard cab, synchro
4320		8,775	G	$6,900	3/5/2010	NENE	Synchro, cab
4430	1973	5,007	G	$27,750	12/18/2013	Online	*BigIron.com,* item in Nebraska, synchro, 8F/2R, 6 cyl. turbo diesel, 125 PTO hp, 18.4x38 rear tires, 10x16 front tires, 2 hyd., 540/1,000 PTO, 6 rear wheel weights
4430	1973		F	$6,500	10/26/2013	SEKS	High hours, rough cab, didn't start on sale day, Case loader, bucket, blade, 540/1,000 PTO, 18.4x38 tires
4430	1973	6,438	G	$9,000	9/14/2013	SEMI	Restored, open station, dual hyd., excellent rubber
4430	1973	8,135	G	$9,750	9/14/2013	SEMI	Cab, diesel
4430	1973		E	$26,500	9/14/2013	NCOK	Cab, air, heat, QR, 3 pt., PTO, 3 hyd., 1,750 hours on complete John Deere engine rebuild, 300 hours on rear end, PTO, clutch, brakes, only 200 hours on new 20.8x38 radials
4430	1973	12,440	G	$13,500	5/8/2013	Online	*IQBID.com,* QR, 2 hyd., 3 pt., Buhler Allied 795 quick attach loader, bale spear
4430	1973	9,622	G	$9,500	4/9/2013	SWSK	2WD, 125 PTO hp, QR, dual PTO, 2 hyd., 20.8x38 rear duals
4430	1973	7,979	G	$15,500	4/6/2013	SWSK	2WD, 125 hp, synchro, dual PTO, 2 hyd., aux. fuel tank, 20.8x38 duals
4430	1973	5,608	G	$16,500	3/27/2013	NWWI	QR shift, Sound Guard cab, 3 pt., 18.4x38 Firestone 23 degree radials, new turbo, rock box
4430	1973	8,250	G	$9,300	3/7/2013	SEIA	2WD, 125 hp, 3 hyd., 3 pt., 16.9x38 rear tires 10%, 10x16 front tires at 40%
4430	1973	5,607	G	$12,850	2/18/2013	Online	*IQBID.com,* QR, SN8377
4430	1973	13,043	F	$10,200	2/6/2013	SESD	2WD, cab, air, heat, QR, 2 hyd., 3 pt., 18.4x38 tires, diff. lock is out
4430	1973	6,869	G	$20,000	1/26/2013	WCIL	QR, cab, aux. fuel tank, 3 pt., quick hitch, dual PTO, 2 hyd., 6 front weights, 4 rear weights, 18.4x38 tires, new style steps, chrome exhaust
4430	1973		G	$8,250	12/14/2012	SWKY	Cab
4430	1973		G	$16,000	11/24/2012	WCIL	Cab, air, heat, new 20.8Rx38 rubber, new paint approximately 2 yrs
4430	1973	9,480	G	$16,500	11/24/2012	SEMN	Cab, air, heat, QR, 38" radial duals
4430	1973	9,021	G	$10,890	6/13/2012	Online	*PurpleWave.com,* item in Kansas, 6 cyl., manual, diff. lock, joystick loader control, 540/1,000 PTO

Model	Year	Hours	Condition	Price	Date	Area	Comments
4430	1973	3,862	G	$13,750	6/13/2012	Online	*BigIron.com,* item in Kansas, 2WD, loader, 16F/6R QR, 6 cyl. turbo diesel, 125 PTO hp, 3 hyd., 540/1,000 PTO, block heater, 3 pt., no radio
4430	1973	6,900	G	$12,500	3/3/2012	SEMN	18.4x38 duals, QR, 2 hyd., rock box, 540/1,000 PTO, SN 002528R
4430	1973	10,000	G	$14,000	3/2/2012	WCMN	Diesel, Sound Guard cab, comfort steps, 18.4Rx38 tires, 540/1,000 PTO, 3 pt., 2 hyd., runs
4430	1973	7,500	G	$10,750	1/28/2012	ECMO	QR, dual PTO, open station
4430	1973	9,425	G	$10,100	1/11/2012	Online	*BigIron.com,* item in South Dakota, QR, diesel, 2 hyd., 540/1,000 PTO, heater works, air does not work
4430	1973		P	$6,750	12/7/2011	NCIA	Needs work, 18.4x38 tires
4430	1973	4,171	G	$8,100	9/14/2011	Online	*BigIron.com,* item in Utah, 2WD, 6 cyl. diesel, QR, 2 hyd., single axle, cab, new paint and seat
4430	1973	6,212	G	$12,500	8/27/2011	SWIL	2WD, QR, 2 hyd., 540/1,000 PTO
4430	1973	9,632	G	$10,025	7/28/2011	Online	*IQBID.com,* cab, air, heat, QR, 3 hyd., 3 pt., 540/1,000 PTO, 18.4x38 duals
4430	1973	1,405	G	$8,800	5/25/2011	Online	*BigIron.com,* item in Kansas, RC, QR, diesel, 2 hyd. 540/1,000 PTO, 3 pt.
4430	1973	4,057	G	$12,500	5/18/2011	SEWY	Diesel, WF, 3 pt., FH 236 loader and grapple
4430	1973	6,565	G	$9,300	2/1/2011	NEIN	PS, dual hyd., HFWD, rear weights
4430	1973	6,365	F	$7,500	12/8/2010	NECO	WF, diesel
4430	1973	7,466	G	$13,500	11/4/2010	NEKS	Cab, QR, 20.8x34 rear tires, 10x16 front tires, 2 hyd., 540/1,000 PTO, 3 pt., rear wheel weights, 10 front end weights, air
4430	1973	7,686	F	$7,250	9/11/2010	WCMI	Diesel, cab, air, heat, synchro, 18.4x38 tires, rear wheel weights, 2 hyd., 540 PTO
4430	1973	7,929	G	$11,000	9/3/2010	SCMN	QR, cab, air, heat, 2 hyd., 3 pt., PTO, rock box, updated air
4430	1973	8,559	F	$8,500	8/26/2010	SCNE	3 pt., 3 hyd., 540/1,000 PTO
4430	1973	5,082	G	$11,000	6/17/2010	SEIA	Cab, air, heat, QR, clamp on duals
4430	1973	87	G	$15,000	5/4/2010	WCOK	5500 KD long-reach loader, cab, air, 3 pt., PTO
4430	1974		G	$14,750	3/15/2014	ECKS	Quick attach John Deere 158 loader, hours unknown, QR, duals
4430	1974	7,606	G	$12,000	3/8/2014	NEMO	QR, 2 hyd., one owner, 18.4x38 duals
4430	1974	2,647	G	$14,001	3/5/2014	Online	*BigIron.com,* item in Nebraska, QR, diesel, 135 hp, 3 hyd., 3 pt., 8 rear wheel weights, new interior, aux. lights
4430	1974	5,115	G	$15,700	2/24/2014	SWMN	18.4x38 singles, QR, 2 hyd., 540/1,000 PTO, rear wiper
4430	1974	8,041	G	$7,750	2/22/2014	ECMI	Diesel, QR, cab, WF, 3 pt., PTO, 2 hyd., 18.4x38 rear duals
4430	1974	4,700	G	$11,250	9/7/2013	SEON	2nd owner, cab, air (working) QR, 20.8x38 rear tires
4430	1974	8,261	G	$10,000	8/20/2013	WCIL	QR, 2 hyd., both PTO, 18.4x38 tires, front and rear weights, right fender has damage

TRACTORS

John Deere

Model	Year	Hours	Condition	Price	Date	Area	Comments
4430	1974	10,215	G	$10,000	4/10/2013	Online	*BigIron.com,* item in Nebraska, row crop, QR, 16F/R, 404 cu. in., 6 cyl., turbo, intercooled 126 diesel, 105 drawbar, 2 hyd., 540/1,000 PTO, Sound Guard cab, air, heat
4430	1974	5,275	G	$12,000	4/3/2013	NEND	2WD, cab, air, heat, 8 sp PS, 3 pt., 540/1,000 PTO, 2 hyd.
4430	1974	6,135	G	$13,200	12/12/2012	SEMN	PS, 3 pt., 2 hyd., 18.4x38 tires 80%
4430	1974	2,002	G	$8,500	10/24/2012	NECO	Diesel, WF, no 3 pt. arms
4430	1974	6,974	G	$19,500	8/14/2012	SWMN	18.4x38 tires and duals
4430	1974	7,667	G	$11,550	7/11/2012	Online	*PurpleWave.com,* item in Kansas, 6 cyl. diesel, 125 hp, QR, air, heat, spring seat, tilt steering wheel, 3 pt., drawbar, 3 rear hyd., 7' Koyker loader
4430	1974	6,156	F	$9,500	6/14/2012	SEND	Cab, air, heat, GEAR., 2 hyd., 3 pt., 540/1,000 PTO, front fuel tank, front suitcase weights, 18.4x38 hub duals
4430	1974	10,875	G	$28,000	5/2/2012	WCSK	2WD, John Deere 158 front end loader, 126 hp PTO, QR, 2 hyd., PTO, 4 rib front, joystick
4430	1974	4,800	E	$27,000	3/17/2012	WCOH	Cab, QR, perfect condition
4430	1974	12,400	G	$8,400	3/14/2012	WCNE	3 pt., dual hyd., 18.4x38 rubber, duals and hubs, OH, 125 hp
4430	1974		F	$10,750	3/7/2012	SEIA	Fully equipped cab, PS, 18.4x38 tires and duals, 4 hyd., 3 pt., 540/1,000 PTO, low time on new motor (1 year ago)
4430	1974	8,730	G	$15,750	2/21/2012	Online	*IQBID.com* online dealer sale, QR, 2 hyd., 3 pt., 540/1,000 PTO, 14.9x46 press steel duals, 11x16 fronts, SN 30203
4430	1974	4,519	G	$8,200	2/7/2012	WCOK	3 pt., PTO, weights, synchro, John Deere 158 front-end loader
4430	1974	6,449	G	$10,250	2/7/2012	WCOK	QR, cab, air, 3 pt., PTO, dual hyd. front weights
4430	1974		G	$10,400	1/28/2012	ECMO	110 hp, 18.4x38 rears, QR, cab, air, heat, radio, 2 hyd., dual PTO, 3 pt.
4430	1974	5,578	G	$12,500	12/30/2011	NCIA	18.4Rx38, QR, quick hitch, 540/1,000, 2 hyd., 4 rear weights, block heater, diff. lock
4430	1974	2,402	G	$10,350	12/28/2011	Online	*BigIron.com,* item in Nebraska, QR, diesel, 2 hyd., PTO, side shield missing
4430	1974	5,440	G	$17,900	11/27/2011	ECIA	QR, 2 hyd., 3 pt., 18.4x38 tires, clamp-on duals, Sound Guard cab, air, heat
4430	1974	10,840	G	$13,500	11/19/2011	NCIA	New paint
4430	1974	52,603	G	$12,500	9/14/2011	Online	*BigIron.com,* item in Nebraska, MFWA, QR, 6 cyl. turbo diesel, 108 drawbar, 125 PTO hp, 540/1,000 PTO, cab, heat, air does not work, 3 pt.
4430	1974	11,000	G	$10,200	7/30/2011	ECMO	9700 hours on OH
4430	1974	11,000	G	$14,800	7/30/2011	ECMO	125 hp, QR, diesel, cab, air, heat, radio, 2 hyd., dual PTO, 3 pt., Cat II quick hitch, new cab kit, top link, 4,600 hours on OH
4430	1974		G	$12,500	6/18/2011	SWMN	High crop, SN 23268, synchro, 4 post ROPS, 3 pt., 2 hyd., repainted

John Deere

Model	Year	Hours	Condition	Price	Date	Area	Comments
4430	1974		G	$3,800	4/1/2011	Online	*AuctionTime.com,* item in Arkansas, 130 hp, 2WD, synchro, 4 post canopy, 2 hyd., 540/1,000 PTO, cranks and runs well
4430	1974		G	$7,100	3/19/2011	SEIA	Synchro
4430	1974	7,244	G	$10,600	3/18/2011	SWIL	ROPS, QR, dual PTO, 2 hyd., 3 pt., wiring hookup, good rubber
4430	1974	8,905	G	$7,400	3/15/2011	WCIL	QR, 2 hyd., 540/1,000 PTO
4430	1974		G	$12,900	12/11/2010	NEMI	Cab, air, heat, QR, direct axle duals, 2 hyd., Power Beyond, 6 front. weights, push bar
4430	1974		F	$8,900	12/10/2010	NWMO	2,000 hours on OH, 18.4x34 duals, Koyker loader
4430	1974	4,843	F	$6,300	12/6/2010	NEMO	18.4x38 and 10x16 tires, synchro, 2 hyd., dual PTO, cab
4430	1974	4,651	G	$9,570	5/26/2010	Online	*PurpleWave.com,* item in Kansas, John Deere 6 cyl. diesel, QR, 2 rev, 540 PTO
4430	1974	9,922	G	$8,910	4/28/2010	Online	*PurpleWave.com,* item in Kansas, John Deere 6 cyl. diesel, 16F/2R gears, suspension seat, 2 hyd., InterchangeE 540/1,000 PTO, cab, air, heat
4430	1974	7,641	G	$10,500	3/10/2010	ECND	3 hyd., 3 pt., 540/1,000 PTO, duals
4430	1974		G	$13,900	1/30/2010	WCIL	Cab, air, heat
4430	1975	11,000	G	$10,250	3/15/2014	WCIL	
4430	1975		G	$18,000	3/15/2014	NCOR	QR, cab
4430	1975	11,393	G	$12,750	3/4/2014	ECND	QR, 2 hyd., 3 pt., OH, 540/1,000 PTO, diff. lock, rock box, clamp on hub duals
4430	1975		G	$12,000	8/15/2013	ECMN	QR, 2 hyd., 3 pt.
4430	1975		G	$10,250	7/10/2013	Online	*BigIron.com,* item in Texas, row crop, some gauges not working
4430	1975	2,797	G	$14,750	7/3/2013	Online	*BigIron.com,* item in Nebraska, 2WD, 404 cu. in. diesel 125 engine
4430	1975	4,048	G	$7,500	4/4/2013	NWWA	HFWD, QR, 14.9R46 and 13.6x24 tires, 3 pt., PTO, 2 hyd., first hour meter 8,500, second hour meter
4430	1975	6,985	G	$14,750	4/2/2013	ECIA	QR, 2 hyd., 3 pt., aux. fuel tank, duals, new cab kit, batteries and axle bearings
4430	1975	7,000	G	$19,000	3/20/2013	NCOK	Loader, very clean
4430	1975	10,914	G	$11,000	3/7/2013	ECIA	
4430	1975	11,123	G	$8,500	11/30/2012	SCMT	Power QR, SGC, dual PTO, 2 hyd., 125 hp 14.9Rx46 10%, 15 piece front weights,
4430	1975	7,446	G	$14,000	8/8/2012	Online	*BigIron.com,* item in Kansas, 2WD, QR 16F/6R, 6 cyl. turbo diesel, 125 PTO hp, 2 hyd.,6' loader, 3 pt. quick hitch
4430	1975	12,212	G	$11,500	4/11/2012	SEAB	2WD, 126 PTO hp, PS, 2 hyd., PTO, 4 rib front tires, plumbed for front-end loader, hyd. and joystick
4430	1975	10,844	G	$9,500	4/10/2012	NEND	Cab, air, heat, QR, 3 pt., 540/1,000 PTO, 2 hyd.
4430	1975		G	$10,500	3/22/2012	ECMN	Cab, air, heat, PS, 2 hyd., 3 pt., PTO, diff. lock
4430	1975	3,361	F	$9,000	2/24/2012	NEKS	2 hyd., 3 pt., PTO, 2 sets rear weights, duals, new air

John Deere

Model	Year	Hours	Condition	Price	Date	Area	Comments
4430	1975	4,741	G	$11,250	1/28/2012	ECMO	Cab, air, heat, 3 hyd., hyd. lift assist, QR, clean solid
4430	1975	13,092	G	$8,200	1/25/2012	Online	*BigIron.com,* item in Nebraska, PS, 404 cu. in. turbo 6 cyl. diesel, 2 hyd., 540/1,000 PTO
4430	1975	10,161	G	$10,500	11/30/2011	ECND	3 hyd., 3 pt.
4430	1975	7,600	G	$21,500	10/7/2011	NWSD	Newer Buhler/Allied 795 loader, joystick, PTO, 3 pt., 3 hyd.
4430	1975	4,800	G	$17,000	9/1/2011	NCIA	Cab, QR, quick coupler, 2 hyd., $8,500 OH 743 hours ago, new radiator, added step, 3 sets of rear weights
4430	1975		G	$12,500	8/27/2011	WCIL	Cab, diesel, 900 hours on OH
4430	1975	7,000	G	$21,500	8/27/2011	NCOH	Cab, air, heat, QR, bolt on duals, 2 hyd., 2,000 hours on new John Deere 466 engine
4430	1975	9,005	G	$10,751	3/23/2011	Online	*BigIron.com,* item in Nebraska, QR, diesel, cab, air, dual hyd., radio, 3 pt., rear weights, axle duals
4430	1975	10,074	G	$14,500	2/19/2011	ECNE	Front weights, diesel
4430	1975	9,046	G	$10,100	12/1/2010	WCIL	Fully equipped cab, QR, 18.4x38 tires, axle mount duals, 2 hyd., one owner, 540/1,000 PTO
4430	1975	8,260	G	$8,000	11/19/2010	SENE	PS, cab, air, heat, 2 hyd., 18.4x38 duals
4430	1975	5,772	G	$15,700	9/21/2010	SEMN	PS, John Deere 720 loader, 18.4-38 tires, quick hitch, 540/1,000 PTO, 2 hyd.
4430	1975	7,085	G	$16,000	9/11/2010	WCMI	Diesel, cab, air, heat, QR, 2 hyd., 3 pt., quick hitch, 540 PTO, 18.4Rx38 tires, axle radial duals, rear weights, complete OH at 5,550 hours
4430	1975	6,999	F	$8,000	7/30/2010	NCNE	2 hyd., 3 pt., QR, 18.4Rx38 rear tires
4430	1975	11,316	G	$13,750	7/15/2010	ECND	2WD, cab, air, heat, QR, 3 pt., QH, 540/1,000 PTO, 2 hyd., front. aux. tank, hub duals
4430	1975	9,100	F	$7,800	6/9/2010	ECIA	
4430	1975	4,535	G	$14,000	3/19/2010	SEIA	Fully equipped cab, 18.4x38 and 10x16 tires, 540/1,000 PTO, 2 hyd., QR, front and rear weights, 2nd owner
4430	1976	9,889	F	$10,600	7/24/2013	Online	*IQBID.com*
4430	1976	9,591	G	$14,000	6/19/2013	Online	*BigIron.com,* item in Nebraska, 8 speed PS, 130 diesel
4430	1976	6,865	G	$13,500	3/20/2013	NCOK	18.4x34 tires, 3 pt., PTO
4430	1976	8,000	G	$14,500	2/23/2013	ECMI	PFWD, 3 pt., PTO, 3 hyd., 14.9x38 rears, eng and clutch rebuilt
4430	1976	9,659	G	$11,500	2/18/2013	Online	*IQBID.com,* QR, SN52630
4430	1976	6,793	G	$18,500	2/12/2013	WCIL	
4430	1976	10,888	G	$19,700	12/8/2012	SWIA	Cab, air, PS, 2 hyd., near new rubber, not OH
4430	1976	7,093	G	$18,000	11/24/2012	SEMN	Cab, air, heat, QR, 2 hyd.
4430	1976	6,900	E	$27,800	11/24/2012	SCIA	QR, cab, 3 sets of rear weights, front fenders, 3 hyd., quick attach, 18.4x38 rubber, one owner, sharp, SN 054923
4430	1976	10,250	G	$10,000	9/13/2012	SEIA	QR, 3 hyd.

John Deere

Model	Year	Hours	Condition	Price	Date	Area	Comments
4430	1976	9,562	G	$12,300	8/22/2012	Online	*BigIron.com,* item in Nebraska, 8 speed PS, diesel, 130 hp, 540/1,000 PTO, 10 front suitcase weights, 3HD hyd., fluid filled tires
4430	1976	4,220	G	$25,250	8/16/2012	NCIA	Cab, QR, 2 hyd., rear weights, 18.4x38 clamp on duals, front tank and weights, quick coupler
4430	1976		G	$11,750	3/28/2012	ECND	2WD, cab, air, heat, QR, 3 pt., 540/1,000 PTO, 2 hyd., duals
4430	1976	5,750	G	$16,750	3/21/2012	ECMN	QR, 3 pt., PTO, 2 hyd., 18.4x38
4430	1976	7,136	G	$12,000	3/14/2012	ECND	QR, 2 hyd., 3 pt., 540/1,000 PTO, duals
4430	1976	7,286	G	$19,500	3/5/2012	NWIN	Cab, 8, speed synchro, duals, weights, quick hitch
4430	1976	8,748	F	$12,750	2/7/2012	SEIA	QR, 3 pt., 2 hyd., duals sell separate
4430	1976	6,576	G	$19,000	1/19/2012	ECIL	QR, 18.4x38 snap on duals, 2 hyd., full front weights
4430	1976	14,785	G	$14,750	12/28/2011	Online	*BigIron.com,* item in Nebraska, 2WD, PS, 2 hyd., 540/1,000 PTO, OH at 12,000 hours, new cab kit and seat
4430	1976		G	$13,500	10/7/2011	NWSD	John Deere 148 loader, joystick control, PS, PTO, 3 pt., 3 hyd.
4430	1976	6,196	G	$10,750	8/13/2011	WCIL	18.4Rx38 rear tires, 2 hyd., QR, 540/1,000 PTO, OH at 5,400 hours
4430	1976	4,500	G	$8,000	7/30/2011	ECMO	
4430	1976	8,729	G	$10,250	6/8/2011	Online	*BigIron.com,* item in Nebraska, QR, 404 cu. in. diesel, 125 hp, 540/1,000 PTO, 2 hyd., air, block heater
4430	1976	4,621	G	$16,750	5/25/2011	NECO	Diesel, WF, John Deere 158 loader and big square fork and 7' bucket
4430	1976	4,361	E	$24,000	4/16/2011	NWOH	One owner, QR, new 18.4x38 tires, not used much in past year, cab, 2 hyd., 6 front weights
4430	1976	3,326	G	$9,000	3/19/2011	SEWY	WF, 3 pt., diesel
4430	1976		G	$9,700	3/15/2011	WCIL	2 hyd., 540 PTO
4430	1976		G	$10,500	3/5/2011	NWMO	
4430	1976	8,921	G	$20,500	3/2/2011	ECND	QR, 3 hyd., 3 pt., PTO, WF, front fuel tank, Goodyear 18.4x38 hub duals
4430	1976		G	$15,600	2/1/2011	NEIN	HFWD, PS
4430	1976	9,811	G	$8,400	12/30/2010	ECMN	Cab, air, heat, QR, 2 hyd., 3 pt., 1,000 PTO, third arm
4430	1976	7,762	G	$8,500	5/22/2010	NWOK	Degelman dozer blade, 3 pt., PTO
4430	1976	6,880	G	$17,000	3/20/2010	NWIA	QR, 3 pt., 2 hyd.
4430	1976		G	$14,000	3/5/2010	NCMO	PS, 3 pt., 2 hyd., cab, air, heat
4430	1976	10,300	G	$10,100	3/1/2010	NEKS	Synchro 8 speed, Sound Guard cab, 18.4Rx38 tires good, diesel
4430	1977	7,592	G	$14,250	3/26/2014	Online	*BigIron.com,* item in Illinois, QR, 16F/6R
4430	1977	9,119	G	$17,000	2/15/2014	ECMO	Fully equipped cab, QR, 18.4Rx38 axle duals, 10x16 front tires, 2 hyd., 540/1,000 PTO, 5 front weights, one owner, 500 hours on major OH, SN 4430H070428R
4430	1977	12,000	G	$8,250	6/24/2013	SWSK	2WD, John Deere 148 front-end loader, 125 PTO hp, QR, dual hyd., dual PTO, 18.4x38 rear duals

John Deere

Model	Year	Hours	Condition	Price	Date	Area	Comments
4430	1977	7,725	E	$18,500	3/20/2013	NCOK	New paint, injectors, air, hyd. pump, injection system, 3 pt., PTO, 2 hyd., 200 hours on new OH
4430	1977	12,000	G	$10,000	11/28/2012	ECND	PS, air, heat, 2 hyd., 3 pt., 540/1,000 PTO, 18.4x38 rears
4430	1977		G	$8,550	8/11/2012	NWIL	Cab, QR, 10 front suitcase weights, 18.4x38, hub duals
4430	1977		G	$18,700	4/25/2012	Online	*PurpleWave.com,* item in Kansas
4430	1977	7,200	G	$17,000	4/7/2012	SWIN	Cab, air, heat, QR, original
4430	1977		G	$8,000	1/28/2012	ECMO	18.4x38 tires, dual PTO, 2 hyd., 3 pt.
4430	1977	6,600	G	$9,100	1/28/2012	ECMO	
4430	1977	8,708	G	$13,500	12/22/2011	Online	*IQBID.com,* 2WD, cab, air, heat, QR, 2 hyd., 3 pt., 540/1,000 PTO, quick hitch, new water pump, alternator and batteries
4430	1977	9,416	G	$12,100	11/30/2011	Online	*PurpleWave.com,* item in Oklahoma, 6 cyl. diesel, partial PS, air, heat, AM/FM, 3 pt., drawbar, aux. outlet, 540/1,000 PTO
4430	1977	6,194	E	$21,000	11/12/2011	SCWI	Cab, air, heat, QR, 18.4x38 tires and duals, rear weights, SN 068695R, sharp
4430	1977		G	$12,500	8/27/2011	WCIL	Cab, diesel
4430	1977		G	$8,500	7/30/2011	ECMO	Farmhand F258 loader
4430	1977	9,244	G	$12,000	7/27/2011	ECND	QR, 3 hyd., 3 pt., PTO, front fuel tank, hub duals
4430	1977	6,309	G	$16,000	4/27/2011	NECO	WF, diesel, front weights and duals
4430	1977	8,900	F	$7,100	4/20/2011	NWMI	Diesel, cab, heat, QR, 3 hyd., 20.8x38 tires and duals
4430	1977	6,046	G	$15,500	3/26/2011	WCIA	Cab, QR, 18.4x38 rubber, SN 068719R
4430	1977	6,624	G	$9,800	2/1/2011	NEIN	PS, cab
4430	1977	6,675	E	$19,000	9/6/2010	NCOH	Cab, air, heat, cast inner wheels, duals, QR, quick hitch, 2 hyd., looks like new
4430	1977	9,131	G	$12,000	7/28/2010	ECND	QR, 2 hyd., 3 pt., PTO, duals
4430	1977		G	$10,000	4/10/2010	NCTN	
4430			G	$5,000	3/26/2014	ECMS	Enclosed cab
4430		9,630	G	$8,500	3/26/2014	Online	*BigIron.com,* item in South Dakota, 18.4x38 rear tires, 10x16 front tires, diesel, 3 pt., PTO, QR, air
4430		9,630	G	$8,500	3/26/2014	Online	*BigIron.com,* item in South Dakota, 3 pt., PTO
4430			G	$10,000	3/22/2014	ECSD	QR
4430			G	$11,200	3/22/2014	ECSD	PS, 3 pt., 2 hyd.
4430		7,800	G	$9,000	2/22/2014	NEIN	18.4x38 tires, 2 hyd., 3 pt., PTO, recent OH
4430		7,341	G	$9,400	1/4/2014	ECOH	Cab, air, heat, clean
4430		8,280	G	$13,750	1/4/2014	ECOH	
4430			G	$13,000	12/4/2013	WCSD	QR, diesel, 3 pt., cab, air, heat, 18.4-38 rears, Farmhand F258 loader, grapple
4430		10,125	G	$12,500	9/14/2013	WCIA	QR, well maintained, buyer's dad was H.S. classmate/Korean war buddy of the seller (81-year-old farmer retiring)
4430		9,732	G	$8,700	9/12/2013	SEIA	QR, 3 pt., 2 hyd., 18.4x38, 10 front weights, rear wheel weights
4430			G	$9,410	9/10/2013	ECND	Cab, air, heat, QR, 2 hyd., 540/1,000 PTO

TRACTORS

Model	Year	Hours	Condition	Price	Date	Area	Comments
4430			F	$7,250	9/7/2013	ECIA	Rolled, cut off cab, cobbled up
4430		10,375	G	$11,250	8/24/2013	NWMO	Diesel, cab, 3 pt., 2 hyd., 540/1,000 top link, 18.4x38 rubber, aux. fuel tank, QR, slight damage to cab front top right, SN 045526
4430		7,465	G	$7,250	8/15/2013	ECMN	Cab, air, heat, 2 hyd., 3 pt., 540 PTO
4430			G	$7,700	7/10/2013	NETX	Westendorf loader, bucket
4430		264	G	$16,252	6/25/2013	WCMN	2WD, PS, 2 hyd., 3 pt., no top link, differential lock, K&M step kit, 8 HID lights, R134 A/C system, 14.9x38 hub duals, 9.5Lx15 3 rib front tires, SN 59771R
4430			G	$7,000	6/22/2013	SESC	Duals
4430		1,006	G	$7,650	5/15/2013	Online	*BigIron.com,* item in Arkansas, 8F/4R PS
4430		10,000	G	$11,251	5/8/2013	Online	*BigIron.com,* item in Nebraska, loader, QR
4430		5,193	G	$16,000	5/1/2013	Online	*BigIron.com,* item in South Dakota, John Deere 158 loader, PS, 6 cyl. diesel
4430			G	$9,000	4/10/2013	NETX	Cab, air, QR, 18.4x38 tires
4430		5,931	G	$12,500	4/10/2013	NETX	Cab, air, 2WD, NH1200 ER Bison loader, 18.4Rx38 and 11x16 tires
4430			G	$11,100	3/23/2013	NEIN	QR, repainted, dual hyd., 3 pt., runs
4430		5,700	G	$11,750	2/12/2013	WCIL	
4430			G	$9,250	1/19/2013	NEMS	
4430			G	$9,300	1/9/2013	Online	*BigIron.com,* item in Nebraska, QR, John Deere 6 cyl. turbo diesel, 125.8 PTO hp, 18.4x38 rear tires, 10x16 front tires, 2 hyd., 540/1,000 PTO, 2500 hours on OH, 3 pt.
4430		6,911	G	$13,900	12/11/2012	SEPA	Cab, QR, 2 hyd.
4430			G	$5,100	12/8/2012	ECTX	High clearance, 4 post canopy, 18.4x38 rear tires, 750x20 tires, 3 pt., PTO, 2 hyd.
4430		4,123	G	$10,500	11/13/2012	NWTX	Total trans OH and other improvements in 2012, no leaks, great tires
4430			G	$14,000	11/13/2012	NCIA	PS
4430		6,824	G	$8,400	10/24/2012	WCWI	18.4x38 tires
4430		8,428	G	$16,000	9/20/2012	ECIN	Cab, QR, 428 hours on OH, 2 hyd., quick coupler, front and rear weights, 18.4x34 tires
4430		4,727	G	$19,000	9/20/2012	ECIN	Cab, PS, 3 front weights, quick coupler, 2 hyd., 18.4x38 tires
4430		3,087	G	$8,100	8/30/2012	SEMN	20.8x38 duals, QR
4430			F	$9,500	8/16/2012	Online	*IQBID.com,* item in Minnesota, 2WD, cab, air, heat, QR, 3 hyd., PTO, 3rd arm, 18.4x38 tires, one season on OH, hours unknown
4430			G	$3,500	7/27/2012	SWKY	
4430			G	$9,000	7/27/2012	SWKY	Duals, radio needs work
4430			G	$9,500	7/27/2012	SWKY	
4430		4,430	P	$4,400	6/20/2012	ECIL	18.4x38, 4 rear weights, 2 hyd., 1 PTO, does not run
4430		7,095	G	$12,000	6/20/2012	ECIL	18.4x38, 3 pt., 2 hyd., PTO

John Deere

Model	Year	Hours	Condition	Price	Date	Area	Comments
4430			P	$10,000	6/9/2012	ECNE	Hyd. front, WD, cab, 3 pt., PTO, dual hyd., synchro, doesn't run
4430			G	$12,250	6/9/2012	ECNE	High crop, dual hyd., 3 pt., synchro, 4 post ROPS, runs, repainted
4430		5,500	G	$18,500	6/2/2012	SEMN	QR, duals, many repairs with all paper work
4430		999	G	$10,858	4/25/2012	Online	*BigIron.com,* item in Nebraska, QR, 540/1,000 PTO, 2WD, 2 hyd., front weight bracket, no weights, needs new cab kit
4430			G	$9,500	3/24/2012	SETX	QR, cab, air, duals, top link
4430		2,039	G	$17,000	3/24/2012	SWMI	6 cyl. John Deere diesel, WF, dual hyd., 540/1,000 PTO, 8 wheel weights, front weight, 18.4x38 rear tires
4430		10,650	G	$4,100	3/22/2012	ECMN	Cab, air, heat, QR, 2 hyd., 3 pt., PTO
4430		13,740	G	$11,250	2/25/2012	WCMI	WF, cab, heat and air, 3 pt., 540/1,000 PTO, 2 hyd., 18.4x38 rear tires
4430			G	$15,000	2/4/2012	ECSC	Loaders
4430			G	$8,750	1/28/2012	ECMO	John Deere 725 loader, QR, cab, air, heat, duals
4430			G	$10,750	1/28/2012	ECMO	
4430		5,700	G	$16,000	1/28/2012	ECMO	4 post, new clutch, dual PTO, 4 post
4430		12,000	G	$12,000	1/14/2012	WCIA	
4430			G	$9,500	12/17/2011	NETX	Cab, air, QR, 2 hyd., 540/1,000 PTO, 3 pt., 10 front weights
4430			G	$12,250	12/9/2011	SWKY	Cab, duals, John Deere 265 loader
4430			F	$9,750	11/29/2011	SWMN	QR, 3 hyd., 3 pt., 18.4x38 tires
4430		6,694	F	$9,400	11/19/2011	NCMO	QR, rough
4430		4,000	G	$13,000	11/19/2011	NCMO	QR
4430		5,988	F	$10,000	11/4/2011	SEWA	MFWD, cab, air, 8 speed PS, 3 pt., dual PTO, 3 hyd., 18.4Rx38 rear tires, 12.4Rx24 front tires, Case quick attach loader, 7' bucket
4430			F	$8,100	10/22/2011	NECO	High crop, 3 pt., quick coupler
4430			G	$9,200	7/30/2011	ECMO	
4430		5,121	G	$10,230	6/29/2011	Online	*PurpleWave.com,* item in Kansas, 6 cyl. diesel, QR, air, heat unknown if working, AM radio
4430		6,681	G	$15,000	5/13/2011	NWOK	Diesel, PS, hyd., 3 pt., PTO, John Deere 158 loader
4430		9,500	G	$16,000	4/14/2011	NCND	2 hyd.
4430			F	$11,250	3/26/2011	NCKS	Cab, air, heat, PTO, 3 pt., 2 hyd., John Deere 158 loader, joystick controls, bucket AND grapple fork, Winkel round bale spear
4430			G	$14,000	3/18/2011	SWIL	Diesel, dual hyd., QR, 8 front weights, new tires
4430			G	$15,500	3/4/2011	NWIA	Tach. said 2,623 hours but was closer to 9,000, diesel, WF, QR, 3 pt., 2 hyd., cab, air, heat, 480/80Rx38 rear rubber
4430		9,200	G	$11,500	1/29/2011	ECMO	
4430		3,500	G	$6,800	1/8/2011	ECMI	

John Deere

Model	Year	Hours	Condition	Price	Date	Area	Comments
4430			G	$8,750	11/27/2010	SEMN	Cab, QR, 3 pt. dual hyd., PTO, 18.4Rx38
4430			G	$9,700	11/27/2010	SEMN	Cab, 3 pt., dual hyd., PTO, 18.4x38
4430			G	$11,500	11/27/2010	SEMN	Cab, PS, 3 pt., dual hyd., PTO, 18.4x38
4430			G	$4,100	11/20/2010	NCLA	Duals, 3 pt.
4430		4,247	G	$10,100	11/20/2010	SEIA	ROPS, synchro
4430			G	$8,600	11/18/2010	SEOK	
4430			G	$4,750	11/17/2010	ECMS	
4430		8,329	F	$8,000	10/15/2010	Online	*IronPlanet.com,* item in Illinois
4430			G	$10,250	9/4/2010	NEIN	High crop, PS
4430			G	$10,700	8/9/2010	WCMO	
4430			G	$8,300	5/26/2010	ECSD	
4430			G	$10,150	5/26/2010	ECSD	
4430			G	$13,750	5/26/2010	ECSD	
4430		11,945	G	$10,100	3/23/2010	SEND	Bottom end OH, QR, 2 hyd.
4430			G	$11,500	3/16/2010	SEMI	Open station, 3,800 hours on OH, PS, weights
4430			F	$7,000	3/6/2010	SEMN	Hours unknown, 20.8x38 tires, QR
4430			F	$6,900	2/11/2010	NENC	Cab, creeper
4430			F	$7,500	2/6/2010	SEVA	Open station
4440	1978	8,500	G	$22,000	2/15/2014	ECMO	Fully equipped cab, PS, 20.8Rx38 axle duals, 11x16 front tires, 2 hyd., 540/1,000 PTO, 12 front weights, one owner, approx. 3,000 hours on OH, SN 4440P011849
4440	1978	13,371	G	$15,500	2/5/2014	SESD	QR, cab, air, heat, 2 hyd., 3 pt., 20.8x38 tires, Ride-N-Drive
4440	1978	8,036	G	$20,000	12/21/2013	WCIL	Fully equipped cab, QR, 18.4x38 and 11x15 tires
4440	1978	8,316	G	$20,000	12/19/2013	WCMN	Cab, air, heat, PS, 3 pt., PTO, full weight set, new cab kit, new front tires, 18.4x38 hub duals, 4,000 hours on new engine
4440	1978	13,248	G	$10,750	11/26/2013	ECND	Cab, air, heat, QR, 3 pt. quick hitch, 540/1,000 PTO, 2 hyd.
4440	1978	6,100	G	$16,000	9/12/2013	SEIA	3 pt., 540/1,000 PTO, 2 hyd., QR, 18.4x38 on rear
4440	1978	9,086	G	$20,350	8/14/2013	Online	*PurpleWave.com,* item in Kansas, John Deere 6 cyl. diesel, PS
4440	1978	5,874	G	$17,300	2/6/2013	SESD	QR, cab, air, heat, 2 hyd., 3 pt., 18.4x38 duals, 10-bolt, Ride-N-Drive
4440	1978	8,691	G	$14,500	11/28/2012	ECND	Cab, air, heat, QR, 3 hyd., 3 pt., 540/1,000 PTO, 14.9x46 tires on 88" centers
4440	1978	6,748	G	$30,750	11/8/2012	ECNE	Diesel, PS, 8 speed, 3 pt., PTO, 2 hyd., cab, air, heat, AM/FM, Firestone 18.4Rx38 radial tires
4440	1978	8,326	F	$15,600	8/1/2012	NCIA	QR, front weights, good rubber, 2 hyd.
4440	1978	6,500	G	$9,000	1/28/2012	ECMO	Cab, air, heat, QR, front. weights
4440	1978	1,729	F	$16,500	1/14/2012	NENC	PS, cab, air, heat, 2 hyd., single lift assist, 540 PTO, aux. live hyd. Power Beyond planter dump valve, retrofitted R134A air, doors tight, 9-hole duals, no weights, weak cab kit, 18.4x38 tires

John Deere

Model	Year	Hours	Condition	Price	Date	Area	Comments
4440	1978	8,300	G	$27,600	9/17/2011	SEMN	QR, new air parts, showed 6,000 hours but owner said about 8,300 hours, spray paint on front corner of side hood, average appearance
4440	1978	4,900	G	$26,000	9/10/2011	ECIA	QR, 18.4x38 tires, 10 front weights, 2 hyd., 3 pt., 2WD
4440	1978	9,476	G	$15,000	8/11/2011	WCMN	Cab, air, heat, 3 pt., PTO, hub duals
4440	1978	1,136	G	$16,750	8/10/2011	Online	*BigIron.com,* item in Nebraska, 8F/4R, PS, 6 cyl. turbo, 7.6L, diesel, 540/1,000 PTO
4440	1978	6,200	G	$22,500	8/2/2011	ECNE	
4440	1978	7,425	G	$22,000	6/18/2011	SESK	2WD, Leon 790 front-end loader, 130 PTO hp, QR, dual PTO, 3 hyd., duals, 3 rib front, reinforced quick detach front-end loader, 7' bucket
4440	1978	8,097	G	$18,500	6/10/2011	WCSK	2WD, 130 PTO hp, QR, 2 hyd., PTO, 3 rib front
4440	1978	13,312	G	$22,000	4/20/2011	WCSK	2WD, Buhler front-end loader, 130 PTO hp, 16 speed, QR shift, 3 hyd., dual hyd., factory duals, 7' bucket, grapple
4440	1978	6,285	G	$27,500	4/9/2011	WCNE	Diesel, duals, front weights
4440	1978	5,000	G	$25,000	3/26/2011	SWIA	Sound Guard cab, QR, 3 hyd., 18.4x38 rubber and duals, front and wheel weights., SN 4440H017327R, looked new, fire 15 years ago, one owner
4440	1978		G	$13,750	3/5/2011	NWMO	
4440	1978	6,077	G	$27,500	1/11/2011	WCIL	QR, 3 hyd., power beyond, 3 pt., quick hitch, 12 front weights, 540/1,000 PTO
4440	1978	5,454	E	$27,500	11/13/2010	NEKS	QR, 3 hyd., 18.4Rx38 rubber 60%, had been used as loader
4440	1978	6,574	G	$17,000	11/12/2010	ECIL	3 pt., weights, 3 hyd., quick hitch, 18.4x38 duals
4440	1978		F	$13,500	11/2/2010	ECOK	Cab, air, 3 pt., 2 hyd.
4440	1978	6,440	G	$21,000	7/30/2010	ECIA	Cab, air, heat, PS, 18.4x38 duals, 3 hyd.
4440	1978	11,700	G	$16,001	6/14/2010	Online	*BigIron.com,* item in South Dakota, QR, diesel, 3 hyd., 3 pt., new paint
4440	1978		G	$14,100	5/26/2010	ECSD	
4440	1978		G	$14,300	5/26/2010	ECSD	QR
4440	1978	603	G	$15,950	4/28/2010	Online	*PurpleWave.com,* item in Kansas, John Deere 6 cyl. diesel, PS, 8F/4R, work lights, 2 hyd., 540/1,000 PTO
4440	1978	2,205	E	$32,500	2/26/2010	NEMO	QR, 2 hyd., cast duals
4520	1969		G	$10,000	4/1/2014	WCMN	8 speed, WF, synchro side console, PTO, 3 pt., QH, 3 hyd., fenders, open canopy
4520	1969		G	$5,500	9/21/2013	WCMI	Diesel, cab, 3 pt., PTO, 2 hyd., 18.4x38 rear tires, not restored
4520	1969		G	$6,500	6/9/2012	ECNE	Standard, PS, PTO, dual hyd., original, runs, missing cab door
4520	1969		F	$5,400	3/7/2012	SEIA	Factory cab, synchro, hub mount duals, 1,000 PTO, 3 hyd., 3 pt., new engine
4520	1969		G	$4,510	12/28/2011	Online	*PurpleWave.com,* item in Kansas
4520	1969		G	$9,000	8/13/2011	WCIL	Cab, 8 speed, synchro, new clutch, 2 hyd., 1,000 PTO, 20.8Rx38 tires, front weights

John Deere

Model	Year	Hours	Condition	Price	Date	Area	Comments
4520	1969	4,596	G	$6,200	4/11/2011	Online	*AuctionTime.com*
4520	1969		G	$4,200	4/1/2011	Online	*AuctionTime.com,* item in Arkansas, 130 hp, 2WD, PS, 2 hyd., 38" duals, 1,000 PTO, cranks, runs and drives well
4520	1969		G	$6,300	12/2/2010	NWIA	20.8x38 tires
4520	1969		G	$7,100	3/5/2010	NCMO	Cab
4520		902	G	$6,750	12/4/2013	Online	*BigIron.com,* item in Nebraska, synchro, diesel, 150 hp, 18.4x42 rear tires, 14Lx15 front tires, 2 hyd., 1,000 PTO, factory cab, roll bar, missing interior
4520		1,969	G	$6,900	9/26/2013	NWOH	Diesel, 18.4x38 tires, 11.6x16 fronts, 540 PTO, 3 pt., 1 hyd., splitter, SN T813R002583R
4520		5,985	G	$4,500	8/15/2013	ECMN	2WD, 2 hyd., third arm, front weights, 18.4x38 dual tires
4520			F	$6,000	7/27/2013	WCIL	Original motor, SN TS130002935
4520			G	$8,500	3/23/2013	NEIN	3 pt., cab, original, runs
4520			G	$26,000	3/23/2013	NEIN	Dual hyd., no 3 pt., older repaint, PS, 4WD, runs
4520		10,190	F	$6,200	4/13/2012	WCMI	Year Round cab, 3 hyd., 1,000 PTO, synchro, front weights, 18.4x38 hub axle duals, 2,200 hours on OH
4520			G	$11,500	3/24/2012	NEIN	Diesel, PS, standard, cab, 2 set rear weights, dual hyd., runs
4520		5,560	G	$11,500	3/10/2012	NWIL	John Deere 158 loader, 2 hyd., side console, no cab
4520		5,486	G	$4,100	9/14/2011	Online	*BigIron.com,* item in Colorado, 6 cyl. diesel, 2 hyd., 540/1,000 PTO, 3 pt., weighted duals, cab, air
4520		9,426	F	$3,050	4/12/2011	Online	*IQBID.com,* cab, 3 pt., 2 hyd., PTO, may need trans repair
4520			F	$2,250	1/15/2011	ECAR	
4520			G	$7,400	12/18/2010	ECMI	
4520		5,550	G	$7,100	11/13/2010	NCIA	Factory cab, air, original paint
4620	1971	7,530	G	$9,551	7/10/2013	Online	*BigIron.com,* item in Nebraska, 8 speed, 130 plus hp, 1,000 PTO
4620	1971	13,000	G	$4,500	3/14/2012	WCNE	3 pt., PTO, dual hyd., synchro, 18.4x38 tires at 30%, 135 hp
4620	1971	8,900	G	$19,000	1/28/2012	ECMO	New clutch, 10 hole duals
4620	1971	7,810	G	$18,500	12/10/2011	SEMN	PS, 20.8x38 Firestone tires, duals 90%, 16.5Lx4 rib front tires, cab, R134 air, extension fuel tank, full set of front weights, inside and outside rear wheel weights, new style step, 3 pt., 2 hyd., very sharp, SN 011285R
4620	1971	6,920	G	$8,750	12/3/2011	NWIL	18.4Rx38 tires 75%, synchro, 2 hyd. updated to new style, less than 1,200 hours on OH and clutch, mechanically sound, Year Round cab, SN 010727R
4620	1971		G	$15,500	6/18/2011	SWMN	Synchro, SN 11289, synchro, front wheel drive, 2 hyd., new tires, original
4620	1972	1,800	G	$5,200	8/15/2013	ECMN	2WD, factory cab, heat, diesel, PS, 2 hyd., 3 pt., 1,000 PTO, rock box, 18.4x38 tires

John Deere

Model	Year	Hours	Condition	Price	Date	Area	Comments
4620	1972	3,728	G	$6,750	6/13/2013	SEAB	2WD, 135 PTO hp diesel, 8F/2R synchro, cab, 2 hyd., 18.4x38 duals
4620	1972	7,514	G	$5,200	6/8/2011	Online	*BigIron.com,* item in Nebraska, diesel, PTO, air, heat, 3 pt.
4620	1972	998	G	$15,000	3/1/2011	SCNE	Cab, PS, 20.8x38 rear tires, clamp on duals, 10x16 front tires, 3 hyd., 3 pt., John Deere quick hitch, 500 lb. inside rear wheel weights, new batteries, oil and filters in December 2010
4620	1972		G	$14,500	2/14/2011	SWNE	PS, Farmhand XL1140 loader, grapple, cab, duals
4620	1972		G	$9,000	5/29/2010	NCIL	Diesel, new front rubber and batteries
4620	1972	7,500	F	$4,070	2/24/2010	Online	*PurpleWave.com,* item in Kansas, 135 hp 6 cyl. diesel, 1,000 PTO, 540 adaptor, PTO is not working
4620			G	$8,300	2/5/2014	SESD	WF
4620			G	$6,000	10/3/2013	NCIN	
4620			G	$12,000	3/23/2013	NEIN	PS, original, diesel, dual hyd., duals, quick coupler, runs
4620		1,885	G	$3,200	2/7/2013	SEAR	Diesel, single range 8 speed, 1,000 PTO, duals
4620		7,934	G	$13,250	8/16/2012	Online	*IQBID.com,* item in Minnesota, PS, cab, air, heat, rock box, 2 hyd., 3 pt., 1,000 PTO, 20.8x38 duals, 11x16 front
4620		1,203	G	$24,000	8/16/2012	Online	*IQBID.com,* item in Minnesota, 2WD, diesel, open station, PS, side console, 2 hyd., 3 pt., 540/1,000 PTO, quick hitch, diff. lock, 90% tires, front weights, restored
4620			G	$6,000	3/24/2012	NEIN	3 pt., synchro, dual hyd., set of rear wheel weights, Hinlker cab, runs
4620			G	$8,250	1/27/2012	SEAL	No top link, duals
4620			G	$2,510	9/14/2011	Online	*BigIron.com,* item in Colorado, 6 cyl. diesel, 540 PTO, 3 pt.
4620			G	$5,400	9/4/2010	NEIN	Synchro, dual hyd.
4620			G	$9,000	9/4/2010	NEIN	Dual hyd., quick hitch
4630	1973		G	$8,750	12/5/2013	SEMN	Row crop
4630	1973	7,265	G	$9,600	12/5/2013	NEIN	Cab, air, heat
4630	1973	9,258	F	$13,000	10/22/2013	WCSK	2WD, 150 PTO hp, QR trans, 2 hyd., 1,000 PTO, 24.5x32 rear
4630	1973		G	$9,700	12/3/2012	WCIL	Cab, synchro, 2 hyd., complete OH at 10K hours, Power Beyond, 18.4x38, no duals, one owner
4630	1973	7,530	G	$10,750	3/14/2012	WCNE	18.4x38 rubber 50%, 3 pt., 3 hyd., cab, air, heat
4630	1973	9,294	F	$12,500	12/29/2011	WCIL	PS, average 18.4x38 axle duals, poor cab interior
4630	1973	7,003	G	$7,800	12/28/2011	Online	*BigIron.com,* item in Nebraska, 8F/4R, PS, 6 cyl. diesel, 150 hp, 2 hyd., 540/1,000 PTO, 3 pt., left side platform step, front fender damage
4630	1973		P	$5,000	12/7/2011	NCIA	Rough, 18.4x38 duals

John Deere

Model	Year	Hours	Condition	Price	Date	Area	Comments
4630	1973	5,872	G	$11,000	11/30/2011	SEMN	Synchro, 18.4x38 tires
4630	1973	2,723	G	$7,500	7/27/2011	ECND	Synchro, 2 hyd., 3 pt., quick hitch, 1,000 PTO, diff. lock
4630	1973	6,685	G	$9,000	7/27/2011	ECND	PS, 3 hyd., 3 pt., quick hitch, 1,000 PTO, band duals
4630	1974	12,000	G	$8,250	2/22/2014	SCNE	2WD, QR, 38" tires 80%, front weights, well maintained, excellent paint, 30" spacing
4630	1974		G	$11,000	12/12/2013	ECNE	QR
4630	1974	1,363	G	$10,800	5/29/2013	Online	*BigIron.com,* item in Kansas, loader, 8F/4R PS
4630	1974	8,775	G	$11,550	3/27/2013	NWWI	Sound Guard cab, QR shift, 2 hyd., 3 pt., 20.8x38 Firestone radial tires, front fuel tank, deluxe steps, 1,000 PTO
4630	1974		G	$12,500	11/24/2012	WCIL	
4630	1974		G	$7,480	4/25/2012	Online	*PurpleWave.com,* item in Kansas
4630	1974	2,727	G	$7,480	4/25/2012	Online	*PurpleWave.com,* item in Kansas, 6 cyl. diesel, QR, 16F/4R gears, air, heat, spring ride seat, tilt wheel, sun shade, AM/FM, 3 pt., drawbar, 1,000 PTO
4630	1974	915	G	$8,806	8/24/2011	Online	*BigIron.com,* item in Nebraska, 8 speed PS, 3 hyd., 1,000 PTO, duals, radio and air work, 3 pt. quick hitch
4630	1974	8,066	G	$11,500	5/25/2011	Online	*BigIron.com,* item in Nebraska, 8 speed PS, 6 cyl. diesel, duals, 2 hyd., 1,000 PTO, 3 pt., master disconnect switch, 10 front suitcase weights
4630	1974	9,980	G	$16,500	4/18/2011	WCSK	2WD, QR, 3 hyd., 1,000 PTO, duals, 3 rib front
4630	1974	10,150	G	$8,000	3/23/2011	ECMN	QR, cab, air, heat, 3 pt., PTO, 3 hyd., duals, 4,000 hours on engine OH, rock box, quick coupler
4630	1975		G	$14,005	1/29/2014	Online	*BigIron.com,* item in Nebraska, 16 speed QR, 6 cyl., 20.8Rx38 rear tires, 14Lx16.1 front tires, diesel, 164 hp, 3 hyd., 3 pt. drawbar, new interior, 320 hours on new tach., 1,000 PTO, weights on front
4630	1975	10,259	G	$9,150	5/29/2013	Online	*BigIron.com,* item in Nebraska, QR, 404 cu in. 6 cyl. turbo
4630	1975		G	$6,500	12/6/2012	Online	*IQBID.com,* SN RW4630T012301
4630	1975		G	$6,500	12/6/2012	SEIA	QR, 1,000 PTO, 2 hyd.
4630	1975	745	G	$8,520	6/13/2012	Online	*BigIron.com,* item in Wyoming, QR, 6 cyl. diesel, 18.4x38 dual tires, 2 hyd., 1,000 PTO, 3 pt., third link, radio, air
4630	1975	5,593	G	$11,100	5/19/2012	WCIL	Cab, PS, good tires, diesel
4630	1975	8,241	G	$9,800	2/7/2012	WCOK	Cab, air, 8 speed, PS, 3 hyd., 18.4x38 rubber, 158 loader
4630	1975	7,875	G	$13,100	7/13/2011	Online	*BigIron.com,* item in Colorado, Westendorf loader, QR, diesel, 3 hyd., 1,000 PTO, 8' bucket, seat ripped
4630	1975	10,000	G	$11,000	5/25/2011	NECO	Diesel, WF, duals, Farmhand 1140 loader and grapple

John Deere

Model	Year	Hours	Condition	Price	Date	Area	Comments
4630	1975	8,063	G	$16,000	5/4/2011	WCSK	2WD, John Deere 158 front end loader, 150 PTO hp, QR, 2 hyd., 1,000 PTO, 7' bucket
4630	1975	6,245	G	$13,000	12/17/2010	WCIL	PS, 20.8x38 duals, recent OH, 2 hyd., 1,000 PTO
4630	1975	7,392	G	$11,100	7/28/2010	ECND	QR, 2 hyd., 3 pt., quick hitch, diff. lock, 1,000 PTO, duals
4630	1976	10,032	G	$11,000	4/11/2014	SWSK	2WD, 150 hp PTO, QR, 16F/6R, 2 hyd., 1,000 PTO, 18.4x38 rear, 4 rib front, duals
4630	1976	8,007	G	$15,100	3/8/2014	NEMO	PS, 3 pt., front weights, 18.4x38 duals
4630	1976	8,130	G	$23,000	2/22/2014	SENE	150 hours on complete OH, 3 hyd., 18.4x38 rubber good, PS, new interior kit, fast hitch, SN 024295R
4630	1976	13,500	G	$15,000	2/5/2014	SESD	QR, 2 hyd., 3 pt. quick hitch, rock box, OH at 10K hours, 20.8x38 duals, rear weights
4630	1976	12,356	F	$13,500	6/7/2013	ECAB	2WD, 150 PTO hp, 8 speed PS, 1,000 PTO, 2 hyd., 18.4x38/24.5x32 rear duals, rear wheel weights, 14Lx16.1 front tires, 4 rib front, greenlight in 1999 and 2005, 300 hours on OH
4630	1976	6,308	F	$7,250	5/31/2013	NCOK	3 pt., PTO, 3 hyd., 150 hp, 20.8-38 tires
4630	1976	6,514	G	$20,750	11/24/2012	SEMN	Cab, air, heat, 3 hyd., QR
4630	1976	8,193	G	$8,250	6/27/2012	Online	*PurpleWave.com,* item in Kansas, 6 cyl. diesel, QR
4630	1976		G	$9,150	5/19/2012	WCIL	Open station, ROPS, new attach, unknown hours, diesel, duals
4630	1976		G	$16,000	3/2/2012	WCMN	Diesel, Sound Guard cab, QR, comfort steps, good 20.8x38 tires, hub duals, 3 pt., 2 hyd., 400 hours on OH, approx. $9K in repairs in 2010
4630	1976	9,816	G	$13,250	2/25/2012	WCMI	PFWD, cab, heat, QR, 3 pt., PTO, 2 hyd., 18.4x38 rear duals, 10 front weights
4630	1976	5,975	G	$14,750	2/2/2012	NEIN	2WD, 18.4x38 rear tires, duals, QR, 2 hyd., quick hitch, 10 front weights, 14Lx16.1 front tires
4630	1976	8,100	G	$13,750	12/22/2011	Online	*IQBID.com,* cab, air, heat, 150 hp, 3 pt., PTO, 2 hyd., duals
4630	1976	1,152	G	$12,100	11/30/2011	Online	*PurpleWave.com,* item in Kansas, 6 cyl. diesel, PS, air, heat, spring ride seat, tilt wheel, AM/FM, 3 pt. quick attach, drawbar, 1,000 PTO
4630	1976	14,545	G	$8,500	8/3/2011	ECND	Cab, air, heat, 8 speed PS, 3 pt., quick hitch, 1,000 PTO, 3 hyd., 18.4x42 duals, air
4630	1976	6,184	G	$10,000	7/30/2011	ECMO	
4630	1976	4,995	G	$15,000	7/20/2011	NEND	Standard, QR, 3 hyd., front. fuel tank, hours on OH
4630	1976	12,473	G	$7,550	6/22/2011	Online	*BigIron.com,* item in Nebraska, QR, 6 cyl. diesel, 3 hyd., 1,000 PTO, 3 pt., inside rear wheel weights, front weight bracket
4630	1976	4,354	G	$6,500	6/8/2011	SWSK	2WD, 150 PTO hp, QR, 3 pt., dual hyd., snap on duals, attach cab, air, heat, OH approximately 2,500 hours

John Deere

Model	Year	Hours	Condition	Price	Date	Area	Comments
4630	1976	6,387	G	$8,750	5/25/2011	NECO	WF, diesel, front weights, quick hitch
4630	1976	10,610	F	$9,750	5/5/2011	SCKS	Diesel, QR, air, PTO, 3 pt.
4630	1976	9,666	G	$11,250	4/16/2011	SWMB	2WD, QR, dual hyd., new cab liner, rack and pinion rear tire adj., factory duals
4630	1976		G	$13,400	4/11/2011	Online	*AuctionTime.com*
4630	1976		G	$12,500	3/15/2011	WCIL	2 hyd., 1,000 PTO
4630	1976	2,715	F	$9,800	3/9/2011	Online	*BigIron.com,* item in Kansas, 8 speed PS, diesel, 2 hyd., small 1,000 PTO, quick hitch, dent in front, cast rims in rear
4630	1976	7,500	G	$9,500	12/17/2010	WCIL	Cab, synchro, 1,000 PTO, 2 hyd., 18.4x38 duals
4630	1976	6,902	G	$15,500	12/3/2010	NEMO	Fully equipped cab, air seat, QR, 18.4x38 rear tires and 10-bolt axle-mount duals, 11x16 front tires, 10 front weights, 3 hyd., 1,000 PTO, John Deere cast Cat. II/III quick hitch, SN 20550
4630	1976	8,155	G	$13,000	12/1/2010	ECND	QR, 3 hyd., 3 pt., PTO, rock box, 60 series step, aux. lights, 18.4x38 duals, 11Lx16 front tires
4630	1976		G	$12,500	3/15/2010	WCIL	2 hyd., 1,000 PTO
4630	1976		G	$12,000	3/10/2010	ECND	Cab, air, heat, QR, 2 hyd., 3 pt., quick hitch, 1,000 PTO, press steel duals
4630	1977	8,441	F	$9,300	7/9/2013	Online	*IQBID.com,* cab, air, heat, PS, 3 hyd., 3 pt., PTO
4630	1977	9,645	G	$8,500	6/5/2013	Online	*BigIron.com,* item in Nebraska, 16 speed QR, John Deere engine
4630	1977	44,688	F	$8,000	5/31/2013	NCOK	3 pt., PTO, 3 hyd., 150 hp, 20.8x38 duals
4630	1977	1,858	G	$13,750	2/12/2013	WCIL	
4630	1977	1,637	G	$7,500	12/6/2012	SEIA	PS, 3 hyd., 1,000 PTO, 20.8x38
4630	1977	7,678	G	$11,300	11/7/2012	SCNE	QR, 18.4x38 duals, rear and front weights, 3 hyd.
4630	1977	6,168	G	$17,000	1/19/2012	ECIL	QR, 18.4x38 snap on duals, 2 hyd., full front weights
4630	1977	4,400	G	$10,760	11/23/2011	Online	*BigIron.com,* item in Kansas, 2WD, QR 16F/6R, diesel, 160 hp, 2 hyd., single axle, 1,000 PTO, air
4630	1977	8,603	G	$15,500	11/22/2011	WCIL	One owner, QR, 10 front suitcase weights, 2 hyd., 1,000 PTO, quick hitch
4630	1977	9,919	G	$8,950	7/21/2011	Online	*IQBID.com,* QR, 3 hyd., 3 pt., 1,000 PTO, diff. lock
4630	1977	10,000	G	$8,500	5/4/2011	ECSK	2WD, QR, dual Pioneer hyd., single speed, PTO, 1,000 rpm, cab, air, duals, flotation front tires, 12V batteries
4630	1977	2,014	G	$8,000	4/27/2011	NECO	Diesel, WF, front weights, duals, quick hitch
4630	1977	4,611	G	$15,500	12/8/2010	NECO	WF, diesel, John Deere 725 loader and grapple
4630	1977	7,898	G	$10,900	8/11/2010	ECMN	Cab, air, heat, QR, 2 hyd., 3 pt., 1,000 PTO, John Deere quick hitch, Tilt-O-Matic rock box, cast hub duals, OH 3,000 hours ago
4630	1998		G	$12,000	4/14/2011	NCND	1998 Woods loader, grapple
4630		6,948	G	$11,500	4/4/2014	SEND	PS, 3 pt., PTO, rebuilt PTO

John Deere

Model	Year	Hours	Condition	Price	Date	Area	Comments
4630		8,239	G	$20,000	3/13/2014	SCID	8 speed PS, 2 hyd., 1,000 PTO, 3 pt., 18.4x38 rubber, duals
4630		6,365	G	$10,099	3/5/2014	Online	*BigIron.com,* item in Wyoming, 16 speed QR, 6 cyl., diesel, 150 hp, 3 hyd., 1,000 PTO, extra fuel tank
4630		674	G	$9,000	2/22/2014	SWAR	Cab, quick hitch
4630		1,384	G	$15,250	1/22/2014	Online	*BigIron.com,* item in Colorado, PS, 6 cyl., rear tires 18.4Rx42, 11x16 front tires, diesel, 1,000 PTO, hyd., quick attach loader, bucket, new fuel line
4630		6,900	G	$12,000	1/1/2014	SWOH	QR, cab, air, heat
4630			G	$8,000	12/20/2013	SCSD	Cab, air, PS, like new rubber
4630		4,500	G	$7,500	12/5/2013	SCIA	2WD, PS, front fuel cell, new starter
4630			G	$9,100	12/5/2013	SCIA	
4630		3,281	G	$7,500	12/4/2013	ECIN	20.8x38 and 11x16 tires, quick hitch, 2 hyd.
4630		377	G	$9,500	12/4/2013	ECIN	2WD, synchro, 18.4x42 and 11x16 tires, 2 hyd., 1,000 PTO
4630		5,249	G	$16,000	9/10/2013	ECND	Cab, air, heat, QR, PTO, 3 pt., 14.9x46 duals, 3 pt. arms, quick hitch
4630			G	$7,000	6/22/2013	SESC	4 post, duals
4630			G	$13,250	6/22/2013	SESC	Cab, 2 WD
4630		2,599	G	$17,350	5/15/2013	Online	*BigIron.com,* item in Nebraska, QR, 6 cyl.
4630		20,683	G	$7,850	4/10/2013	Online	*BigIron.com,* item in Kansas, QR, diesel, dual hyd., 3 pt. quick attach, 1,000 PTO, rear weights, dual hubs, no duals, headliner loose
4630			G	$9,500	3/2/2013	NCWI	4 wheel assist, PS, differential lock, 3 pt., 2 hyd., 20.8x38 tires
4630		4,600	G	$4,500	2/7/2013	SEAR	Diesel, open ROPS, PS, PTO
4630		7,535	G	$9,750	12/3/2012	WCIL	Fwd, QR, 20.8x38 tires and duals, 14.9x24 front tires
4630		2,648	G	$17,030	9/12/2012	Online	*IQBID.com,* item in North Dakota, QR, 3 hyd., 20.8x42 band duals, 14Lx16.1 fronts, 158 loader
4630		6,636	G	$10,500	8/22/2012	ECMN	PS, duals, 2 hyd., PTO, 3 pt., quick coupler, front light unit, 2 owner
4630		11,855	G	$9,000	8/8/2012	Online	*BigIron.com,* item in Colorado, PS, diesel, 3 hyd., 1,000 PTO, 3 pt., John Deere quick attach, 10 front wheel weights, tool box
4630			G	$8,500	8/4/2012	NEAR	6 cyl. diesel, synchro, cab, air, dual hyd., 3 pt., 1,000 PTO
4630			G	$5,400	7/28/2012	SWTN	4 post canopy duals, dual hyd., QR
4630			G	$8,000	7/27/2012	SWKY	Duals
4630			P	$4,700	6/20/2012	ECIL	Does not run, 2 hyd., 18.4x38 tires, PTO, no top link
4630		9,656	G	$9,600	6/20/2012	ECIL	QR, 3 hyd., 18.4x34 tires, 11x16 tires, quick hitch , 1 PTO
4630		8,606	G	$10,000	6/20/2012	ECIL	20.8x38R and 11x16F tires, QR, 3 hyd., 1 PTO, no top link
4630			F	$11,000	4/23/2012	WCSK	2WD, John Deere 158 front end loader, 150 hp PTO, PS, 3 pt., 2 hyd., 18.4x38 duals, bucket

John Deere

Model	Year	Hours	Condition	Price	Date	Area	Comments
4630			G	$11,000	3/24/2012	NEIN	HFWD, cab, QR, front weights, quick coupler, dual hyd., PTO, duals, runs
4630		9,608	G	$10,250	3/22/2012	ECMN	Cab, air, heat, PS, 2 hyd., 3 pt., 1,000 PTO, top link, duals
4630		6,000	G	$14,000	2/25/2012	NWFL	
4630			G	$6,250	2/4/2012	NENC	Diesel, synchro, cab, 2 dual hyd., 18.4Rx38 duals
4630			G	$6,600	2/4/2012	ECSC	Cab, duals
4630		6,194	G	$13,750	1/31/2012	NEIN	Synchro, 18.4x42 duals, 3 hyd.
4630			G	$10,500	1/28/2012	SEAB	
4630			G	$11,000	1/28/2012	ECMO	Cab, air, heat, 1,000 PTO, 2 hyd., 3 pt., duals
4630		13,690	G	$12,000	11/15/2011	ECND	QR, 3 hyd., 3 pt., PTO, front. weights, steel hub duals, cast insides
4630			F	$7,000	11/4/2011	SEWA	2WD, cab, air, 3 pt., PTO, 2 hyd., high hours, QR, 20.8x38 rear rubber
4630			F	$13,500	8/19/2011	NWIL	Duals
4630			G	$17,200	8/16/2011	Online	*BidNow.us,* LG 420x46 tires, 3 pt. quick hitch, 3 hyd.
4630			G	$10,250	7/30/2011	ECMO	
4630		7,500	G	$9,000	7/9/2011	ECND	QR, 3 pt., PTO, 18.4x42 duals
4630		2,069	G	$7,500	4/27/2011	Online	*BigIron.com,* item in Kansas, QR, diesel, 2 hyd., small 1,000 PTO, cast wheels, 8 suitcase weights, dent in front end, 3 pt., leak under dash
4630		10,080	G	$14,000	4/16/2011	WCSD	Koyker 565 loader, joystick
4630		8,332	G	$11,500	4/4/2011	ECSD	1,000 PTO, 3 pt.
4630		4,202	G	$8,100	3/18/2011	SWIL	QR, 2 hyd., 3 pt., front weights, duals, leaky seal on PTO
4630		8,300	G	$11,000	3/17/2011	ECMN	2WD, cab, air, heat, PS, 3 pt., 1,000 PTO, 3hyd.
4630		8,636	E	$15,000	3/10/2011	Online	*IQBID.com,* QR, 2 hyd., 3 pt., diff. lock, quick hitch, PTO,158 loader, very clean
4630		6,587	G	$12,500	2/28/2011	SCMI	2WD, 3 pt., PTO, dual hyd., WF, cab, heat and air
4630		5,589	G	$12,500	2/28/2011	SCMI	Cab, heat, 3 pt., PTO, WF, 3 hyd., 4WD, rear duals, 8 front weights, hyd. pump, new drive shaft and seals
4630			G	$9,000	1/29/2011	ECMO	2WD, cab, air, heat, duals and front weights, 3 hyd., 3 pt.
4630			G	$7,900	11/20/2010	NCLA	Cab, air, duals
4630			G	$7,500	11/18/2010	SEOK	John Deere 725 loader, forks, no bucket, duals
4630		10,000	G	$9,500	6/5/2010	NWIA	New clutch, 4,400 hours on OH, trans. work 1,000 hours ago
4630			F	$7,000	4/9/2010	NECO	Cab, 3hyd., weights, quick hitch, QR, hub duals
4630			G	$10,000	3/5/2010	NENE	2WD, QR, 1,600 hours on engine OH
4640	1978	7,108	G	$19,000	4/3/2014	NEIN	
4640	1978		P	$11,100	3/21/2014	ECIA	Duals, needs TLC
4640	1978	3,481	G	$16,000	3/4/2014	ECND	PS, 3 hyd., Power Beyond, 3 pt., quick hitch, 1,000 PTO, rock box, 14.9x46 press steel duals

John Deere

Model	Year	Hours	Condition	Price	Date	Area	Comments
4640	1978	3,647	E	$32,500	2/15/2014	SCKS	New rubber duals, quick hitch, 4 hyd., cab, air
4640	1978	6,187	E	$23,000	1/25/2014	NCOH	2WD, cab, air, heat, 3 hyd., rear weights, rear cast wheels, 8 front weights, block heater, quick coupler hammer strap, axle duals
4640	1978	6,363	G	$9,020	11/13/2013	Online	*PurpleWave.com,* item in Kansas, John Deere diesel, 155 hp, PS, diff. lock
4640	1978	9,280	G	$17,600	9/25/2013	Online	*PurpleWave.com,* item in Minnesota, John Deere 6 cyl. diesel, QR, air, heat, AM/FM, Kenwood 2-way radio, Raven GPS, 3 pt., drawbar
4640	1978	8,350	F	$15,500	7/24/2013	Online	*IQBID.com,* PS, 3hyd.
4640	1978	8,593	G	$12,000	4/22/2013	SWSK	2WD, 156 PTO hp, 8 speed, PS, big 1,000 PTO, diff. lock
4640	1978	5,044	G	$20,000	4/16/2012	NWOH	Cab, air, QR, no duals, weights or quick hitch
4640	1978	6,941	G	$23,000	2/6/2012	ECIL	Sound Guard cab, QR, 2 hyd., PTO, 3 pt., front weights, duals
4640	1978		F	$24,500	3/26/2011	NEIA	PS, new paint, complete OH, SN 4403, 18.4x42 axle mount duals, kind of rough
4640	1978	10,000	G	$14,000	8/6/2010	NWIL	Cab, 12 front suitcase weights, quick hitch, new front tires, duals
4640	1978	7,083	G	$27,250	1/6/2010	ECIL	2,000 hours on OH, cab, air, 3 hyd., quick hitch, weights, 18.4x38 tires, duals
4840	1978	7,915	G	$18,000	3/19/2014	Online	*BigIron.com,* item in Minnesota, PS
4840	1978	2,069	G	$17,000	8/30/2013	NCIA	PS
4840	1978		G	$10,000	7/25/2013	ECND	PS, cab, air, heat, 3 pt., quick hitch, PS, front weights, new hyd. pump
4840	1978	11,147	G	$17,500	12/27/2012	NCIA	SN P002428R, 3 hyd., 20.8x38 tires, duals, 1,000 PTO, 3 pt., quick hitch, diff. lock, 8 speed, PS, FR fuel tank, 10,000 hours on reman. engine
4840	1978	6,850	G	$13,000	8/27/2011	WCIL	Diesel, cab, PS, 1,000 PTO, 20.8x8 tires, duals, weights
4840	1978	6,726	G	$15,000	7/27/2011	Online	*BigIron.com,* item in Kansas, PS, diesel, 180 hp, 3 hyd., 1,000 PTO, OH at 6352 hours, quick hitch, shades
4840	1978		G	$14,500	3/25/2011	SCWA	Cab and duals
4840	1978		G	$14,500	3/25/2011	SCWA	Cab, duals
4840	1978	5,696	G	$26,000	3/24/2011	ECMT	PS, 3 pt., 2 hyd., PTO, duals, 180 hp
4840	1978	9,100	G	$13,000	8/11/2010	ECMN	50 series motor, PS, 2 hyd., 1,000 PTO, duals, 10 bolt hubs
4840	1978		F	$13,000	2/11/2010	NENC	Very good tires, duals, quick hitch, clean
5010	1963	6,800	G	$4,200	3/23/2012	WCNE	Diesel, 24.5x32 rubber 20%, fenders, 2 hyd., 1,000 PTO, SN 5010 32T1521
5010	1963		G	$25,000	6/18/2011	SWMN	SN 3236, front weights, new tires, dust shields, 2 hyd., PTO, repainted
5010	1967	5,400	E	$8,250	10/24/2012	NECO	Diesel, WF, PTO, Wheatland
5010		995	G	$4,500	4/11/2013	SEID	2WD, 105 hp, cab, synchro, drawbar, 2 hyd., 24.5x32 on cast wheels, inside rear wheel weights
5010			G	$9,500	3/24/2012	NEIN	Repainted, 3 pt., dual hyd., PTO, runs

John Deere

Model	Year	Hours	Condition	Price	Date	Area	Comments
5010			G	$10,000	3/24/2012	NEIN	Standard, dust shields, fenders, 32" tires, dual hyd., PTO, straight, original, runs
5010			G	$5,600	8/14/2010	WCMN	New rubber, WF, dual hyd., 3 pt., PTO
5010			F	$3,500	5/26/2010	ECSD	Wheatland, runs
5020	1966		G	$5,250	9/21/2013	WCMI	Diesel, 3 pt., PTO, 2 hyd., 18.4x38 rear tires, restored
5020	1967		G	$7,000	8/20/2013	WCIL	2 hyd., quick hitch, 1,000 PTO, 18.4Rx38 rear tires, axle mount duals, 1,160 hours on OH
5020	1967	8,675	G	$9,200	7/10/2013	NCIA	Cab, WF, 3 pt., quick hitch
5020	1967	4,550	E	$17,250	8/25/2012	NEIA	Row crop, open station, 18.4x38 tires and axle duals, 3 pt., synchro, original condition, flat top fender
5020	1967		G	$4,725	8/8/2012	Online	*BigIron.com,* item in Kansas, synchro, diesel, small 1,000 PTO, 2WD, dual hyd., standard 3 pt., standard hyd. system
5020	1967	7,421	F	$3,150	6/22/2011	Online	*BigIron.com,* item in Nebraska, Wheatland, synchro, 6 cyl. diesel, 2 hyd., 1,000 PTO, swinging drawbar, inside and outside wheel weights, engine bad
5020	1967		G	$11,250	4/1/2011	Online	*AuctionTime.com,* item in Nebraska, parade ready, completely repainted, OH 50 hours ago, rear end has been done
5020	1967	5,282	G	$20,100	2/25/2011	ECIL	New 24.5x32 tires, $7K OH
5020	1967	4,319	G	$4,070	5/26/2010	Online	*PurpleWave.com,* item in Kansas, John Deere 6 cyl. 141 hp diesel, 1,000 PTO
5020	1968		G	$7,500	3/8/2014	NWLA	Canopy, dual hyd., nice
5020	1968	6,890	F	$6,900	6/20/2012	SESD	Diesel, Western cab, 3 pt., category 3, Western front, axle mounted cart duals
5020	1968	3,124	G	$9,000	3/13/2010	WCIL	18.4x38 and 14.1x16.1 tires
5020	1969	296	G	$3,550	7/17/2013	Online	*BigIron.com,* item in Oklahoma, 2WD, 8 speed synchro, John Deere engine
5020	1969		G	$3,800	12/15/2011	Online	*IQBID.com,* cab, synchro, 2 hyd., PTO, 3 pt., front weight, 20.8x38 rears
5020	1970	6,995	G	$7,900	8/11/2011	WCMN	Diesel, row crop, 2 hyd., 3 pt., PTO, factory 12V, quick hitch
5020	1970	6,602	G	$3,750	3/16/2011	ECSD	Open station, synchro, 2 hyd., no 3 pt., PTO
5020	1971	7,628	G	$9,100	7/14/2012	SWMN	18.4x38 rear tires, duals, 2 hyd., rock box
5020			G	$9,600	3/8/2014	NWWI	Diesel, open station, 619 John Deere motor, motor has 2,161 hours and dynos at 280 hp, SN T313R,0268922, ROPS, Speeco Cat 3 quick hitch, pioneer hyd., 20.8x38 hub duals, was Mennonite tractor on steel, shifted hard
5020		1,133	G	$8,450	12/4/2013	ECIN	18.4x38 and 11x15 tires, quick hitch, 2 hyd.
5020		6,164	G	$3,750	6/12/2013	Online	*BigIron.com,* item in Nebraska, 2WD, 8 speed, 6 cyl.
5020			G	$7,500	3/23/2013	NEIN	PTO, dual hyd., nice original, 24.5x32 tires, runs

John Deere

Model	Year	Hours	Condition	Price	Date	Area	Comments
5020			G	$10,000	3/23/2013	NEIN	Dual hyd., PTO, rear weights, 18.4R38 duals, original, runs
5020			G	$7,100	2/7/2013	NEIN	24.5x32 tires, 2 hyd., 2WD
5020			G	$7,100	2/7/2013	NEIN	Cab
5020			G	$6,000	6/2/2012	SEMN	Diesel, Wheatland, 20.8x34 duals, synchro, 1,000 PTO, cab, 2 hyd.
5020		5,367	G	$4,400	2/1/2012	SEND	3 pt., PTO
5020			G	$4,500	1/29/2011	ECMO	18.4x38 duals, axle mount duals, top link
5020			P	$1,600	1/15/2011	ECAR	
5020			G	$4,000	12/18/2010	ECMI	Duals
5020			G	$8,100	8/14/2010	WCMN	3 pt., 2 hyd., PTO, 24.5x32 tires
5020		5,616	G	$10,300	8/14/2010	WCMN	Diesel, heavy offset cast duals, 3 pt., PTO, 2 hyd., row crop special, major out of frame OH, new clutch, WF
5020			F	$2,500	7/17/2010	NEMT	Needs work
5020			F	$4,000	5/26/2010	ECSD	Wheatland, runs
5020			G	$10,300	2/13/2010	SWIA	
6030	1972	9,600	G	$16,500	12/22/2011	Online	*IQBID.com,* factory cab, air, heat, 3 pt., PTO, quick hitch, K&M rock box, new turbo and exhaust manifold, rear wheel weights
6030	1972		E	$25,000	11/13/2010	NCIA	Factory open station, restored 2009
6030	1973		E	$31,000	8/10/2013	NCIA	SN 0334175, factory open station, cover, restored
6030	1973		G	$17,000	3/7/2012	SEIA	Factory cab, synchro, 540 PTO, rear weights, original
6030	1973		G	$17,000	6/18/2011	SWMN	SN 34448, 38" duals, front weights, ROPS, fenders, quick coupler, 2 hyd.
6030	1975		E	$40,000	11/13/2010	NCIA	Restored, factory open station, a beauty
6030	1975	9,600	F	$10,500	4/17/2010	ECNE	Row crop, ROPS, cab, air, diff. lock, 3 pt., 2 hyd., inner rear weights, duals
6030	1976	9,000	G	$17,500	7/31/2013	ECND	200 hp, synchro, cab, air, heat, 2 hyd., 3 pt., 1,000 PTO
6030	1976		G	$13,300	12/5/2012	Online	*AuctionTime.com,* item in Illinois, 2WD, cab
6030	1977	5,703	F	$24,000	4/5/2013	WCIL	Cab, weights, 20.8x38 rear tires and duals, 14Lx16.1SL front tires, 2 hyd., 1,000 PTO, 3 pt., may have shifting problems, SN B313R036643R
6030		4,816	G	$17,500	7/9/2011	ECND	20.8 hub duals, second owner
6030			G	$17,000	4/2/2011	ECMN	Cab
6030			G	$9,200	1/29/2011	ECMO	Sound Guard cab, cold air
6030			G	$9,250	9/4/2010	NEIN	3 pt., dual hyd.
6030		3,690	G	$17,500	1/12/2010	WCIL	Cab, new 20.8Rx38, original 14Lx16 front tires, 3 hyd., quick hitch, very nice straight original collector quality
7020	1973	5,222	F	$3,000	12/4/2010	SEWY	3 pt., diesel, PTO, 12' Degelman dozer
7020	1974	9,838	G	$4,250	4/2/2013	ECIA	5 speed Hi/Lo 3 pt., quick attach, 540/1,000 PTO, clamp on duals, OH
7020	1979	10,124	G	$9,250	6/21/2012	ECND	Cab, air, heat, 2WD, PS, 3 pt., 540/1,000 PTO, 3 hyd., front weights, 14.9x46 duals, one owner

John Deere

Model	Year	Hours	Condition	Price	Date	Area	Comments
7020			G	$15,000	9/4/2010	NEIN	
7020			P	$1,100	3/16/2010	SEND	4WD, needs work, jobber 3 pt., synchro
7520	1973		G	$12,250	9/21/2013	WCMI	Articulated, diesel, cab, 3 pt., PTO, 3 hyd., 18.4x34 duals all the way around, restored
7520	1973	6,958	E	$38,000	3/28/2013	ECOH	4WD, 18.4x34 duals, 3 pt., PTO, 2 hyd., OH
7520	1973	10,190	F	$8,250	3/14/2012	ECND	Cab, air, heat, 3 hyd., 1,000 PTO, hub duals, two new major OH at 7,000 hours
7520	1973	7,558	F	$9,000	3/7/2012	SEIA	4WD, axle mount duals, 2 hyd., 1,000 PTO, 3 pt.
7520	1973	8,604	G	$18,500	12/10/2011	SEMN	4WD, 18.4x38 duals all around, 2 hyd., 3 pt., 1,000 PTO, R134 air, very clean, SN 003037R, OH at 5,000 hours
7520	1973	7,499	G	$11,200	11/4/2010	NEKS	4WD, diesel, synchro, OD, 18.4x34 tires, hub mount duals, 2 hyd., 1,000 PTO, 3 pt., quick hitch, 1,500 hours on new engine, clutch and ring gear
7520	1974	5,695	G	$10,000	6/13/2013	SEAB	4WD, 175 PTO hp diesel, 8F/2R synchro, 2 hyd., 1,000 PTO, 18.4x34 duals
7520	1974	6,300	G	$13,000	8/28/2010	WCIL	4WD, PTO, 3 pt., 18.4x34 tires excellent, 800 hours on OH
7520	1975		G	$4,000	6/26/2013	Online	*BigIron.com,* item in Kansas, 4x4, 16 speed manual, 6 cyl. diesel, 3 hyd. blade
7520	1976	7,350	G	$8,700	12/31/2010	SWOH	4WD, 18.4x34 tires
7520			G	$12,250	3/23/2013	NEIN	4WD, original, duals, 3 hyd., 3 pt., quick coupler, PTO, runs
7520		9,048	G	$5,060	5/30/2012	Online	*PurpleWave.com,* item in Kansas, 6 cyl. diesel, synchro, AM/FM, PTO always runs, 3 hyd.
7520		6,550	G	$7,500	3/26/2011	SEIL	4WD, 25 hours on total service, tires 95%, good paint
7520		3,463	G	$6,500	2/28/2011	SCMI	Articulated, 4WD, 3 pt., cab, heat, 3 hyd.
7520		4,700	G	$8,100	8/14/2010	WCMN	4WD, 20.8x34 duals, new inside tires, 3 pt., PTO, 3hyd., John Deere ROPS cab, original paint
7520			F	$4,750	3/31/2010	ECND	4WD, cab, air, heat, PTO, 3hyd., 18.4-x8 duals
8020	1964		G	$90,000	10/2/2010	SESK	4WD, detroit diesel, 3 hyd., 18.4x34 duals, 23.1x26 single original tires and rims, SN 62T 1014 so 14th of only 100 made
8430	1975	1,000	G	$16,000	11/6/2010	SEMN	4WD, 50 series, 3 pt., PTO, 2 hyd., 18.4x34 duals, SN 001209R
8430	1975		G	$20,200	3/20/2010	NEIA	4WD, 3 pt., PTO
8430	1976	8,159	G	$10,100	8/15/2013	ECMN	4WD, cab, air, heat
8430	1976	7,180	G	$6,000	3/20/2013	NCOK	8440 update, new air, 2 new tires 18.4x38, PTO
8430	1976	9,000	G	$9,000	7/27/2011	ECND	3 hyd., 3 pt., quick hitch, PTO
8430	1976	7,000	G	$14,000	1/29/2011	ECMO	MFWD, cab, air, heat
8430	1977	5,850	G	$8,100	12/6/2013	NWIA	4WD, 3 pt., PTO, 3 hyd., 50 Series motor, 20.8x34 rubber

John Deere

Model	Year	Hours	Condition	Price	Date	Area	Comments
8430	1977	6,370	G	$18,600	5/4/2013	WCSD	4WD, 178 hp, 466 cu. in. turbo diesel, 16F/4R, cab, air, heat, radio, 3 hyd., PTO, 3 pt. quick hitch, 18.4x38 duals all around, SN D43011004402R, mtd. John Deere 12' hyd. lift blade
8430	1977	5,077	G	$15,500	2/6/2013	NEIL	4WD, 3 pt., PTO, 3 hyd., 18.4x38 rear tires, axle duals, 12' blade, John Deere 8440 updated engine put in at 2,200 hours, rebuilt fuel injection pump, air converted to R134A, head manafluxed, heads and valves reground, SN 005132R
8430	1977	7,895	G	$1,910	7/11/2012	Online	*BigIron.com,* item in Nebraska, diesel, 3 hyd., 1,000 PTO, 3 pt., trans out
8430	1977	9,100	G	$9,750	4/23/2012	WCSK	4WD, QR, 100 PTO, 18.4-38 duals
8430	1978	11,760	G	$10,500	11/7/2013	NEND	4WD, complete new 50 series, QR, 1,000 PTO, 3 hyd., Raven Quick Trax auto guidance
8430	1978	7,264	G	$20,000	6/27/2013	SWSK	4WD, 250 PTO hp, QR, 18.4x38 factory duals, PTO, 3 hyd.
8430	1978	9,274	G	$12,250	5/1/2013	Online	*BigIron.com,* item in Iowa, QR, 16F/4R
8430	1978	6,307	G	$8,600	8/8/2012	Online	*IQBID.com,* item in North Dakota, 4WD, cab, air, heat, 16 speed, 3 hyd., no 3 pt., PTO, 95% rubber, new batteries, new hour meter shows 369 hours
8430	1978	6,921	G	$7,900	7/11/2012	Online	*BigIron.com,* item in Wyoming, 4WD, QR 16F/4R, 6 cyl. diesel, 178 hp, 3 hyd., tandem axle
8430	1978	1,341	G	$18,000	2/7/2012	SEIA	4WD, PTO, 3 pt., duals
8430	1978	5,865	G	$21,500	3/3/2011	ECMI	4WD, cab, air, heat, QR, 2 hyd., 3 pt., 1,000 PTO, 40 series, 18.4x38 duals 90%, diesel
8430	1978	5,865	G	$21,500	3/3/2011	WCMI	4WD, cab, air, heat, QR, 2 hyd., 3 pt., 1,000 PTO, 40 series, duals
8430	1978		G	$14,300	9/3/2010	SCMN	4WD, cab, air, heat, QR, 3hyd., PTO, quick hitch, rock box, hub duals 75%
8430		7,898	G	$16,000	4/10/2014	SWSK	4WD, 200 PTO hp, QR, 1,000 PTO, 3 hyd.
8430			G	$7,200	3/1/2014	SEMN	1,000 PTO, 3 pt., 3 hyd.
8430		6,096	G	$10,000	8/20/2013	WCIL	4WD, 2 hyd., 3 pt., 1,000 PTO, 18.4Rx38 tires, axle mount duals
8430		6,425	G	$18,000	2/23/2013	NCIL	4WD, 50 series, 3 pt., 3 hyd.
8430			G	$14,250	2/7/2013	NEIN	4WD
8430		9,098	G	$14,250	2/7/2013	NEIN	4WD, QR, 18.4x34, bolt on duals, 4 hyd., quick hitch, hammer strap
8430		8,500	G	$14,800	2/1/2013	Online	*IQBID.com,* 50 series, SN 5298R
8430			G	$16,000	12/14/2012	SWKY	4WD, 3 pt., PTO
8430		275	F	$9,500	8/16/2012	Online	*IQBID.com,* item in Minnesota, 4WD, cab, air, heat, 50 series, 2 hyd., 3 pt., LG 1,000 PTO, quick hitch, 18.4x34 tires, hub duals
8430		9,970	G	$8,500	4/23/2012	WCSK	4WD, QR, 1,000 PTO, 3 hyd., 18.4x38 duals
8430		8,827	G	$9,500	3/22/2012	ECMN	Cab, air, heat, 50 series at 6,000 hours, 3 pt., PTO, duals
8430		6,800	G	$12,250	7/21/2011	WCIL	4WD, 3 pt., 50 series, 3 hyd.

John Deere

Model	Year	Hours	Condition	Price	Date	Area	Comments
8430		8,500	G	$9,750	3/25/2011	ECWI	Cab, air, heat, QR, 3 pt., PTO
8430		4,909	G	$10,000	11/27/2010	SEMN	4WD QR, 3 pt., quick hitch, PTO, dual hyd., 18.4x34 duals
8430		7,108	F	$8,500	11/26/2010	WCOH	4WD, 3 pt., PTO, axle duals
8430		3,925	G	$7,750	8/26/2010	SCNE	4WD, QR, 2 hyd., duals, PTO, 3 pt.
8430		7,584	G	$10,000	3/6/2010	SEMN	4WD, 3 pt., PTO, 3 hyd., 18.4x38 rear tires
8630	1974	9,400	G	$7,550	9/12/2012	Online	*IQBID.com,* item in North Dakota, 16 speed, 3 hyd., PTO, 24.5 duals, new hyd. pump, 30 series motor, 2300 hours on OH
8630	1975	10,318	G	$4,750	11/26/2013	ECND	4WD, cab, air, heat, QR, 1,000 PTO, 3 hyd., John Deere factory front hyd. dozer, duals
8630	1975	581	G	$10,340	3/27/2013	Online	*PurpleWave.com,* item in Kansas, 4WD, John Deere 6 cyl. diesel, QR PS
8630	1975	2,345	G	$10,000	8/16/2012	Online	*IQBID.com,* item in Minnesota, cab, air, heat, QR, 3 hyd., 3 pt., PTO, quick hitch, 18.4x34 tires, 95% rubber
8630	1975	6,200	G	$8,250	7/22/2010	ECND	3 hyd., 1,000 PTO, 50 series, duals
8630	1976	10,309	G	$10,230	3/27/2013	Online	*PurpleWave.com,* item in Kansas, John Deere 6 cyl. diesel, QR, diff. lock, 4WD
8630	1976	6,801	G	$19,500	4/11/2012	SEAB	4WD, 226 PTO hp, 290 hp, QR, 3 hyd., PTO, duals
8630	1976	5,900	F	$13,000	3/7/2012	SEIA	4WD, fully equipped cab, synchro, 3hyd., big 1,000 PTO, 3 pt., recent engine work and new clutch
8630	1976	4,620	G	$8,000	1/28/2012	ECMO	3 pt., PTO
8630	1976	6,629	G	$19,000	11/9/2011	Online	*BigIron.com,* item in Montana, articulated 4WD, QR, 16F, 50 series, 6 cyl. diesel, 225 hp, 3 hyd., 1,000 PTO, extra lights
8630	1976	9,900	F	$11,500	1/29/2011	ECMO	Cab, air, heat, 4x4, quick hitch
8630	1976	8,116	G	$17,750	1/29/2011	ECMO	4WD, cab, air, heat, QR
8630	1976	7,557	G	$24,000	12/3/2010	NEMO	4WD, fully equipped cab, 18.4Rx38 inside tires new, duals, 3 hyd., 3 pt., PTO, John Deere cast Cat. II/III quick hitch, SN 8630H004426R
8630	1976	7,491	G	$11,200	11/23/2010	NEKS	4WD, 18.4x38 duals good, 3 pt., large 1,000 PTO
8630	1977	7,579	G	$6,100	6/26/2013	Online	*BigIron.com,* item in Oklahoma, QR, John Deere 6 cyl., diesel, 225 PTO hp, 3 hyd., drawbar, LG PTO 1,000, 3 pt. no lift arms
8630	1977	7,946	G	$8,690	4/25/2012	Online	*PurpleWave.com,* item in Kansas, 4WD, 6 cyl. diesel, replacement engine, QR partial PS, 16F/4R gears, tilt, AM/FM, 3 pt., drawbar
8630	1977	6,312	F	$5,600	6/22/2011	NECO	Diesel, 4x4 duals, 3 pt., 3 hyd., needs work
8630	1977	6,399	G	$15,500	8/31/2010	WCIL	4WD, 20.8x34 tires and duals, cast iron wheels, updated 50 series motor, 3 pt., 1,000 PTO, 3 hyd., opt. air seat

John Deere

Model	Year	Hours	Condition	Price	Date	Area	Comments
8630	1977		F	$3,000	8/11/2010	ECMN	4WD, 16 speed, 50 series, 3 pt., PTO, hub duals, engine issues
8630	1978	7,012	G	$27,000	8/17/2013	SCKY	4WD, 12' front dozer blade, 3 hyd., 3 pt., PTO, 20.8x38 axle duals
8630	1978	9,357	G	$13,000	4/24/2013	Online	*BigIron.com,* item in South Dakota, 16 speed QR, 4WD, articulated
8630	1978	9,438	G	$10,002	4/3/2013	Online	*BigIron.com,* item in Nebraska, 4WD, synchro, John Deere 6 cyl. diesel, 275 hp, 18.4Rx38 tires, 3 hyd., 1,000 PTO, 3 pt.
8630	1978	4,015	G	$13,000	3/28/2013	NEIA	4WD, 3 pt., PTO
8630	1978	8,317	F	$19,000	4/24/2012	SESK	4WD, 275 hp, QR, 1,000 PTO, 20.8x38 duals, 3 hyd.
8630	1978		G	$15,250	3/20/2012	WCIL	4WD
8630	1978	7,610	F	$17,000	12/29/2011	WCIL	4WD, 3 pt., 1,000 PTO, good 20.8x38 hub duals, average cab interior, average paint
8630	1978	7,005	G	$18,500	12/29/2011	WCIL	4WD, 3 pt., 1,000 PTO, poor 20.8x38 hub duals, recent trans. rebuild, 2 hyd., good paint
8630	1978	6,947	G	$16,000	11/17/2010	WCKS	4WD, 3 pt., 4,213 hours on 50 series motor
8630		681	G	$92,250	4/3/2014	NEIN	18.4x38 duals, 3 pt., quick hitch, 3 hyd., QR
8630			G	$6,250	1/4/2014	WCNY	Front blade
8630			G	$5,500	12/19/2013	SCNY	Articulated, duals, 3 pt., PTO
8630		11,090	G	$5,550	12/18/2013	Online	*BigIron.com,* QR 16 speed, 3 hyd., 3 pt., drawbar
8630		7,537	G	$7,600	12/18/2013	Online	*BigIron.com,* 16 speed QR, 6 cyl. diesel, 1,000 PTO, 3 hyd., 3 pt. missing top link
8630		8,091	G	$10,450	12/18/2013	Online	*BigIron.com,* QR, 3 hyd. hyd., 3 pt., drawbar, 14' push blade, hyd. lift, glass intact
8630			G	$9,680	12/16/2013	NWWI	3 pt., PTO, 3 hyd.
8630		8,823	G	$8,200	12/11/2013	Online	*BigIron.com,* item in Nebraska, 50 series, 18.4-38 tires, 3 hyd., 3 pt., quick hitch, John Deere dozer, starts, QR
8630		5,630	G	$9,240	8/26/2013	NWWI	Duals, 3 pt., PTO
8630			G	$12,650	4/23/2013	Online	*HansenandYoung.com,* recent OH
8630		7,000	G	$20,000	3/9/2013	WCPA	4WD, articulated, cab, QR, 20.8x38 duals all around, 3 hyd., 3 pt., PTO, clean
8630			F	$8,100	5/8/2012	Online	*IQBID.com,* 4WD, 50 series, 3 hyd., PTO, 14.9x46 tires, set up at 120" for sprayer, Outback steering valve
8630			G	$6,750	2/4/2012	ECSC	
8630			G	$13,000	1/27/2012	SEAL	MFWD
8630		2,800	G	$36,000	11/19/2011	NCIA	4WD, Kinze Repower, 855 Cummins engine, duals
8630		9,000	F	$10,000	3/16/2011	NWIA	4WD, not shedded, tires poor
8630		7,463	F	$15,000	2/28/2011	SCMI	Articulated, 3 pt., PTO, 3 hyd., shaft broken on PTO, duals

Model	Year	Hours	Condition	Price	Date	Area	Comments
8630		3,080	G	$6,300	11/27/2010	SEMN	4WD QR, 3 pt., PTO, 3 hyd., 18.4x38, duals, quick hitch
A	1934		F	$2,500	11/20/2010	ECFL	Open shaft, unstyled
A	1935		G	$3,750	6/30/2012	NEIA	Brass tag, oil pressure pin, unstyled
A	1935		G	$6,300	8/24/2011	ECMN	Early '35, NF, PTO, open fan, on round spoke, front and rear, new 12.4x36 rubber
A	1935		G	$3,600	11/20/2010	NCKY	On original rubber, old restoration
A	1935		F	$2,000	6/5/2010	ECMN	Gas, NF, brass tag, brass carburetor
A	1936		G	$2,600	12/19/2013	WCMN	Gas, NF, GP, restored
A	1936		G	$3,750	9/21/2013	SEMN	Factory round spokes, like new tires
A	1936		G	$1,100	9/12/2013	SEIA	NF, unstyled, oversized piston, new radiator core, cast rear wheels
A	1936		E	$3,750	8/10/2013	NCIA	SN 437181
A	1936		G	$1,150	3/7/2013	ECIA	Unstyled, spoke front
A	1936		F	$1,100	8/25/2012	NWIL	Gas, cutoff rears and fronts
A	1936		G	$12,000	8/25/2012	NWIL	Gas, unstyled, new tires, 2R John Deere #25 picker
A	1936		G	$1,250	6/30/2012	NEIA	Unstyled
A	1936		G	$6,000	6/13/2012	Online	*BigIron.com,* item in Wyoming, 2 speed Hi/Lo, gas, 11.2x36 rear tires, 9.00x10 front tires, 540 PTO, SF, unstyled
A	1936		G	$2,000	5/28/2012	ECMO	Unstyled, spoke wheels
A	1936		G	$2,400	5/19/2012	SWMI	NF, 13.6x38 tires, fenders, unstyled
A	1936		G	$1,750	9/1/2011	WCMN	NF, rubber on round spokes, older restoration
A	1936		G	$2,000	6/22/2011	Online	*BigIron.com,* item in Colorado, gas, 50" rear tires, 24" front tires, restored, magneto was removed, 540 PTO, 2 pt. lift, drawbar, hand clutch
A	1936		G	$4,500	7/10/2010	ECOK	Unstyled, original round spoke rear and front
A	1937		G	$3,200	11/16/2013	SCVA	GP, 2 cyl. gas, 540 PTO, partially restored, like new
A	1937		G	$2,750	9/21/2013	WCMI	Gas, PTO, hand start, unstyled, loop drawbar, 13.6x38 rear tires, restored
A	1937		G	$1,815	8/14/2012	Online	*PurpleWave.com,* item in Kansas, gas, manual, 540 PTO, drawbar, 11x36 rears, 5.50x16 fronts, tires work and cracked
A	1937		G	$3,600	6/13/2012	Online	*BigIron.com,* item in Wyoming, 2 speed Hi/Lo, gas, 11.2x36 rear tires, 9x10 front tires, 1 hyd., 540 PTO, 3 pt., SF, unstyled
A	1937		G	$1,900	2/25/2012	WCMI	Unstyled, working shutters, restored
A	1937		G	$3,600	10/29/2011	NCNC	Rebuilt carburetor
A	1937		G	$2,400	10/12/2011	NWOH	SN 455682, NF, hand start, unstyled, rebuilt mag, new radiator core, recent head work, excellent tires
A	1937		P	$1,450	8/6/2011	NCIA	Spokes, rough
A	1937		G	$1,350	6/22/2011	NECO	Gas
A	1937		F	$2,000	2/21/2011	WCIL	Gas, unstyled
A	1937		G	$850	11/20/2010	ECFL	Unstyled, round spoke rear wheels, restorable, runs, PTO

John Deere

Model	Year	Hours	Condition	Price	Date	Area	Comments
A	1937		G	$1,050	6/5/2010	ECMI	NF
A	1938		G	$3,400	6/13/2012	Online	*BigIron.com,* item in Wyoming, 2 speed Hi/Lo, gas, 11.2x36 rear tires, 9x10 front tires, 1 hyd., 540 PTO, 3 pt., drawbar, unstyled
A	1938		G	$1,700	6/25/2011	ECIA	Unstyled, SN 447149, rear round spokes, older repaint
A	1938		G	$2,500	11/16/2010	ECNE	Unstyled, NF, 11x38 rear tires, splined axles, shop-built spoke wheels, Behlen road gear
A	1939		F	$900	6/23/2010	Online	*BigIron.com,* item in Nebraska, narrow front end, 5.5x16 spoked wheels, rear steel skeleton wheels, parade ready rubber, Behlen OD, belt pulley
A	1939		G	$850	6/5/2010	ECMI	1938 unstyled converted to 1939 styled, 1 of 472
A	1941		G	$1,100	9/12/2013	SEIA	NF, 540 PTO, 11.2x30 rears, hand start, styled, 6 speed
A	1941		F	$1,700	5/31/2013	NCOK	New rubber front
A	1941		G	$3,750	11/24/2012	SEMN	WF, fenders, 6 speed, starter, slant dash, new tires, painted
A	1941		G	$1,800	8/4/2012	ECMN	New rubber, completely restored
A	1942		G	$2,750	6/22/2013	SEWA	NF, 2 cyl., gas, hand flywheel start, PTO, right side belt drive, SN 560461
A	1943		G	$3,100	4/7/2012	NWMI	Gas, restored, NF, Roll-O-Matic, PTO drawbar hitch
A	1944		G	$2,000	7/9/2013	Online	*IQBID.com,* restored, NF, electrical start, 12V PTO
A	1944		G	$1,100	12/6/2012	SEIA	Completely restored 1 year ago
A	1944		G	$1,100	12/6/2012	Online	*IQBID.com*
A	1944		F	$1,000	1/17/2012	SCKS	Styled
A	1944		G	$2,200	6/25/2011	ECIA	Styled, SN 530847, new tires, hand start, repainted
A	1945		G	$4,100	9/9/2011	ECND	WF, fenders, electric start, PTO, new 13.6x38 tires, restored, runs
A	1945		G	$1,200	5/1/2010	NCOH	Electric start, runs well, older restoration
A	1946		F	$880	3/27/2013	Online	*PurpleWave.com,* item in Kansas, John Deere 2 cyl. gas, manual
A	1946		F	$850	9/22/2010	NECO	Double front, gas
A	1946		G	$2,900	7/10/2010	ECOK	
A	1946		G	$3,750	1/2/2010	NWOH	Gas, row crop, new front tires, restored
A	1947		F	$1,550	11/19/2013	WCMI	2 cyl., gas, NF, electric start, 12V system, hyd. 3 pt., PTO, 13x38 rear tires
A	1947		G	$2,350	4/14/2012	NEIA	Real good 12.4x38 rear tires, excellent paint, SN 592726, major OH in 2007
A	1947		G	$900	6/5/2010	ECMI	3 pt.
A	1947		G	$900	6/5/2010	ECMI	OH, long hood
A	1947		G	$935	2/24/2010	Online	*PurpleWave.com,* item in Iowa, PTO, drawbar
A	1948		G	$1,200	9/15/2012	SCMN	Power steering, NF, front wheel weights, 3 pt.
A	1948		G	$1,850	9/9/2011	ECND	Factory WF, electric start, 1 hyd., PTO, rock shaft, runs

John Deere

Model	Year	Hours	Condition	Price	Date	Area	Comments
A	1948		G	$1,300	3/26/2011	SEWI	Rare 3 pt., new paint, power steering, good tires, good SN tag
A	1948		G	$3,000	9/4/2010	SEVA	2 cyl., gas, all original
A	1948		G	$800	7/10/2010	SEIA	Cast rear wheels, 12V, Roll-O-Matic
A	1948		G	$2,750	7/10/2010	ECOK	Fenders
A	1948		G	$1,125	6/23/2010	Online	*BigIron.com,* item in Nebraska, 6 speed Hi/Lo, gas, 540 PTO, restored, all tinwork including wheels sanded and primed prior to being spray painted, has 12v electrical system
A	1948		G	$1,750	2/20/2010	NCIL	Pressed frame, NF, runs, mounted 10"x24' grain flat storage auger, gas
A	1949		G	$2,900	3/24/2012	SEOH	Styled
A	1949		F	$1,050	10/7/2011	NWSD	NF, hyd., PTO, bell mount Woods mower, straight sheet metal, good runner, easy restoration
A	1949		F	$800	7/27/2011	Online	*BigIron.com,* item in Nebraska, 2 speed, 4 gear, gas, seat needs new cushions, lights front and back, right rear tire is no good, flat now
A	1949		G	$1,200	4/11/2011	Online	*AuctionTime.com*
A	1949		G	$4,500	10/23/2010	SCPA	
A	1949		G	$2,800	9/19/2010	NEPA	Very good, PTO
A	1949		G	$875	6/23/2010	Online	*BigIron.com,* item in Nebraska, cable controlled factory John Deere dozer blade, ran when parked
A	1949		G	$1,450	6/23/2010	Online	*BigIron.com,* item in Oklahoma, 6F/1R, 2 cyl. gas, rear tires 12.4x38, front tires 5.5x16, 1 hyd., 540 PTO, all new tires, totally restored
A	1949		G	$2,200	4/24/2010	SEMN	Newer tires, Roll-A-Matic, Powr Trol, John Deere 45 trip bucket loader
A	1950		G	$2,500	9/21/2013	WCMI	Gas, PTO, electric start, 14.9x38 rear tires, restored
A	1950		G	$2,300	9/12/2013	SEIA	
A	1950		G	$2,000	7/25/2013	WCSK	2WD, 38 belt hp gas, square fenders, WF axle, 14.9x26 rubber, electric start, new battery, PTO, 1 hyd., John Deere hyd. ram included, 2 cyl. club letter, running
A	1950		E	$2,000	3/16/2013	NEIL	Original John Deere live hyd. pump
A	1950		G	$1,300	11/30/2011	SEMN	Good rubber, NF
A	1950		F	$2,600	11/12/2011	NEIA	Electric start, rear wheel weights, did not run
A	1950		G	$1,700	3/19/2011	ECIA	New tires
A	1950		F	$1,000	10/23/2010	ECMO	Styled, SN 654039, does not run
A	1950		F	$800	9/22/2010	NECO	SF, gas
A	1951		G	$1,600	12/26/2013	Online	*BigIron.com,* item in Nebraska, 6 speed, 13.6x38 rear tires, 6x16 front tires, rear tires 2 years old
A	1951		F	$1,500	7/17/2013	NEND	WF, PTO, not running, motor is free
A	1951		G	$1,700	6/15/2013	WCMI	NF, 13.6x38 tires, Powr Trol, Roll-A-Matic, SN668987
A	1951		G	$1,700	10/24/2012	NECO	SF, PTO, 3 pt.

John Deere

Model	Year	Hours	Condition	Price	Date	Area	Comments
A	1951		G	$1,800	8/21/2012	WCIL	
A	1951		G	$1,025	8/8/2012	Online	*BigIron.com,* item in Montana, 2WD, 2 cyl. gas, 33 hp, 540 PTO, factory WF, power steering, aftermarket 3 pt.
A	1951		G	$3,000	3/24/2012	SEOH	Styled
A	1951		F	$2,500	7/10/2010	SEIA	Repainted
A	1951		F	$2,802	6/23/2010	Online	*BigIron.com,* item in Nebraska, 6 speed, 2 cyl. gas, 2 live Baker add on valves, restored, straight tin work, new seat, steering wheel cracked
A	1951		G	$1,800	4/17/2010	ECNE	Electric start
A	1952		F	$1,800	1/30/2012	NEIA	Gas, NF
A	1952		G	$4,400	1/30/2012	NEIA	Gas, 226 2R mounted picker
A	1952		G	$925	8/24/2011	Online	*BigIron.com,* item in Kansas,runs, 6 speed, Norden front end, factory hyd., cast iron centers on rear wheels, power steering added, electric start, flotation tires
A	1952		G	$3,500	12/30/2010	ECMN	Late model with split pedestal, new rear tires
A	1952		E	$5,050	7/24/2010	WCIA	New rubber
A	1952		G	$1,100	6/23/2010	Online	*BigIron.com,* item in Nebraska, 2 cyl. gas, 5 speed
A	1952		G	$1,750	6/5/2010	ECMI	New rear rubber
A	1952		G	$1,750	5/1/2010	NCOH	John Deere 6' sickle bar mower
A			F	$1,200	3/22/2014	NWNJ	Completely disassembled
A			G	$3,400	3/22/2014	WCMO	Fully restored, new rubber
A			G	$1,200	12/5/2013	SCIA	New rubber
A			G	$1,402	10/22/2013	Online	*HansenandYoung.com,* Powr Trol, starts, runs, drives
A			G	$800	9/12/2013	SEIA	NF, 540 PTO, 13.6x38 tires
A			G	$1,500	8/24/2013	NEMD	New carburetor, new wiring harness, new brake shoes, new battery, new clutch shoe
A			G	$3,600	8/24/2013	SEMI	Unstyled, 12 spline axles, 9 bolt wheels
A			G	$2,250	8/3/2013	ECMN	NF, 12.4x38 tires
A			G	$3,000	8/3/2013	ECMN	NF, 12.4x38 tires, PS live hyd.
A			G	$4,500	8/3/2013	ECMN	Unstyled, 12.4x36 tires, front and rear round spoke
A			G	$1,017	6/24/2013	ECMN	Unstyled, runs, factory round spoke front rims, cut off rear rims
A			F	$1,595	6/24/2013	ECMN	Unstyled, factory front spoke rims, rear cut off rims, new rear tires 11.2x36, runs
A			G	$900	6/8/2013	NEND	Styled, lights, PTO, hyd. rock shaft, factory WF
A			G	$950	5/11/2013	NCOH	Styled, water pump, runs
A			G	$1,000	5/11/2013	NCOH	Styled, hand start, older repaint, runs
A			G	$1,100	5/11/2013	NCOH	Styled, electric start, repainted, runs
A			G	$1,450	5/11/2013	NCOH	Styled, electric start, repainted, runs
A			G	$1,700	5/11/2013	NCOH	Styled, square axle, older repaint, runs
A			G	$2,200	5/11/2013	NCOH	Repainted, factory 3 pt., water pump, runs

Model	Year	Hours	Condition	Price	Date	Area	Comments
A			G	$2,300	5/11/2013	NCOH	Unstyled, older repaint, new tires, cut off spoke wheels, runs
A			G	$1,100	5/8/2013	Online	*BigIron.com,* item in Colorado, 2 cyl., all original, PTO, motor stuck
A			G	$775	4/17/2013	Online	*BigIron.com,* item in Wyoming, manual, does not start now, stored
A			G	$877	4/17/2013	Online	*BigIron.com,* item in South Dakota, manual, ran when parked, does not start now, stored
A			G	$4,800	3/23/2013	NEIN	Unstyled, repainted, round spokes, new rear tires, runs
A			G	$5,200	3/22/2013	NWMN	Unstyled, restored, new tires, fenders, runs
A			G	$2,800	3/2/2013	NETN	Cultivator
A			G	$3,200	2/1/2013	Online	*IQBID.com,* dual wheel NF, PTO, unstyled
A			G	$2,750	12/18/2012	ECWI	11.2x38 tires, clam shell fenders, repainted, Powr Trol, electric start
A			G	$1,900	11/13/2012	NWTX	3 pt., NF
A			G	$2,400	10/20/2012	ECIL	Late model, new rear rubber
A			G	$4,000	9/22/2012	NEOR	Unstyled, NF
A			G	$850	8/30/2012	SEMN	Loader
A			G	$1,000	8/30/2012	SEMN	
A			G	$1,100	8/21/2012	WCIL	Styled
A			G	$2,200	8/21/2012	WCIL	
A			G	$2,100	7/21/2012	ECIA	Unstyled, runs, original, spoke wheels, runs
A			G	$2,400	7/21/2012	ECIA	Open fan shaft, rear steel, front spokes, runs
A			G	$7,250	7/21/2012	ECIA	High crop, no tag, not running
A			G	$17,500	7/21/2012	ECIA	High crop, restored, runs
A			G	$2,900	6/16/2012	ECIN	Unstyled, set up for pulling, new tires
A			G	$7,750	6/16/2012	ECIN	Unstyled, rare WF assembly, front and rear steel wheels extensions, repainted
A			G	$3,600	3/24/2012	NEIN	Unstyled, full steel, restored, runs
A			G	$8,750	3/24/2012	NEIN	Unstyled, WF, fenders, front/rear round spokes, runs
A			G	$3,100	3/22/2012	ECMN	Restored, 540 PTO, hand clutch, new 12.4x38 rears, Roll-O-Matic fronts
A			G	$3,600	1/21/2012	NEMS	WF
A			G	$1,100	12/9/2011	SCIA	2 cyl., NF
A			G	$2,200	11/26/2011	NCOH	Styled, clean, original
A			G	$3,000	11/12/2011	WCMI	6 speed, PTO, 1 hyd., NF, Roll-O-Matic
A			G	$1,650	10/29/2011	ECMN	
A			G	$1,400	10/22/2011	NECO	Electric start, new rear tires
A			G	$1,600	10/22/2011	NECO	Square axle, WF
A			G	$3,000	10/22/2011	NECO	Unstyled, full steel, repainted
A			G	$7,800	10/22/2011	NECO	Open fan, full steel
A			G	$9,250	10/22/2011	NECO	Orchard, all fuel
A			G	$14,000	10/22/2011	NECO	Unstyled, WF, new tires, front and rear round spokes
A			G	$17,500	10/22/2011	NECO	High crop, new rear tires

John Deere

TRACTORS

Model	Year	Hours	Condition	Price	Date	Area	Comments
A			G	$1,010	9/14/2011	Online	*BigIron.com,* item in Colorado, 2 cyl. gas, 540 PTO, tricycle front end, recent rebuilt, new tires
A			G	$1,150	7/30/2011	ECMO	
A			G	$4,300	6/25/2011	ECIA	Unstyled, SN 451394, new tires, cultivator, power,lift, repainted
A			G	$1,450	4/26/2011	SWMN	Rear fenders
A			G	$1,000	3/15/2011	WCIL	NF
A			G	$1,100	12/30/2010	ECMN	1 hyd., 540 PTO, hand clutch, lights
A			F	$1,050	12/17/2010	WCIL	
A			G	$1,650	11/13/2010	NCIA	OD
A			G	$2,700	9/18/2010	ECMO	Round spokes, fenders, repainted
A			G	$4,100	9/18/2010	ECMO	Fenders, power block, repainted
A			G	$11,750	9/18/2010	ECMO	Open fan, front and rear round spokes, restored
A			G	$1,250	9/11/2010	SEIA	
A			G	$2,600	9/4/2010	NEIN	
A			G	$3,000	9/4/2010	SEVA	Gas, 2 cyl., all original
A			G	$4,500	9/4/2010	NEIN	
A			G	$14,000	9/4/2010	NEIN	Front and rear rounds
A			G	$17,000	9/4/2010	NEIN	High crop
A			P	$2,750	9/3/2010	NEIN	Full steel, dead row, needs work and may not run or drive, as is
A			G	$1,500	8/14/2010	WCMN	NF, good rubber, 1 hyd., PTO, John Deere 45 trip loader, like new, no welds
A			G	$1,750	8/11/2010	ECMN	NF, new paint
A			G	$1,300	8/7/2010	SEWI	Electric start, runs good
A			G	$1,500	8/7/2010	SCMN	NF, unstyled, PTO, 12.4x36 tires, SN 475302
A			G	$2,000	8/7/2010	SCMN	NF, unstyled, PTO, new 11.2x38 tires, SN 452122
A			G	$3,300	8/7/2010	SCMN	NF, Roll-O-Matic, PTO, John Deere Powr Trol, 12.4x38s, SN 675076
A			G	$3,500	7/31/2010	NWIL	Unstyled, spoke wheels front and back, like new rubber on rear
A			G	$950	7/17/2010	NEMT	
A			G	$1,100	7/17/2010	NEMT	
A			F	$1,150	7/17/2010	NEMT	Stuck
A			G	$1,250	7/17/2010	NEMT	Smooth back
A			G	$3,100	7/17/2010	NEMT	
A			G	$5,100	7/17/2010	NEMT	Open fan shaft
A			F	$2,850	6/23/2010	Online	*BigIron.com,* item in Colorado, rear tires 11.2x38 new, front tires 6x16 bad
A			G	$1,050	6/11/2010	SEAB	Styled, row crop gas, fenders, hyd., PTO, belt pulley
A			G	$1,500	6/11/2010	SEAB	Styled, row crop gas, belt pulley, Powr Trol, no arms, 10x38 rear rubber
A			G	$3,200	6/11/2010	SEAB	42" rear wheels, older restoration, WF axles
A			G	$1,200	6/5/2010	WCMO	Unstyled, press steel wheels
A			G	$1,650	6/5/2010	NETN	NF
A			G	$1,750	6/5/2010	ECMN	Diesel, NF, complete OH

John Deere

Model	Year	Hours	Condition	Price	Date	Area	Comments
A			G	$2,100	6/5/2010	WCMO	Unstyled, front rounds
A			G	$4,200	6/5/2010	WCMO	Unstyled, factory front and rear rounds, Behlem OD
A			F	$1,900	5/7/2010	NEAR	GP, 1930s
A			G	$1,500	4/10/2010	ECNE	
A			G	$2,100	4/10/2010	NCTN	
A			G	$2,400	4/10/2010	ECNE	
A			G	$4,400	4/10/2010	ECNE	
A			G	$935	2/24/2010	Online	*PurpleWave.com,* item in Kansas
A			G	$2,100	2/13/2010	SWIA	
A			G	$2,800	2/13/2010	SWIA	5th from last built
A			G	$4,000	2/13/2010	SWIA	
AN	1936		G	$2,800	9/1/2011	WCMN	SF, on full steel, rebuilt carburetor, restored
AN	1938		E	$5,400	10/24/2012	NECO	SF, PTO, gas
ANH	1945		G	$7,000	9/1/2011	WCMN	Slant dash, SF wheel, power lift, electric start, lights, complete restoration
AO	1936		G	$3,700	9/1/2011	WCMN	New front tires, cast rear wheels, unrestored
AO	1941		G	$4,500	6/15/2013	WCMI	WF, styled, orchard fenders, hyd., new front tires, 16.8x26" tires, SN276623
AO	1943		G	$11,000	8/6/2011	SEWI	1 of 35 built in 1943, factory electric start and headlights, factory orchard type fenders, 2 cyl., documentation
AO	1949		G	$6,800	6/25/2011	ECIA	Unstyled, SN 271383, new tires, electric start, lighting, shutters, repainted
AO			G	$3,250	3/23/2013	NEIN	Styled, older repaint, runs
AO			G	$2,400	6/9/2012	ECNE	Unstyled, hand start, original, shutters, PTO, runs
AO			G	$6,600	3/24/2012	NEIN	Unstyled, electric start, lights, repainted, PTO, shutters, runs
AO			G	$12,500	9/4/2010	NEIN	
AO			P	$1,000	9/3/2010	NEIN	Electric start, dead row, needs work and may not run or drive, as is
AO			F	$1,200	7/17/2010	NEMT	Stuck
AO			G	$3,900	7/17/2010	NEMT	
AO			G	$4,700	7/17/2010	NEMT	Full tin
AO			G	$3,200	6/5/2010	WCMO	Electric start
AOS			G	$11,000	3/23/2013	NEIN	PTO, factory steel, repainted, runs
AOS			G	$5,000	3/24/2012	NEIN	Sheet metal in primer, original underneath, runs
AOS			G	$8,000	10/22/2011	NECO	Full steel
AOS			G	$24,500	9/18/2010	ECMO	Factory fronts, citrus fenders, restored
AOS			G	$5,800	9/4/2010	NEIN	
AOS			G	$14,500	9/4/2010	NEIN	PTO
AR	1936		E	$4,500	9/29/2012	ECTN	Restored, gas
AR	1941		F	$1,700	9/1/2011	WCMN	Electric start, PTO, battery box, lights, new front. rubber
AR	1945		G	$2,000	9/1/2011	WCMN	PTO, original unrestored, sold by John Deere Plow Company decals
AR	1945		G	$2,000	9/1/2011	WCMN	PTO, shutters, 14.9x26 rubber
AR	1946		G	$2,200	11/9/2013	SWON	Bug eye unstyled

John Deere

Model	Year	Hours	Condition	Price	Date	Area	Comments
AR	1947		F	$1,000	6/20/2013	ECSK	2WD, 27 hp drawbar, 30 hp belt, 13x26 rear tires, motor interior is good, starter rebuilt
AR	1947		G	$5,000	8/24/2011	ECMN	Electric start, PTO, lights, new 14.9x26 rubber
AR	1948		F	$4,000	11/16/2013	SCVA	2 cyl., partially restored
AR	1950		G	$3,300	9/21/2013	SEMN	Standard
AR	1950		G	$5,500	8/24/2011	ECMN	PTO
AR	1951		G	$3,600	11/9/2013	SWON	Styled
AR	1951		G	$3,600	11/9/2013	SWON	
AR	1951		G	$5,500	3/26/2011	SEWI	
AR	1951		G	$2,100	5/29/2010	NCIL	Gas, new tires
AR	1952		G	$2,300	7/25/2013	WCSK	2WD, styled, 30 belt hp, WF axle, 14.9x26 rubber, electric start, 2 cyl. club letter, running
AR	1952		F	$3,000	6/10/2013	WCSK	Gas, 26 drawbar hp, original paint, 14.9x26 tires, hyd. kit, less than 100 hours on motor
AR	1952		G	$3,500	7/24/2010	WCIA	
AR	1952		G	$1,200	6/23/2010	Online	*BigIron.com,* item in Kansas, gas, 30 hp, rear tires 14x26, front tires 7.5x16, 540 PTO, stuck, rust on fenders, new grill, new starter and fly, wheel cover
AR	1954		G	$2,200	4/23/2012	WCSK	1 hyd., recent batteries
AR			G	$5,000	8/3/2013	ECMN	WF, new 14.9x26 tires
AR			F	$1,400	6/11/2013	SWSK	2WD, running condition, 14.9/13x26 rear
AR			G	$1,000	6/8/2013	NEND	Styled, good rear rubber, starter, lights, PTO, factory hyd.
AR			G	$2,500	6/8/2013	NEND	Styled, starter, lights, PTO, factory hyd.
AR			G	$2,800	3/23/2013	NEIN	Styled, repainted, runs
AR			G	$900	3/22/2013	NWMN	Custom built, repainted, runs
AR			G	$2,650	2/1/2013	Online	*IQBID.com,* gas, PTO, SN 283669
AR			F	$1,700	1/9/2013	Online	*IQBID.com,* 2 cyl., 14.9x26 tires, engine turns over, has not been run in several years, not restored, SN 274514
AR			G	$1,759	1/9/2013	Online	*IQBID.com,* WF, PTO, 14.9x24 tires, unstyled, SN 251610
AR			G	$2,650	11/24/2012	SEMN	Unstyled, WF
AR			G	$1,900	10/22/2011	NECO	Styled
AR			G	$2,600	10/22/2011	NECO	Unstyled
AR			G	$3,900	10/22/2011	NECO	Unstyled
AR			G	$3,300	9/11/2010	NCIL	Gas, WF
AR			G	$2,100	9/4/2010	NEIN	PTO
AR			G	$2,400	9/4/2010	NEIN	PTO
AR			P	$1,500	9/3/2010	NEIN	Brass tag, dead row, needs work and may not run or drive, as is
AR			P	$1,900	9/3/2010	NEIN	Full steel, dead row, needs work and may not run or drive, as is
AR			F	$1,750	7/17/2010	NEMT	Brass tag, stuck
AR			G	$1,900	7/17/2010	NEMT	
AR			G	$2,100	7/17/2010	NEMT	

John Deere

Model	Year	Hours	Condition	Price	Date	Area	Comments
AR			F	$2,500	7/17/2010	NEMT	Locked in 2 gears
AR			G	$4,150	7/17/2010	NEMT	
AR			G	$6,500	7/17/2010	NEMT	
AR			G	$3,900	6/11/2010	SEAB	PTO, gas, 12V restored
AR			G	$2,750	6/5/2010	WCMO	New tires
AR			G	$3,300	4/17/2010	SESK	PTO, restored
AW	1940		E	$3,025	9/29/2012	ECTN	Restored, gas
AW	1944		G	$2,700	11/13/2010	NWIL	Styled, factory WF, dual FUEL
AW	1946		G	$4,600	8/24/2011	ECMN	Starter, PTO, lights, complete engine OH, new 13.6x38 rubber
AW			G	$1,500	7/17/2010	NEMT	
AW			G	$12,000	7/17/2010	NEMT	
AWH	1941		G	$9,000	9/1/2011	WCMN	Power lift, new 5.5x16 rubber fronts, orginal 9x40 rear rubber on round spokes, complete restoration
AWH	1951		G	$5,000	8/24/2011	ECMN	Factory 3 pt., PTO, clam shell fenders, new 12.4x42 rubber
B	1935		G	$4,300	11/9/2013	SWON	Unstyled, brass tag, factory round spoked rear wheels
B	1935		G	$2,600	3/7/2013	ECIA	Unstyled, good rubber, spoke front and rears
B	1935		G	$3,300	8/14/2012	Online	*PurpleWave.com,* item in Kansas, 4-bolt, gas, manual, 540 PTO, drawbar, 5x12 front tires, 12.4x36 rear tires
B	1935		E	$16,500	6/30/2012	NEIA	GP B, early model, 4-bolt front pedestal, on steel and skeleton rear steel
B	1935		G	$1,750	5/28/2012	ECMO	Unstyled, tricycle, older restoration
B	1935		F	$1,100	11/20/2010	ECFL	4-bolt, 10 spline wheels, extra parts
B	1935		G	$2,500	11/20/2010	NCKY	Old restoration, newer rubber
B	1935		F	$2,000	10/23/2010	ECMO	Unstyled, brass tag, runs, flat spoke wheels, new rear tires, PTO, SN 7288
B	1935		G	$2,500	7/10/2010	SEIA	New radiator, hood, reconditioned head blocks, new rings
B	1936		G	$2,400	3/22/2014	NWNJ	Good restoration and paint, needs decals, not currently running, needs minor clean up of electrical contact points as there is no spark
B	1936		F	$1,600	9/21/2013	SEMN	Rear steel, round spokes, front with new rubber
B	1936		G	$1,250	6/30/2012	NEIA	On rubber, unstyled
B	1936		G	$2,500	5/19/2012	SWMI	Short frame, 9x36 tires, full factory round spoke wheels front and back, unstyled
B	1936		G	$6,000	8/7/2010	SEWI	Unstyled, trailer
B	1936		G	$1,700	7/24/2010	WCIA	GP, factory flat spoke and new rubber
B	1936		G	$1,900	7/10/2010	ECOK	GP, unstyled, flat spoke rear
B	1936		G	$2,700	7/10/2010	ECOK	Unstyled, flat spoke rear, round spoke front
B	1937		G	$1,900	4/1/2014	WCMN	NF, PTO, spoke tires
B	1937		G	$4,100	12/12/2012	NCIL	GP B, on all steel, been in family since bought new, auction buyer was from exteneded family, SN 38448
B	1937		F	$1,300	8/25/2012	NWIL	Gas, unstyled, Woods belly mower

John Deere

Model	Year	Hours	Condition	Price	Date	Area	Comments
B	1937		G	$1,850	8/21/2012	WCIL	Round spoke wheels
B	1937		G	$2,000	5/9/2012	Online	*BigIron.com,* item in Nebraska, unstyled, 2 speed 2 ranges, 2 cyl. gas, 540 PTO, tires like new
B	1937		G	$3,250	11/12/2011	NEIA	Unstyled, spoke wheels on rubber, older restoration
B	1937		G	$3,200	8/25/2011	ECND	NF, SF on rubber, rear 50" steel on flat spoke, runs
B	1937		G	$2,500	11/20/2010	ECFL	Round spoke, cut off wheels, runs, PTO, spot on floor is from previous exhaust
B	1937		F	$2,200	10/23/2010	ECMO	Unstyled, full steel, runs, all fuel, PTO, SN 33738
B	1937		G	$3,500	8/14/2010	SEMN	On steel
B	1938		G	$1,600	5/9/2012	Online	*BigIron.com,* item in Nebraska, row crop, 4F/1R, 149 cu. in., 2 cyl. gas, 540 PTO, hand crank
B	1938		G	$3,300	8/24/2011	ECMN	NF, short frame, PTO, cast wheel, new 11.2x36 rubber
B	1938		F	$1,450	8/6/2011	NCIA	Spokes, new tires, cracked block
B	1938		G	$2,200	12/11/2010	WCMI	2R mechanical lift cultivator
B	1938		F	$3,200	10/23/2010	ECMO	Unstyled, round spokes, runs, SN 51447
B	1938		E	$3,900	9/22/2010	NECO	Restored, gas, DF, flat spoke wheels
B	1939		G	$850	6/15/2013	WCMI	NF, styled, factory front round spoke wheels, 11x38 tires, flywheel start, SN60228
B	1939		G	$1,155	8/14/2012	Online	*PurpleWave.com,* item in Kansas, row crop, John Deere 2 cyl. gas, 16 hp, manual, spring seat, 15 gal. fuel cap, drawbar, 540 PTO, 5x1T fronts, 11x38 rears
B	1939		G	$3,300	9/1/2011	WCMN	NF, original unrestored, fenders, rear steel wheels, rubber fronts, runs good, low hours
B	1939		G	$1,000	1/29/2011	ECMO	Hand crank
B	1940		G	$2,950	10/27/2012	NEIA	Redone, new rubber
B	1940		F	$1,100	9/1/2011	WCMN	Original unrestored
B	1940		G	$1,300	8/13/2011	WCIL	PTO, 11.2x38 tires, runs well
B	1941		G	$1,300	2/22/2014	SCNE	NF, hand start, older repaint
B	1941		G	$1,400	2/22/2014	SCNE	NF, hand start, runs, straight, rockshaft
B	1941		G	$1,950	5/22/2013	Online	*BigIron.com,* item in Iowa, 4F/1R, 2 cyl.
B	1941		G	$2,250	11/6/2010	WCOH	Templeton loader
B	1941		G	$1,550	6/23/2010	Online	*BigIron.com,* item in Nebraska, 6 speed, 2 cyl. gas, rear tires 11.2x38R1, front tires 5x15, 540 PTO, water temperature and oil pressure guages are new, rear tires are new
B	1941		G	$1,100	5/29/2010	NCIL	NF, new back rubber
B	1942		G	$2,600	8/10/2013	NCIA	SN 141676
B	1942		G	$2,250	6/22/2013	SEWA	NF, 2 cyl., gas, direct start, adj. rear wheel width, rear PTO, SN 177839
B	1942		F	$925	8/6/2011	NCIA	Hand start, 2R cultivator, stuck
B	1942		G	$1,400	8/2/2011	ECNE	

John Deere

Model	Year	Hours	Condition	Price	Date	Area	Comments
B	1942		G	$2,000	6/29/2011	NEND	Styled, NF, running, complete, stored inside
B	1943		G	$2,500	7/25/2013	WCSK	2WD, row crop, styled, 16 belt hp, NF axle, 12.2x36 rubber, manual start, 2 cyl. club letter, running
B	1943		G	$1,700	8/25/2012	NWIL	War time frame, new tires, gas
B	1943		F	$975	11/12/2011	NEIA	Electric start, front spoked wheels on rubber, new tires
B	1943		G	$2,600	7/10/2010	ECOK	
B	1944		G	$1,200	4/24/2013	Online	*BigIron.com,* item in Missouri, 6 speed Hi/Lo, 2 cyl.
B	1944		G	$4,900	3/4/2012	ECNE	All fuel, electric start factory, new 11.2x38 tires, good factory original, SN 171067
B	1944		G	$1,900	9/9/2011	ECND	NF, hand start, PTO
B	1944		G	$3,000	8/6/2011	WCOK	Completely restored, new rubber, parade ready
B	1944		G	$1,100	6/22/2011	Online	*BigIron.com,* item in Kansas, 540 PTO, electric start 6V, cast rear wheels, crank handle, power lift, needs muffler
B	1944		G	$2,000	5/22/2010	SEMN	New 11.2x38 tires
B	1945		G	$2,900	6/25/2011	ECIA	Styled, SN 182906, new tires, hand start, repainted
B	1946		G	$875	5/23/2012	Online	*BigIron.com,* item in Nebraska, 6 speed, 2 cyl. gas, NF, 2 pt. shaft, adj. rear tires, solid rim rear wheel, electric start
B	1947		G	$1,705	10/16/2013	Online	*PurpleWave.com,* item in Kansas, 2 cyl. gas, 6 speed, 540 PTO
B	1947		G	$1,980	10/31/2012	Online	*PurpleWave.com,* item in Nebraska, 2.4L, 2 cyl. gas, 12 hp, manual, spring seat, drawbar, 540 PTO, Powr Trol, front/rear lights, 12V system, manual steering
B	1947		G	$2,500	3/22/2012	ECMN	NF, electrical start, PTO, hand clutch, older restoration
B	1947		G	$2,300	12/16/2010	NCMI	Restored, new tires, NF, electric start, new 12.4x38 tires
B	1947		F	$1,800	6/23/2010	Online	*BigIron.com,* item in South Dakota, 6 speed, 2 cyl. gas, rear tires 12.4x38, front tires 5.5x16SL, 540 PTO, new radiator, new seat, all new tires, OH in the late 60s
B	1947		G	$825	2/24/2010	Online	*PurpleWave.com,* item in Iowa, PTO, drawbar
B	1948		G	$3,200	2/9/2013	SWOH	Good, older restoration
B	1948		G	$900	6/22/2011	Online	*BigIron.com,* item in Colorado, 6 speed, SF, new battery, runs
B	1948		E	$5,000	9/6/2010	NCOH	
B	1949		F	$1,300	7/14/2012	SWMN	11.2x38 tires
B	1949		G	$1,800	4/14/2012	NEIA	12.4x38 rear tires, SN 247001, good to excellent paint, electronic ignition installed in 2008
B	1949		F	$1,300	10/7/2011	NWSD	PTO, belly mount Woods mower, straight sheet metal, good runner, easy restoration, NF

John Deere

Model	Year	Hours	Condition	Price	Date	Area	Comments
B	1949		G	$1,000	10/2/2010	SWWI	
B	1949		G	$1,200	5/26/2010	ECSD	
B	1950		G	$2,600	9/28/2013	NEIA	Engine OH, good paint, new seat
B	1950		G	$1,540	8/14/2012	Online	*PurpleWave.com,* item in Kansas, gas, manual, rear hyd. plugs, 540 PTO, drawbar, 5.5x16 fronts, 12.4x38 rears
B	1950		G	$1,800	6/9/2012	ECNE	Square axle, new tires, PTO, runs, repainted
B	1950		G	$1,500	4/7/2012	NWMI	Gas, Roll-O-Matic, NF, electric start, fenders
B	1950		F	$1,100	11/12/2011	NEIA	Did not run, new tires, electric start
B	1950		G	$1,000	4/26/2011	SWMN	Seller's dad bought new, rear fenders
B	1951		G	$1,700	9/21/2013	WCMI	Gas, PTO, electric start, 12.4x38 rear tires, restored
B	1951		G	$2,400	9/12/2013	SEIA	New tires, parade ready
B	1951		G	$825	8/24/2013	WCMN	New seat and paint
B	1951		G	$1,100	4/16/2011	SWMB	Tricycle, PTO rock shaft, hyd., electric start
B	1951		G	$1,850	3/23/2011	ECMN	New rear rubber
B	1951		F	$900	11/13/2010	NWIL	Styled, square axle, gas, NF, new tires
B	1951		G	$1,700	8/7/2010	SEWI	Styled, restored, nice paint, good tires
B	1951		G	$2,900	7/24/2010	WCIA	
B	1951		G	$2,200	6/5/2010	ECMN	Restored, new rubber
B	1951		F	$1,100	5/26/2010	ECSD	
B	1951		G	$1,500	5/4/2010	WCOK	Recently rebuilt, hours unavailable
B	1952		G	$1,018	3/27/2013	Online	*PurpleWave.com,* item in Kansas, John Deere 2 cyl. gas, manual
B	1952		G	$1,100	7/14/2012	NWIA	NF, clean, carburetor OH
B	1952		G	$2,650	1/13/2012	NCIA	NF, new tires
B			G	$3,200	3/22/2014	WCMO	Fully restored, new rubber
B			G	$900	1/17/2014	SEOK	
B			G	$880	10/22/2013	Online	*HansenandYoung.com*
B			G	$1,017	10/22/2013	Online	*HansenandYoung.com,* new rear tires, 3 pt., starts, runs
B			G	$1,925	10/22/2013	Online	*HansenandYoung.com,* unstyled, new rear tires
B			G	$1,870	9/11/2013	Online	*PurpleWave.com,* item in Missouri, 2 cyl. gas, manual Hi/Lo, 540 PTO, drawbar
B			G	$3,100	8/3/2013	ECMN	NF, new 11.2x38 tires
B			F	$1,017	6/24/2013	ECMN	Unstyled, 1 factory rear round spoke, 1 cut off rear rim, runs
B			G	$1,100	6/15/2013	WCMI	Unstyled, on steel, SN56454
B			G	$3,000	6/15/2013	WCOH	Styled, live hyd., PTO, restored, John Deere 45 loader, runs
B			G	$3,300	6/15/2013	WCOH	New tires, restored, electric start, lighting, runs
B			G	$1,200	6/8/2013	NEND	Unstyled, PTO, NF, running when parked
B			G	$1,850	6/8/2013	NEND	WF, starter, lights, rock shaft
B			G	$950	5/11/2013	NCOH	Electric start, lighting, repainted, runs, styled
B			G	$1,300	5/11/2013	NCOH	Styled, hand start, repainted, runs
B			G	$1,400	5/11/2013	NCOH	Styled, electric start, nice original, runs

John Deere

Model	Year	Hours	Condition	Price	Date	Area	Comments
B			G	$1,550	5/11/2013	NCOH	Styled, electric start, lighting, older repaint, runs
B			G	$1,600	5/11/2013	NCOH	Unstyled, long frame, new tires, cut down spoke wheels, older repaint, runs
B			G	$2,100	5/11/2013	NCOH	Styled, older repaint, live hyd., runs
B			G	$2,400	5/11/2013	NCOH	Unstyled, older repaint, cut down spokes, new tires
B			G	$875	4/24/2013	Online	*BigIron.com,* item in Nebraska, 5 speed, 2 cyl. gas
B			G	$1,300	3/27/2013	Online	*BigIron.com,* item in Wyoming, as is for parts or to be restored, does not work
B			G	$2,400	3/23/2013	NEIN	Styled, hand start, fenders, repainted, runs
B			G	$4,000	3/23/2013	NEIN	Unstyled, factory flat spokes, repainted, runs
B			G	$5,000	3/23/2013	NEIN	Slant steer, repainted, new tires, electric start, lights, runs
B			G	$1,400	3/16/2013	NEIL	
B			G	$1,152	2/1/2013	Online	*IQBID.com,* dual wheel NF, PTO, unstyled, SN 6135
B			G	$1,300	2/1/2013	Online	*IQBID.com,* dual wheel NF, PTO, unstyled
B			G	$1,700	2/1/2013	Online	*IQBID.com,* dual wheel NF, PTO, styled, SN 100668
B			G	$1,200	1/9/2013	Online	*IQBID.com,* dual wheel NF, round fenders, 10x38 tires, styled
B			G	$1,500	12/29/2012	WCMI	NF, 1 hyd., PTO
B			G	$850	11/24/2012	WCIL	
B			G	$2,050	11/17/2012	SWMN	Near new 11.2x38 rubber
B			G	$2,550	11/3/2012	SWMI	2 cyl. gas, WF, PTO, straight bar, orchard fenders, 12.4x28 rear tires
B			G	$4,000	9/22/2012	NEOR	Unstyled, NF
B			G	$1,200	8/21/2012	WCIL	
B			G	$2,000	7/21/2012	ECIA	Styled, repaint, new tires, hand start, runs
B			G	$2,750	7/21/2012	ECIA	Styled, repainted, fenders, all fuel, new rear tires, runs
B			G	$4,400	7/21/2012	ECIA	Unstyled, restored, front and rear round spokes, runs
B			G	$4,250	6/16/2012	ECIN	Unstyled, 2,way plow
B			G	$9,400	6/16/2012	ECIN	Unstyled, long frame, front and rear round spokes, runs, rare WF assembly
B			F	$2,000	6/13/2012	SWOH	Row crop, open flywheel, froze
B			F	$751	5/23/2012	Online	*BigIron.com,* item in Nebraska, 2 cyl., gas, 540 PTO
B			F	$1,425	3/24/2012	SCMN	NF, gas, complete OH, 11.2x38 new rear tires, 2nd owner
B			G	$3,600	3/24/2012	NEIN	Unstyled, long frame, repainted, new tires, PTO, shutters, runs
B			F	$800	3/17/2012	SEMN	Like new tires, not running
B			F	$1,100	11/3/2011	Online	*PurpleWave.com,* item in Kansas, NF
B			F	$950	10/29/2011	SEMN	Styled, cultivator, does not run
B			F	$1,050	10/29/2011	SEMN	Half round fenders, styled, loader, does not run

John Deere

Model	Year	Hours	Condition	Price	Date	Area	Comments
B			G	$1,375	10/25/2011	Online	*BidNow.us,* rebuilt engine
B			G	$1,100	10/22/2011	NECO	John Deere #5 mower
B			G	$1,250	10/22/2011	NECO	SF, 42" rear fenders
B			F	$1,300	10/22/2011	ECTX	
B			G	$1,700	10/22/2011	NECO	New rear tires, add on WF
B			G	$2,800	10/22/2011	NECO	Round spoke rears, SF steel
B			G	$2,900	10/22/2011	NECO	WF, fenders
B			G	$3,000	10/22/2011	NECO	Texas sand wheel, skeleton rear
B			G	$3,250	10/22/2011	NECO	Full steel
B			G	$26,000	10/22/2011	NECO	Converted to high crop
B			G	$2,750	9/15/2011	ECIA	Restored, NF
B			G	$3,750	9/15/2011	ECIA	Restored, NF
B			G	$1,251	9/14/2011	Online	*BigIron.com,* item in Colorado, 2 cyl. gas, 540 PTO, has John Deere 38 7' sickle mower, needs front tire
B			G	$1,800	8/31/2011	SEMN	11.2x38 tires
B			G	$800	8/11/2011	WCMN	NF, 1 hyd., PTO, fenders
B			G	$1,000	7/30/2011	ECMO	
B			G	$2,100	7/27/2011	ECND	Late model, 6 speed, like new rear tires, dual wheels
B			G	$1,950	6/25/2011	ECIA	Styled, unreadable tag, new tires, repainted
B			G	$2,400	4/7/2011	SEIA	Electric start, repainted
B			G	$2,000	4/2/2011	ECMN	On steel
B			G	$1,150	3/25/2011	WCIL	NF, rough
B			G	$1,800	12/15/2010	SEMI	One owner, 12.4x38 tires 90% tread
B			F	$1,700	11/6/2010	SEMN	Flat rear spokes
B			G	$2,200	10/23/2010	SWWI	Unstyled
B			P	$850	10/2/2010	SWWI	Doesn't run
B			G	$1,100	10/2/2010	ECMN	NF
B			G	$1,400	10/2/2010	ECMN	Roll-O-Matic, NF
B			G	$3,000	9/18/2010	ECMO	Fenders, restored
B			G	$3,100	9/18/2010	ECMO	Replica, homemade
B			G	$4,300	9/18/2010	ECMO	
B			G	$6,000	9/18/2010	ECMO	3 pt., fenders, new tires, restored
B			F	$1,050	9/11/2010	NCIL	Not running, stuck
B			G	$3,300	9/4/2010	NEIN	LP
B			G	$4,600	9/4/2010	NEIN	4-bolt
B			G	$7,500	9/4/2010	NEIN	Duals, WF
B			P	$1,500	9/3/2010	NEIN	Unstyled, dead row, needs work and may not run or drive, as is
B			F	$800	8/14/2010	SEMN	
B			G	$2,350	8/14/2010	WCMN	Hi/Lo, PTO, new rubber, flat spoke wheel, all fuel, repainted
B			G	$2,900	8/14/2010	WCMN	Water pump, new rear rubber
B			G	$1,400	8/7/2010	SCMN	NF, electric start, PTO, flat spoke rear rims, 11.2x36 tires, round spoke front rims, SN 140354
B			G	$1,400	8/7/2010	SCMN	NF, PTO, new 11.2x38 tires, SN 196107
B			G	$1,500	8/7/2010	SCMN	NF, Roll-O-Matic, PTO, 13.6x38 tires, unable to verify VIN

John Deere

Model	Year	Hours	Condition	Price	Date	Area	Comments
B			G	$2,200	8/7/2010	WCMN	Gas, NF
B			G	$4,250	7/31/2010	NWIL	Unstyled, NF, round spoke front and rear, like new rubber on rear, restored
B			F	$900	7/17/2010	NEMT	
B			G	$1,100	7/17/2010	SCON	Canadian sale, row crop
B			G	$1,250	7/17/2010	NEMT	
B			F	$1,350	7/17/2010	NEMT	Stuck
B			G	$1,500	7/17/2010	NEMT	
B			G	$1,600	7/17/2010	NEMT	
B			G	$3,000	7/17/2010	NEMT	
B			G	$4,000	7/17/2010	NEMT	
B			G	$5,000	7/17/2010	NEMT	
B			G	$1,100	6/23/2010	Online	*BigIron.com,* item in Nebraska, 2 speed Hi/Lo, gas, rear tires 10x38, front tires 5.5x16SL, 540 PTO, draw bar, hand crank started on first pull, 6th gear add on
B			F	$1,000	6/17/2010	SEIA	Unstyled
B			G	$1,900	6/5/2010	WCMO	Unstyled, long frame
B			G	$1,900	6/5/2010	WCMO	Unstyled, original, long frame, shutters
B			G	$2,900	6/5/2010	WCMO	Unstyled, rear rounds, front cut downs, brass tag
B			F	$900	5/26/2010	ECSD	
B			G	$1,200	5/26/2010	ECSD	
B			G	$1,500	5/1/2010	SENE	
B			E	$1,650	5/1/2010	NCOH	Restored, fenders, no serial tag
D			G	$3,000	4/17/2010	SESK	PTO, restored
B			F	$800	4/10/2010	ECNE	
B			G	$1,300	4/10/2010	ECNE	
B			G	$852	2/24/2010	Online	*PurpleWave.com,* item in Kansas, no carburetor
B			F	$1,350	2/13/2010	SWIA	
BI			G	$21,000	10/22/2011	NECO	New tires
BI			G	$14,750	9/4/2010	NEIN	PTO, winch
BI			G	$9,500	7/17/2010	NEMT	
BN	1946		G	$3,500	8/24/2011	ECMN	Starter, PTO, lights, fenders, SF wheel, new 11.2x38 rubber
BN			G	$3,600	3/23/2013	NEIN	Styled, SF, restored, new tires, PTO, runs
BN			G	$2,900	7/21/2012	ECIA	Styled, 42" rear wheels, repainted, runs
BN			G	$4,800	6/16/2012	ECIN	Unstyled, full steel, fenders, power lift, repainted
BN			P	$1,300	9/3/2010	NEIN	Cultivators, SF, dead row, needs work and may not run or drive, as is
BN			G	$1,150	7/17/2010	NEMT	No tag, stuck
BN			G	$1,900	7/17/2010	NEMT	
BN			G	$2,900	7/17/2010	NEMT	No tag
BN			F	$4,000	7/17/2010	NEMT	Stuck
BNH	1945		G	$16,000	9/1/2011	WCMN	Power lift, electric start, lights, original 7x40 rear rubber on round spokes, new 6x16 front tire, complete restoration
BNH	1951		G	$950	11/9/2013	SWON	SF, 42x9 front wheels
BNH			G	$4,700	3/24/2012	NEIN	Styled, runs

John Deere

Model	Year	Hours	Condition	Price	Date	Area	Comments
BNH			G	$2,600	10/22/2011	NECO	42" tires
BNH			G	$9,000	10/22/2011	NECO	No serial tag, 40" rears, new tires
BO	1937		G	$3,900	8/22/2012	Online	*BigIron.com,* item in Montana, orchard, unknown hours, 8-ply nylon general farm tires, 2 cyl. gas, 12 hp claimed, fully restored, new tires
BO	1946		G	$4,350	6/25/2011	ECIA	Bo Lindeman, SN 336168, steers good, repainted
BO			G	$5,100	7/21/2012	ECIA	Repainted, front round spokes, rare rear wheels, runs
BO			G	$6,400	3/24/2012	NEIN	Restored, spoke wheels, runs
BO			G	$3,800	10/22/2011	NECO	Rear steel, front cut offs
BO			G	$3,800	10/22/2011	NECO	Rear steel, front cut offs
BO			G	$6,000	9/18/2010	ECMO	New tires, restored
BO			G	$11,750	9/18/2010	ECMO	Lindeman, citrus fenders
BO			G	$3,100	9/4/2010	NEIN	
BO			G	$3,750	9/4/2010	NEIN	On steel
BO			G	$3,600	7/17/2010	NEMT	
BO			G	$15,000	7/17/2010	NEMT	Lindeman
BR	1936		P	$3,200	11/20/2010	ECFL	Unstyled, round spoke and cut off wheels
BR	1937		G	$2,700	11/9/2013	SWON	Factory spoked wheels
BR	1937		G	$2,700	11/9/2013	SWON	Standard, factory spoked wheels
BR	1938		G	$5,000	10/23/2010	SCPA	
BR	1946		F	$3,750	8/7/2010	SEWI	Original decals and tags from dealer in Canada, complete original, factory shutters and lights
BR	1947		G	$7,500	8/24/2011	ECMN	Electric start, PTO, lights, original 10x26 Firestone tires, original low hour
BR			G	$2,800	1/9/2013	Online	*IQBID.com,* WF, PTO, steel wheels, unstyled, SN 327556
BR			G	$3,200	7/21/2012	ECIA	Repainted, starts, new tires, runs
BR			G	$4,600	7/21/2012	ECIA	Cut off front wheels, new tires, runs
BR			G	$4,900	10/22/2011	NECO	Electric start, lights, repainted
BR			G	$4,500	9/4/2010	NEIN	Full steel, electric start, lights
BR			G	$4,200	7/17/2010	NEMT	
BR			G	$8,600	7/17/2010	NEMT	
BW	1941		G	$2,700	11/20/2010	ECFL	War time, no tag, older restoration
BW	1946		F	$2,000	11/13/2010	NWIL	Styled, electric start, stuck, gas
BW	1948		G	$4,300	8/24/2011	ECMN	Hyd., PTO, long axle, fenders
BW	1952		G	$9,400	9/6/2012	Online	*IQBID.com,* item in Minnesota, complete restoration
BW			G	$9,200	9/4/2010	NEIN	Front and rear rounds
BW			G	$23,000	9/4/2010	NEIN	Front and rear rounds, light kit
BW			G	$9,250	7/31/2010	NWIL	Gas, restored, WF, round spokes, unstyled
BW			G	$3,150	7/17/2010	NEMT	
BW			G	$15,000	7/17/2010	NEMT	
BWH	1945		G	$12,500	9/1/2011	Online	*IQBID.com,* power lift, electric start, lights, new fronts, original 7x40 rear rubber on round spokes, complete restoration

John Deere

Model	Year	Hours	Condition	Price	Date	Area	Comments
BWH	1945		G	$12,500	9/1/2011	WCMN	Power lift, electric start, lights, new fronts, original 7x40 rear rubber on round spokes, complete restoration
BWH			G	$20,000	10/22/2011	NECO	Unstyled, 40" rear roundS, both blocks in front end
C			G	$100,000	7/17/2010	NEMT	
D	1924		G	$14,500	11/9/2013	SWON	Spoker, factory round spoke wheels all around
D	1925		E	$28,000	10/28/2013	SCKS	Restored, all original spoked flywheel, SN 33051, rare
D	1925		E	$17,000	9/15/2011	ECIA	Spoke wheels, restored, SN 34580
D	1925		F	$7,100	7/17/2010	NEMT	Disassembled
D	1925		G	$7,500	7/17/2010	NEMT	
D	1925		F	$15,000	6/23/2010	Online	*BigIron.com,* item in Nebraska, spoker fly wheel, original John Deere steering steel wheels, 2 cyl. gas, Hi/Lo and reverse, runs
D	1926		F	$12,500	7/17/2010	NEMT	Nickel hole flywheel, stuck
D	1927		G	$3,500	8/25/2012	NWIL	On all steel wheels, rear wheel extensions, unstyled
D	1927		G	$3,000	8/14/2010	SEMN	On steel
D	1927		G	$4,800	7/17/2010	NEMT	
D	1927		G	$5,100	7/17/2010	NEMT	
D	1928		G	$1,000	11/20/2010	ECFL	Does not run, very restorable condition, side shaft PTO, sand wheels
D	1928		F	$2,300	10/23/2010	ECMO	PTO, new old stock block and major OH, runs good
D	1929		G	$1,595	10/10/2012	Online	*PurpleWave.com,* item in Iowa, John Deere 2 cyl. gas, manual, spring seat, drawbar
D	1929		G	$2,200	7/24/2010	WCIA	On steel
D	1929		G	$2,090	6/23/2010	Online	*BigIron.com,* item in Nebraska, 2 cyl. gas, motor is stuck, extensions on rear wheels, comes with carburetor, block may be cracked
D	1931		G	$1,800	7/17/2010	NEMT	
D	1932		G	$6,300	7/17/2010	NEMT	
D	1935		F	$1,900	1/17/2012	SCKS	Engine stuck
D	1935		G	$2,000	9/9/2011	ECND	PTO
D	1935		G	$2,800	11/20/2010	ECFL	Round spoke wheels, PTO, nearly new tires, runs
D	1935		G	$2,200	6/5/2010	ECMI	
D	1936		E	$6,500	9/21/2013	SEMN	Junior built from a 1936 John Deere B, fenders, like new tires
D	1936		G	$2,600	5/19/2012	SWMI	WF, 14x28 tires, fenders, spoke front wheels, unstyled
D	1936		G	$2,400	9/22/2010	NECO	PTO, gas, older restoration
D	1937		G	$2,750	6/30/2012	NEIA	On rubber, block welded, runs good
D	1937		G	$2,400	12/11/2010	WCMI	On rubber, steel wheels available
D	1938		G	$1,700	6/22/2011	Online	*BigIron.com,* item in Colorado, gas, rear tires 44", 27" front tires, restored and has been sitting out for 6 mos, 540 PTO, drawbar, hand clutch

John Deere

Model	Year	Hours	Condition	Price	Date	Area	Comments
D	1939		G	$925	6/11/2010	SEAB	Styled, gas, hand start
D	1941		G	$850	8/22/2012	ECMN	PTO, loose, not running
D	1942		G	$2,500	5/29/2013	Online	*BigIron.com,* item in Iowa, standard tread, 3F/1R, 8.2L, 2 cyl., 23.5 gal. fuel tank, manual flywheel start
D	1944		G	$3,250	7/25/2013	WCSK	2WD, styled, 27 belt hp, manual start, 13x30 rubber, 2 cyl. club letter, running
D	1945		G	$4,500	6/5/2010	ECMN	Gas, WF
D	1946		G	$5,100	8/24/2011	ECMN	Starter, PTO, lights, new 16.9x30 rubber
D	1946		G	$3,100	2/1/2011	NEIN	Nice original
D	1947		G	$6,000	8/7/2010	SEWI	WF, new tires, electric start, lights, good tag, original fenders, nice restoration
D	1948		G	$2,000	11/9/2013	SWON	PTO, electric start
D	1948		G	$2,000	11/9/2013	SWON	Styled, PTO and electric start
D	1948		F	$2,000	12/15/2012	WCMI	Gas, W.F., fenders, poor tires
D	1948		G	$2,500	5/23/2012	Online	*BigIron.com,* item in South Dakota, 3 speed, 2 cyl. gas, rear tires bad, missing starter selenoid
D	1948		G	$3,500	5/23/2012	Online	*BigIron.com,* item in South Dakota, 3 speed, 2 cyl. gas, electric start
D	1948		G	$3,500	1/31/2012	NEIN	Styled, completely restored
D	1948		G	$950	1/18/2012	Online	*BigIron.com,* item in Oklahoma, 3F/1R, 2 cyl. gas, 38 hp, electric start
D	1948		E	$2,800	9/22/2010	NECO	Restored, gas, PTO
D	1949		G	$1,750	8/25/2012	NWIL	Styled hand crank, gas
D	1949		G	$1,600	9/9/2011	ECND	Styled, electric start, original
D	1949		G	$2,250	9/1/2011	WCMN	Live hyd., complete unit, lights, starter, new 7.5x16 front tires, original unrestored
D	1949		G	$2,900	7/24/2010	WCIA	
D	1949		G	$3,200	7/10/2010	ECOK	
D	1950		F	$2,100	6/20/2012	SESD	Good tin, 14x30 rears, good fenders, stored inside, not run in 10 years
D	1950		G	$6,250	10/23/2010	SCPA	
D	1952		G	$1,800	6/11/2010	SEAB	Styled, gas, new motor
D	1953		G	$4,000	9/21/2013	WCMI	Gas, PTO, electric start, 16.3x30 rear tires, restored
D			G	$4,000	4/16/2014	ECAB	2WD, for restoration, steel wheels
D			F	$1,600	3/22/2014	NWNJ	Partially disassembled, has fenders, a good project, we believe most parts are here, there are multiple extras of some parts
D			G	$4,400	8/24/2013	SEMN	Good tin, good paint, runs good
D			G	$1,500	8/14/2013	WCMN	Electric start, 16.9x30
D			G	$3,200	8/3/2013	ECMN	16.9x30 tires, electric start
D			F	$2,500	7/27/2013	WCIL	On rubber, WF, spoke style rims
D			G	$800	6/8/2013	NEND	Unstyled, flat rear spokes, round front
D			G	$1,250	6/8/2013	NEND	Unstyled, round spoke front wheels
D			G	$2,700	6/8/2013	NEND	Unstyled, on steel, good sheet metal, flat spokes, was running when parked
D			G	$2,500	5/11/2013	NCOH	Styled, older repaint, hand start, runs
D			F	$2,600	2/6/2013	SESD	On steel, not running

John Deere

Model	Year	Hours	Condition	Price	Date	Area	Comments
D			G	$1,125	1/9/2013	Online	*IQBID.com,* WF, electric start, PTO, 18.4x30 tires, styled, SN 50051
D			G	$1,380	1/9/2013	Online	*IQBID.com,* WF, steel wheels, unstyled, SN 103428
D			G	$3,575	12/18/2012	ECWI	Electric start, 18.4x30 tires, restored
D			G	$1,600	11/24/2012	WCIL	
D			G	$3,500	9/22/2012	NEOR	Electric start, WF
D			G	$5,200	7/27/2012	SWKY	
D			G	$11,500	6/16/2012	ECIN	Spoke fly wheel, older repaint, motor turns over, front and rear steel wheels, new fenders
D			G	$3,300	5/28/2012	ECMO	Complete, older restoration
D			G	$3,600	3/24/2012	NEIN	Styled, repainted, hand start, PTO, runs
D			G	$3,700	3/24/2012	NEIN	Runs
D			G	$4,000	3/24/2012	NEIN	Unstyled, full steel, repainted, runs
D			G	$4,500	3/24/2012	NEIN	Electric start, lighting, PTO, new tires, restored, runs, styled
D			F	$2,250	3/20/2012	WCIL	
D			F	$1,540	11/3/2011	Online	*PurpleWave.com,* item in Kansas
D			F	$1,925	11/3/2011	Online	*PurpleWave.com,* item in Kansas
D			F	$1,980	11/3/2011	Online	*PurpleWave.com,* item in Kansas
D			F	$2,145	11/3/2011	Online	*PurpleWave.com,* item in Kansas, flat front tire
D			G	$3,410	11/3/2011	Online	*PurpleWave.com,* item in Kansas
D			G	$2,300	10/22/2011	NECO	Unstyled
D			G	$3,300	10/22/2011	NECO	Diesel, altered to orchard use
D			G	$3,750	10/22/2011	NECO	Electric start, PTO
D			G	$4,500	10/22/2011	NECO	Styled, turning brakes, repainted
D			G	$4,800	10/22/2011	NECO	Diesel, full steel, PTO
D			G	$8,000	10/22/2011	NECO	Full steel, nickel hole flywheel
D			G	$12,000	10/22/2011	NECO	Spoke flywheel, PTO
D			G	$3,000	5/7/2011	SWMB	
D			G	$2,300	5/4/2011	WCSK	2WD, running
D			G	$6,400	9/18/2010	ECMO	Round spokes
D			F	$1,250	9/11/2010	NCIL	On steel, not running
D			G	$10,000	9/9/2010	NWWI	
D			G	$3,200	9/4/2010	NEIN	
D			G	$4,000	9/4/2010	NEIN	Full steel
D			G	$16,000	9/4/2010	NEIN	True corn bore, comes W/original hood
D			G	$20,000	9/4/2010	NEIN	Full steel, spoke
D			P	$1,000	9/3/2010	NEIN	Dead row, needs work and may not run or drive, as is
D			P	$1,300	9/3/2010	NEIN	Full steel, dead row, needs work and may not run or drive, as is
D			G	$3,500	8/14/2010	SEMN	On rubber
D			G	$2,000	8/7/2010	SCMN	WF, spoke front and rear rims, PTO, 15.2x28 tires, SN 145335
D			G	$2,000	7/31/2010	NWIL	Unstyled, WF, on rubber, spoke fronts, original paint, radiator repaired
D			G	$7,500	7/31/2010	NWIL	Spoker, gas, unstyled, flywheel cracked and welded on key way, rebuilt carburetor and magneto

John Deere

Model	Year	Hours	Condition	Price	Date	Area	Comments
D			F	$800	7/17/2010	NEMT	Stuck
D			F	$900	7/17/2010	NEMT	Stuck
D			F	$950	7/17/2010	NEMT	Stuck
D			F	$950	7/17/2010	NEMT	Stuck
D			F	$1,100	7/17/2010	NEMT	No tag, stuck
D			F	$1,150	7/17/2010	NEMT	Stuck
D			F	$1,200	7/17/2010	NEMT	Stuck
D			F	$1,600	7/17/2010	NEMT	No tag
D			F	$1,750	7/17/2010	NEMT	Cracked block
D			F	$1,800	7/17/2010	NEMT	Stuck
D			F	$1,900	7/17/2010	NEMT	No tag, stuck
D			F	$2,500	7/17/2010	NEMT	Stuck
D			G	$3,400	7/17/2010	NEMT	Hyd.
D			F	$3,750	7/17/2010	NEMT	Stuck
D			F	$4,000	7/17/2010	NEMT	Stuck, keyed flywheel
D			G	$15,000	7/17/2010	NEMT	Plow
D			G	$32,500	7/17/2010	NEMT	
D			G	$36,000	7/17/2010	NEMT	Exhibit B
D			G	$50,000	7/17/2010	NEMT	Exhibit A
D			F	$875	6/23/2010	Online	*BigIron.com,* item in Colorado, free, complete, tires are poor
D			F	$1,100	6/23/2010	Online	*BigIron.com,* item in Colorado, gas motor seized, tires are poor
D			F	$1,410	6/23/2010	Online	*BigIron.com,* item in Colorado, styled, seized, electric start, tires poor
D			F	$2,000	6/23/2010	Online	*BigIron.com,* item in Colorado, unstyled D, on factory iron lugs
D			F	$2,501	6/23/2010	Online	*BigIron.com,* item in Colorado, bad, modified steering, extra steering parts, seized
D			G	$1,075	6/11/2010	SEAB	Styled, gas, spoked front wheels, electric start
D			G	$2,000	6/5/2010	WCMO	Unstyled, full factory found spokes
D			G	$2,500	6/5/2010	WCMO	Styled
D			G	$1,900	4/17/2010	SESK	PTO, restored
D			G	$2,400	4/10/2010	ECNE	
D			G	$2,100	3/27/2010	SWIA	
D			G	$2,650	3/27/2010	SWIA	
D			G	$1,000	2/13/2010	SWIA	
D			G	$1,600	2/13/2010	SWIA	
D			G	$3,000	1/30/2010	NETX	New tires, unstyled
D			G	$3,400	1/30/2010	NETX	Unstyled, full steel
G	1938		G	$4,700	1/22/2014	Online	*BigIron.com,* item in Missouri, unstyled, manual 4F/1R, 2 cyl., 380x80R38 rear tires, 6.00x16 front tires, gas, drawbar, new exhaust
G	1938		G	$4,950	11/9/2013	SWON	Unstyled
G	1938		G	$4,950	11/9/2013	SWON	Unstyled
G	1938		F	$3,750	8/25/2012	NWIL	Round spoke rear wheels, gas
G	1938		G	$3,600	8/21/2012	WCIL	

John Deere

Model	Year	Hours	Condition	Price	Date	Area	Comments
G	1938		G	$12,500	9/1/2011	WCMN	Low radiator, skeleton wheels, rubber on front, NF, flat back, full restoration including engine, radiator gauges, and wiring
G	1938		G	$4,850	8/6/2011	NCIA	Puller
G	1938		G	$4,000	8/14/2010	SEMN	On rubber
G	1938		G	$12,000	5/29/2010	NCIL	Low radiator, complete restore, steel wheels
G	1939		G	$7,000	5/23/2012	Online	*BigIron.com,* item in South Dakota, unstyled, 4 speed, 2 cyl. gas, new front tires, runs, shedded
G	1939		G	$3,960	11/3/2011	Online	*PurpleWave.com,* item in Kansas, 20 hp 2 cyl., 6 speed, 540 PTO, hyd.
G	1940		G	$6,600	8/24/2011	ECMN	NF, PTO on cast, new 12.4x36 rubber, OH
G	1941		G	$4,000	9/21/2013	WCMI	Gas, PTO, hand start, unstyled, 12.4x38 rear tires
G	1941		G	$4,900	8/29/2013	NWIA	NF, spoked tires, restored
G	1941		E	$8,700	7/24/2010	WCIA	GP
G	1942		G	$3,900	10/23/2010	ECMO	Unstyled, PTO, SN 11295
G	1946		F	$1,101	6/23/2010	Online	*BigIron.com,* item in Nebraska, 6 speed Hi/Lo, gas, rear tires 14.9x38, front tires 7x16, 1 hyd., 540 PTO
G	1947		G	$3,095	11/15/2011	Online	*IQBID.com,* hyd., PTO
G	1948		G	$1,100	6/22/2013	SEWA	NF, 2 cyl., gas, electric starter to flywheel start, rear mounted hyd. unit, SN G33978
G	1948		G	$2,970	3/27/2013	Online	*PurpleWave.com,* item in Kansas, row crop, John Deere G 6.8L, 2 cyl. gas, 38 hp, manual
G	1948		G	$2,145	10/10/2012	Online	*PurpleWave.com,* item in Iowa, John Deere 2 cyl. gas, manual, drawbar, 540 PTO
G	1948		F	$2,500	8/25/2012	NWIL	Gas, electric start
G	1948		E	$7,800	12/3/2011	NWIL	Clamshell fenders, 14.9x38, fresh OH, older restoration, SN 32394
G	1948		G	$1,700	4/11/2011	Online	*AuctionTime.com*
G	1949		G	$5,700	5/23/2012	Online	*BigIron.com,* item in Nebraska, collectible, 6 speed, 2 cyl., gas, 38 hp, 540 PTO, 2 hyd., NF, rear hyd., adj. rear tires, electric start
G	1949		G	$6,000	3/28/2012	ECND	Factory WF, Powr Trol, rock shaft, 540 PTO, live power, dual hyd. loader, bucket
G	1949		G	$4,000	6/25/2011	ECIA	SN 35346, fenders, 3 pt., power steering, repainted
G	1950		G	$4,500	3/20/2013	WCMN	
G	1950		G	$4,400	2/9/2013	SWOH	Older restoration
G	1950		G	$3,100	5/23/2012	Online	*BigIron.com,* item in South Dakota, 6 speed, 2 cyl. gas, 1 hyd., 540 PTO, electric start
G	1950		G	$2,500	7/10/2010	SEIA	Original
G	1950		G	$1,500	6/23/2010	Online	*BigIron.com,* item in Nebraska, 6 speed Hi/Lo, 2 cyl. gas

TRACTORS

John Deere

Model	Year	Hours	Condition	Price	Date	Area	Comments
G	1951		G	$1,485	7/31/2012	Online	*PurpleWave.com,* item in Kansas, 2 cyl. all fuel, 20 hp, 6 speed, 540 PTO
G	1951		G	$2,500	7/10/2010	ECOK	
G	1952		E	$12,500	1/11/2013	NWIN	PS
G	1952		G	$1,073	7/31/2012	Online	*PurpleWave.com,* item in Kansas, 2 cyl. all fuel, 20 hp, 6 speed, 540 PTO
G	1952		E	$10,200	7/24/2010	WCIA	Original rubber
G	1952		G	$1,100	7/10/2010	ECOK	
G	1952		G	$5,000	5/29/2010	NCIL	Styled, NF
G			G	$2,200	2/22/2014	SCNE	NF, electric, runs
G			G	$4,500	11/16/2013	SCVA	2 cyl., 540 PTO, 3 pt., Roll-O-Matic front end, runs, partially restored, SN 51000
G			G	$1,760	10/22/2013	Online	*HansenandYoung.com*
G			G	$2,000	9/28/2013	SWMN	SN 42460
G			G	$5,300	8/3/2013	ECMN	NF, new 13.6x38 tires
G			G	$3,500	5/11/2013	NCOH	Repainted, runs
G			G	$4,000	5/11/2013	NCOH	Styled, older repaint, runs
G			G	$6,000	5/11/2013	NCOH	New tires, WF, 3 pt., repainted, runs
G			G	$4,150	1/9/2013	Online	*IQBID.com,* dual wheel NF, PTO, rock shaft, unstyled, SN G2259
G			G	$4,950	1/9/2013	Online	*IQBID.com,* dual wheel NF, PTO, round fenders, 13x36 tires, spoke rims, SN G7781
G			G	$5,500	9/15/2012	SCMN	NF, new rubber, electric start
G			F	$1,975	7/14/2012	SWMN	Water pump, 12x36 rears, needs valve cover gasket, flywheel seal and one rear tire
G			G	$2,100	1/28/2012	SEAB	
G			F	$1,870	11/3/2011	Online	*PurpleWave.com,* item in Kansas
G			F	$3,000	10/22/2011	NECO	Mismatched rear rubber, as is
G			F	$3,500	10/22/2011	NECO	Gas, unstyled, motor stuck
G			G	$3,500	10/22/2011	NECO	Unstyled, new front tires
G			G	$3,700	10/22/2011	NECO	WF
G			G	$3,700	10/22/2011	NECO	WF, gas
G			G	$4,250	10/22/2011	NECO	WF, fenders
G			G	$5,250	10/22/2011	NECO	Unstyled, shutters, repainted
G			G	$30,000	10/22/2011	NECO	High crop
G			F	$1,900	9/1/2011	WCMN	
G			G	$4,000	12/4/2010	SEMN	Styled, high compression head, Roll-O-Matic, power steering, new tire on front
G			G	$4,300	11/6/2010	SEMN	Styled, electric start, runs good
G			G	$5,800	9/18/2010	ECMO	Water pump, fenders, repainted
G			G	$14,000	9/18/2010	ECMO	Fenders, low rod, round spoke wheels, restored
G			G	$5,000	9/4/2010	NEIN	Unstyled
G			G	$8,200	9/4/2010	NEIN	Unstyled
G			G	$9,500	9/4/2010	NEIN	Pulling tractor
G			P	$800	9/3/2010	NEIN	Dead row, needs work and may not run or drive, as is

John Deere

Model	Year	Hours	Condition	Price	Date	Area	Comments
G			P	$2,050	8/14/2010	WCMN	PTO, rough
G			G	$4,000	8/7/2010	SCMN	NF, electric start, power steering, PTO, gas, 13.6x38 tires, SN 30447
G			G	$4,000	7/31/2010	NWIL	Gas, unstyled, original paint
G			G	$6,500	7/31/2010	NWIL	Gas, unstyled, original, restored radiator, NF, spoke wheels, solid rear rims
G			G	$1,850	7/17/2010	NEMT	
G			G	$3,200	7/17/2010	NEMT	
G			G	$5,000	7/17/2010	NEMT	
G			G	$9,300	7/17/2010	NEMT	Low radiator
G			G	$4,450	6/23/2010	Online	*BigIron.com,* item in Nebraska, 3 speed, 2 cyl. gas, rear tires spoked, one cutoff, 12x36 tires, front tires 6.00x16, steel plate front rims, engine free
G			P	$3,050	6/17/2010	SEIA	Non running
G			G	$4,000	6/5/2010	WCMO	1 hyd., WF
G			G	$4,700	6/5/2010	WCMO	Unstyled, 1 hyd., shutters
G			G	$6,500	6/5/2010	WCMO	Unstyled, rear rounds, front cut downs, PTO, fenders, new rubber
G			G	$1,100	2/13/2010	SWIA	
G			G	$2,700	2/13/2010	SWIA	
G			G	$4,500	2/13/2010	SWIA	
G			G	$3,200	1/30/2010	NETX	Styled
GM	1945		G	$2,400	9/21/2013	WCMI	Gas, PTO, electric start, power lift, NF, 13.x38 rear tires, restored
GM	1946		F	$2,600	11/13/2010	NWIL	Not running, 1 new rear tire, gas
GM	1947		G	$4,750	10/23/2010	SCPA	
GM			G	$4,500	7/21/2012	ECIA	Hand start, repainted, new tires, runs
GM			G	$4,000	6/25/2011	ECIA	SN 13077, older repaint
GM			G	$4,000	9/18/2010	ECMO	New rear, electric start, repainted
GM			G	$6,000	9/4/2010	NEIN	Hand start
GM			F	$1,300	7/17/2010	NEMT	Stuck
GM			G	$900	2/13/2010	SWIA	
GP	1929		F	$2,600	2/6/2013	SESD	On steel, not running
GP	1929		G	$5,300	12/19/2012	ECWI	
GP	1929		G	$2,860	10/10/2012	Online	*PurpleWave.com,* item in Iowa, John Deere 2 cyl. gas, manual, spring seat
GP	1929		G	$2,100	8/25/2012	NWIL	Old restoration, gas
GP	1929		G	$5,000	5/28/2012	ECMO	On full steel, original, tin good
GP	1929		G	$3,300	5/23/2012	Online	*BigIron.com,* item in South Dakota, 3 speed, 2 cyl., gas, runs, shedded
GP	1929		G	$8,500	3/24/2012	NEIN	New tires, front/rear round spokes, fully restored, runs
GP	1929		G	$4,500	7/22/2011	SEMN	Flat spoke steel rear with lugs, rubber tire fronts on round spoke, older restoration
GP	1930		G	$4,000	8/10/2013	NCIA	SN 223307
GP	1931		G	$1,350	11/9/2013	SWON	Wide tread, original, on full steel, partial cultivator
GP	1931		G	$12,500	8/7/2010	SEWI	Rare "Beaner" model, designed primarily for Michigan bean farmers, WF

John Deere

Model	Year	Hours	Condition	Price	Date	Area	Comments
GP	1934		G	$2,600	11/9/2013	SWON	Standard
GP	1934		G	$2,600	11/9/2013	SWON	Standard
GP	1934		G	$5,000	6/5/2010	ECMI	Steel wheels, beaner
GP	1934		G	$7,000	6/5/2010	ECMI	Rubber tires, PTO, beaner
GP	1935		G	$14,000	8/7/2010	SEWI	Expo quality restoration, rare orchard style exhaust, manifold and unique air cleaner found only on 1935 models
GP			G	$1,500	6/16/2012	ECIN	Full steel, not running, older repaint
GP			G	$1,600	6/16/2012	ECIN	Complete, not running
GP			G	$2,600	6/16/2012	ECIN	Rear steel, front spokes, incomplete
GP			G	$2,750	6/16/2012	ECIN	Full steel, PTO power lift, complete slant plug cyl. head, low air cleaner, rare 2-way plow
GP			G	$3,600	6/16/2012	ECIN	Big bore, full steel, incomplete, last 1931 built
GP			G	$3,750	6/16/2012	ECIN	Wide tread, 3R cultivator
GP			G	$4,200	6/16/2012	ECIN	Big bore, full round spokes, not running
GP			G	$4,400	6/16/2012	ECIN	Full steel, PTO power lift, 3R corn planter, older restoration
GP			G	$4,400	6/16/2012	ECIN	Full steel, repainted
GP			G	$4,500	6/16/2012	ECIN	Full steel, not running, original
GP			G	$4,700	6/16/2012	ECIN	Full steel, not running
GP			G	$7,000	6/16/2012	ECIN	Full steel PTO, power lift, 3R cultivator, older restoration
GP			G	$7,100	6/16/2012	ECIN	3R planter
GP			G	$7,500	6/16/2012	ECIN	Bean special, repainted, front and rear round spokes, motor turns over, swing seat, new tires
GP			G	$9,000	6/16/2012	ECIN	Bean axle, full round spokes, PTO power lift, swing seat, 18" front round spokes, restored
GP			G	$9,000	6/16/2012	ECIN	Bean axle, full steel extension and road bands, swing seat, PTO power lift, restored
GP			G	$10,000	6/16/2012	ECIN	Bean axle, full round spokes, swing seat, PTO power lift, restored
GP			G	$10,000	6/16/2012	ECIN	Bean axle, full steel, swing seat, restored
GP			G	$11,000	6/16/2012	ECIN	Bean axle, full round spokes, screw on front round spokes, swing seat, restored
GP			G	$22,000	6/16/2012	ECIN	2,way plow
GP			G	$25,000	6/16/2012	ECIN	Experimental bean axle, complete, stuck
GP			G	$48,000	6/16/2012	ECIN	Wide tread, sickle bar mower
GP			G	$5,600	3/24/2012	NEIN	Repainted, front/rear round spokes, new tires, runs
GP			G	$6,300	3/24/2012	NEIN	Cut off front/rear spokes, new turf tires, restored, runs
GP			G	$1,250	10/22/2011	NECO	No serial tag, PTO, power lift, incomplete
GP			F	$2,400	10/22/2011	NECO	New rear tires, motor now stuck
GP			G	$3,100	10/22/2011	NECO	
GP			G	$3,600	10/22/2011	NECO	Big bore

John Deere

Model	Year	Hours	Condition	Price	Date	Area	Comments
GP			G	$3,800	10/22/2011	NECO	New rear tires, Vortec air breather
GP			G	$4,100	10/22/2011	NECO	New rear tires
GP			G	$4,400	10/22/2011	NECO	Full steel, power lift, PTO
GP			G	$7,500	10/22/2011	NECO	Full steel, slant plug head
GP			G	$8,300	6/25/2011	ECIA	GP A, open fan shaft, SN 410708, new tires, fenders, repainted
GP			G	$3,700	9/18/2010	ECMO	Repainted, steel wheels, small bore, no serial tag
GP			G	$4,800	9/18/2010	ECMO	No tag, full steel
GP			G	$24,000	9/18/2010	ECMO	Bean axle, spokes
GP			P	$900	9/11/2010	NCIL	On steel, not running, stuck
GP			G	$4,900	9/9/2010	NWWI	
GP			G	$2,800	9/4/2010	NEIN	
GP			G	$3,500	9/4/2010	NEIN	Full steel
GP			G	$6,250	9/4/2010	NEIN	
GP			G	$9,900	9/4/2010	NEIN	
GP			P	$2,400	9/3/2010	NEIN	Big bore, dead row, needs work and may not run or drive, as is
GP			P	$2,400	9/3/2010	NEIN	Dead row, needs work and may not run or drive, as is
GP			G	$3,000	7/31/2010	NWIL	Unstyled, old restoration, round spoke on front and rear, 2R cultivator on front and rear
GP			G	$3,700	7/31/2010	NWIL	Gas, unstyled, repainted
GP			F	$2,350	7/17/2010	NEMT	Stuck
GP			G	$2,700	7/17/2010	NEMT	
GP			G	$4,300	7/17/2010	NEMT	
GP			G	$5,200	7/17/2010	NEMT	Tricycle
GP			G	$5,700	7/17/2010	NEMT	Full steel with extension rims
GP			G	$7,100	7/17/2010	NEMT	
GP			G	$3,100	6/23/2010	Online	*BigIron.com,* item in Nebraska, front spoke rims, broken muffler, all pieces there
GP			G	$2,000	6/5/2010	WCMO	New tires
GP			G	$2,600	6/5/2010	WCMO	Cut off wheels
GPWT			G	$5,000	6/16/2012	ECIN	Full steel, front sand steel, PTO power lift, 2R cultivator, older restoration
GPWT			G	$8,000	6/16/2012	ECIN	Full steel, road bands, Texas sand front wheels, PTO power lift 2R Lister planter, completely restored
GPWT			G	$9,000	6/16/2012	ECIN	No tag, top steer, carcass
GPWT			G	$9,300	6/16/2012	ECIN	Wide tread, front and rear steel wheels, front Texas sand wheels, swing seat, big bore, repainted
GPWT			G	$10,500	6/16/2012	ECIN	PTO, power lift, full steel, rare over band rear steel, button lugs, swing seat, 1 of 2 extremely rare GPWT sickle bar mower, restored
GPWT			G	$15,000	6/16/2012	ECIN	Full steel rare potato rear steel, side hill drawbar shifter
GPWT			G	$23,000	6/16/2012	ECIN	Top steer
GPWT			G	$70,000	6/16/2012	ECIN	2R Lister planter

TRACTORS

TRACTORS

John Deere

Model	Year	Hours	Condition	Price	Date	Area	Comments
GPWT			G	$7,500	10/22/2011	NECO	PTO, swing seat, 6" bore
GPWT			G	$7,900	10/22/2011	NECO	6" bore, converted to top steer, full steel
GPWT			G	$18,000	10/22/2011	NECO	Top steer, PTO, power lift, front cut offs
GPWT			G	$12,500	7/31/2010	NWIL	Wide tread, new rubber, NF, 4 round spokes, repainted and primed, ready for coat
GPWT			G	$5,700	7/17/2010	NEMT	
GPWT			G	$22,000	7/17/2010	NEMT	Top steer
GW	1951		G	$5,750	9/6/2012	Online	*IQBID.com,* item in Minnesota, older restoration
GW	1952		G	$6,600	8/24/2011	ECMN	PTO, clam shell fenders, new rubber
GW			G	$8,500	3/22/2013	NWMN	Repainted, WF, 3 pt., fenders, weights, runs
GW			G	$5,900	7/21/2012	ECIA	New tires, repainted, water pump, runs
GW			G	$7,000	6/25/2011	ECIA	SN 63484, new tires, WF, water pump, repainted
GW			G	$5,100	8/14/2010	WCMN	OH and restored, new rubber, nice straight, WF
GW			G	$5,700	7/17/2010	NEMT	
H	1939		G	$6,500	9/6/2012	Online	*IQBID.com,* item in Minnesota, complete restoration
H	1939		G	$1,750	5/19/2012	SWMI	NF, new 9.5x32 tires, fenders, no PTO, styled
H	1940		G	$1,800	11/10/2012	NCNC	
H	1940		G	$4,250	10/23/2010	SCPA	
H	1941		G	$2,250	9/1/2011	WCMN	NF, PTO, older restoration
H	1941		G	$4,900	9/1/2011	WCMN	Electric start, 6V lights, wheel weights, new front. tires, restored
H	1941		G	$1,600	11/20/2010	ECFL	Older restoration, no PTO
H	1942		G	$3,250	6/22/2013	SEWA	NF, 2 cyl., gas to hand flywheel start, right side belt drive, rear PTO, SN H-33266
H	1942		G	$5,100	8/24/2011	ECMN	Hyd., PTO, starter, lights, fenders, new 9.5x32 rubber
H	1942		G	$2,250	6/23/2010	Online	*BigIron.com,* item in Nebraska, 3F/1R, 2 cyl. gas, rear tires 9x32, front tires 4x15, 540 PTO, wheel weights not included
H	1944		G	$2,800	7/10/2010	ECOK	
H	1946		G	$2,500	10/12/2011	NWOH	PTO, rear wheel weights, repainted
H			G	$4,600	3/22/2014	WCMO	Fully restored, new rubber
H			F	$2,800	11/16/2013	SCVA	2 cyl., 540 PTO, 3 pt., partially restored
H			G	$1,622	10/22/2013	Online	*HansenandYoung.com,* electric start, hyd. PTO
H			G	$2,400	8/3/2013	ECMN	NF, 9x32 tires, hand start
H			G	$3,125	5/11/2013	NCOH	Runs, electric start, lighting, older repaint
H			G	$3,400	3/23/2013	NEIN	Repainted, fenders, runs
H			G	$3,900	3/23/2013	NEIN	Fenders, repainted, new tires, runs
H			G	$2,900	11/17/2012	SWMN	Electric starter, like new rubber, cultivator
H			G	$2,000	9/22/2012	NEOR	Manual start, NF
H			G	$3,000	9/22/2012	NEOR	Electric start
H			G	$2,000	6/16/2012	ECIN	Rare 1 bottom plow

Model	Year	Hours	Condition	Price	Date	Area	Comments
H			G	$3,400	3/24/2012	NEIN	Repainted, new tires, electric start, lighting, hyd.
H			G	$2,420	11/3/2011	Online	*PurpleWave.com,* item in Kansas
H			P	$2,200	10/22/2011	NECO	Engine stuck
H			F	$3,300	10/22/2011	NECO	Electric start, new rear tires, as is
H			G	$2,700	3/23/2011	ECMN	All original
H			F	$1,750	11/20/2010	NCOH	Complete, not running
H			P	$950	9/3/2010	NEIN	Dead row, needs work and may not run or drive, as is
H			G	$3,000	8/7/2010	SCMN	NF, electric start, PTO, 19.5x32 tires, SN 52832
H			F	$1,400	7/17/2010	NEMT	Stuck
H			G	$1,500	7/17/2010	NEMT	
H			G	$1,600	7/17/2010	NEMT	
H			G	$2,300	7/17/2010	NEMT	
H			G	$3,000	7/17/2010	NEMT	
H			G	$2,500	6/5/2010	WCMO	Electric start
HWH	1941		G	$38,000	9/1/2011	Online	*IQBID.com,* hyd. pump, 10x38 rear rubber, complete restoration, 126 made
HWH			G	$7,000	6/25/2011	ECIA	SN 22914, WF welded, rear rims welded, sheet metal rough, older repaint, does not archive as a true HWH
HWH			F	$7,250	7/17/2010	NEMT	Stuck
HWH			G	$23,000	7/17/2010	NEMT	Stuck
L	1937		G	$3,600	11/9/2013	SWON	Unstyled, belt pulley and partial cultivators
L	1938		G	$5,500	6/25/2011	ECIA	Unstyled, SN 621439, new tires, repainted
L	1938		F	$9,000	3/26/2011	WCOH	Stored inside
L	1938		G	$6,500	10/23/2010	SCPA	Unstyled
L	1939		F	$900	11/20/2010	ECFL	Hand crank, very restorable
L	1939		G	$4,600	10/23/2010	SCPA	
L	1942		G	$3,500	9/15/2011	ECIA	Restored, Johnny Popper L
L	1942		G	$11,000	8/24/2011	ECMN	Starter, PTO, lights, new 7.5x22 rubber
L	1943		G	$2,600	4/11/2011	Online	*AuctionTime.com,* 2WD
L			F	$2,100	11/16/2013	SCVA	2 cyl., cultivators, hand cranks, equipped with electric starter
L			G	$6,250	8/3/2013	ECMN	Unstyled, 750x22 tires
L			G	$1,650	6/15/2013	WCMI	WF, SN L640439
L			G	$2,050	5/11/2013	NCOH	Repainted yellow, new tires, runs
L			G	$2,300	5/11/2013	NCOH	Repainted yellow, electric start, runs
L			G	$2,300	5/11/2013	NCOH	Styled, new tires, repainted, hand start, runs
L			G	$2,700	5/11/2013	NCOH	Electric start, new tires, repainted, runs
L			G	$3,800	3/23/2013	NEIN	Styled, belt pulley, nice original, OH motor, runs
L			G	$3,200	10/22/2011	NECO	New rear tires, 1R cultivators
L			G	$3,400	10/22/2011	NECO	Unstyled, welded block and pulley
L			G	$13,250	1/6/2011	NENC	Unstyled
L			G	$3,800	9/18/2010	ECMO	Lights, restored
L			G	$8,500	9/9/2010	NWWI	Unstyled, 1 bottom plow

John Deere

Model	Year	Hours	Condition	Price	Date	Area	Comments
L			G	$2,600	9/4/2010	NEIN	
L			G	$3,000	9/4/2010	NEIN	
L			G	$4,600	9/4/2010	NEIN	Unstyled
L			G	$1,300	7/31/2010	NWIL	Styled, on rubber, rear wheel weights
L			G	$3,000	7/31/2010	NWIL	Unstyled, WF, painted primer, good rubber on back
L			G	$3,000	7/17/2010	NEMT	
L			G	$7,500	7/17/2010	NEMT	Unstyled
L			G	$1,600	6/5/2010	WCMO	Cultivators, serial tag
L			G	$2,100	6/5/2010	WCMO	Serial plate
L			G	$2,800	6/5/2010	WCMO	Cultivator brackets
LA	1941		G	$2,600	9/21/2013	WCMI	Gas, electric start, drawbar, 10x24 rear tires, restored
LA	1941		E	$3,750	10/15/2011	ECIA	WF, parade ready, 10x24 rear tires
LA	1941		G	$3,200	8/20/2011	NEMN	Restored, 1 bottom plow and cultivator, SN AL2084t
LA	1942		G	$5,500	10/23/2010	SCPA	
LA	1944		F	$1,250	11/9/2013	SWON	Needs starter
LA	1946		G	$9,500	9/6/2012	Online	*IQBID.com,* item in Minnesota, complete restoration
LA	1946		G	$3,250	10/12/2011	NWOH	Cast iron rear wheels, 24" tires
LA	1949		G	$2,100	10/7/2011	NWSD	PTO, hyd., older restoration, sheet metal very straight
LA	1949		G	$4,000	8/7/2010	WCMN	Gas, engine good
LA			G	$6,500	8/3/2013	ECMN	New 9.5x25 tires, pulley
LA			G	$2,700	5/11/2013	NCOH	1 bottom plow, new tires, repainted, runs
LA			G	$3,000	3/23/2013	NEIN	Repainted, electric start, runs
LA			G	$5,050	12/19/2012	ECWI	
LA			G	$4,510	11/3/2011	Online	*PurpleWave.com,* item in Kansas
LA			G	$2,900	10/22/2011	NECO	New tires, electric start
LA			G	$3,100	10/22/2011	NECO	Sickle mower
LA			G	$3,500	6/25/2011	ECIA	No tag, new tires, electric start, lights, repainted
LA			G	$2,600	9/4/2010	NEIN	
LA			G	$2,750	9/4/2010	NEIN	Cultivator, belt pulley
LA			G	$3,500	7/17/2010	NEMT	No tag
LA			G	$5,200	7/17/2010	NEMT	
LA			G	$2,500	6/11/2010	SEAB	Gas, belly mount, sickle mower
LA			G	$4,000	6/11/2010	SEAB	Gas
LA			G	$2,300	6/5/2010	WCMO	No serial tag, hand start
LA			G	$2,600	6/5/2010	WCMO	Belt pulley, 2-way plow, no serial tag
LA			G	$2,800	6/5/2010	WCMO	Electric start, serial tag
LI	1947		G	$3,400	10/12/2011	NWOH	Repainted, electric start
LI	1947		G	$3,750	10/12/2011	NWOH	Repainted, electric start, lights, gas pedal, drawbar, new front and 22" rear tires
LI			G	$4,500	12/4/2013	ECIN	Lights work, replacement tag, new front tires 4x15, rear tires 9.5x24 95%
LI			G	$1,800	5/11/2013	NCOH	Belt pulley, runs
LI			G	$2,950	7/21/2012	ECIA	Styled, sickle mower, green, runs good

John Deere

Model	Year	Hours	Condition	Price	Date	Area	Comments
LI			G	$3,700	3/24/2012	NEIN	Electric start, lighting, foot throttle, new tires, repainted, runs
LI			G	$5,100	3/22/2012	ECMN	Industrial, older restoration, runs good
LI			G	$4,000	6/25/2011	ECIA	SN 50463, hyd., eclectic start, lighting, repainted
LI			G	$5,000	7/17/2010	NEMT	
LI			G	$2,200	6/5/2010	WCMO	Serial tag
M	1947		G	$2,650	8/6/2011	NCIA	Industrial
M	1948		G	$3,300	12/1/2011	SEMN	
M	1948		F	$3,025	11/19/2011	SEIA	Professionally restored, newer rubber, 6V system, parade ready
M	1948		G	$3,900	9/1/2011	WCMN	New front tires, restored
M	1948		G	$2,500	8/20/2011	NEMN	Restored, nice, good rubber, SN M23535
M	1948		G	$3,000	6/25/2011	ECIA	SN 11930, new tires, cultivator, repainted
M	1949		E	$6,000	4/14/2014	SCSK	11.2/10x24 rear tires, 5x15SL front tires, fully restored, running
M	1949		G	$1,250	5/28/2012	ECMO	Restored, new tires, runs
M	1949		G	$3,000	9/15/2011	ECIA	Restored, blade, SN SM23750
M	1949		E	$2,100	9/22/2010	NECO	WF, gas, restored
M	1949		G	$3,750	5/29/2010	NCIL	
M	1950		G	$2,600	9/21/2013	WCMI	Gas, PTO, 3 pt., electric start, 11.2x24 rear tires, unrestored
M	1950		G	$4,500	5/1/2013	WCSK	18 hp, 1.6L, 2 cyl. gas, shedded
M	1950		G	$2,250	11/17/2010	ECMS	WF, gas, wheel weights
M	1951		G	$3,900	8/24/2011	ECMN	PTO, 6 bolt hubs
M	1951		G	$2,800	6/22/2011	NECO	WF, gas, PTO
M			G	$1,600	1/4/2014	WCNY	Cultivator and plow
M			G	$2,750	9/18/2013	ECMT	Restored, gas, 4 speed, PTO, 3 pt., new front tires and alternator, good runner
M			G	$5,000	8/3/2013	ECMN	WF, new 11.2x24 tires, rear weights
M			G	$3,500	6/22/2013	SEWA	2 cyl., gas, direct electric start, rear PTO, 3 pt., attached sickle mower, SN M-18903
M			G	$5,000	6/15/2013	WCOH	Weights, restored, John Deere 2 bottom M plow, runs
M			G	$2,050	5/11/2013	NCOH	Rear weights, older repaint, runs
M		108	G	$1,250	4/2/2013	ECIA	WF, 2 pt., 540 PTO, hand crank electrical start
M			G	$2,150	3/23/2013	NEIN	Repainted, new tires, runs
M			G	$2,000	9/22/2012	NEOR	John Deere No. 5 mower, WF
M			G	$1,200	7/28/2012	NWSC	
M			P	$800	6/9/2012	ECNE	Not running, PTO
M			G	$1,650	3/24/2012	SWMI	2 cyl. gas, WF, hyd. drawbar, PTO, 12.4x24 rears
M			G	$1,400	2/4/2012	NENC	
M			G	$960	12/28/2011	Online	*BigIron.com,* item in Nebraska, WF, 6-ply tires
M			G	$2,100	10/22/2011	NECO	
M			F	$2,200	10/22/2011	NECO	New tires, as is
M			G	$3,850	9/14/2011	Online	*BigIron.com,* item in Kansas, manual, gas, WF, 3 pt., shedded, new battery and fuel bowl in fuel line, 2R plow

John Deere

Model	Year	Hours	Condition	Price	Date	Area	Comments
M			G	$2,500	9/18/2010	ECMO	Restored
M			G	$2,000	7/17/2010	NEMT	
M			G	$3,250	7/17/2010	NEMT	
M			G	$975	6/5/2010	NCTN	
M			G	$1,800	6/5/2010	WCMO	
M			G	$2,350	6/5/2010	ECMN	WF, 60" belly mower
M			G	$2,500	6/5/2010	WCMO	Front and rear weights
M			G	$2,650	6/5/2010	WCMO	Nice, original
M			G	$1,700	1/30/2010	NETX	
M			G	$2,100	1/30/2010	NETX	
MI	1949		G	$4,000	10/12/2011	NWOH	Orange, Detroit harvester sickle bar mower, PTO, new tires
MI			G	$2,900	3/24/2012	NEIN	Repaint, new tires, runs
MI			G	$2,500	10/12/2011	NWOH	Yellow, rebuilt engine, repainted
MI			G	$2,900	10/12/2011	NWOH	Yellow
MI			G	$6,900	8/14/2010	WCMN	6' side mount sickle mower, WF
MI			F	$2,500	7/17/2010	NEMT	Stuck, no tag
MT	1949		G	$3,750	8/24/2011	ECMN	WF, PTO, new 11.2x34 rubber
MT	1950		G	$4,200	9/6/2012	Online	*IQBID.com,* item in Minnesota, complete restoration
MT	1950		G	$2,400	9/1/2011	WCMN	PTO, fenders, 11.2x34 rubber, long axles, restored
MT	1950		G	$3,200	8/24/2011	ECMN	NF, 3 pt., PTO, mounted 2R cultivator, new 11.2 and 10x34 rubber
MT	1950		G	$2,800	7/24/2010	WCIA	
MT	1951		F	$1,950	6/20/2012	SESD	Tricycle front
MT	1951		G	$2,241	11/15/2011	Online	*IQBID.com*
MT	1951		G	$3,100	9/15/2011	ECIA	Restored, NF, SN 22973
MT	1951		G	$1,500	4/8/2011	WCMI	Gas, NF, PTO, flat puller, drawbar hitch, rolls free, 10x34 tires
MT	1951		G	$1,900	11/20/2010	ECFL	Very restorable, PTO, runs
MT	1951		F	$4,200	11/13/2010	NWIL	Factory WF, super straight, original, gas
MT			G	$2,035	10/22/2013	Online	*HansenandYoung.com,* starts, runs, drives
MT			G	$1,050	8/14/2013	WCMN	10x34, good tires, SN 16379
MT			G	$2,900	8/3/2013	ECMN	NF, 11.2x34 tires, pulley
MT			G	$1,800	5/11/2013	NCOH	Older repaint, new tires, runs
MT			G	$2,200	3/23/2013	NEIN	Repainted, runs
MT			G	$3,600	2/6/2013	SESD	
MT			G	$2,100	8/16/2012	Online	*IQBID.com,* item in Minnesota, NF, 95% tires, restored
MT			G	$1,700	7/21/2012	ECIA	NF, new tires
MT			G	$2,100	7/21/2012	ECIA	WF, new tires, repainted
MT			G	$2,600	6/16/2012	ECIN	Front and rear weights, SF, repainted
MT			G	$1,050	3/24/2012	SWMI	
MT			F	$1,300	3/20/2012	WCIL	
MT			G	$1,550	1/31/2012	NEIN	
MT			G	$1,100	10/22/2011	NECO	
MT			G	$1,925	6/29/2011	Online	*PurpleWave.com,* item in Kansas, 2 cyl. gas, manual, 4F/1R, 3 pt., 540 PTO

John Deere

Model	Year	Hours	Condition	Price	Date	Area	Comments
MT			P	$1,175	3/5/2011	SEMN	John Deere sickle mower, NF, fenders, not running
MT			F	$800	11/18/2010	SEOK	
MT			G	$3,250	9/4/2010	NEIN	
MT			G	$2,600	8/14/2010	WCMN	Belt pulley, good rubber, new front tires, new paint, dual Touch-O-Matic, NF
MT			G	$1,900	8/7/2010	SCMN	NF, 11.2/10x34 tires, SN 11770
MT			G	$1,050	7/17/2010	NEMT	
MT			G	$2,150	7/17/2010	NEMT	
MT			G	$2,300	7/17/2010	NEMT	
MT			G	$2,000	6/5/2010	WCMO	Belly mower
MT			G	$2,100	6/5/2010	ECMN	NF
MT			G	$2,000	1/30/2010	NETX	
N	1934		G	$2,900	11/20/2010	ECFL	Open fan shaft, cut off wheels, PTO
R	1949		G	$6,800	11/9/2013	SWON	Diesel, original, PTO
R	1949		G	$4,600	10/7/2011	NWSD	PTO, hyd., restored
R	1950		G	$4,290	10/16/2013	Online	*PurpleWave.com,* item in Kansas, 2 cyl. diesel, 2 cyl. gas Pony motor, 540 PTO, drawbar
R	1950		G	$7,500	8/7/2010	SEWI	
R	1950		G	$4,900	7/10/2010	SEIA	Diesel, straight, original
R	1950		G	$3,000	5/29/2010	NCIL	WF, diesel
R	1951		G	$3,500	2/1/2011	NEIN	Nice original
R	1951		G	$5,000	7/24/2010	WCIA	New rubber
R	1952		G	$5,000	9/6/2012	Online	*IQBID.com,* item in Minnesota, original condition
R	1952		G	$7,000	10/23/2010	SCPA	
R	1953		G	$4,250	12/19/2013	WCMN	WF, diesel, hyd., 540 PTO, hand clutch, 18.4x34 tires, 7.5x18 tires
R	1953		G	$2,500	11/20/2010	ECFL	Diesel, very restorable, runs
R	1954		G	$8,200	8/24/2011	ECMN	PTO, new 16.9x34 rubber
R	1962		G	$4,750	6/22/2013	SEWA	2 cyl., gas, flywheel electric starter, right side belt drive, SN 13415
R			F	$3,500	4/14/2014	SCSK	Running
R			G	$7,250	8/3/2013	ECMN	Standard diesel, Pony start, new 16.9x34 tires
R			G	$3,900	5/11/2013	NCOH	Older repaint, PTO, runs
R			G	$5,100	3/23/2013	NEIN	Older repaint, Pony, runs
R			G	$5,250	3/23/2013	NEIN	All new tires, PTO, hyd., original, runs
R			G	$6,500	9/22/2012	NEOR	WF
R			G	$6,250	7/21/2012	ECIA	23.1 tires, original paint, very good condition
R			G	$4,200	3/24/2012	NEIN	Repainted, fender extensions, rear weights, PTO, hyd., Pony runs well
R			G	$6,250	3/24/2012	NEIN	PTO, hyd., repainted, weights, runs
R			G	$4,500	1/31/2012	NEIN	Older repaint, PTO, hyd.
R			G	$2,800	10/22/2011	NECO	PTO
R			G	$3,900	10/22/2011	NECO	Diesel, rear weights, PTO
R			G	$3,900	10/22/2011	NECO	Diesel, rear weights, PTO
R			G	$4,900	5/4/2011	WCSK	2WD, diesel, starter Pup rebuilt, 18.4x34 RR, 2 hyd., belt pulley, running

John Deere

Model	Year	Hours	Condition	Price	Date	Area	Comments
R			G	$6,700	9/11/2010	NCIL	Diesel, standard, Pony motor, good rubber
R			G	$5,750	9/4/2010	NEIN	
R			G	$6,700	8/14/2010	WCMN	Good Pony, new radiator, new rubber, 3 pt., PTO, 1 hyd., some engine work, new paint
R			G	$8,000	8/7/2010	SCMN	Diesel, WF, Pony start, PTO, 18.4x34 tires, SN 4447
R			F	$2,900	7/17/2010	NEMT	No tag, stuck
R			G	$4,100	6/5/2010	WCMO	PTO, 1 hyd., running
R			F	$1,250	1/30/2010	NETX	
R			G	$2,500	1/30/2010	NETX	

Lanz

Model	Year	Hours	Condition	Price	Date	Area	Comments
N/A	1958		G	$6,250	9/21/2013	WCNY	25 hp

Leader

Model	Year	Hours	Condition	Price	Date	Area	Comments
16-32	1920		G	$80,000	9/21/2013	WCNY	
N/A	1946		G	$1,200	3/22/2013	WCMI	WF, 9.5x24 rear tires, runs
N/A	1948		G	$4,250	10/23/2010	SCPA	
N/A	1949		G	$4,250	10/23/2010	SCPA	

Long

Model	Year	Hours	Condition	Price	Date	Area	Comments
1100	1975		F	$2,800	6/9/2010	ECIA	2WD

Massey Ferguson

Model	Year	Hours	Condition	Price	Date	Area	Comments
20	1969		G	$2,300	9/28/2011	Online	*BigIron.com,* item in Nebraska, loader, blade, harrow, 3 speed, Hi/Lo, 3 cyl. 2.5L, gas, 42 hp, 540 PTO
20			G	$1,700	12/5/2013	SCIA	Gas, loader
20			G	$3,100	1/26/2012	SEAL	Front loader
20			G	$2,250	4/9/2010	WCFL	Loader
30	1954		G	$2,860	5/9/2012	Online	*PurpleWave.com,* item in Kansas, Continental 4 cyl. gas, 28 hp, Hi/Lo Sherman OD, 3 pt., 540 PTO, dust cover
30	1978	1,672	G	$4,900	4/3/2013	Online	*BigIron.com,* item in Oklahoma, forward and reverse foot pedal, auto with no clutch, industrial hydro, Perkins diesel, 45 hp, 2 hyd., box blade with 6 rippers
30			G	$1,600	4/18/2011	SESK	
35	1960	1,911	G	$2,900	3/24/2012	SETN	6 speed, 37 hp, gas, ag tires at 70%, filled

Massey Ferguson

Model	Year	Hours	Condition	Price	Date	Area	Comments
35	1961	3,200	G	$3,500	2/22/2014	NEIN	Gas, PS, live PTO, new paint
35	1961		G	$1,600	4/11/2011	Online	*AuctionTime.com,* 2WD
35	1962		F	$2,000	1/11/2012	Online	*BigIron.com,* item in Iowa, hour meter inoperable, 3 speed Hi/Lo, 4 cyl. gas, 35 hp, 540 PTO, starts
35	1962		G	$3,300	5/26/2010	ECSD	Deluxe
35	1963	1,158	G	$1,800	2/22/2014	ECMI	Diesel, 2WD, WF, 3 pt., 540 PTO, 1 hyd., 12.4x28 rear tires
35		29,093	G	$1,050	3/22/2014	WCWA	Classic, great running condition
35			G	$1,600	1/25/2014	NWMD	
35			G	$2,600	11/9/2013	SWON	Gas, 3 pt. blade, SN 199185
35			G	$2,500	4/25/2013	SWSK	2WD, gas, 3 pt., 540 PTO, 11.2x28 rubber
35			G	$1,750	3/30/2013	NWIL	Gas, live power, power steering, 3 pt., runs, drives
35			G	$1,600	3/2/2013	NETN	Loader
35			G	$925	1/19/2013	NEMS	
35			G	$2,250	11/30/2012	SCMT	Deluxe, gas, 3 pt., PTO, 35 hp
35			F	$1,000	2/4/2012	NEAR	4 cyl. gas, 3 pt., 540 PTO, 12.4x28 rears
35			F	$1,750	10/29/2011	ECMN	Loader
35			F	$2,000	5/7/2011	SWMB	Loader, 3 pt., clutch problems
35			G	$1,900	11/20/2010	SCKY	
35			F	$2,500	11/20/2010	SCKY	
35			G	$2,000	11/18/2010	SEOK	
35			G	$1,250	11/4/2010	SEON	4 cyl. gas
35			G	$2,650	10/16/2010	NCTN	Gas
35			G	$1,400	5/7/2010	WCOH	Diesel on hard rubber wheels
35			G	$1,550	5/7/2010	WCOH	Diesel
35			G	$1,700	5/7/2010	WCOH	Diesel, 3 cyl., power steering

It's kind of amazing how down right beautiful a 40-year-old tractor can look, isn't it? Lay your eyes on this 1971 Massey Ferguson 165 with 2,026 hours, and tell me it's not pretty to look at. It was always shedded and is just beautiful. Apparently bidders at the April 26, 2013, farm auction in east-central Alberta, Canada thought this tractor was pretty too, as it went for $13,500. How high is that? The next-highest sale price I've seen on a Massey Ferguson 165 tractor during the past 18 years was $6,500 for a 165 all-the-way back at a May 7, 2000, collector auction in eastern Maryland. That Massey Ferugson 165 had just 2,638 hours on it, but it also sold with a loader.

PETE'S PICK

Massey Ferguson

Model	Year	Hours	Condition	Price	Date	Area	Comments
50	1958		G	$1,750	10/7/2011	NWSD	Unrestored, power steering, 3 pt., hyd., spin-out rims, straight, new rubber
50			F	$963	3/27/2013	Online	*PurpleWave.com,* item in Kansas, 4 cyl. LP, manual, spring suspension seat, 3 pt.
50		5,283	G	$1,430	8/31/2011	Online	*PurpleWave.com,* item in Kansas, 4 cyl., 3 pt., top link missing, 540 PTO
50			G	$3,500	5/11/2011	ECAB	4 cyl. gas, PTO, standard
50			F	$1,700	11/20/2010	SCKY	
50			G	$1,900	5/7/2010	WCOH	Gas, power steering
50		3,497	G	$2,250	5/4/2010	WCOK	3 pt., PTO, gas
50		7,849	G	$1,650	4/10/2010	ECON	
65	1956		G	$3,600	7/10/2010	SEIA	Gas, complete rebuild, new paint
65	1958		G	$2,860	11/13/2013	Online	*PurpleWave.com,* item in Kansas, 4 cyl. gas, 43 hp, 6 speed, 3 pt.
65	1958	1,628	P	$770	10/23/2013	Online	*PurpleWave.com,* item in Minnesota, 540 PTO, 3 pt.
65	1958	3,415	E	$5,250	4/26/2013	ECAB	Gas, 40 hp, 3 pt., 13.6x28 rear tires, SN SGM655667
65	1959	5,420	F	$1,900	10/24/2012	NECO	Diesel, WF, 3 pt., loader
65	1959		G	$2,100	6/11/2010	SEAB	Gas, 3 pt., 540 live PTO, rubber, motor rebuilt 40 hours ago
65	1960		F	$800	7/10/2010	SEIA	Diesel
65	1962	4,850	G	$3,000	4/27/2011	NECO	WF, gas, 3 pt., front weights
65	1963		G	$2,800	12/14/2011	WCMN	Diesel, WF, hyd. loader, runs off PTO
65	1964	6,188	F	$3,600	7/16/2013	SESK	2WD, 40 hp Continental gas, Multi-Power, 3 pt., 2 hyd., PTO, 14.9x28 rear
65			G	$1,900	3/15/2014	WCIL	1 hyd., 540 PTO, 3 pt., 14.9x28 rear tires, hyd. loader and 5' bucket
65			G	$2,977	3/5/2014	Online	*BigIron.com,* item in Wyoming, loader, gas, 2-13.6x28 rear tires, 540 PTO
65		198	G	$3,200	3/4/2014	SWMN	WF, high clearance, open station, diesel, 2 hyd., 3 pt., 540 PTO, 18.4x30 tires, Power Slide rims
65		1,924	G	$1,910	12/18/2013	Online	*BigIron.com,* item in Nebraska, 4 cyl., 1 hyd. drawbar, 3 pt.
65			P	$935	8/27/2013	Online	*PurpleWave.com,* item in Kentucky, Continental 2.9L, 4 cyl. gas, 40 hp, manual, 3 pt.
65		498	G	$2,200	7/25/2013	ECND	3 pt.
65			G	$2,100	3/30/2013	NWIL	Gas, live power, power steering, 3 pt., runs, drives
65			F	$3,000	3/28/2013	SCMN	WF, PTO, fenders, rear wheel weights
65			G	$2,500	3/2/2013	NCWI	Diesel Matic, Multi-Power, 15.5x38 tires, diff. lock, 3 pt., PTO
65			G	$2,900	2/7/2013	NEIN	NF, 12.4x38 tires, gas
65			G	$2,300	3/24/2012	SETN	Bush Hog
65			G	$3,000	1/21/2012	SEVA	Loader, attachments
65			G	$2,000	7/30/2011	ECMO	
65			G	$2,600	7/30/2011	ECMO	
65			G	$1,705	6/29/2011	Online	*PurpleWave.com,* item in Kansas, Continental 6176 4 cyl. gas, 6F/2R, 3 pt., drawbar

Massey Ferguson

Model	Year	Hours	Condition	Price	Date	Area	Comments
65			G	$1,500	5/7/2010	WCOH	Gas, power steering
65			G	$3,250	5/7/2010	WCOH	Diesel, power steering, 1 hyd., repaint
65			E	$4,000	4/10/2010	ECIA	WF, mint
65			F	$3,250	1/30/2010	WCIL	WF, 3 pt., loader
65			F	$1,600	1/9/2010	ECTX	WF, starts and runs well
65			F	$3,000	1/9/2010	ECTX	Gas, hours unknown, WF, runs fine
85	1959		G	$3,800	3/9/2011	SEVA	High crop, SN CGM800152
85	1959		G	$2,200	9/3/2010	SCMN	WF, gas, 3 pt., PTO, Schwartz hyd. loader
85	1960	6,588	G	$2,100	3/27/2013	Online	*BigIron.com,* item in Kansas, 4 speed Hi/Lo, 4 cyl.
85			G	$1,200	1/4/2014	WCNY	Fender tractor, 3 pt., PTO
85		7,521	G	$3,000	2/7/2013	SEAR	4 cyl. gas, Hi/Lo 4 speed, PTO, canopy
85			G	$1,050	8/4/2012	NEAR	4 cyl. gas, 3 pt., 540 PTO, 16.9x30 rears
85			G	$1,600	6/9/2012	ECNE	3 pt., PTO, hyd., runs
85			F	$1,500	8/20/2011	NEMN	Gas, WF, 3 pt., power steering, Paulson hyd. loader, snow bucket
90	1963		F	$2,500	4/12/2013	WCSK	2WD, Multi-Power, dual hyd.
90	1963	5,504	G	$2,600	5/18/2011	SEWY	Diesel, WF, 3 pt., Massey Ferguson 85 loader
97	1962	3,771	G	$2,700	3/28/2012	ECND	Hand clutch, 1 hyd., standard PTO, power steering, 5 speed, rear weights
97	1964		G	$4,500	3/22/2012	ECMN	PTO, 2 hyd., restored in two years, rebuilt engine and rear end
98	1960		E	$19,500	10/7/2011	NWSD	Rare, drawbar 61 hp, 84 PTO hp, Oliver made 250 to 500 of these models 2 sold on this sale, restored
98	1960		G	$20,000	8/7/2010	WCMN	Diesel, engine rebuilt
130			G	$1,750	10/22/2011	NECO	Diesel
135	1966	3,238	G	$2,100	5/28/2012	ECMO	Multi-Power, add on hyd., old restoration
135	1969		F	$1,000	6/29/2012	NETX	45 hp, gas, 2WD, open station, 12.4x28 tires
135	1970	3,008	G	$3,050	4/11/2011	Online	*AuctionTime.com,* loader, 2WD
135			G	$3,900	12/4/2013	WCSD	3 pt., diesel
135		2,977	G	$5,000	8/24/2013	NWIL	14.9x24 rears, NF, tire chains, Massey Ferguson 235 loader
135			G	$4,100	6/22/2013	SESC	
135			G	$2,100	2/22/2013	SWKY	Diesel
135			G	$2,200	2/22/2013	SWKY	Gas
135		4,620	G	$1,400	12/6/2012	Online	*IQBID.com,* SN SGW641008228
135		4,620	G	$1,400	12/6/2012	SEIA	Partial PS, 540 PTO, 1 hyd.
135		1,904	F	$1,705	9/26/2012	Online	*PurpleWave.com,* item in Kansas, 3 cyl. gas, 3-speed Hi/Lo
135			G	$1,600	8/1/2012	NEOK	
135			G	$2,600	7/28/2012	SWTN	Diesel, power steering
135			G	$1,400	6/20/2012	ECIL	
135			G	$4,500	2/18/2012	ECIL	WF
135			G	$3,000	1/26/2012	SEAL	
135		1,500	E	$4,500	5/14/2011	NETN	Gas
135			G	$1,700	5/7/2011	SWMB	

Massey Ferguson

Model	Year	Hours	Condition	Price	Date	Area	Comments
135			G	$5,500	5/7/2011	SWMB	3 pt., PS, cab, diesel
135			G	$1,900	4/1/2011	Online	*AuctionTime.com,* item in Oregon, 6F/2R, standard 3 pt., 1 hyd., 540 PTO, 6x16 front, 14.9x24 rear
135			G	$2,300	3/25/2011	WCIL	Gas, Multi-Power, 540 PTO, 3 pt.
135			G	$2,000	1/29/2011	ECMO	Gas, top link
135			F	$1,350	11/20/2010	SCKY	
135			F	$2,450	11/20/2010	SCKY	
135		1,399	G	$5,500	11/20/2010	NCKY	Gas, power steering
135			G	$1,600	11/18/2010	SEOK	
135		1,581	G	$2,700	11/18/2010	SCMS	Diesel, brand new tires
135			G	$3,700	11/17/2010	ECMS	
135			P	$2,650	10/7/2010	NCOH	Gas, rough
135		167	G	$1,725	6/23/2010	Online	*BigIron.com,* item in Oklahoma, 4 Speed, 3 cyl. Perkins Diesel, 12.4/11x28 rear tires, 6x16.00 front 540 PTO
135			G	$2,100	6/5/2010	NETN	
135			G	$2,150	6/5/2010	NETN	
135			G	$2,750	6/5/2010	NETN	Power steering
135		3,544	G	$2,600	5/7/2010	WCOH	Gas, repaint
135		3,544	G	$3,750	5/7/2010	WCOH	Diesel, 250 on OH, power steering
135			G	$3,100	4/3/2010	ECTN	Diesel
135		3,755	G	$3,600	2/20/2010	ECPA	Original, straight tin
135			F	$1,250	1/9/2010	ECTX	Gas, was running when parked, been sitting about 3-4 months, SN 9A28373
150	1967	3,000	G	$3,000	3/22/2012	ECMN	WF, gas, 1 hyd., 3 pt., 540 PTO, 2 hyd., Power Slide wheels, 13.6x28 rears with fluid, 6x16 fronts
150	1967		G	$8,500	3/22/2012	ECMN	WF, 2 hyd., 3 pt., PTO, Power Slide wheels
150		2,005	G	$1,489	6/5/2013	Online	*BigIron.com,* item in Kansas, manual 3 speed Hi/Lo, 3 cyl. gas
150		3,892	G	$2,750	5/16/2012	Online	*PurpleWave.com,* item in Arkansas, Perkins 3 cyl. diesel, 44 hp, power steering
150			G	$3,300	1/27/2012	SEAL	
150			G	$2,700	3/25/2011	WCIL	1 hyd., 540 PTO, Multi-Power, turf tires
150			F	$3,300	5/8/2010	NETN	No cab, WF, front-end loader, 1 hyd., bale spear, 3 pt.
150			G	$2,300	5/7/2010	WCOH	Gas
150			G	$2,800	4/3/2010	ECTN	
165	1966	4,108	G	$4,700	7/11/2012	Online	*BigIron.com,* item in Wyoming, 3 speed Hi/Lo, Perkins 4 cyl. diesel, 2 hyd., 540 PTO, canopy, drawbar, 3 pt., third link
165	1966		G	$2,400	3/1/2012	NWTX	
165	1966		G	$5,200	1/28/2012	ECMO	
165	1967	2,023	G	$4,000	7/27/2013	NCOH	Diesel, WF, 15.5x38 tires, SN 9A 16124
165	1967	5,005	G	$4,310	5/9/2012	Online	*BigIron.com,* item in Wyoming, 4 speed Hi/Lo, 3 cyl. diesel, 65 hp, 1 hyd., 3 pt., swing drawbar, rebuilt hyd. pump, 12V system

Massey Ferguson

Model	Year	Hours	Condition	Price	Date	Area	Comments
165	1968	3,364	F	$2,950	11/26/2011	WCOH	WF, 300 hours on complete engine overhaul, Perkins diesel, 2 hyd., power steering, like new rubber
165	1969	6,683	G	$3,100	7/30/2011	ECMO	Perkins gas, 12 speed Multi-Power, diff lock, power steering, live PTO, 2 stage clutch, loader
165	1969	1,640	G	$4,600	7/13/2011	Online	*BigIron.com,* item in Wyoming, 3 speed Hi/Lo, 4 cyl. Perkins diesel, 1 hyd., 540 PTO, cab, 3 pt., tool box, 8 front weights, Float-O-Matic seat
165	1971	2,026	E	$13,500	4/26/2013	ECAB	Shedded, 52 PTO hp, diesel, Multi-Power, 3 pt., PTO, 2 hyd., 3 rib front, 18.4x26 rear tires, front weights, Float-O-Matic ride with suitcase weights, SN 9A 116352
165	1972	3,246	G	$2,530	8/15/2012	Online	*PurpleWave.com,* item in Illinois, Perkins 4 cyl. gas, manual, diff. lock, spring seat, 3 pt., drawbar, 41 hp, aux. hyd., 47 hp, 18.5 gal. fuel capacity, Massey Ferguson 5' loader
165			G	$2,500	3/26/2014	ECMS	Trencher
165		3,215	E	$7,000	11/16/2013	SEMN	Gas, Vaughn loader, open station, 13.6x38 tires 85%, square fenders, 3 pt., 540 PTO, 2 hyd., very clean
165		4,028	G	$2,200	10/28/2013	NWWI	WF, 3 pt., 540 PTO, 15.5x38 rear tires, diesel
165			G	$1,200	7/10/2013	NETX	
165		3,538	G	$2,500	6/29/2013	SWIA	Diesel, open station, WF
165			G	$3,500	4/11/2013	SEID	2WD, 50 hp, Perkins diesel, Multi-Power partial PS, 3 pt., 540 PTO, 16.9x38 tires
165			G	$3,600	3/7/2013	SEIA	Loader, PS, PTO
165			G	$5,200	12/12/2012	SESD	
165			G	$1,925	10/31/2012	Online	*PurpleWave.com,* item in Oklahoma, Perkins 4 cyl. diesel, manual, 3 pt., 540 PTO, 2 rear hyd., 16.9x28 rear tires
165			G	$4,250	6/9/2012	ECNE	Front weights, PTO, 3 pt., older repaint
165			G	$3,000	2/4/2012	ECSC	
165			G	$2,800	1/27/2012	SEAL	
165			F	$1,850	10/22/2011	ECTX	Diesel
165			G	$2,950	9/14/2011	Online	*BigIron.com,* item in Colorado, 6 cyl. diesel, ran when parked, 540 PTO, 3 pt. hitch
165		4,924	P	$625	8/24/2011	SCMI	Did not run, open, diesel
165		5,004	G	$2,800	8/13/2011	WCIL	Diesel, Bush Hog loader, 15.5x38 rear tires, 1 hyd., PTO
165			G	$2,075	6/21/2011	Online	*BidNow.us,* gas, loader, 7-style wire wheel rake, good front tires
165		6,145	G	$2,000	5/13/2011	ECMS	Diesel
165			G	$3,400	4/2/2011	ECMN	Loader
165		5,263	G	$2,400	1/8/2011	ECMI	2WD
165			F	$2,500	12/17/2010	WCIL	Diesel, loader
165			F	$1,800	11/18/2010	SEOK	
165			G	$2,800	11/18/2010	SEOK	

Massey Ferguson

Model	Year	Hours	Condition	Price	Date	Area	Comments
165			G	$2,800	11/18/2010	SEOK	
165			G	$2,200	6/5/2010	NETN	OROPS, diesel
165			G	$2,250	6/5/2010	NETN	Diesel
165			G	$4,000	5/7/2010	WCOH	Multi-Power diesel, repaint
165			G	$2,000	5/1/2010	SETX	
165			G	$2,600	4/10/2010	ECON	Diesel
175	1967		G	$1,800	4/11/2011	Online	*AuctionTime.com,* 2WD
175	1969	5,500	G	$4,000	2/7/2012	WCOK	Diesel, ROPS, 3 pt., PTO
175	1973	4,493	G	$2,900	11/7/2013	WCMI	Diesel, 3 pt., PTO, SN 176445
175			G	$3,500	3/26/2014	ECMS	Diesel
175			G	$1,750	1/17/2014	SEOK	Canopy
175		1,982	G	$2,585	10/28/2013	NWWI	WF, 3 pt., 540 PTO, spin out rear rims
175		3,105	G	$3,200	6/28/2013	NEMO	WF, 3 pt., 540 PTO, 1 hyd., 16.9x28 rubber, 1 owner, S/N 9A16501
175		4,986	G	$3,000	3/14/2013	NENE	WF, propane, 16.9Rx28 rear tires, dual hyd., 540 PTO, 3 pt., fenders
175		3,727	G	$3,750	1/31/2012	NEIN	3 pt., diesel, PTO, fenders
175		6,166	E	$3,000	10/23/2010	NCMD	
175			P	$900	9/3/2010	NEIN	Diesel, spin out rims, dead row, needs work and may not run or drive, as is
175		3,687	G	$2,200	6/5/2010	NETN	
180	1067	3,895	G	$3,600	8/20/2013	WCIL	Multi-Power, 1 hyd., hyd. loader, 60" bucket, bale fork, diesel
180	1958	4,428	G	$3,005	4/12/2011	Online	IQBID.com, gas, 3 speed Hi/Lo, 2 hyd., PTO, Du-Al hyd. loader, 8' bucket, new cutting edge on bucket
180	1966		G	$2,600	6/19/2013	Online	*BigIron.com,* item in Colorado, manual 3F/2R, 4 cyl. gas
180	1966	5,557	F	$1,200	2/12/2013	WCIL	
180	1967	4,503	G	$4,000	7/27/2013	NCOH	Diesel, WF, 15.5x38 rear tires, SN 9A26860, Kelley loader
180	1967	3,895	G	$3,600	7/20/2013	WCIL	Diesel, Multi-Power, 1 hyd., hyd. loader, 60" bucket, bale fork
180	1967	9,000	G	$2,400	9/13/2012	SEIA	WF, 3 pt., PTO, new tires, new clutch, Perkins diesel
180	1968	3,605	G	$3,000	4/22/2013	SWSK	2WD, 63 hp Perkins diesel, 18.4x30 rubber
180	1973		G	$2,500	7/10/2010	SEIA	Diesel, repainted, new timing, new power steering pump, rear tires
180		4,353	G	$2,520	12/18/2013	Online	*BigIron.com,* 4 speed, Hi/Lo, 4 cyl. diesel, 540 PTO, 2 hyd.
180			G	$3,700	4/13/2013	SEMN	Diesel, open station, 3 pt., 2 hyd., Du-Al 340 hyd. loader
180		868	G	$5,100	9/22/2012	NCCO	
180		2,686	G	$3,410	8/15/2012	Online	*PurpleWave.com,* item in Kansas, Ford 4 cyl. diesel, manual, 3 pt., drawbar, 1 hyd., 59.5" loader bucket
180		901	G	$3,850	5/9/2012	Online	*PurpleWave.com,* item in Kansas, 4 cyl. diesel, manual Hi/Lo 3F/2R, block heater, tilt steering wheel, 6' loader bucket, PTO driven hyd. pump
180			G	$3,500	3/24/2012	SWMI	WF, 4 cyl. Perkins diesel, 3 pt., PTO, 2 hyd., 15.5x38 rears

Massey Ferguson

Model	Year	Hours	Condition	Price	Date	Area	Comments
180			F	$4,700	2/4/2012	NENC	Loader
180			G	$3,500	7/30/2011	ECMO	Diesel, good rubber, no top link
180			G	$3,400	1/29/2011	ECMO	
180			F	$2,900	12/11/2010	NCOH	
180			G	$4,000	5/7/2010	WCOH	4WD, cab, loader, custom built, one of a kind
180		4,000	G	$4,000	1/30/2010	WCIL	WF, 3 pt.
205			F	$2,250	11/18/2010	SEOK	4x4
220	1949		G	$1,350	9/22/2010	NECO	Gas, WF, older restoration
235			G	$2,500	7/27/2012	SWKY	Diesel, 8 speed
235			G	$2,600	2/4/2012	ECSC	
235			G	$2,800	1/28/2012	ECMO	Rebuilt engine, gas
235		3,010	F	$2,500	11/13/2010	ECTX	
245		1,502	E	$5,900	8/27/2013	NCWI	Gas, WF, 3 pt., rear wheel weights, grill guard, like new, SN 9A-283626
245		391	E	$8,500	5/5/2013	WCNC	Bush Hog 2345QT front-end loader, diesel, clean
245		1,455	G	$4,000	5/13/2011	ECMS	
245			G	$3,200	11/18/2010	SEOK	
245		2,605	G	$5,000	11/2/2010	ECOK	3 pt., PTO, diesel, ROPS, canopy, dual hyd., Master 700 front-end loader
245			G	$3,800	6/5/2010	NETN	Diesel
245		2,456	G	$3,900	5/7/2010	WCOH	Gas, 1 hyd.
245			G	$4,600	4/3/2010	ECTN	
255	1976	4,454	F	$2,000	7/11/2012	Online	*BigIron.com,* item in Utah, 4 speed Hi/Lo, Perkins diesel, 50HP, 1 hyd., 540 PTO, 3 pt., swing drawbar, seat worn, grill missing, engine oil leak, 12v system
265	1976	2,189	G	$3,000	11/6/2012	ECOK	Diesel, 3 pt. PTO, 1 owner
275	1975		G	$4,100	1/21/2012	SEIL	100 hours on OH
275	1976		F	$3,600	2/24/2012	NETX	2WD, 67 hp, cab, 16.9x28 tires, 1 hyd.
275	1976		G	$5,100	12/7/2011	NCIA	WF, 2 hyd.
285	1976	5,200	G	$7,000	11/26/2011	WCIN	Diesel, utility, 3 pt., PTO, 2 hyd., 6 speed Multi-Power, 18.4x34 radials, SN 253348
285	1976		F	$6,000	6/9/2011	SWSK	2WD, Leon front-end loader, 81 PTO hp, Perkins diesel, standard, 540 PTO, 2 hyd., power steering, 4 rib front, bucket
300			G	$2,201	6/12/2013	Online	*BigIron.com,* item in Iowa, 2WD, hydro, Perkins AD4203 gas
356	1962		F	$800	3/19/2010	SEIA	Bucket tractor, shuttle transmission, 4 cyl., 13x24 tires
1080	1971	7,512	G	$5,500	11/26/2011	WCIN	Diesel, open station, 3 pt., PTO, 2 hyd., 6 speed Multi-Power, new 16.9x38 radials, SN 29525
1080	1972	6,670	F	$3,500	11/26/2011	WCIN	Diesel, turbo, open station, 3 pt., 2 hyd., 6 speed Multi-Power, 16.9x38 Dyna-Torque radials, SN 34520, PTO not working
1080			G	$6,250	1/28/2012	SEAB	MF 246 loader
1080			F	$2,600	6/14/2011	WCSK	2WD, 81 PTO hp, Perkins diesel, standard, 540 PTO, 2 hyd., roll bar
1080			F	$2,700	12/17/2010	WCIL	Diesel, 18.4x34 tires, 2 hyd., 540 PTO

Massey Ferguson

Model	Year	Hours	Condition	Price	Date	Area	Comments
1080		4,711	F	$3,600	12/11/2010	NCOH	S/N 7B29156, 16.9x38 Firestone rear tires, 20% tread, 10x16 Firestone front, 90% tread, diesel, rear cast weights, day cab, 2 spool valves
1085	1973	5,116	G	$5,200	4/11/2011	Online	*AuctionTime.com*
1085	1974	6,389	G	$6,500	12/8/2012	ECIA	Diesel, WF, factory cab, 3 pt., 18.4x34 tires
1085	1974	3,327	G	$7,200	1/21/2010	SCMI	Diesel, original hours, new sleeves, valve work, water pump and radiator in 2007, WF, quick hitch
1085	1975	3,821	G	$8,100	4/13/2011	Online	*BigIron.com,* item in Wyoming, 3 speed Hi/Lo, 4 cyl. Perkins diesel, 2 hyd., 540 PTO, 3 pt., cab, quick couple loader, grapple fork, 72" bucket, 3 spool valve
1100	1967	1,783	G	$6,505	4/27/2011	Online	*BigIron.com,* item in Missouri, 2WD, 12F/4R, 94 hp, radial tires, 2 hyd., 540/ 1,000 PTO, power steering, wet brakes
1100	1967		F	$7,750	4/5/2011	SWSK	2WD, cab, Leon 707 front-end loader, Perkins diesel, Multi-Power, dual hyd., dual PTO, 5' bucket
1100	1968	5,324	G	$3,500	4/29/2013	WCSK	2WD, cab, 94 PTO hp, Perkins diesel, Multi-Power, 12F/4R, 540 PTO, 2 hyd., 18.4x34 rubber
1100	1969	8,090	F	$5,000	11/17/2010	WCIL	Diesel, WF, no cab, 18.4x34 rear tires, 11x16 front tires, tires good, weights
1100		5,335	G	$5,500	3/14/2013	NENE	Cab, Hi/Lo, 18.4x38 rear tires, 1 hyd., 540 PTO, Multi-Power, front mount dozer
1100		4,500	G	$5,000	3/2/2013	ECMN	Loader, cab, 18.4x34 tires, 540 PTO, 3 pt.
1100			G	$2,250	8/30/2012	SEMN	Diesel, 18.4x38 tires, PTO, 2 hyd., 3 pt.
1100			G	$4,950	1/30/2012	SEPA	Diesel, WF, 2 hyd., good condition
1100			G	$3,000	10/28/2011	NETX	Loader
1100			G	$1,600	8/27/2011	NEIA	Gas, WF, 3 pt., faded paint, straight tin, good runner
1100		7,000	G	$3,000	8/6/2011	NEIA	WF, 3 pt., 2 hyd., no cab, 1105 motor, turbo, runs
1100			G	$2,600	11/18/2010	SEOK	
1100			G	$3,000	11/18/2010	SEOK	Great Bend 800 loader
1100			G	$3,150	6/23/2010	Online	*BigIron.com,* item in Nebraska, Perkins diesel, Multi-Power 3 speed Hi/Lo
1100		7,200	G	$3,300	3/6/2010	SEMN	Diesel, open station, 3 pt., 2 hyd., 2nd owner, 18.4x34 tires
1105	1973		F	$5,500	11/7/2013	WCMI	Diesel, ROPS, canopy, 3 pt., 2 hyd., SN 36728
1105	1973	4,649	G	$7,250	3/31/2012	SWSK	2WD, 110 PTO hp, Perkins, air, 2 hyd., dual PTO
1105	1973	6,570	G	$5,300	11/26/2011	WCIN	Diesel, open station, 3 pt., PTO, 2 hyd., 6-speed Multi-Power, good 18.4x38 tires with hub duals, roll bar, SN 40698
1105	1973	3,975	G	$8,250	11/26/2011	WCIN	Diesel, cab, air, heat, 3 pt., PTO, 2 hyd., front weights, 6 speed Multi-Power, 18.4-38 tires with duals, one owner, SN 41860

Massey Ferguson

Model	Year	Hours	Condition	Price	Date	Area	Comments
1105	1974	2,771	G	$8,500	11/7/2013	WCMI	Diesel, cab, heat, 1 owner, 18.4x38 tires, 2 hyd., 540/1,000 PTO, SN 49808
1105	1974	3,443	G	$4,500	7/27/2013	NCOH	Open station, 18.4x34 tires, SN 9B46622
1105	1974	5,346	G	$5,650	5/19/2012	WCIL	Diesel, good tires
1105	1974	4,873	G	$8,000	4/10/2012	WCSK	2WD, 111 PTO hp, Multi-Power, 2 hyd., PTO, updated air, 3 rib front
1105	1974	5,833	G	$5,800	1/21/2012	SEVA	2WD, cab, air, heat, 540 PTO, 3 hyd.
1105	1974	7,435	F	$3,900	6/10/2011	WCSK	2WD, 111 PTO hp, 2 hyd., 540 PTO, 4 rib front
1105	1975	6,635	G	$6,500	4/23/2011	SWSK	2WD, Leon 707 loader, 111 PTO hp, Perkins diesel, dual PTO, 2 hyd., 6' bucket
1105	1975	7,827	G	$7,000	4/18/2011	WCSK	2WD, 6 cyl. Perkins diesel, Multi-Power, 540/1,000 PTO
1105		5,948	F	$825	12/18/2013	Online	*BigIron.com,* 4 speed, 2 ranges Hi/Lo, 6 cyl. diesel, 540/1,000 PTO
1105			G	$4,600	12/4/2013	Online	*BigIron.com,* item in Nebraska, 6 speed, 6 cyl., 18.4x38 rear tires, 11x16 front tires, diesel, 2 hyd., drawbar
1105			G	$1,900	7/28/2012	SWTN	6 cyl. diesel, dual hyd.
1105			G	$3,000	1/27/2012	SEAL	
1105		6,596	G	$5,500	4/7/2011	WCMI	Diesel, cab, heat, good 18.4x38 tires, 2 hyd., 3 pt., 540 PTO
1130	1967		G	$1,500	6/22/2011	Online	*BigIron.com,* item in Nebraska, 3 speed Hi/Lo, 6cyl. diesel, 2 hyd., does not run, 3 pt., missing third link
1130	1968	5,332	G	$3,700	8/30/2013	NCIA	Duals
1130	1971	8,100	F	$5,000	4/12/2013	WCSK	2WD, Ezee-On 100 front-end loader, 2 hyd., 540/1,000 PTO, 4 rib front, 23.1x34 rear
1130	1971		G	$2,860	10/10/2012	Online	*PurpleWave.com,* item in Kansas, hours unknown, 6 cyl. diesel, manual, spring seat
1130			G	$3,300	7/30/2011	ECMO	Loader
1130		9,162	G	$1,600	3/23/2011	Online	*BigIron.com,* 6 cyl. Perkins diesel, 3 pt., 540 PTO, 2 hyd.
1135	1973	4,886	G	$6,250	12/4/2010	SEWY	WF, diesel, Westendorf WL42 loader
1135	1974		G	$9,000	6/17/2011	WCSK	Leon front-end loader, bucket, duals, cab, air, heat, standard, PTO 5980
1135	1975	4,893	G	$6,600	12/7/2011	NCIA	Cab, WF, 2 hyd., 540/1,000 PTO, 3 pt.
1135	1976	2,436	G	$3,190	8/28/2013	Online	*PurpleWave.com,* item in Missouri, Perkins 5.8L, 6 cyl. diesel, partial PS, cab, air, heat, Multi-Power, drawbar, 540 PTO, cosmetic damage
1135	1976		G	$4,730	5/9/2012	Online	*PurpleWave.com,* item in Kansas, 6 cyl. diesel, manual, hard top canopy on two post roll bar, ROPS, work lights, block heater, 3 pt., drawbar, aux. outlet, 540 PTO
1135	1976	7,244	G	$5,500	3/31/2012	SWSK	2WD, 120 PTO hp, Perkins, 3 hyd., dual PTO, factory duals
1135	1976	3,376	G	$4,070	1/27/2010	Online	*PurpleWave.com,* item in Colorado, 540 PTO, 3 pt.

Massey Ferguson

Model	Year	Hours	Condition	Price	Date	Area	Comments
1135	1977	3,850	G	$6,900	4/23/2011	SESK	2WD, 6 cyl. D engine, standard, Multi-Power, 540 rpm PTO, dual hyd., cab, air, heat, rear duals
1150		2,451	G	$7,500	11/26/2010	WCOH	Open station, duals
1155	1976	5,444	G	$5,500	12/1/2011	NEIN	18.4x38 with snap-on duals, 60%, 2 hyd., QH, 10' weights, 1,000 hours on OH, 1 owner
1155	1976	3,450	G	$1,610	8/10/2011	Online	*BigIron.com,* item in Nebraska, 4 speed Hi/Lo, V8 diesel, 2 hyd., 540 PTO, 3 pt., dual hubs & wheel centers, missing front windshield
1155	1977	4,818	F	$4,750	4/13/2012	SWSK	2WD, 140 hp PTO, 8 cyl. Perkins, 1,000 PTO, 2 hyd., 18.4x38 factory duals
1505		4,061	G	$3,700	6/26/2013	Online	*BigIron.com,* item in Wyoming, blade, Cat 3208 diesel, 185 hp
1805	1974	4,810	G	$5,000	8/24/2010	NEMO	4WD, fully equipped cab, clamp on duals, Cat 3208, 3 hyd., 3 pt., 1,000 PTO
1805	1978		G	$3,000	2/28/2011	SCMI	13' Leon push blade, 3 pt., 3 hyd., cab, heat, duals, PTO not hooked up
1805			G	$5,500	7/27/2011	ECND	3 hyd., 2,500 hours on 3208 Cat
1805			F	$3,050	12/11/2010	NCOH	4WD, 3 pt., new clutch
2675	1978	1,833	G	$6,050	8/22/2012	Online	*PurpleWave.com,* item in Kansas, Perkins 6 cyl. diesel, 103 hp, PS
2805	1978	2,358	F	$4,800	8/30/2013	NCIA	V8, WF
Super 90	1964	2,827	G	$3,700	9/3/2010	SCMN	WF, diesel, open station, 3 pt., PTO
Super 90	1965		G	$5,500	7/20/2011	NCIA	Diesel, WF, spin out wheels, 3 pt.
Super 90		4,331	G	$1,350	3/5/2011	SEMN	Diesel, WF, PTO

Massey-Harris

Model	Year	Hours	Condition	Price	Date	Area	Comments
2			G	$18,000	9/21/2013	WCNY	Project tractor, missing head, stuck, lugs
2			G	$45,000	9/21/2013	WCNY	Loose, Buda engine 12-22, repainted
20			G	$2,000	3/28/2013	SCMN	NF, fenders, PTO
20			G	$1,100	6/5/2010	ECMN	NF, gas
22	1948		F	$775	5/19/2012	WCIL	All new tires
22	1948		E	$3,750	10/15/2011	ECIA	Row crop, parade ready, average Goodyear 10x28 rear tires
22	1948		G	$2,700	8/11/2010	ECMN	Belt horsepower, live hyd., new clutch, engine has new rings and pistons, steering wheel, shift knob and boots all new, new front tires, parade ready
22	1950		G	$2,250	4/3/2014	NEIN	540 PTO, 3 pt., NF, 18.4x28 tires
22			G	$1,050	3/22/2014	SWMI	
22			G	$1,076	9/9/2013	NWWI	New tires, Firestone 9.5x32 rear, electric start
22			G	$1,100	5/11/2013	NCOH	Original, factory 3 pt., runs, no tag
22			G	$1,300	10/2/2010	SWWI	
22			G	$2,325	7/17/2010	SCON	Canadian sale

Massey-Harris

Model	Year	Hours	Condition	Price	Date	Area	Comments
22			G	$2,250	6/19/2010	SWIL	Running, restored, fenders, PTO, motor rebuilt, older paint, parade tractor
22			G	$3,600	5/22/2010	SEMN	New paint, new 11.2x34 rubber, runs, NF
25			G	$2,000	2/6/2013	SESD	On round spokes, old restoration, runs
30	1949		G	$666	8/24/2011	Online	*BigIron.com,* item in Nebraska, engine free, one tire flat
30	1952		F	$660	5/16/2012	Online	*PurpleWave.com,* item in Oklahoma, 4 cyl. gas, manual, drawbar, 540 PTO, 11.2/10x38 tires
30	1952		G	$950	6/22/2011	Online	*BigIron.com,* item in Nebraska, 4 cyl. gas, 1 hyd., 540 PTO, wheel weights, loader, 4' bucket, 2 hyd.
30			F	$875	8/24/2013	SEMI	NF
30			G	$1,500	12/11/2010	NCOH	3 pt., hyd., NF
30			G	$3,750	10/23/2010	SCPA	
30			G	$775	10/2/2010	SWWI	
30			G	$1,550	4/10/2010	NCTN	
33	1953		G	$3,750	1/11/2013	ECIL	Weights, good 12.4x38 tires, low hours
33	1953		F	$800	6/20/2012	SESD	Stanhoist Loader, NF, 1 hyd., Powersteam, 13.6x38 tires, runs
33	1954		G	$4,000	10/23/2010	SCPA	Standard
33			G	$900	6/6/2013	ECAB	Running
33			G	$2,101	8/22/2012	Online	*BigIron.com,* item in Nebraska, gas, 12.4x38 rear and 6x16 front tires, loader
33			F	$875	6/20/2012	SESD	NF, 3pt., PTO, 15.5x38 tires, shedded, should run
33			F	$900	12/17/2010	WCIL	
33			F	$1,100	5/26/2010	ECSD	Running
44	1948		G	$826	5/9/2012	Online	*BigIron.com,* item in Nebraska, RC, 5F/1R, 249 cu. in. Continental 4 cyl. gas, 31 belt hp, 45 engine hp, 540 PTO, standard drawbar, rear fenders

I grew up on Highway 12 in Benson, Minn., out in the far west-central part of the state. About two hours east on Highway 12 toward the Twin Cities is the wonderful town of Cokato. There was quite a nice farm auction in Cokato back on March 28, 2013, a sale by Henslin Auctions Inc. I like these kind of farm auctions–some modern equipment, such as the 1999 John Deere 7710 tractor with 2,988 hours that sold for $68,000, but also some antique tractors. This auction had a few really nice Massey-Harris models, including the 1941 Super Twin 101 narrow front with new 13.6x38 tires pictured here. It sold for $6,250.

PETE'S PICK

Massey-Harris

Model	Year	Hours	Condition	Price	Date	Area	Comments
44	1949		G	$1,100	10/7/2011	NWSD	PTO, gas, 3 pt., unrestored, straight sheet metal, left fender has some rust
44	1951		G	$1,500	5/31/2013	SWSK	2WD, gas, rubber belt pulley, 16.9x30 rear
44	1951		G	$3,000	8/24/2011	ECMN	PTO, new 16.9x30 rubber
44	1951		F	$800	12/4/2010	SEWY	SF, gas
44	1952		F	$1,265	11/3/2011	Online	*Purplewave.com,* item in Kansas, 4 cyl. gas
44	1952		G	$6,500	10/23/2010	SCPA	Standard
44	1956		F	$2,000	1/2/2010	NWOH	Row crop, 3 pt., WF, fenders, lights, original rear case cracked
44			G	$1,000	4/3/2014	NEIN	Special, NF, 15.5x38, 3 pt., 540 PTO
44			G	$1,500	8/24/2013	SEMI	Standard, WF, 4 cyl. engine
44			G	$900	5/11/2013	NCOH	Older repaint, fenders, runs
44			E	$3,000	4/26/2013	ECAB	44 PTO hp, gas, PTO, pulley, 6.5x16 rear tires, 14x30 front tires
44			F	$850	3/28/2013	SCMN	NF, PTO
44			F	$1,200	3/28/2013	SCMN	WF, fenders, gas, PTO
44			G	$1,900	3/28/2013	SCMN	NF, rear wheel weights, fenders, 13.8x38 tires
44			F	$800	3/22/2013	WCMI	NF, power steering, 13x38 rear tires, runs
44			F	$900	1/21/2013	NCIA	NF, loader
44			F	$1,125	12/12/2012	NCIL	Gas, SN GB 14659
44			G	$1,900	8/21/2012	WCIL	Diesel
44			G	$950	8/4/2012	ECMN	WF, gas
44			F	$1,300	10/29/2011	ECMN	Loader
44			G	$1,000	8/27/2011	NEIA	NF, drawbar, gas, amateur restoration
44			G	$1,500	7/30/2011	ECMO	
44			G	$850	5/7/2011	SESK	2WD, gas, PTO, 1 hyd., 14x30 tires
44			F	$1,000	4/11/2011	NEIA	Rough, no paint left, bad water pump leak, smoked like crazy
44			G	$1,350	4/7/2011	WCMI	Gas, power steering, power adjust rear wheels
44			G	$1,000	10/2/2010	SWWI	Standard
44			F	$950	7/19/2010	NCIA	Live pump
44			G	$1,900	6/19/2010	SWIL	Running, restored, PTO, lights, deluxe seat, belt pulley
44			F	$900	5/1/2010	SENE	Special
44			G	$1,100	5/1/2010	SENE	
44			G	$1,200	5/1/2010	SENE	Standard
50			G	$2,300	8/21/2012	WCIL	
50			G	$4,250	9/2/2010	ECND	2WD, 3 pt., PTO, newer paint
55	1952		G	$2,900	10/7/2011	NWSD	Diesel, hyd., PTO, older restoration
55			F	$962	11/3/2011	Online	*PurpleWave.com,* item in Oklahoma
81	1941		G	$5,000	10/23/2010	SCPA	
81	1944		G	$3,600	4/1/2014	WCMN	NF, mechanical lift and pulley, 1 of 10 made, PTO
81	1945		G	$2,550	3/22/2013	WCMI	NF, 9.5x32 rear tires, runs
81	1946		G	$900	6/11/2010	SEAB	Belt pulley, PTO
81			E	$3,000	4/26/2013	ECAB	26 PTO hp Continental gas, 4F/1R, PTO, pulley, 11.2x28 rear tires recent, 5x15 front tires

Massey-Harris

Model	Year	Hours	Condition	Price	Date	Area	Comments
81			G	$3,100	4/17/2010	SESK	Restored, PTO
81			F	$1,800	2/19/2010	WCIL	NF, teardrop fenders, 11x28 tires
101	1940		F	$3,400	3/22/2013	WCMI	Senior, NF, 13.6x38 rear tires, runs
101	1941		G	$6,250	3/28/2013	SCMN	Super Twin 101, NF, PTO, new 13.6x38 tires
101	1941		G	$5,750	10/23/2010	SCPA	
101	1947		G	$1,100	10/2/2010	SWWI	Senior
101			G	$3,200	3/28/2013	SCMN	Junior, NF, PTO, 11.2x38 tires
101			G	$1,350	3/22/2013	WCMI	Junior, NF, 12.4x25 rear tires, runs
101			G	$2,200	2/6/2013	Online	Item in Illinois, 101 Junior, Twin Power, standard, SN 3814101944, belt pulley
101			G	$2,100	6/20/2012	SESD	Junior, restored in 1995
101			G	$850	10/2/2010	SWWI	Junior Twin Power
101			G	$6,000	7/17/2010	SCON	Canadian sale, Twin Power
101			F	$175	6/23/2010	Online	*BigIron.com,* item in Nebraska, Senior, rear tires 12.4x38, front tires 5.5x16, stuck
101			G	$1,150	5/1/2010	SENE	
101			G	$2,700	5/1/2010	SENE	Junior
102			E	$2,600	4/26/2013	ECAB	102 Senior, 6x16 front tires, 14.9x26 rear tires, PTO, pulley
102			F	$2,600	3/28/2013	SCMN	Junior Twin Power, WF, original paint, standard, new tires and fenders, PTO
102			G	$1,100	6/11/2010	SEAB	Senior, gas 6 cyl., rebuilt
203			P	$4,600	9/3/2010	NEIN	Standard, 6 cyl., dead row, needs work and may not run or drive, as is
333	1956		G	$4,500	8/24/2011	ECMN	WF, PTO, rock shaft, fenders, Power Slide rear wheels, new 13.6x38 rubber, complete eng OH
333			E	$6,000	4/26/2013	ECAB	37 PTO hp, 5.5x16 front tires, 13.6x28 rear tires, hyd. and low range trans., 3 tone paint
333			G	$1,000	3/30/2012	SEND	Loader
444	1956	1,957	G	$2,860	10/10/2012	Online	*PurpleWave.com,* item in Iowa, Massey-Harris 277G 4 cyl. gas, manual, spring seat, 3 pt.
444	1956		G	$1,451	9/28/2011	Online	*BigIron.com,* item in Nebraska, 10F/2R, 4 cyl. gas, 1 hyd., 540 PTO, 277 cu. in. engine, adj. rear wheels
444	1956		F	$1,150	5/26/2010	ECSD	Older restoration
444	1957		G	$1,500	5/19/2012	WCIL	Gas, NF
444	1958		F	$1,475	5/19/2012	WCIL	Gas, WF, bad clutch, good tires
444			G	$4,000	4/29/2013	WCSK	2WD, Shaver post pounder, gas, 16.9x30 rear recent, 3 rib front/1 new, 540 PTO
444			E	$3,500	4/26/2013	ECAB	48 PTO hp, 7.5x16 front tires, 16.9x30 rear tires, recent rubber, hyd. engine work, 3 tone paint
444			F	$2,100	3/28/2013	SCMN	NF, power steering, PTO
444			G	$4,800	9/4/2010	NEIN	LP
555			E	$5,300	4/26/2013	ECAB	71 PTO hp, diesel, hyd. power steering, new 18.4x24 rear tires, 7.5x18 front tires, 3 tone paint

TRACTORS

Massey-Harris

Model	Year	Hours	Condition	Price	Date	Area	Comments
Challenger			G	$900	6/5/2010	WCMO	
Colt	1953		G	$7,000	8/24/2011	ECMN	WF, 3 pt., PTO, new 11.2x28 rubber
GP	1930		E	$17,500	5/10/2014	SCMN	4WD, on steel, 4 cyl., crank and electric start, new radiator
GP	1930		G	$22,000	10/23/2010	SCPA	4WD
GP	1932		F	$5,500	5/10/2014	SCMN	4WD, on steel, new battery, 6 cyl., gas tank needs repair, runs
GP	1937		G	$14,000	5/10/2014	SCMN	4WD, 12.4x28 new tires, PTO, 6 cyl., new battery, runs
GP			G	$8,500	9/21/2013	WCNY	4WD, loose, original, full steel with extensions, SN 302643
GP			G	$12,000	9/21/2013	WCNY	GP, on skeleton steel, 4WD, needs a radiator
GP			G	$13,500	9/21/2013	WCNY	4WD, older restoration, on steel, no lugs
GP			G	$14,000	3/23/2013	NEIN	4WD, repainted, full steel, runs
GP			G	$10,000	9/18/2010	ECMO	4x4, full steel wheels, repainted
GP			G	$8,000	5/1/2010	SENE	4 wheel
Mustang	1953		G	$4,500	8/24/2011	ECMN	WF, 3 pt., PTO, new rubber
Pacemaker			G	$4,300	3/24/2012	NEIN	Restored, new tires, PTO, belt pulley, runs
Pacer	1954		G	$3,600	8/24/2011	ECMN	PTO, new 9.5x24 rubber
Pacer	1954		G	$4,500	10/23/2010	SCPA	
Pacer			G	$4,700	10/7/2011	NWSD	Loader, PTO, 3pt., handy little snow mover
Pacer			G	$3,700	9/15/2011	ECIA	Restored, SN PGA 51852, WF
Pony	1949		G	$1,700	10/7/2011	NWSD	Needs some cosmetic work, WF
Pony	1950		G	$1,500	5/19/2012	SWMI	1 bottom plow, WF, 9.5x24 Turf tires, fenders, hyd. lift
Pony	1951		G	$3,000	10/23/2010	SCPA	
Pony	1954		E	$5,000	10/15/2011	ECIA	Parade ready, adj. WF, Goodyear Super Grip 9x24 rear tires
Pony			G	$1,150	1/4/2014	WCNY	Blade, disk, plow, cultivator
Pony			G	$1,705	8/28/2013	Online	*PurpleWave.com*, item in Kansas, Continental N62 4 cyl. gas, manual, 540 PTO, 4x15 front tires, 8.3x24 rear tires
Pony			G	$3,000	4/26/2013	ECAB	8x24 rear tires, 4x15 front, front wheel weights, no hyd. or PTO
Pony			F	$1,250	3/22/2013	WCMI	WF, 8.3x24 rear tires, runs
Pony			G	$3,100	8/24/2011	ECMN	Black engine, PTO, belt pulley
Pony			G	$2,200	7/17/2010	SCON	Canadian sale
Pony			G	$1,350	6/5/2010	WCMO	
Pony			G	$2,900	6/5/2010	WCMO	Repainted
Pony			G	$2,250	5/1/2010	NCOH	Woods belly mower, nice
Pony			F	$1,150	4/10/2010	ECON	Plow

McCormick-Deering

Model	Year	Hours	Condition	Price	Date	Area	Comments
0-6			E	$11,000	8/24/2013	SEMI	Orchard, restored, automotive paint
0-12	1934		G	$2,300	8/25/2011	ECND	PTO, front wheel weights, 24" rears, loose

McCormick-Deering

Model	Year	Hours	Condition	Price	Date	Area	Comments
0-14			G	$5,600	8/24/2013	SEMI	Orchard, 1 of 636 produced
10-20	1925		G	$1,100	8/9/2012	NEIL	
10-20	1927		G	$3,200	6/30/2012	NEIA	McCormick, with extra wheels
10-20	1928		G	$1,450	5/19/2012	SWMI	WF, steel wheels with rubber cover, fenders, belt pulley
10-20	1931		F	$2,700	7/10/2010	SEIA	Restored, rebuilt magneto with two year warranty
10-20			G	$1,300	2/22/2014	SCNE	On steel
10-20			G	$900	9/12/2013	SEIA	WF, spoke wheels
10-20			F	$800	2/22/2013	NWIN	Full steel, original, complete
10-20			F	$950	5/19/2012	NWMI	
10-20			F	$950	1/28/2012	ECMO	On covered steel
10-20			F	$900	10/29/2011	SEMN	One side curtain, steel flat spoke wheels, does not run
10-20			F	$1,350	11/20/2010	NCOH	On steel, complete, not running
10-20			F	$800	7/17/2010	SCON	Canadian sale, on steel
10-20			G	$1,200	5/1/2010	SENE	
15-30	1928		F	$725	8/25/2011	ECND	On full steel with lugs, stuck
15-30	1929		F	$800	8/25/2011	ECND	Side curtains, on full steel with lugs, stuck
15-30			G	$1,475	1/29/2014	Online	*BigIron.com,* item in Iowa, 3F/1R, liquid cooled 4 cyl., kerosene, drawbar, runs
15-30			F	$963	8/14/2012	Online	*PurpleWave.com,* item in Kansas, 4 cyl. kerosene engine, 30 hp, manual, crank start, drawbar, steel seat, 14x30 rears need replacement
15-30			F	$850	6/20/2012	SESD	On steel, motor is loose
15-30			G	$1,000	5/19/2012	NWMI	
15-30			G	$2,600	10/7/2011	NWSD	Steel wheels
22-36			F	$800	6/20/2012	SESD	On steel, missing some parts, motor loose
22-36			G	$3,080	11/3/2011	Online	*PurpleWave.com,* item in Kansas, 36 hp, drawbar load 22
22-36			G	$2,700	7/22/2011	SEMN	Full steel with lugs, rebuilt engine, older restoration
22-36			G	$800	5/14/2011	SWSK	36 hp, drawbar 22 hp, steel wheeled, has lugs, belt pulley
22-36			G	$900	6/5/2010	WCMO	
A	1940		G	$2,035	5/30/2012	Online	PurpleWave.com, item in Missouri, Culti-Vision
F14	1939		G	$2,750	7/31/2010	NWIL	Gas, restored Farmall, on rubber
F20			F	$1,500	11/23/2011	Online	*BigIron.com,* item in Nebraska, Farmall, 11.2x38 rears, 6x16 fronts
F30			F	$875	6/23/2010	Online	*BigIron.com,* item in Colorado, restored, gas tank leaks
Super W-6			G	$1,500	1/30/2010	NETX	
Super WD9			G	$2,100	9/12/2013	SEIA	WF, PTO, rear wheel weights
W12	1935		F	$875	8/25/2011	ECND	PTO, flat spoke, cut off rear, round spoke fronts, stuck, parts for restoration
W30	1939		F	$1,000	8/25/2011	ECND	WF, belt pulley, hand clutch, 14x28 rears, loose, complete

TRACTORS

McCormick-Deering

Model	Year	Hours	Condition	Price	Date	Area	Comments
W30			G	$2,000	1/28/2012	ECMO	On steel and has rubber
W30			G	$2,475	11/3/2011	Online	PurpleWave.com, item in Kansas, steel wheels
W4	1944		F	$1,000	8/25/2011	ECND	Standard, gas, PTO, belt pulley, rear weights, 13x26 rears, loose
W4			G	$2,850	8/24/2013	SEMI	Needs carburetor kit
W4			G	$1,425	1/9/2013	Online	*IQBID.com,* WF, gas, 11x28 tires, front and rear steel rims sold with tractor, SN 31201
W4			G	$800	10/2/2010	ECMN	WF
W4			G	$1,400	6/11/2010	SEAB	
W40	1938		G	$3,300	8/25/2011	ECND	Gas, electric start, belt pulley, rebuilt engine, 14x32 tires on round spoke wheels, round spoke front, runs
W6	1941		G	$1,300	8/25/2011	ECND	Standard, gas, PTO, belt pulley, 14x30 rears, runs
W6	1951		G	$1,250	9/9/2011	ECND	Standard, PTO
W-6	1947		G	$2,900	6/11/2010	SEAB	Standard gas, PTO, belt pulley, new rubber, new radiator, complete OH on motor, parts book
W-6			G	$1,700	9/12/2013	SEIA	WF, PTO, wheel weights
W-6			G	$3,100	8/24/2013	SEMI	
W-6			G	$1,700	7/17/2010	SCON	Canadian sale, standard
W-9	1946		G	$1,800	5/23/2012	Online	*BigIron.com,* item in Nebraska, standard collectible, 4x2, 2WD, 4 cyl. gas, 49 hp, 2 hyd., electric start
W-9	1951		F	$850	8/25/2011	ECND	Standard, gas, PTO, rear weights, 16.9x34 rears, stuck
W-9			G	$2,400	5/1/2010	SENE	
WD-6	1952		G	$1,000	7/25/2013	WCSK	16.9x30 rubber, 8' blade
WD-9	1946		G	$6,700	5/18/2013	SEON	
WD-9			G	$3,000	12/12/2013	Online	
WD-9			G	$1,300	9/12/2013	SEIA	Standard, WF, PTO
WD-9			G	$1,600	9/9/2010	NWWI	
WD-9			G	$1,700	6/23/2010	Online	*BigIron.com,* item in Oklahoma, diesel, rear tires 18.4x34, front tires 7.5x18SL, 2 hyd., PTO, rear tires cracking, right better than left, will run if pull start
WD-40			G	$10,000	6/5/2010	WCMO	Diesel
WK-40			F	$1,500	6/20/2012	SESD	Gas, spoke wheels, complete - except tires
WK-40			G	$3,700	5/19/2012	NWMI	
WK-40			F	$2,585	11/3/2011	Online	*PurpleWave.com,* item in Kansas, International Harvester engine
WK-40			G	$1,750	6/5/2010	WCMO	
WK-40			G	$4,500	6/5/2010	WCMO	
WK-40			G	$6,500	6/5/2010	WCMO	Round spokes, rear wheel weights
WK-40			G	$10,000	6/5/2010	WCMO	

Minneapolis

Model	Year	Hours	Condition	Price	Date	Area	Comments
12-25			G	$65,000	9/21/2013	WCNY	
17-30			G	$7,500	9/9/2010	NWWI	Type B
22-24			G	$115,000	9/21/2013	WCNY	
25-50	1912		G	$135,000	5/15/2014	NCKS	2nd owner, same family since 1957, original condition, proceeds from sale to go to local County Community Foundation Fund
35-70			G	$110,000	9/21/2013	WCNY	
39-57			G	$18,000	6/5/2010	WCMO	Rear steel

There's quite a story on the 1912 Minneapolis 25-50 tractor that sold for $135,000 at a May 15, 2014, auction in Munden, Kan. The tractor had been in the same family since 1957. Pre-sale literature by Aumann Auctions Inc. said the tractor was running in the late '80s and early '90s according to the Strnad family who owned it. It sat on the east side of Munden until 1998 when it was relocated to a grain elevator building. The tractor became a part not only of the Strnad family history but also of Munden.

Proceeds from the auction were donated to the Republic County Community Foundation. How cool is that? A special 102-year-old tractor giving back to the town that had been home to it for 57 years.

PETE'S PICK

Minneapolis-Moline

Model	Year	Hours	Condition	Price	Date	Area	Comments
4 Star			G	$4,500	6/5/2010	SWIA	Running, restored, WF, gas
4 Star			G	$5,000	6/5/2010	SWIA	Running, restored, NF, gas
5 Star	1958		G	$1,800	10/7/2011	NWSD	Restored, gas, PTO, TA, right rear tire is newer
5 Star	1958		G	$1,900	10/7/2011	NWSD	PTO, hyd., restored, diesel
5 Star			G	$900	6/8/2013	NEND	PTO, lights, hyd., rear weights
5 Star			G	$1,300	12/6/2012	SEIA	Freeman loader
17-30			G	$7,000	6/19/2010	SWIL	Running, old restoration and repaint, fenders, duals, belt pulley
27-44			G	$16,500	9/21/2013	WCNY	Cross motor, loose and greasy, looks like a runner, older restoration
39-57	1929		G	$32,000	7/22/2011	SEMN	V-belts on fan, on full steel with lugs, flat spoke, extra carts, 1 of 12 built
335		2,639	G	$850	11/20/2010	SEIA	3 pt., PTO, runs
336-4		2,800	F	$1,760	1/11/2012	Online	*PurpleWave.com,* item in Kansas, loader, 4 cyl. gas, 5 speed Hi/Lo, 3 pt., 540 PTO, dual cyl. loader

Minneapolis-Moline

Model	Year	Hours	Condition	Price	Date	Area	Comments
445	1956	1,255	F	$798	8/14/2012	Online	*PurpleWave.com,* item in Kansas, Universal, gas, manual, power steering, 540 PTO, drawbar, 3 pt.
445	1956		F	$2,400	6/20/2012	SESD	LP gas, 3 pt., original paint
445	1956		G	$1,820	7/27/2011	Online	*BigIron.com,* item in Nebraska, New Idea 501 loader, 5 speed manual, 4 cyl. gas, 40 hp, 2 hyd., adj. front axle, adj. rear tread, electric starter, 12V system
445	1957		G	$2,650	5/23/2012	Online	*BigIron.com,* item in South Dakota, 5 speed, TA, 4 cyl. gas, 1 hyd., 540 PTO, 1400 Schwartz loader
445			G	$800	7/31/2013	ECND	WF, gas, 1 hyd., 3 pt., live power, PTO
445			G	$1,000	11/13/2012	NCIA	Loader
445			G	$1,900	8/11/2011	WCMN	WF, 2 hyd., 3 pt., PTO, White 1610 loader, Power Slide rims
445			F	$800	10/2/2010	SWWI	
504			G	$11,000	6/5/2010	SWIA	Running, restored, FWA, rear wheel weights
670			G	$2,000	5/26/2010	ECSD	Diesel
1355			G	$5,000	8/31/2011	ECMN	
A4T-1600			G	$10,000	3/23/2013	NEIN	Diesel, 3 pt., dual hyd., original, runs
A4T-1600			P	$1,000	6/30/2012	SESK	Motor seized
AT1400			G	$1,900	6/19/2010	SWIL	Running, old restoration and repaint, PTO, lights
AT1600			P	$1,300	8/31/2010	WCIL	A4T-1600 4WD tractor, 18.4-34 tires, salvage, tractor not at auction site
BF			G	$2,200	3/23/2013	NEIN	3 pt., original, runs
BF			G	$4,750	10/23/2010	SCPA	
BFW	1953		G	$3,900	3/23/2012	WCNE	WF, gas, PTO, hyd., runs, straight
BFW	1953		E	$4,500	10/15/2011	ECIA	WF, parade ready, average Firestone 11.2x28 rear tires
D			G	$1,600	6/11/2010	SEAB	540 PTO, hyd., new front tires, calcium-filled rear tires, rear wheel weights

The Comfortractor combined a tractor and a car into one. Good idea? Bad? Well, it didn't work out very well for Minneapolis-Moline back in the late 1930s when the UDLX model was introduced. Not many were made because sales were so bad. But now the UDLXs turn heads whenever they show up, which isn't often. This one (pictured) attracted a tad more buyer attention than when it rolled off the line new back in the late '30s. It sold for a whopping $105,000 at an Oct. 24, 2009, auction for the Gary Parker collection in Churubusco, Ind.

— PETE'S PICK —

Minneapolis-Moline

Model	Year	Hours	Condition	Price	Date	Area	Comments
G	1948		G	$6,750	10/23/2010	SCPA	
G			G	$1,430	10/31/2012	Online	*PurpleWave.com,* item in Kansas, 4 cyl. gas, 5 speed, push button start, hand start, 540 PTO, hyd., adj. angle drawbar, pressed seat, WF
G			G	$850	6/27/2012	NEND	Standard tread, PTO
G			G	$3,400	3/24/2012	NEIN	Diesel, original, dual PTO, dual hyd., runs
G			G	$12,500	3/24/2012	NEIN	Vista, diesel, open station, dual hyd., dual PTO, 3 pt., runs
G			G	$1,800	9/4/2010	SEVA	4 cyl., LP, original, out of Texas
G1000	1966	5,611	G	$3,520	10/10/2012	Online	*PurpleWave.com,* item in Kansas, actual hours unknown, 6 cyl. diesel, manual, 3 pt.
G1000		2,027	G	$4,850	12/15/2011	Online	*IQBID.com,* Wheatland, gas LP, 2 hyd., 23.1x34 rears
G1000			G	$5,750	9/4/2010	NEIN	LP
G1000			G	$6,750	9/4/2010	NEIN	Vista, nice repaint, new rubber
G1000			G	$7,500	9/4/2010	SEVA	Vista, 6 cyl., diesel, out of North Carolina
G1000			G	$2,900	5/26/2010	ECSD	LP
G1050			G	$4,800	9/4/2010	NEIN	
G6			G	$5,000	6/5/2010	SWIA	Running, restored, WF, diesel
G704	1962		F	$3,000	6/20/2012	SESD	Diesel, FWA, runs, 1 of 123
G704			G	$4,600	9/4/2010	NEIN	MFWD
G705	1963		G	$2,100	3/28/2012	ECND	2hyd., 540 PTO
G705			F	$1,600	5/26/2010	ECSD	Wheatland, LP, not running
G705			G	$1,900	5/26/2010	ECSD	LP
G706			G	$4,000	3/24/2012	NEIN	Diesel, 4WD, runs
G707	1965		F	$2,250	6/20/2012	SESD	Diesel, runs, rusted, 1 of 415
G750			G	$8,500	9/4/2010	NEIN	
G750		6,690	G	$15,000	6/19/2010	SWIL	Running, restored, PTO, lights, deluxe seat, 3 pt., power steering
G850			G	$8,300	9/4/2010	NEIN	
G900			G	$4,100	1/29/2011	ECMO	
G900			G	$5,750	9/4/2010	NEIN	Diesel, toplink
G900			G	$8,750	6/19/2010	SWIL	Diesel, running, restored, rear wheel weights, fenders, PTO, lights, hyd., front weight, deluxe seat, 3 pt., power steering
G900			G	$3,000	6/5/2010	SWIA	Running, original, diesel, WF
G900			G	$31,000	6/5/2010	SWIA	Running, FWA, original
G950	1972	3,665	G	$7,850	12/18/2013	Online	*BigIron.com,* clamp on duals
G955			G	$4,250	3/22/2013	NWMN	3 pt., PTO, diesel, original, runs
G955			G	$8,500	9/4/2010	NEIN	
GB			G	$2,600	3/24/2012	NEIN	LP, STD, repainted, runs
GB		1,351	G	$3,000	9/4/2010	SEVA	4 cyl., LP, cab, item from Kansas, all original
GB			G	$16,500	9/4/2010	NEIN	Very rare experimental Ellwood, MFWD, diesel
GV1000			F	$450	6/8/2013	NEND	hyd., PTO, standard tread, good tin work
GVI	1961		G	$1,800	8/11/2010	ECMN	2hyd., 540 PTO

Minneapolis-Moline

Model	Year	Hours	Condition	Price	Date	Area	Comments
GVI			G	$4,100	9/4/2010	NEIN	MFWD
GVI			G	$7,000	9/4/2010	NEIN	MFWD, LP
Jet Star	1959		F	$1,700	9/1/2011	WCMN	Gas, WF, PTO, belt pulley, fenders, unrestored, rebuilt carburetor and TA
Jet Star	1961		G	$8,500	2/18/2010	SEND	LP, WF, 3 pt., PTO, 14.9x28 rear tires
Jet Star	1969		G	$2,100	4/8/2011	WCSK	2WD, 44 PTO hp, 4 cyl. gas, PTO
Jet Star			G	$11,750	3/23/2013	NEIN	Orchard, gas, full orchard sheet metal, runs
Jet Star			G	$4,300	7/16/2011	SCMN	Loader and buckets
Jet Star			G	$2,600	4/23/2011	WCMI	Gas, 3 pt., PS, 540 PTO, 1 hyd., belt pulley
Jet Star			G	$1,000	9/4/2010	SEVA	4 cyl., gas, out of Texas
Jet Star			G	$3,500	9/4/2010	SEVA	Jetstar 3, 4 cyl., gas, out of Pennsylvania, all original
Jet Star 2	1963		G	$1,100	7/10/2010	SEIA	WF, 3 pt.
Jet Star 3	1967	592	G	$6,500	9/1/2011	WCMN	301 industrial gas, PTO, 1 hyd., power steering, Mars cab, 191 total built, used at Grand Fork, N.D., Air Force base
JT			G	$16,250	3/23/2013	NEIN	Orchard, full orchard sheet metal, runs
JTO			G	$8,500	9/21/2013	WCNY	Twin City
M-5			G	$4,200	6/5/2010	SWIA	Running, restored, NF, SF
M-602	1963		G	$2,600	3/28/2013	NEIA	Gas
M-602	1963	4,513	G	$1,100	6/14/2010	Online	*BigIron.com,* item in Oklahoma, 2WD, 10F/2R, 4 cyl. LP, 64 drawbar hp
M-602	1964		G	$2,650	5/19/2012	WCIL	Diesel, WF, good tires and paint
M-670	1967	3,068	G	$2,750	11/28/2012	Online	*PurpleWave.com,* item in Kansas, 4 cyl. LP, manual, Welco front loader, spring suspension seat, bale spear, drawbar, 540 PTO
M-670	1969	8,145	G	$3,225	4/13/2011	Online	*BigIron.com,* item in Kansas, super, 5 speed TA, 366-A4 LP, 70 hp, 1 hyd., other axle, 540 PTO, 3 pt.
M-670		8,145	G	$3,202	12/26/2013	Online	*BigIron.com,* item in Colorado, 4 cyl. LP, 18.4x38 rear tires, 6.5x16 front tires, 3 pt., 540 PTO, PS, 1 hyd., TA works
M-670			G	$2,700	8/31/2011	SEMN	
M-670		2,123	G	$800	6/8/2011	Online	*BigIron.com,* item in Nebraska, 6 speed, LP, 540 PTO, WF, radiator damage, power steering, 3 pt.
M-670		3,361	G	$3,175	4/13/2011	Online	*BigIron.com,* item in Nebraska, diesel, 5 speed, TA, 75 hp, bias rear tires, 540 PTO, 3 pt., internal engine block heater, lights
M-670		3,633	G	$4,250	4/13/2011	Online	*BigIron.com,* item in Nebraska, diesel, 75 hp, WF, radial rear tires, 5 speed, 540 PTO, 3 pt., 2 hyd., external block heater
M-670			G	$2,000	9/4/2010	SEVA	4 cyl., LP

Minneapolis-Moline

Model	Year	Hours	Condition	Price	Date	Area	Comments
M-670		1,235	G	$2,400	9/4/2010	SEVA	Super standard, 4 cyl., diesel, out of Kansas, all original
M-670			G	$2,500	9/4/2010	SEVA	Tricycle front
M-670			F	$1,300	8/9/2010	WCMO	Wheel weights
M-670			G	$6,000	6/19/2010	SWIL	Running, restored, fenders, PTO, lights, 1 hyd., deluxe seat, 3 pt., power steering, new paint
R	1950		G	$4,500	10/23/2010	SCPA	
R			G	$2,800	5/11/2013	NCOH	WF, repainted, new tires, runs
R			G	$1,700	2/6/2013	SESD	Fenders
R			G	$1,500	11/16/2010	ECNE	NF, gas, 4 speed, 540 PTO
R			G	$16,750	9/18/2010	ECMO	Cab, repainted
R			G	$26,000	6/5/2010	SWIA	Running, restored, cab, like new rubber
R			G	$1,300	4/1/2010	NCIN	540 PTO, 9.5x36 70% tires
RI	1951		F	$1,550	9/1/2011	WCMN	Industrial, power steering, wheel weights, complete rebuilt engine with Lull model DTS front forklift, first one built in 1951
RT	1939		G	$2,750	3/27/2013	Online	*PurpleWave.com,* item in Kansas, row crop, Minneapolis-Moline 2.7L, 4 cyl. gas, 23 hp, manual, spring seat
RT	1939		E	$2,250	9/22/2010	NECO	Wheatland, gas, totally restored
RTI			G	$2,855	4/27/2011	Online	*BigIron.com,* item in Missouri, 4 speed, 4 cyl. gas, new clutch, restored in 2009, rebuilt generator and starter and new battery, 4F/1R, starts and runs
RTN			G	$1,250	4/27/2011	Online	*BigIron.com,* item in Wyoming, SF, 4 speed, 4 cyl. gas, 540 PTO, drawbar, electric start, hand clutch
RTS	1949		F	$907	11/3/2011	Online	*PurpleWave.com,* item in Oklahoma
RTU	1948		G	$1,225	5/1/2010	NCOH	Older restoration, runs well
RTU			G	$900	5/11/2013	NCOH	Repainted, runs
RTU			F	$700	10/2/2010	SWWI	
RTU			G	$1,600	10/2/2010	ECMN	
RTU			G	$1,000	8/7/2010	SEWI	
U	1945		G	$2,350	3/6/2010	SEMN	48 HP, older restoration
U	1947		G	$4,750	10/23/2010	SCPA	
U	1948		E	$1,800	10/7/2011	NWSD	Restored, WF
U	1950		G	$2,000	9/1/2011	WCMN	Standard, LP, PTO, hyd. cylinder, original unrestored, second owner, 14x30 rubber
U	1951		G	$3,050	1/11/2013	ECIL	power steering, weights, belt pulley, overhauled, new 13.6x38 tires
U	1952		G	$1,350	6/22/2011	Online	*BigIron.com,* item in Oklahoma, 5F/1R, 4 cyl. LP, 1 hyd., 540 PTO, rear wheel weights
U	1955		F	$800	10/7/2011	NWSD	Standard, PTO stuck, grill and hood straight, left fender bent up some, right fender ok
U			G	$3,100	9/12/2013	SEIA	Restored, NF, 540 PTO, 1 hyd.
U			F	$800	6/2/2012	SEMN	Gas, runs, good sheet metal
U			G	$2,250	3/24/2012	NEIN	Special LP, repainted, new tires, PTO, runs

Minneapolis-Moline

Model	Year	Hours	Condition	Price	Date	Area	Comments
U			G	$1,150	11/13/2010	NCIA	
U			G	$1,000	5/26/2010	ECSD	Standard, LP gas, runs
U302	1966		G	$5,000	8/7/2010	SEWI	Super U302, complete new paint job, new 13.6x38 and 6.5x16 tires, new seat cushions and steering wheel, all gauges work, torque and clutch good
U302			G	$990	8/28/2013	Online	*PurpleWave.com,* item in Missouri, 4 cyl. gas, 6 speed, 3 pt., 15.5x38 rear tires
U302			G	$4,000	3/24/2012	NEIN	Diesel, PTO, 3 pt., hyd., motor OH, WF, fenders, original, runs
U302			G	$3,750	9/4/2010	NEIN	Gas
UB		518	F	$1,810	12/18/2013	Online	*BigIron.com,* item in Kansas, special, 5 speed, 4 cyl., 14.9x38 rear tires, 6x16 front tires, 3 pt., adj. drawbar, 540 PTO, O-ring seal needs replacement
UB			G	$3,800	3/24/2012	NEIN	Gas, special, PTO, hyd., repainted, runs
UB			G	$4,400	3/24/2012	NEIN	Special diesel, factory WF, new rear tires, PTO, hyd., fenders, repainted, runs
UB			F	$950	11/20/2010	ECFL	Runs
UB			G	$950	9/24/2010	ECMN	Power assist steering, PTO, Farmhand F11 loader, bucket, fork attachment
UB			G	$1,200	9/4/2010	SEVA	4 cyl., LP, Schwartz front end, out of Texas
UB			G	$1,700	8/26/2010	SCNE	Propane, WF
UB			G	$1,550	6/5/2010	WCMO	WF
UB			F	$1,050	5/22/2010	SEMN	Did not start, not used for years but looked pretty good
UB			G	$2,000	5/1/2010	SENE	
UB			F	$800	2/13/2010	SWIA	
UB			G	$1,500	2/13/2010	SWIA	Standard
UBE	1954		G	$1,950	9/1/2011	WCMN	Diesel, PTO, unrestored
UT			G	$900	9/12/2013	SEIA	Wheel weights
UTA	1948		F	$425	8/24/2013	WCMN	Engine stuck
UTB			F	$850	4/8/2010	SCMB	Diesel, shedded, not run for two years
UTC	1948		G	$15,000	9/1/2011	WCMN	LP, high crop, new Firestone, new fronts, restored
UTS	1947		G	$925	5/23/2012	Online	*BigIron.com,* item in South Dakota, 5 speed, 4 cyl. gas, 540 PTO, runs, shedded
UTS	1952		G	$5,600	8/24/2011	ECMN	STD, PTO, new 16.9x30 rubber
UTS			G	$926	7/27/2011	Online	*BigIron.com,* item in Nebraska, 5F/1R, gas, 540 PTO, Farmhand F10 loader, 9x32 deep bucket, hyd. pump
UTS			G	$1,250	5/26/2010	ECSD	Wheatland, LP, engine free
UTU	1941		G	$2,500	8/24/2011	ECMN	NF, PTO, 1 piece block, full fenders
UTU	1949		G	$950	9/3/2010	SCMN	NF, gas, converted to 12V, PTO, cast rims
UTU			G	$825	2/1/2013	Online	*IQBID.com,* item in North Dakota, NF, gas, 1 piece block, 5 speed, PTO, SN 114900845
UTU			G	$900	11/3/2012	SWMO	Starts, runs, new tires on back
UTU			G	$1,575	4/27/2011	Online	*BigIron.com,* item in Wyoming, WF, 5 speed, 4 cyl. LP, bareback, drawbar

Minneapolis-Moline

Model	Year	Hours	Condition	Price	Date	Area	Comments
Z	1942		G	$1,400	12/3/2011	NCOH	
Z	1950		G	$1,200	8/24/2013	WCMN	New paint and restored
Z	1951		G	$1,500	4/6/2013	ECWI	Universal Z, restored
Z	1951		E	$1,600	10/7/2011	NWSD	Restored, WF
Z	1951		G	$3,600	10/23/2010	SCPA	
Z	1953		G	$1,350	5/1/2010	NCOH	Runs well, hydro., tin straight, original
Z			E	$1,750	7/27/2013	WCIL	Gas, NF, fenders, new rubber, professionally restored and parade-ready, 2 sold on this sale
Z			E	$2,350	7/27/2013	WCIL	Gas, NF, fenders, new rubber, professionally restored and parade-ready, SN 0185004071
Z			F	$900	7/28/2012	NWSC	
Z			F	$900	6/20/2012	SESD	NF, 12.4x38 tires, fenders, restored, will run, shedded
Z			F	$900	10/7/2011	NWSD	WF, PTO, rubber pretty decent with some weather cracks
Z			F	$800	10/2/2010	SWWI	
Z			F	$900	10/2/2010	ECMN	NF
Z			P	$800	9/3/2010	NEIN	High crop, dead row, needs work and may not run, as is
Z			G	$1,200	7/31/2010	NWIL	NF, original paint
Z			G	$1,075	5/22/2010	SEMN	Runs but needs a starter, new paint, good rubber, looked good, new 13.6x-36 tires
ZA	1950		G	$1,200	9/12/2013	SEIA	Runs
ZA			G	$1,800	8/11/2011	WCMN	Adj. WF, gas, PTO, fenders
ZAN	1950		G	$1,250	11/30/2011	ECND	Adj. WF, hyd., PTO
ZB	1955		E	$5,300	8/25/2012	NEIA	New tires, parade ready
ZB			F	$2,450	11/19/2013	WCMI	Gas, NF, PTO, 1 hyd., 12.4x38 rear tires
ZB			F	$950	7/10/2010	SEIA	NF, hand clutch
ZBE	1953		G	$4,200	8/24/2011	ECMN	WF, PTO, rock shaft, Power Slide wheels, new 13.6x38 rubber
ZTE	1948		G	$3,750	8/24/2011	ECMN	WF, PTO, fenders, new 13.6x38 rubber
ZTS	1942		G	$1,900	4/4/2012	ECSK	PTO, 11.2x38 rear tires
ZTU	1939		E	$3,700	6/6/2013	ECAB	4 cyl. engine, new tires
ZTU	1948		G	$1,300	10/7/2011	NWSD	NF, PTO, restored
ZTU			G	$1,320	10/31/2012	Online	*PurpleWave.com,* item in Kansas, 4 cyl. gas, 5 speed, push button start, hand start crank included, 540 PTO, drawbar, pressed seat, tricycle front

Moline

Model	Year	Hours	Condition	Price	Date	Area	Comments
Universal			G	$65,000	9/21/2013	WCNY	Gas pull, rare, SN 842, loose, repainted
Universal			G	$14,000	9/21/2013	WCNY	2 cyl., plow, very complete, very original angle lugs
Universal			G	$4,000	9/21/2013	WCNY	Cart, some missing parts, sat outside
Universal			G	$2,000	9/21/2013	WCNY	
Universal			G	$9,500	9/9/2010	NWWI	Plow, motor SN R32232
Universal			G	$14,000	6/19/2010	SWIL	Running, style D, restored, PTO, lights, belt pulley

Oliver

Model	Year	Hours	Condition	Price	Date	Area	Comments
55	1955		G	$6,100	4/17/2014	WCMN	2WD, diesel, cab, 3 pt., 354.4 natural Perkins diesel engine out of a White 8900 combine
55		715	G	$6,100	4/17/2014	WCMN	Gas, 3 pt., 540 PTO, 2 hyd. with valve
55			G	$850	6/28/2013	NEMO	SN 12910-518
55			G	$1,400	6/5/2010	WCMO	Diesel, 1 hyd.
60	1941		G	$3,750	10/12/2013	NEOH	Row crop, cultivators
60	1941		G	$4,000	10/12/2013	ECOH	Row crop, cultivators
60	1941		G	$5,100	3/24/2012	NEIN	Row crop, PTO, runs
60	1941		G	$1,300	8/25/2011	ECND	Row crop, factory WF, PTO, fenders, lights, 9x32 tires, loose
60	1942		F	$925	8/25/2011	ECND	Standard, PTO, rear weights, 11x24 rears, stuck
60	1945		E	$3,050	10/15/2011	ECIA	Parade ready, near new Firestone 12.4x28 tires
60	1946		G	$1,050	10/2/2010	SWWI	Row crop, gas
60	1947		G	$4,700	8/25/2012	NEIA	Row crop, new tires, new paint
60	1947		G	$1,100	5/19/2012	SWMI	Row crop, NF, 9.5x32 tires, fenders, newer paint
60	1948		G	$6,000	10/12/2013	ECOH	Standard
60	1948		G	$1,485	5/30/2012	Online	*PurpleWave.com,* item in Missouri, row crop, Oliver 4 cyl. gas, 18 hp, manual, 2WD
60			G	$3,100	6/15/2013	WCOH	Fenders, new tires, ES, lights, PTO, restored, runs
60			G	$900	5/11/2013	NCOH	Older repaint, runs
60			G	$900	5/11/2013	NCOH	Repainted, runs
60			G	$1,350	5/11/2013	NCOH	Older repaint, electric start, lights
60			G	$2,800	5/11/2011	Online	*BigIron.com,* row crop, PTO
60			F	$1,000	10/2/2010	ECMN	NF, row crop
60			G	$3,600	7/24/2010	SWIL	Fender extensions, power lift, side curtains
60			G	$2,100	6/19/2010	SWIL	Running, restored, fenders, PTO, lights, belt pulley
66	1949		G	$4,500	8/7/2010	WCMN	Row crop, gas, engine rebuilt
66	1950		G	$6,000	10/12/2013	ECOH	Standard
66	1950		G	$17,000	10/12/2013	ECOH	Orchard
66	1950		G	$3,200	6/20/2012	SESD	Row crop, NF
66	1950		G	$2,200	8/27/2011	NEIA	Gas, fenders, side curtains, SN 423934, new clutch and pressure plate in 2009 ($2,366 in repairs), used for spraying around the farm, shedded, tires are usable
66	1950		G	$6,500	3/18/2011	NWIA	Row crop, tractor NF, side pulley, SN 423218C66C
66	1950		G	$4,200	7/24/2010	SWIL	Row crop, Hydra-Power, all new tires
66	1951		G	$30,000	10/12/2013	ECOH	Row crop, high clearance, restored, running, WF, fenders, lights, belt pulley, like-new tires
66	1953		G	$2,750	10/12/2013	ECOH	Row crop
66	1953		G	$4,750	10/12/2013	ECOH	Row crop
66	1953		G	$5,250	10/12/2013	ECOH	Row crop

Oliver

Model	Year	Hours	Condition	Price	Date	Area	Comments
66			G	$3,100	6/28/2013	NEMO	11x38 rubber, SN 42963066, row crop
66			G	$2,800	6/15/2013	WCOH	Pulley, new tires, PTO, hyd., repainted, runs
66			G	$1,550	5/11/2013	NCOH	Factory WF, original, runs
66			G	$9,250	3/22/2013	NWMN	Orchard, full orchard sheet metal, original, runs
66			G	$2,500	9/22/2012	NEOR	Standard, WF
66			G	$1,500	9/15/2012	SCMN	Row crop, NF, fenders, side tins, repainted
66			G	$1,300	10/2/2010	SWWI	Row crop, gas
66			P	$3,000	10/2/2010	SWWI	Diesel, row crop, motor is loose, doesn't run, fuel problem
66			P	$1,050	9/3/2010	NEIN	Sprayer tractor, dead row, needs work and may not run or drive, as is
66			G	$2,750	7/31/2010	NWIL	Diesel, row crop, NF, old repaint, has side panels, rare
66			G	$1,750	6/23/2010	NEWI	66 row crop, screens, hour meter, very snappy
66			G	$4,500	6/19/2010	SWIL	No tag, running, restored, fenders, lights, deluxe seats, belt pulley, new gauges
66			G	$1,750	6/5/2010	WCMO	Row crop, new tires
66			G	$2,600	6/5/2010	WCMO	Diesel, WF, running
70	1935		F	$1,500	8/11/2011	WCMN	NF, PTO, on full steel, row crop, original

March 17, 2012, was an amazing day. I think I received five or six auction sale price reports on that early spring Saturday. Each sale was "red hot." So which sale to focus on and blog about? That Saturday evening I decided to go with a farm estate auction from the Waterloo, Iowa area. One of the deciding factors was the White 6100 six-row planter on this auction that sold for $20,500, a new record price by a mile. No, by two miles.

Also on this sale was this 1973 Oliver 2255 front-wheel assist with 4,844 hours. It sold for $28,500, another new record price. I blogged that night along the lines of..."See folks, it really does pay to take great care of your equipment." The next morning I got an email from Dave, son of the man whose estate auction this was for. Dave relayed how auction day went by and he was fine, but upon reading my blog Saturday night, he broke into tears. He was proud of his dad. Dave emailed me again three months later when another nice 2255 with 3,900 hours sold for $26,000 at an auction in east-central Iowa. Dave wrote: "Pete, Dad still has the record!"

PETE'S PICK

TRACTORS

Oliver

Model	Year	Hours	Condition	Price	Date	Area	Comments
70	1936		G	$7,250	10/12/2013	ECOH	Row crop
70	1938		G	$15,000	10/12/2013	ECOH	Orchard
70	1939		G	$1,500	9/1/2011	WCMN	NF, belt pulley, fenders w/ext., canvas seat, original unrestored
70	1940		G	$3,000	10/12/2013	ECOH	Row crop
70	1941		G	$1,500	10/12/2013	ECOH	Row crop
70	1941		G	$5,000	10/12/2013	ECOH	Row crop, cultivators
70	1941		E	$6,000	6/7/2013	ECSD	SN 239035, fenders, side panel, runs, good rubber, recent paint, parade ready unit
70	1942		G	$2,000	5/26/2010	ECSD	Restored
70	1944		P	$875	1/26/2013	WCIL	Not running, belt pulley
70	1945		P	$1,025	10/11/2011	Online	*BidNow.US*, NF, PTO, belt pulley, new carburetor, aluminum sheet metal, engine seized
70	1947		F	$1,000	8/27/2011	NCIN	Row crop, NF
70	1949		G	$925	10/2/2010	SWWI	Row crop, gas
70			F	$925	3/21/2014	ECIA	Gas, 13.6x38 tires
70			G	$2,400	6/15/2013	WCOH	PTO, hyd., lights, electric start, older repaint, runs
70			G	$2,800	6/15/2013	WCOH	Full steel with extensions, fenders, PTO, electric start, lights restored, runs
70			G	$3,600	6/15/2013	WCOH	Factory WF, electric start, lights, PTO, restored, runs
70			G	$900	5/11/2013	NCOH	Older repaint, belt pulley, runs
70			G	$1,200	5/11/2013	NCOH	Electric start, lights, repainted, runs
70			G	$1,500	5/11/2013	NCOH	Repainted, electric start, lights, runs
70			G	$825	11/3/2012	SWMO	Side panels and fenders, rear wheel weights, runs
70			G	$1,100	9/22/2012	NEOR	Row crop, mower
70			G	$1,200	9/12/2012	Online	*IQBID.com*, item in North Dakota, gas, runs
70			G	$1,500	11/13/2010	NCIA	Fenders, side panels
70			P	$650	10/2/2010	SWWI	Hart Parr, doesn't run, motor is loose
70			F	$800	10/2/2010	ECMN	NF
70			G	$21,000	9/18/2010	ECMO	Repainted
70			P	$900	9/3/2010	NEIN	Row crop, dead row, needs work and may not run or drive, as is
70			P	$1,500	7/24/2010	SWIL	Belt pulley, doesn't run
70			G	$1,300	7/17/2010	SEIA	Pulling tractor
70			G	$2,900	6/5/2010	WCMO	Standard, gas
70			G	$2,200	5/1/2010	SENE	
70			G	$3,300	5/1/2010	SENE	Industrial
77	1949		G	$2,650	3/18/2011	NWIA	Row crop, tractor, 80% rear rubber, 13. 6x38 rear rubber, NF, rear fenders, side pulley, SN 325552
77	1949		G	$4,250	8/7/2010	WCMN	Standard gas, engine good
77	1949		G	$2,600	7/24/2010	SWIL	Row crop, belt pulley, hyd. side curtains
77	1950		G	$5,500	10/12/2013	ECOH	Standard
77	1950		G	$2,400	10/7/2011	NWSD	Restored, standard, PTO, straight skirt
77	1951		F	$825	8/24/2013	SWWI	Fresh paint

Oliver

Model	Year	Hours	Condition	Price	Date	Area	Comments
77	1951		F	$1,100	12/17/2010	WCIL	Gas, NF, 540 PTO
77	1951		G	$4,500	8/7/2010	WCMN	Row crop, gas, engine rebuilt
77	1951		G	$3,200	7/24/2010	SWIL	Row crop, steps, side curtains
77	1954		G	$4,000	10/12/2013	ECOH	Row crop
77			F	$1,300	3/21/2014	ECIA	Gas, 12.4x38 tires
77			G	$2,250	3/15/2014	WCIL	WF, gas, row crop
77			G	$1,000	12/5/2013	SCIA	Gas, NF
77			P	$1,550	8/24/2013	SWOH	Didn't run, gas, tricycle front, needs repair
77			G	$900	7/18/2013	SCSK	2WD, 32 PTO hp, gas, needs clutch work
77			G	$2,500	6/26/2013	Online	*BigIron.com,* item in Nebraska, 2WD, 6 speed, 1 hyd.
77			F	$1,500	6/15/2013	WCOH	Gas, original, PTO, fenders, lights, hyd., low hour, not running
77			G	$2,300	6/15/2013	WCOH	Gas, PTO, hyd., repainted, runs
77			G	$4,000	6/15/2013	WCOH	WF, gas, fenders, new tires, older repaint, runs
77			G	$1,100	5/11/2013	NCOH	Loader, repainted, runs
77			G	$1,200	5/11/2013	NCOH	Older repaint, belt pulley, runs
77			G	$1,300	5/11/2013	NCOH	Belt pulley, repainted, runs
77			G	$1,400	5/11/2013	NCOH	Original, belt pulley, runs
77			G	$1,500	12/13/2012	WCIA	
77			G	$2,000	9/15/2012	SCMN	Row crop, NF, side tins, fenders
77			G	$1,024	8/22/2012	Online	*BigIron.com,* item in Nebraska, gas, 13.6x38 duals, 11Lx15 front tires, 540 PTO
77			G	$1,400	8/21/2012	WCIL	Diesel
77			G	$1,700	6/30/2012	ECIA	Gas, NF, hyd., disk brakes, fair tires
77			F	$1,900	6/8/2012	ECND	Standard, loader, no curtains
77			G	$2,250	3/24/2012	NEIN	Gas, orchard, runs
77			P	$800	3/20/2012	WCIL	
77			G	$1,000	2/18/2012	ECIL	
77			F	$1,800	8/26/2011	SWOH	Row crop, cab
77			G	$1,200	8/13/2011	SWMN	Loader
77			G	$1,250	7/30/2011	ECMO	
77			G	$4,300	5/14/2011	SWSK	6 cyl. gas, PTO, 1 hyd., 13.6x38 RR tires
77			F	$1,150	4/29/2011	NEOH	Stuck engine, gas, all panels, fenders
77			F	$3,450	3/19/2011	NCPA	Mower and 2 bottom plow
77			G	$3,100	10/2/2010	SWWI	Standard, diesel
77			G	$3,700	9/4/2010	NEIN	Standard
77			G	$29,000	9/4/2010	NEIN	Orchard, diesel
77			P	$1,600	7/24/2010	SWIL	Diesel, side curtains, doesn't run
77			G	$1,900	5/26/2010	ECSD	Du-Al loader, gas
80	1940		G	$2,860	8/14/2012	Online	*PurpleWave.com,* item in Illinois, row crop, Waukesha Oliver 4 cyl. gas, 30 hp drawbar, 39 hp belt, manual, hand crank start, dry disk clutch, 540 PTO
80	1946		G	$3,250	10/12/2013	ECOH	Standard
80	1946		F	$1,600	10/7/2011	NWSD	Standard, PTO, tin fairly straight, good rubber, runs

Oliver

Model	Year	Hours	Condition	Price	Date	Area	Comments
80			F	$1,250	6/15/2013	WCOH	Standard, older repaint, electric start, lights, PTO, nice original, not running
80			G	$1,700	6/15/2013	WCOH	Row crop, NF, original, 40" tires, fenders, PTO, belt pulley, not running
80			F	$2,500	6/15/2013	WCOH	Row crop, repainted, complete, fenders, PTO, NF, original 13x40 closed rear tires, not running
80			G	$8,500	6/15/2013	WCOH	Row crop, factory WF, electric start, lights, pulley, PTO, new 42" tires, restored, runs
80			G	$1,400	5/11/2013	NCOH	Belt pulley, repainted, runs, standard
80			G	$1,500	9/22/2012	NEOR	Standard, electric start, WF
80			F	$1,700	10/29/2011	SEMN	Unstyled, does not run
80			G	$72,000	9/18/2010	ECMO	40" rear, repainted
80			F	$850	7/17/2010	SCON	Standard, WF
80			G	$800	6/5/2010	WCMO	
88	1948		G	$4,000	10/12/2013	ECOH	Standard
88	1948		G	$7,500	10/12/2013	ECOH	Old style, row crop
88	1948		G	$8,250	10/12/2013	NEOH	Row crop
88	1948		F	$1,700	8/24/2013	WCMN	Painted, does need side panels
88	1949		G	$2,768	7/13/2011	Online	*BigIron.com,* item in Kansas, row crop, dual 3F/1R, gas, 45 hp, 1 hyd., 540 PTO, repainted, lights all work
88	1950		G	$4,750	8/7/2010	WCMN	Row crop, diesel, engine good
88	1950		G	$3,500	7/24/2010	SWIL	Standard, belt pulley, new front tires
88	1951		G	$2,100	7/24/2010	SWIL	Row crop, Hydra-Power, side curtains
88	1952		G	$6,000	3/24/2012	NEIN	Wheatland, diesel, standard, repainted, runs
88	1952		G	$1,800	8/27/2011	NEIA	Gas, fenders, side curtains, SN 138906, new starter and ring gear in 2010, runs and drives, at this time it is missing the rear side tins on both sides, $140 spent in 2010, tires are usable
88	1953		G	$1,600	12/6/2012	Online	*IQBID.com*
88	1953		G	$1,600	12/6/2012	SEIA	
88	1954		F	$900	1/26/2011	NECO	WF, gas, 3 pt., FH-F11 loader
88			G	$4,000	3/27/2014	ECNE	Row crop, NF, 6 speed, fenders, hyd. rear, side shields, original
88			F	$1,425	7/27/2013	WCIL	NF, New Idea trip loader
88			G	$2,200	6/15/2013	WCOH	Gas, PTO, hyd., lights, wheel weights, older repaint, runs
88			G	$5,500	6/15/2013	WCOH	Gas, new tires, fenders, lights, PTO, nicely repainted, runs
88			G	$7,750	6/15/2013	WCOH	Diesel, standard, runs, fenders with extensions, dust shields, nice original
88			G	$1,350	5/11/2013	NCOH	Older repainted, runs
88			G	$2,200	5/11/2013	NCOH	Older repaint, runs
88			G	$3,500	5/11/2013	NCOH	Gas, standard, repainted, Western dust shield, runs
88			G	$776	4/10/2013	Online	*BigIron.com,* item in Nebraska, 2WD, PTO pump, gas
88			G	$2,000	9/15/2012	SCMN	Row crop, factory WF, new rubber, fenders, repainted

Oliver

Model	Year	Hours	Condition	Price	Date	Area	Comments
88			G	$2,300	6/30/2012	ECIA	Gas, NF, hyd., 2 sets of steps, clean tractor, older repaint, has Super series frame
88			G	$3,700	6/30/2012	ECIA	Standard, gas, complete engine OH, power steering, hyd. 2 lever, Firestone 16.9x26 tires (road worn), older repaint
88			F	$1,300	6/20/2012	SESD	Gas, WF, hyd., PTO, runs
88			F	$1,600	4/24/2012	SESK	PTO, belt pulley, gas, 12V conversion
88			G	$2,500	3/24/2012	NEIN	Standard, diesel, original, runs
88			F	$2,400	3/23/2012	WCNE	Farmhand loader, snow bucket, complete, straight, SN 820251
88			F	$1,600	8/6/2011	WCIL	Gas, all sheet metal
88			F	$900	4/2/2011	SWSK	2WD
88			F	$1,900	10/2/2010	SWWI	Diesel, good rubber, rear end is welded
88			F	$950	9/9/2010	NWWI	Diesel, WF
88			G	$3,700	9/4/2010	NEIN	LP
88			P	$1,000	9/3/2010	NEIN	Row crop, dead row, needs work and may not run or drive, as is
88			G	$3,800	7/24/2010	SWIL	Standard, hyd., fender extensions, side curtains
88			G	$1,900	6/19/2010	SWIL	Row crop, running, restored, fenders, hyd.
88			G	$4,000	6/19/2010	SWIL	Running, old restoration and repaint, rear wheel weights, fenders, PTO, lights, deluxe seat
88			G	$5,000	6/19/2010	SWIL	Running, old style, old restoration and repaint, fenders, PTO, lights, deluxe seat
88			G	$2,700	6/11/2010	SEAB	Standard gas, PTO belt pulley, power steering, hyd.
88			G	$5,800	6/11/2010	SEAB	Gas, PTO, belt pulley, restored
88			G	$3,100	6/5/2010	WCMO	Standard
88			G	$3,500	6/5/2010	WCMO	Row crop
88			G	$2,700	2/13/2010	SWIA	
90	1941		G	$3,750	10/12/2013	ECOH	Standard
99	1947		G	$2,900	7/22/2011	SEMN	Gas, rear wheel weights, new rear tires, 16.9x30 rubber, repaired block
99	1948		G	$3,750	10/12/2013	NEOH	Standard, early model
99	1948		G	$8,250	10/12/2013	ECOH	Standard
99	1948		G	$1,375	8/22/2012	ECMN	Standard, 4 cyl., factory rear wheel weights, hyd. pump and valve
99	1948		G	$3,850	8/14/2012	Online	*PurpleWave.com,* item in Illinois, 4 cyl. gas, 52 hp drawbar, 62 belt hp, manual, electric start with hand crank, 540 PTO, 7.5x18 fronts, 16.9x30 rears
99	1950		F	$3,410	8/14/2012	Online	*PurpleWave.com,* item in Illinois, 4 cyl. gas, engine stuck, manual, rare dual brakes, electric start with hand crank, 540 PTO
99	1952		F	$2,600	10/7/2011	NWSD	Standard, PTO, unstyled, tin pretty straight, easy restoration or looks pretty good original as it is
99	1952		G	$6,000	8/7/2010	WCMN	Standard gas, engine good

Oliver

Model	Year	Hours	Condition	Price	Date	Area	Comments
99	1953		G	$6,750	10/12/2013	NEOH	Standard
99	1953		G	$9,900	10/1/2011	ECIA	Restored, 302 cu. in., 6 cyl., 4 speed, gas
99	1953		G	$7,500	8/7/2010	WCMN	6 cyl. diesel, engine good
99	1953		G	$8,500	8/7/2010	WCMN	Gas, engine rebuilt
99			G	$5,800	6/15/2013	WCOH	Unstyled, PTO, new tires, electric start, lights, restored, runs
99			G	$1,900	5/11/2013	NCOH	Repainted, no tag, belt pulley, runs
440	1958		G	$13,500	8/7/2010	WCMN	Gas, engine good
440	1960		G	$12,500	10/12/2013	ECOH	
440	1960		G	$12,500	10/12/2013	ECOH	
440	1960		G	$13,000	7/24/2010	SWIL	3 pt.
440			G	$26,000	6/15/2013	WCOH	3 pt., full cultivators, new tires, restored, runs
440			G	$10,000	5/11/2013	NCOH	Older repaint, 3 pt., front/rear weights, runs
440			E	$1,850	3/23/2013	NEIN	Original, cultivators, weights, 3 pt., PTO, runs
440			G	$17,000	3/23/2013	NEIN	3 pt., repainted, new tires, runs
440			G	$8,700	9/4/2010	NEIN	Cultivators
550	1958		G	$8,500	8/7/2010	WCMN	Loader, gas, engine good
550	1958	2,738	F	$3,600	6/23/2010	Online	*BigIron.com,* item in Kansas, gas engine, 40 hp, rear tires 12.4x28, front tires 6.5x16, 540 PTO, PTO OH, live PTO and hyd.
550	1959		G	$6,250	10/23/2010	SCPA	
550	1966		G	$4,400	1/28/2012	ECMO	
550	1968		G	$2,750	10/19/2013	WCIL	Gas, new paint, loader
550	1974		G	$5,000	2/5/2014	SESD	WF
550		4,231	G	$5,400	3/27/2014	ECNE	4 cyl. gas, WF, 3 pt., fenders, PTO, original condition
550			G	$3,750	10/12/2013	NEOH	
550			G	$9,000	6/15/2013	WCOH	Gas, PS, 3 pt., fenders, restored, plastic grill, runs
550			G	$13,000	6/15/2013	WCOH	Diesel, PS, power set wheels, 3 pt., fenders, rear weights, restored, plastic grill, runs
550			G	$2,800	12/29/2012	WCMI	Gas, WF, 3 pt., PTO
550		3,700	G	$4,400	6/30/2012	ECIA	Gas, power steering, 3 pt., drawbar, no hyd. valve, repainted, 13.6x26 rear tires
550		3,300	G	$2,000	9/3/2011	WCIL	Gas
550		4,325	G	$3,100	2/25/2011	NENC	13.6x26 rear tires, 6.5x16SL front tires, 540 PTO, SN 60-713-519
550			G	$1,700	1/8/2011	ECMI	Gas, new battery and alternator
550			G	$3,500	9/4/2010	NEIN	
550			G	$3,900	9/4/2010	NEIN	Industrial
550			G	$6,000	9/4/2010	NEIN	Industrial
550			G	$4,000	7/24/2010	SWIL	Freeman loader, power adj. rear wheels
550			G	$4,250	7/24/2010	SWIL	3 pt., new tires, gas, runs, restored
660	1959		G	$6,500	10/12/2013	ECOH	
660	1959		G	$6,500	8/7/2010	WCMN	Row crop, gas, engine good

Oliver

Model	Year	Hours	Condition	Price	Date	Area	Comments
660	1961		G	$7,000	7/24/2010	SWIL	Row crop, steps
660	1963		G	$12,000	10/1/2011	ECIA	Restored, 155 cu. in., hyd., 3 pt., belt pulley, cast rear wheels, gas
660			G	$6,000	6/15/2013	WCOH	Gas, WF, new tires, fenders, PTO, restored
660			G	$4,200	10/2/2010	SWWI	WF
660			G	$7,000	9/4/2010	NEIN	Diesel, row crop
660			G	$6,000	6/19/2010	SWIL	Running, restored, fenders, PTO, lights, hyd., low hours
660			G	$10,000	6/19/2010	SWIL	Diesel, running, restored, major redo on motor, rebuilt rear end and transmission
770	1958		G	$4,750	10/12/2013	ECOH	
770	1958		G	$2,700	7/24/2010	SWIL	Gas, row crop, 3 pt
770	1959		G	$4,000	10/1/2011	ECIA	216 cu. in., new rear tires, original
770	1959		G	$2,520	5/25/2011	Online	*BigIron.com,* item in Nebraska, gas, hyds. were taken off, NF, shifts a little rough
770	1960		G	$5,000	10/12/2013	ECOH	Goodison
770	1960		F	$2,600	3/18/2011	NWIA	NF, side pulley, rear fenders, 13.6x38 rear rubber, SN 423218C66C
770	1961		G	$4,300	7/24/2010	SWIL	Row crop
770	1964		G	$11,750	10/12/2013	ECOH	LP orchard
770	1964		G	$1,300	11/3/2012	SWMI	6 cyl. gas, NF, live hyd., independent PTO, 14.9x38 rear tires
770	1965		G	$7,100	8/25/2012	NEIA	Gas, good tires, NF, wheel weights
770	1966		G	$3,500	7/24/2010	SWIL	Diesel, square fenders, 3 pt
770		5,108	G	$5,100	3/27/2014	ECNE	Row crop, 6 cyl. gas, 6 speed, PTO, fenders, side shields, 1 hyd., Schwartz hyd. front loader, bucket
770			G	$2,000	2/22/2014	ECIL	Row crop, NF, 3 pt.
770			G	$2,750	11/2/2013	WCWI	NF, snow plow
770			P	$1,800	8/24/2013	SWOH	Gas, tricycle front end, needs repair
770		2,174	G	$2,600	8/24/2013	SEMN	NF, PTO hyd., 15.5x38, new power steering, new generator, new wheel bearings, air in PS
770			G	$4,900	6/15/2013	WCOH	Gas, row crop, new tires, fenders, PTO, hyd., restored, runs
770			G	$9,000	6/15/2013	WCOH	Diesel, front/rear weights, new tires, 3 pt., PTO, fenders, power set wheels, restored, runs
770			G	$4,000	5/11/2013	NCOH	Gas, repainted, PS, fenders, power set wheels, runs
770		9,156	G	$6,000	12/8/2012	ECIA	Fenders, padded seat, 15.5x38
770			F	$1,347	6/7/2012	Online	*HansenandYoung.com,* $1,225 + 10% buyers fee = $1,347, gas, needs carb. cleaned, 2 hyd., Firestone tires good tread
770			F	$975	9/17/2011	SEND	Diesel, tractor not far from running, Farmhand F10 loader good
770			G	$1,800	9/17/2011	SEND	Gas, good runner, F10 Farmhand loader poor, WF, hyd., live power, good rubber

Oliver

Model	Year	Hours	Condition	Price	Date	Area	Comments
770			F	$1,250	9/16/2011	ECND	WF, power steering, hyd. PTO
770			G	$2,500	9/14/2011	Online	*BigIron.com,* item in Nebraska, 6 cyl. gas, 540 PTO, 6F/2R, fenders, one hyd., live power, 3 pt., drawbar
770			G	$3,900	7/16/2011	SCMN	
770			F	$1,400	11/29/2010	ECIA	NF
770			G	$1,900	5/1/2010	SENE	
880	1958		G	$4,250	10/12/2013	ECOH	Goodison
880	1958		G	$6,500	10/12/2013	NEOH	Standard, Wheatland, Goodison
880	1959		G	$6,250	10/12/2013	ECOH	Wheatland
880	1959		P	$1,500	6/29/2011	WCIL	Diesel, PTO, NF
880	1960		G	$9,000	8/7/2010	WCMN	Wheatland diesel, engine good
880	1961		G	$6,200	7/24/2010	SWIL	Row crop
880	1962		G	$8,000	10/1/2011	ECIA	Restored, 265 cu. in., PS rear wheels
880			G	$4,750	10/12/2013	NEOH	
880			G	$2,640	8/26/2013	NWWI	Gas, runs, drives
880			G	$3,000	6/22/2013	SEMN	WF, factory 3 pt., good rubber, 3 pt., dual hyd., PTO
880			G	$6,600	6/15/2013	WCOH	Diesel, standard, new tires, PTO, hyd., fenders with extension, dust shields, restored, runs
880			G	$12,500	6/15/2013	WCOH	Diesel, new tires, PTO, hyd., fenders, power set wheels, restored, runs
880			G	$3,200	4/3/2013	ECMN	WF
880			G	$900	3/22/2013	NESD	Diesel, WF
880			P	$900	10/4/2011	SCMN	Not running, gas, converted from LP
880			F	$3,850	3/26/2011	WCIA	Restorable, diesel, NF
880			G	$2,000	10/2/2010	SWWI	Diesel
880			G	$2,800	9/4/2010	NEIN	
880		3,068	G	$1,150	6/23/2010	Online	*BigIron.com,* item in Nebraska, 6 Speed, 6 cyl. diesel, rear tires 15.5x38, front tires 6x16, 540 PTO, WF, new clutch last year, tractor spun a rod bearing, no battery
880		8,000	G	$1,305	6/23/2010	Online	*BigIron.com,* item in Nebraska, 6 speed Hi/Lo 2 reverses, 6 cyl. diesel
880			G	$4,750	6/19/2010	SWIL	Running, restored, rear wheel weights, fenders, PTO, lights, hyd.
880			G	$3,400	6/5/2010	WCMO	Diesel, nice original, 3 pt., WF, p ower steering
880			F	$3,750	6/5/2010	SEMN	WF
950	1958		G	$8,000	8/7/2010	WCMN	Diesel, engine rebuilt
950	1959		G	$6,500	10/12/2013	NEOH	
950	1959		G	$12,500	10/12/2013	ECOH	Standard
950	1960		G	$12,500	8/7/2010	WCMN	Gas, engine like new
950			G	$6,500	3/27/2014	ECNE	6 cyl. diesel, 2 speed Hi/Lo, fenders, 1 hyd., original
950			G	$8,500	6/15/2013	WCOH	Diesel, PTO, hyd., excellent original, runs
990	1959		G	$12,500	10/12/2013	ECOH	Standard
990	1959		G	$17,500	8/7/2010	WCMN	Diesel, cab, engine good
990	1959		G	$20,000	8/7/2010	WCMN	Pulling tractor, diesel, engine rebuilt
990	1959		G	$20,500	8/7/2010	WCMN	Diesel, engine rebuilt

Oliver

Model	Year	Hours	Condition	Price	Date	Area	Comments
990	1960		G	$16,000	10/1/2011	ECIA	Restored, GM 371, standard size PTO shaft
990	1960		G	$5,600	6/23/2010	Online	*BigIron.com,* item in Nebraska, 6 speed, 353 Detroit Spec. #39-4112 engine, rear tires 18.4x34, front tires 7.5x18, 1 hyd., dual air intake
990			G	$9,500	3/24/2012	NEIN	GM Detroit motor, new 26" tires, PTO, original, runs
990			G	$7,500	9/4/2010	NEIN	GM Detroit diesel
990			G	$18,000	8/7/2010	WCMN	Diesel, engine rebuilt
995	1958		G	$60,000	8/7/2010	WCMN	Diesel, engine rebuilt
995	1959		G	$25,000	10/12/2013	ECOH	
995	1960		G	$39,000	8/7/2010	WCMN	Diesel, engine rebuilt
995			G	$5,700	3/27/2014	ECNE	WF, trans completely rebuilt and refurbished GM diesel, most tinwork and other parts to rebuild tractor included
995			G	$11,500	3/24/2012	NEIN	Original, runs
1250	1965		G	$3,200	3/26/2011	SEWI	Made in Italy by Fiat, power steering
1250	1965		G	$3,800	8/7/2010	SEWI	WF, new paint, power steering, diff. lock, 2 stage clutch controlled a continuous PTO
1250	1967		G	$1,100	4/11/2011	Online	*AuctionTime.com,* 2WD
1250			G	$1,300	1/4/2014	WCNY	1 hyd., 3 pt., PTO
1250		4,983	G	$1,350	11/20/2010	SCKY	
1250			G	$3,250	10/23/2010	SCPA	
1365		2,605	G	$3,400	3/26/2014	Online	*BigIron.com,* item in Kansas, 4F/2R transmission, rear tires
1365			G	$1,800	1/4/2014	WCNY	Diesel, loader, 3 pt., PTO
1365			G	$3,300	6/1/2013	SEMN	3 pt., 540 PTO
1365		4,370	G	$8,030	4/9/2013	NWWI	MFWD, new rear tires 16.9x30, 3 pt., 540 PTO, single hyd., new starter, front tires 9.5x24, newer alternator, clutch and hose heater
1365		4,984	G	$3,400	4/29/2011	NEOH	
1465			G	$3,000	8/21/2012	WCIL	Diesel, 3 pt., 16.9x34 tires
1550	1965	7,095	G	$1,700	12/10/2013	Online	*IQBID.com,* WF
1550	1966		G	$6,700	7/24/2010	SWIL	Wheatland, 3 pt., square fenders, power adj., steps
1550	1968	2,400	G	$3,500	10/19/2013	WCIL	Gas, Hydra-Power, WF, 3 pt., good tires, front/rear weights
1550	1968	8,450	G	$2,750	7/14/2012	SWMN	Diesel, NF, open platform
1550			G	$4,250	7/28/2012	SCNE	Gas, Lion loader and grapple
1550			G	$4,500	3/24/2012	NEIN	Gas, PTO, dual hyd., repainted, runs
1550			G	$9,750	3/24/2012	NEIN	Gas, 3 pt., PTO, hyd., restored, runs
1550			G	$8,750	9/4/2010	NEIN	High crop, 3 pt.
1550			G	$15,500	6/19/2010	SWIL	Running, restored
1550			G	$4,100	5/1/2010	SENE	
1550			G	$3,800	4/17/2010	NEIA	Cozy cab, heater, NF, over/under, 3 pt., spin out wheels, weights, White fully hyd. loader, 2 buckets, old boy paint brush finish on everything, lose the loader and cab = average tractor

Oliver

Model	Year	Hours	Condition	Price	Date	Area	Comments
1555	1974	4,537	G	$4,500	6/20/2012	SESD	Diesel, WF, PS, hyd., fenders, PTO, 18.4x34 tires, good runner
1555	1974		G	$3,200	3/23/2010	SEND	2 hyd.
1555	1975	2,815	G	$7,000	7/17/2013	NEND	Gas, 3 pt., PTO, Leon loader
1555			G	$5,400	12/20/2013	SCSD	Cab, WF, Farmhand 336 loader, grapple
1555			G	$2,050	5/8/2013	Online	*IQBID.com,* Farmhand F11 loader, no chains, needs repair
1555			G	$7,200	4/13/2013	SEMN	Gas, open station, WF, fenders, 3 pt., 2 hyd., 540 PTO, 15.5x38 tires 80%, SN 232-249-504
1555			G	$4,900	3/23/2013	NEIN	Gas, WF, original, runs
1555			F	$2,000	7/9/2011	ECND	Farmhand loader
1555		2,093	G	$4,750	3/16/2011	ECSD	2WD, open station, PTO, gas, 16.5x38 rear tires, one owner
1600	1962	6,273	P	$1,300	5/18/2011	SEWY	Diesel, WF, 3 pt., engine needs work
1600	1963		G	$6,000	10/12/2013	ECOH	
1600	1963		G	$2,000	4/11/2011	Online	*AuctionTime.com,* 2WD
1600	1963		G	$11,000	8/7/2010	WCMN	Diesel, engine good
1600	1964		G	$16,000	10/12/2013	ECOH	High crop
1600	1964		G	$7,500	10/1/2011	ECIA	Restored, 2 speed, 3 pt., PTO, diesel, 265 cu. in.
1600	1972	7,000	G	$3,750	2/11/2010	NENE	Farmhand F11 loader, 3 pt., WF, 1,500 hours on overhaul
1600		3,622	G	$3,410	10/30/2013	Online	*PurpleWave.com,* item in Missouri, Oliver 6 cyl. gas, manual
1600			G	$2,475	8/28/2013	Online	*PurpleWave.com,* item in Kansas, 6 cyl. gas, Oliver 1610 loader, 60" toothed bucket, 3 pt., drawbar, 540 PTO, 18.4x34 tires
1600			G	$1,624	8/8/2012	Online	*BigIron.com,* item in Nebraska, Farmhand F11B loader, manual, diesel, 1 hyd., 540 PTO, 9' hay bucket and grapple, 3 pt.
1600			G	$10,000	3/24/2012	NEIN	Gas, 3 pt., PTO, hyd., restored, runs
1600			F	$1,400	4/14/2011	NCND	Gas
1600		3,816	G	$3,300	2/1/2011	NEIN	Diesel
1600			G	$1,800	1/29/2011	ECMO	NF, gas
1600			G	$3,900	9/4/2010	NEIN	Standard
1600			G	$2,000	7/24/2010	SWIL	
1600			G	$2,400	7/24/2010	SWIL	Row crop, front weights, square fenders
1600			G	$9,750	6/19/2010	SWIL	Running, restored, PTO, lights, hyd., deluxe seat
1650	1965	4,379	G	$3,650	8/20/2013	WCIL	Diesel, 2 hyd., 540 PTO, Bush Hog 3425 QT loader, 84" bucket
1650	1965	4,379	G	$3,650	7/20/2013	WCIL	2 hyd., diesel, 540 PTO, Bush Hog 3425 QT loader, 84" bucket
1650	1965		G	$5,200	11/6/2010	SEMN	Gas, open station, fenders, 3 pt., 2 hyd., front weights, new front tires, clean, SN 154263-452
1650	1966		G	$30,000	10/12/2013	ECOH	Rare HFWA, restored, running, fenders, lights, tires 45%
1650	1966	2,620	G	$4,200	8/27/2011	NCIN	3 pt., WF, 2 hyd., Kelley 800 hyd. loader, 80" material bucket

Oliver

Model	Year	Hours	Condition	Price	Date	Area	Comments
1650	1967	3,261	G	$8,200	3/8/2014	NEMO	Gas, not run in a few years
1650	1967		G	$6,000	2/22/2014	NEIN	WF, dual hyd., 3 pt., PTO
1650	1967	4,010	G	$4,500	6/19/2013	Online	*BigIron.com,* item in Oklahoma, 12F/2R Hydra-Power, 6 cyl. gas
1650	1967		G	$2,430	10/11/2011	Online	*BidNow.US,* WF, Hydra-Power, 3 pt., PTO, 2 hyd., second owner, runs well, new this spring: starter, alternator and seat
1650	1968	4,000	F	$3,000	7/17/2013	NEND	Gas, 3 pt., PTO, 2 hyd.
1650	1968	4,002	G	$1,800	12/30/2010	ECMN	WF, 3 pt., 540 PTO
1650	1969		F	$2,200	7/27/2013	WCIL	Model 26521678, has add on gas tank on front, SN 193326452
1650		7,583	G	$3,900	3/22/2014	SEMN	Gas, WF, 3 pt., PTO, hyd.
1650			G	$3,700	12/5/2013	SCIA	Gas, NF, 3 pt., fenders
1650			G	$3,100	12/4/2013	Online	*BigIron.com,* item in Nebraska, 6 speed, 6 cyl. engine, 18.4x34 rear tires, 6.5x16SL front tires, diesel, 1 hyd., drawbar, 3 pt., 540 PTO
1650		5,944	G	$2,200	9/12/2013	SEIA	3 pt., 540 PTO, gas, WF, 16.9x34 and 9.5x14 tires
1650		3,114	G	$1,800	9/5/2013	WCMN	2WD, WF, gas, 2 hyd., 3 pt., PTO, 16.9x34 tires
1650		5,899	G	$2,950	5/29/2013	Online	*BigIron.com,* item in Nebraska, Hydra-Power, Oliver 283 engine, rear tires
1650			G	$3,000	11/24/2012	SEMN	Cab, Workmaster 880 hyd. loader, 3 pt., hyd. PTO
1650		5,730	G	$1,750	8/16/2012	Online	*IQBID.com,* item in Minnesota, 2WD, gas, open station, over/under, 2 hyd., 3 pt., 540 PTO, third arm, 18.4x34 tires
1650		6,130	G	$2,100	8/4/2012	ECMN	Gas, 540 PTO, 3 pt., New Idea loader
1650		6,400	G	$5,900	6/30/2012	ECIA	Cab, second owner, good rubber, 15.5x38 rear tires, front fenders, rear weights, Cozy cab
1650			F	$2,600	6/7/2012	NEIN	
1650			F	$3,250	2/18/2012	ECIL	
1650			G	$3,900	7/30/2011	ECMO	Loader, diesel, new hoses, brakes replaced last year, new battery cables, has original seat
1650		9,330	G	$3,000	4/27/2011	Online	*BigIron.com,* item in Nebraska, 6 cyl. gas, 6 speed Hydra-Power, 3 pt., one set of hyd., 540 PTO, lights work, always shedded
1650		3,900	G	$5,400	4/9/2011	SCNE	Gas, WF, repainted, nice
1650			F	$4,600	3/16/2011	NWIA	Gas, runs ok, WF
1650			G	$3,000	8/14/2010	NCIL	
1650			G	$2,500	8/9/2010	WCMO	Diesel, tires 25%
1650			G	$2,700	7/24/2010	SWIL	Row crop, square fenders, rear weights
1650			G	$3,000	6/23/2010	NEWI	NF, gas, Hydra-Power
1650			G	$2,350	6/5/2010	ECMN	Rebuilt engine
1650			F	$2,700	6/5/2010	SEMN	Gas, 3 pt., PTO, hyd.
1650		6,171	G	$5,000	4/1/2010	NCIN	3 pt., top link, 2 hyd., engine OH
1655	1970	6,917	G	$4,200	10/3/2013	NCIN	2WD, gas, 16.9x34, over/under, 2R

Oliver

Model	Year	Hours	Condition	Price	Date	Area	Comments
1655	1973	6,033	G	$2,800	3/23/2012	WCMN	Diesel, WF, Hiniker cab, 1 hyd., 3 pt., quick hitch, PTO
1655	1974	2,597	G	$5,200	8/27/2011	NCIN	16.9x34 rubber, 3 pt., WF, 2 hyd., front weight bracket, over/under
1655	1975	1,740	E	$10,900	6/7/2013	ECSD	WF, 3 pt., sale bill said 1,100 hours on engine OH but on sale day auctioneer and neighbor said 1,740 original hours, nice paint, clean
1655	1975	3,800	G	$6,700	7/10/2010	SEIA	Diesel, new radiator/inj pump, 3 speed Hydra-Power
1655		6,396	G	$4,750	1/4/2014	ECOH	Diesel, WF, cab
1655		4,000	G	$8,000	11/2/2013	WCWI	
1655			G	$8,500	10/12/2013	ECOH	
1655			G	$3,200	3/23/2013	NEIN	Gas, WF, 3 pt., fenders, dual hyd., original, runs
1655		5,111	G	$4,100	6/13/2012	Online	*BigIron.com,* item in Nebraska, 18F/6R over/under, diesel, 72 hp, 2 hyd., 540 PTO, 3 pt.
1655			G	$5,250	6/2/2012	SEMN	3 pt., 540 PTO
1655		6,485	G	$5,300	4/27/2011	Online	*BigIron.com,* item in Nebraska, 6 cyl. diesel, 6 speed, over/under, 540 PTO, 3 pt. lift, 3 front weights, shedded
1655			G	$2,100	12/30/2010	ECMN	WF, 1 hyd., 3 pt., PTO, flat top fenders
1655		9,243	G	$3,900	12/30/2010	ECMN	Year-A-Round cab, 3 pt., PTO, over/under
1655			G	$5,900	11/20/2010	NCKY	JD 48 loader, nice, new rear tires
1655			G	$4,100	6/14/2010	WCMO	Tires 80%, gas, 3 pt., nice paint
1750	1967	8,623	F	$4,950	2/26/2014	Online	*PurpleWave.com,* item in Missouri, 6 cyl. diesel, manual, 3 pt
1750	1967		G	$3,800	7/24/2010	SWIL	Row crop, square fenders, step, dual hyd.
1750	1968	3,772	G	$5,000	4/13/2013	SCMI	2WD, diesel, over/under, 2 hyd., 3 pt., 540 PTO, front and rear weights, 18.4x34 tires, SN 211213-247
1750	1968	4,205	G	$4,500	8/24/2011	Online	*BigIron.com,* item in Nebraska, row crop, Hydra-Power, partial PS, 8 gear 3 hydra shifts, 6 cyl. diesel, 3 pt., 540 PTO
1750	1969		G	$3,500	7/13/2011	Online	*BigIron.com,* item in Kansas, 3 speed over/under, diesel, 80 hp, 2 hyd., 540 PTO, adaptable to 1,000 PTO
1750		5,462	F	$4,100	8/24/2013	SWOH	Gas, running condition
1750			G	$4,250	5/11/2013	NCOH	Diesel, WF, 3 pt., fenders, front weights
1750			G	$2,800	11/24/2012	SEMN	Gas, cab, Vaughn hyd. loader, 3 pt., dual hyd., PTO, 18.4x34
1750		5,700	G	$8,500	6/30/2012	ECIA	Diesel, cab, 3 speed, 18.4x34 spin-out rims, Oliver 1610 loader
1755	1973	2,150	E	$13,000	7/17/2010	NCIL	Diesel, WF, 3 pt., 2 hyd., one owner, 18.4x34 tires, like new, seller was former Oliver dealer
1755	1974	3,200	E	$19,100	3/17/2012	NEIA	Cab, front fuel tank, second owner, clamp-on duals
1755	1977	8,060	G	$4,210	5/8/2013	Online	*BigIron.com,* item in Wyoming, 6 speed over/under, 6 cyl. diesel

Oliver

Model	Year	Hours	Condition	Price	Date	Area	Comments
1755		6,400	G	$6,500	11/2/2013	WCWI	WF, good rubber
1755		1,527	G	$9,500	11/2/2013	WCWI	QT cab, WF, good rubber
1755		3,607	G	$2,310	10/28/2013	NWWI	WF, 3 pt., dual hyd., 540 PTO
1755		3,607	G	$3,360	9/9/2013	NWWI	Diesel, WF, 3 pt., dual hyd., 540 PTO
1755		3,505	F	$4,900	8/24/2013	SWOH	Over/under, diesel
1755			G	$5,000	3/23/2013	NEIN	Diesel, PTO, dual hyd., WF, fenders, original, runs
1755		4,642	G	$9,750	6/30/2012	ECIA	Diesel, cab, front fenders, weights on front, nice original paint, Year Round cab, Firestone 23 degree rear tires 75%
1755		6,870	G	$7,300	1/31/2012	NEIN	Diesel, dual hyd., 3 pt., PTO, cab, air
1755		3,992	G	$6,000	4/27/2011	Online	*BigIron.com,* item in Nebraska, Farmhand F27 loader, 6 cyl. gas, hyd. shift, 3 pt., 1 dual hyd., 540 PTO, WF tires 15", 3-tine grapple fork
18-27	1931		G	$3,200	7/22/2011	SEMN	NF, round spoke rear, 13x38 rubber, older restoration
18-27	1935		F	$1,000	8/28/2010	WCIL	Oliver Hart-Parr 18-27, 15.5x38 rear tires, pulling tractor
18-27			G	$900	6/5/2010	WCMO	
18-27			G	$2,200	5/1/2010	SENE	
18-28			G	$2,700	6/23/2010	NEWI	Very nice, owner had paid $5,000 for it few years ago from private seller
1800	1962	8,550	F	$1,100	6/22/2011	Online	*BigIron.com,* item in Nebraska, 6 speed Hydra-Power, direct drive, 6 cyl. diesel, 1 hyd., 540 PTO, does not run, open station, 3 pt., missing third link, swinging drawbar
1800	1962		G	$4,100	4/9/2010	NWMN	3 pt., PTO, hyd. Farmhand loader, 96" bucket
1800	1963		G	$5,500	10/12/2013	ECOH	Wheatland
1800	1963		G	$5,000	10/1/2011	ECIA	Restored, 2 speed, hyd. PTO, power steering, 310 cu. in.
1800		2,200	G	$2,650	1/4/2014	ECOH	Gas, WF
1800			G	$6,000	6/15/2013	WCOH	Gas, row crop, WF, fenders, 3 pt., PTO, new 23.1x34 Firestone tires, restored, runs
1800			G	$2,850	5/11/2013	NCOH	Gas, WF, fenders, 3 pt., older repaint
1800			G	$1,300	8/4/2012	ECMN	Needs work
1800			F	$2,800	6/7/2012	NEIN	
1800			G	$10,500	3/24/2012	NEIN	MFWD, gas, original, fenders, like new tires, dual hyd., PTO, 3 pt., runs
1800			G	$3,700	3/20/2012	WCIL	Loader
1800		3,900	G	$15,250	8/31/2011	SEND	Gas, nice, Farmhand F11 loader (loader fair)
1800			F	$6,700	2/19/2010	WCIL	LP gas, NF, 540 PTO, 2 hyd., 18.4x34 tires
1800C	1964		G	$6,000	8/7/2010	WCMN	Diesel, engine rebuilt
1800C	1964		G	$8,750	8/7/2010	WCMN	Diesel, engine rebuilt
1850	1964		G	$3,000	2/11/2010	NENE	Diesel, WF, 1 hyd., 2 years on water pump, head gasket injectors, batteries, hyd. pump

TRACTORS

Oliver

Model	Year	Hours	Condition	Price	Date	Area	Comments
1850	1966	3,820	F	$5,100	4/3/2013	Online	*BigIron.com,* item in Nebraska, 6 speed Hi/Lo, Perkins diesel, 95 HP, 23.1x34 rear tires, 11Lx15SL front tires, 2 hyd., 540 PTO, Hydra-Power, 3 pt., fluid in rear tires, 9 front weights
1850	1966		G	$5,250	9/29/2010	ECIA	LP, WF, loader
1850	1966		G	$2,800	7/24/2010	SWIL	WF gas, square fenders, step, tool box, 3 pt., dual hyd.
1850	1967	2,343	G	$3,500	8/20/2013	WCIL	Gas, 1 hyd., 540 PTO, 18.4x38 tires, some rust on wheels
1850	1967		G	$6,400	12/1/2012	NCMO	Diesel, sold w/ Oliver hyd. loader
1850	1967	297	G	$3,500	1/30/2012	NEIA	Diesel
1850	1968		G	$15,000	10/12/2013	ECOH	Standard
1850	1968		G	$8,250	10/7/2011	NWSD	Restored, nice Miller loader (no welds), 540/1,000 PTO, 3 hyd., cab
1850			G	$4,000	2/5/2014	SESD	
1850		6,098	G	$3,100	8/22/2013	SEMN	Gas
1850		5,400	G	$6,250	6/4/2013	NWMN	Diesel, Hydra-Power, 3 pt., PTO, hyd., 18.4x34 tires
1850			G	$4,200	2/7/2013	NEIN	Diesel, WF, 2 hyd.
1850			G	$6,250	3/24/2012	NEIN	Diesel, repainted, new tires, 3 pt., PTO, dual hyd., runs
1850			G	$2,800	1/28/2012	ECMO	3 pt., 3 hyd.
1850			P	$1,600	5/11/2011	Online	*BigIron.com,* 6 speed Hi/Lo Hydra-Power, gas, needs work, does not run
1850			G	$981	4/27/2011	Online	*BigIron.com,* item in Nebraska, 12 speed, 2 reverse, 6 cyl. diesel, 2 hyd., 540/1,000 PTO, rare HD set back front axle, 3 pt., top link is missing, cast rear wheels, cast grill, rear fenders
1850			G	$3,500	1/29/2011	ECMO	Loader
1850		6,737	F	$2,900	9/25/2010	SEMN	Diesel, 3 pt., PTO, hyd., 18.4x34 tires
1850			G	$2,100	9/11/2010	WCMI	Gas, Hydra-Power, 15.5x38 tires, rear wheel weights, 3 pt., 2 hyd., PTO
1850			G	$3,750	9/4/2010	NEIN	High crop
1850			G	$3,750	9/4/2010	NEIN	MFWD
1850			G	$5,000	9/4/2010	NEIN	Gas
1850			G	$16,500	9/4/2010	NEIN	MFWD, stack weights, dual hyd.
1850			G	$2,700	5/26/2010	ECSD	Wheatland
1855	1969	6,983	F	$1,900	9/22/2010	NECO	WF, gas, dual loader, grapple
1855	1970	727	G	$17,000	6/19/2010	SWIL	Running, unrestored, original, shipped new to PA, loader added and used only to push snow down doctor's mountain driveway, factory cab, lights
1855	1973	2,600	F	$5,750	2/6/2013	Online	Diesel, WF, 2 hyd., 18.4x34 rear tires, SN 243572
1855	1973	7,400	E	$7,700	8/21/2010	ECPA	Spin out rims, 2 hyd., dual PTO, this tractor spent most of its time on a baler, ran like a top, still had its dealer stickers on the side panel
1855		7,225	G	$2,750	4/4/2014	SESD	
1855		4,523	G	$6,000	2/22/2014	NEIN	WF, dual hyd., 3 pt., over/under

Oliver

Model	Year	Hours	Condition	Price	Date	Area	Comments
1855		2,957	G	$3,900	12/26/2013	Online	*BigIron.com,* item in Colorado, Perkins diesel 6 cyl., 15.5x38 rear tires, 11Lx15 front tires, 2 hyd., 3 pt., 540 PTO, PS, TA works
1855		4,852	G	$6,000	6/30/2012	ECIA	Diesel, open station, front fenders, runs nice, original, 18.4x37 tires (85%, mismatched)
1855			G	$4,300	3/24/2012	NEIN	Diesel, dual hyd., PTO, 3 pt., repainted, runs
1855			G	$2,900	7/30/2011	ECMO	
1855			G	$2,500	5/26/2010	ECSD	Model D
1900	1962		G	$16,500	10/1/2011	ECIA	Restored, front wheel assist, 2 speed, PTO, 3 pt., power steering, GM 453
1900			G	$12,750	3/27/2014	ECNE	6 cyl. Oliver diesel, 6 speed, 2 hyd., PTO, HD rear wheel weights
1900			G	$7,500	10/12/2013	ECOH	Wheatland, checkerboard
1900			G	$5,800	9/4/2010	NEIN	GM Detroit diesel
1900			G	$7,000	9/4/2010	NEIN	MFWD, GM Detroit diesel
1950		3,428	G	$20,000	3/27/2014	ECNE	Over/under, WF, 3 pt., 2 hyd.
1950			G	$14,000	10/12/2013	ECOH	
1950		4,860	G	$11,000	6/30/2012	ECIA	GM-453 GM engine, fender fuel tanks, 2WD, cab, duals, 2 speed, tractor frame has been repainted, rear tires 60%
1950			G	$4,600	3/24/2012	NEIN	Original, 3 pt., PTO, dual hyd., runs
1950			G	$5,400	9/4/2010	NEIN	MFWD, ROPS, canopy
1950T			G	$2,300	8/7/2010	WCMN	Will run but turbo has oil leak, front weights and hubs, front duals
1955	1970		G	$8,300	5/25/2011	Online	*BigIron.com,* item in Nebraska, 6 speed manual, diesel, 108 hp, 540 PTO, started and moved forward and reverse, hour meter changed
1955	1972	7,862	G	$9,050	7/11/2012	Online	*BigIron.com,* item in Nebraska, 12 speed, 310 cu. in. 6 cyl. diesel, 108 PTO hp, 2 hyd., cab with factory air, starts, runs
1955	1974	4,800	F	$6,150	3/18/2011	NWIA	SN 251770-692, 20.8x34 rear rubber, 3 pt., WF, lower 3 speed needs work
1955	1974	2,171	G	$7,300	8/11/2010	ECMN	Factory cab, heat, 2 hyd., 3 pt., dual PTO, front weight bracket
1955		4,762	G	$11,250	3/27/2014	ECNE	6 cyl. diesel, over/under, 3 pt., quick hitch, 2 hyd., PTO, 9 bolt hub duals
1955			G	$5,900	12/4/2013	Online	*BigIron.com,* item in Nebraska, 6 speed over/under, 6 cyl. diesel, 18.4x34 rear tires, 11Lx15 front tires, 2 hyd., drawbar, 3 pt., no third arm, 540 PTO, hyd. pump
1955			G	$6,700	4/3/2013	ECMN	White 2110
1955			G	$11,500	3/24/2012	NEIN	Repaint, Cummins engine repower, front/rear weights, PTO, 3 pt., dual hyd., runs
28-50	1937		G	$2,750	10/23/2010	SCPA	Special
2050	1969		G	$13,750	10/12/2013	ECOH	Standard
2050	1969	4,668	G	$16,500	3/28/2013	ECOH	Over/under, 3 pt., PTO
2150	1969	4,427	G	$9,200	8/30/2013	NCIA	V8, WF

TRACTORS

Oliver

Model	Year	Hours	Condition	Price	Date	Area	Comments
2150	1969	4,300	G	$8,500	3/5/2011	NWMO	MFWD, past engine OH, factory dual hyd., 3 pt., dual power PTO
2150	1969	5,800	G	$10,000	3/5/2011	NWMO	MFWD, 3 pt., dual hyd., 1,000 PTO, Allied 595 front loader, 7' bucket
2150			G	$10,000	10/12/2013	NEOH	
2150			G	$9,300	3/22/2013	NWMN	PTO, hyd., 3 pt., 4WD, original, fenders, runs
2150			G	$10,500	3/24/2012	NEIN	Front wheel drive, original, 3 pt., fenders, PTO, dual hyd., runs
2150		3,799	G	$9,100	4/1/2010	NCIN	2 hyd., top link, 540 PTO
2255	1972	3,900	G	$26,000	6/30/2012	ECIA	Front wheel assist, cab, 3 pt., less than 200 hours on engine OH, 3150 Cat engine with Turbo II air cleaner, factory cab, 3 hyd., 540 PTO
2255	1973		G	$25,000	10/12/2013	ECOH	Front wheel assist
2255	1973	3,200	G	$15,000	11/15/2012	NEIA	V8, cab, air
2255	1973	4,844	E	$28,500	3/17/2012	NEIA	MFWD, second owner, cab, new cab kit, Cat 3150, clamp on duals sold separate for another $1,000
2255	1973		G	$14,000	8/7/2010	WCMN	Diesel, engine good
2255	1974	3,627	G	$8,500	9/29/2010	ECIA	Cab
2255	1974	4,684	G	$10,500	9/26/2010	ECIA	Cab, 3208 Cat V8, WF, clamp-on duals
2255	1974		G	$10,000	8/7/2010	WCMN	Diesel, engine good
2255	1974		G	$12,000	8/7/2010	WCMN	Diesel, engine good
2255	1974		G	$23,000	8/7/2010	WCMN	Front wheel assist, diesel, engine good
2255		3,718	G	$28,500	3/27/2014	ECNE	MFWD, Cat 3150 diesel, Hi/Lo, heavy duty ROPS, canopy, fenders with built-in fuel tanks, tilt steering wheel, 3 pt., 2 cyl. lift assist
2255		3,220	G	$13,250	3/23/2013	NEIN	Cab, original, 3 pt., dual hyd., PTO, runs
2255			G	$22,000	3/22/2013	NWMN	4WD, repainted, 3 pt., 3 hyd., open station, runs
2255			P	$3,400	4/20/2011	NWMI	2WD, for parts, Cat 3208 diesel, bad hyd. power, 20.8x38 duals, front weights
2255			G	$9,000	9/4/2010	NEIN	Cat 3208
2255			G	$9,000	9/4/2010	NEIN	Cat 3208, front stack weights, wheel spacers
2255			G	$15,000	6/19/2010	SWIL	Running, old restoration and repaint, rear wheel weights, fenders, PTO, lights
2255			G	$27,000	6/19/2010	SWIL	Running, restored, rear wheel weights, fenders, PTO, lights, hyd.
2844			G	$2,500	2/6/2013	SESD	On steel, restored, runs
OC3			G	$2,000	5/11/2013	NCOH	Blade, not running, tracks
OC3			G	$4,800	9/18/2010	ECMO	42", restored
OC3			G	$13,500	9/18/2010	ECMO	High crop, restored
OC4			G	$11,750	9/18/2010	ECMO	High crop, restored
OC6			P	$1,500	9/3/2010	NEIN	High track crawler, dead row needs work and may not run or drive, as is
Super 44	1957		G	$17,000	10/23/2010	SCPA	
Super 44	1957		G	$11,500	8/7/2010	WCMN	Gas, engine rebuilt
Super 44			G	$9,000	10/12/2013	ECOH	
Super 44			G	$7,000	3/24/2012	NEIN	Repainted, new tires, runs

Oliver

Model	Year	Hours	Condition	Price	Date	Area	Comments
Super 44			G	$9,250	9/4/2010	NEIN	Rear wheel weights, 3 pt.
Super 55	1955		G	$4,250	7/24/2010	SWIL	No tag
Super 55	1956		G	$4,500	8/7/2010	WCMN	Diesel, good engine
Super 55	1957		G	$5,200	6/20/2012	SESD	Gas, WF, 3 pt., completely restored, motor overhaul and clutch in 2005, nice
Super 55	1957		G	$3,500	8/7/2010	SEWI	WF, new paint and tires, runs great
Super 55		96	G	$4,600	3/27/2014	ECNE	4 cyl. gas, 6 speed, WF, 3 pt., PTO, 1 hyd., original condition
Super 55			G	$3,100	6/15/2013	WCOH	Diesel, 3 pt., weights, original, Oliver 59A loader, runs
Super 55			G	$2,300	5/11/2013	NCOH	Older repaint, 3 pt., runs
Super 55			G	$2,350	5/11/2013	NCOH	Original, 3 pt., runs
Super 55			F	$2,500	4/29/2011	NEOH	Gas, loader
Super 55			G	$1,350	4/11/2011	Online	*AuctionTime.com,* 2WD
Super 55			G	$3,800	9/11/2010	SEIA	
Super 55			F	$2,300	8/21/2010	NCOH	Not run in 10 years, rust/mice/ squirrels had set in
Super 66	1955		G	$3,000	10/12/2013	ECOH	Row crop
Super 66	1955		G	$4,250	10/12/2013	NEOH	Row crop
Super 66	1955		G	$7,000	10/2/2010	SWWI	Diesel
Super 66	1955		G	$4,500	7/24/2010	SWIL	Row crop, all new tires
Super 66	1958		G	$4,500	10/1/2011	ECIA	Restored, 144 cu. in., hyd., cast rear wheels, gas
Super 66			G	$4,800	6/15/2013	WCOH	Tach., WF, fenders, PTO, hyd. with cyl., new tires, restored, runs
Super 66			G	$4,700	6/5/2010	WCMO	Diesel, repainted, new tires
Super 77	1954		G	$4,750	10/12/2013	ECOH	Row crop
Super 77	1955		G	$3,300	9/1/2011	WCMN	Wheatland, gas, original, unrestored, belt pulley
Super 77	1956		G	$3,500	10/12/2013	ECOH	Row crop
Super 77	1956		G	$7,250	10/12/2013	ECOH	Standard
Super 77	1956		G	$4,000	3/18/2011	NWIA	Fenders, NF, 100% rear rubber, SN 52214702, super sharp
Super 77	1957		G	$7,500	10/1/2011	ECIA	Restored, 216 cu. in., hyd., PS rear wheels, diesel
Super 77	1959		G	$2,300	11/3/2012	SWMI	6 cyl. diesel, NF, drawbar, PTO, 13.6-38 rear tires, complete OH 2 yrs ago
Super 77			G	$900	10/12/2013	NEOH	Row crop
Super 77			G	$1,950	8/24/2013	SEMN	Side panels, 13.6x38 tires
Super 77			G	$4,000	6/28/2013	NEMO	WF, 13.6x38 rubber, SN 42600-702
Super 77			G	$4,500	6/15/2013	WCOH	PTO, fenders, hyd., restored, runs
Super 77			G	$7,000	6/15/2013	WCOH	Nice original, 2R picker, runs
Super 77			G	$1,300	5/11/2013	NCOH	Gas, older repaint, runs
Super 77			G	$1,600	5/11/2013	NCOH	Diesel, original, runs
Super 77			G	$2,000	5/11/2013	NCOH	Nice original, runs
Super 77			G	$2,400	5/11/2013	NCOH	Gas, repainted, runs
Super 77			P	$1,650	10/2/2010	SWWI	Cultivator, doesn't run, hyd. leaks, diesel
Super 88	1951		G	$3,100	10/19/2013	WCIL	Diesel, good paint, NF
Super 88	1954		G	$3,400	3/24/2012	NEIN	Diesel, runs
Super 88	1954		G	$2,200	7/24/2010	SWIL	Hyd.

Oliver

Model	Year	Hours	Condition	Price	Date	Area	Comments
Super 88	1955		G	$4,250	8/7/2010	WCMN	Row crop, gas, engine rebuilt
Super 88	1956		G	$7,500	8/7/2010	WCMN	Wheatland diesel, engine rebuilt
Super 88	1957		G	$4,500	10/12/2013	ECOH	Row crop
Super 88	1957		G	$6,000	10/12/2013	ECOH	Row crop
Super 88	1957		G	$3,100	4/13/2013	SCMI	Restored, NF, gas, fenders, 12V electric start, 15.5x38 tires 20%, 1 hyd., PTO, drawbar hitch, SN 49401-801
Super 88	1957	7,752	G	$5,000	12/8/2012	ECIA	Fenders, 14.9x38
Super 88	1957		E	$7,900	8/25/2012	NEIA	Diesel, new tires, NF, umbrella, parade ready
Super 88	1957		G	$4,500	10/1/2011	ECIA	Restored, 285 cu. in., hyd., power steering, gas
Super 88	1957		F	$1,650	1/1/2011	ECKS	WF, motor needs work
Super 88			G	$10,750	10/12/2013	ECOH	Standard
Super 88			G	$10,250	6/15/2013	WCOH	Diesel, standard, tach., restored, PTO, hyd., fenders with extensions, fixed WF, runs
Super 88			F	$11,000	6/15/2013	WCOH	Diesel, WF, fenders with extensions, tach., new tires, PTO, hyd., restored, not running
Super 88			G	$3,400	11/24/2012	SEMN	NF, restored, new 13.6x38 tires
Super 88			G	$3,000	9/22/2012	NEOR	Row crop, new rubber, rock shaft, PTO
Super 88			G	$4,150	8/4/2012	ECMN	Gas, WF, fenders, 15.5x38 tires, good tin
Super 88			F	$1,500	8/6/2011	WCIL	13.6x38 tires, gas, all sheet metal
Super 88			G	$4,900	10/2/2010	SWWI	Diesel
Super 88			G	$4,900	8/7/2010	WCMN	Gas
Super 88			G	$800	6/5/2010	WCMO	Standard, spin-out rims
Super 88			F	$2,000	6/5/2010	SEMN	NF
Super 88			G	$2,800	6/5/2010	WCMO	Diesel, factory WF, running
Super 88			G	$1,900	2/13/2010	SWIA	
Super 99	1954		G	$9,250	10/12/2013	ECOH	
Super 99	1955		G	$18,000	8/7/2010	WCMN	Diesel, engine rebuilt
Super 99	1955		G	$19,000	8/7/2010	WCMN	Diesel, engine rebuilt
Super 99	1956		E	$16,000	10/7/2011	NWSD	GM diesel, wheel weights, hyd., restored
Super 99	1957		G	$16,500	8/7/2010	WCMN	6 cyl. diesel, engine rebuilt
Super 99	1959		G	$11,000	8/7/2010	WCMN	Gas, engine rebuilt
Super 99			G	$11,000	6/15/2013	WCOH	Diesel, hyd., PTO, weights, restored, 18.4x34 Firestone tires, runs
Super 99			G	$49,000	6/15/2013	WCOH	Restored, hyd., PTO, new 20.8x34 Firestone tires, runs
Super 99		1,402	G	$10,000	10/23/2010	ECMO	371 Detroit, diesel, hyd., metal good, good rubber, SN 51981-C99D, runs

Porsche

Model	Year	Hours	Condition	Price	Date	Area	Comments
Junior	1958		G	$18,700	1/18/2011	SCAZ	L model, diesel, 3 pt., 1 cyl., red, restored
Super	1959		G	$25,300	1/18/2010	SCAZ	Diesel, 3 cyl., red, 13% buyer's premium ($3,289), total price $28,589
Standard	1960		G	$11,500	8/7/2010	SEWI	Star model, 2 cyl. diesel, 8 speed, foot accelerator, diff. lock, air cooled

Rumely

Model	Year	Hours	Condition	Price	Date	Area	Comments
6A	1931		G	$10,750	10/23/2010	SCPA	
6A			G	$6,750	9/21/2013	WCNY	On steel, no lugs, wrong fenders, electric start, needs restoration
6A			G	$9,500	9/21/2013	WCNY	Original, older repaint, on full steel with extensions
6A			F	$8,910	11/3/2011	Online	*PurpleWave.com,* item in Kansas
6A			G	$6,700	4/16/2010	NEKS	
8-16			G	$90,000	9/21/2013	WCNY	Oil Pull
12-20			G	$19,000	9/21/2013	WCNY	Oil Pull, all original, rusty but engine is greasy, few original decals, great restoration project
12-20			G	$35,000	9/21/2013	WCNY	Rare, possibly an experimental tractor with chain drive rear wheels, loose, fairly complete, museum item
14-28			G	$40,000	9/21/2013	WCNY	Oil Pull
15-25			G	$8,250	9/21/2013	WCNY	Fairly complete, SN 827
15-25			G	$13,500	9/21/2013	WCNY	Oil Pull, solid fly wheel, one rear extension, fairly complete
15-25			F	$5,610	11/3/2011	Online	Model L, *PurpleWave.com,* item in Kansas
15-25			G	$20,000	9/9/2010	NWWI	Model L Oil Pull, light weight
15-30			G	$190,000	9/21/2013	WCNY	Oil Pull
16-30			G	$40,000	9/21/2013	WCNY	Oil Pull, loose, repainted, SN 9608
18-35			G	$160,000	9/21/2013	WCNY	Road roller
20-30			G	$19,000	9/21/2013	WCNY	Model W Oil Pull, nice, original, very complete, SN 2630
20-30			G	$12,000	4/16/2010	NEKS	
20-35			G	$12,500	9/21/2013	WCNY	Model M, fairly complete, angle lugs, SN 2521
20-35			G	$12,500	9/21/2013	WCNY	Model M, SN 588, original, full steel
20-40	1923		G	$34,100	11/3/2011	Online	Model G Oil Pull, *PurpleWave.com,* item in Kansas, 2 cyl. kerosene, 2 speed, 20 drawbar hp, 40 belt hp
20-40			G	$50,000	9/21/2013	WCNY	Older repaint, very complete, great original, on industrial rubber rear wheels
25-40	1926		E	$22,000	9/22/2012	NEOR	Model R Oil Pull, SN R673, rare spoke flywheel and metal lug wheels
25-40	1928		F	$6,050	11/3/2011	Online	Model X, *Purplewave.com* online auction, item in Kansas, 2 cyl. kerosene engine, 3 speed, 25 drawbar hp, 40 belt hp
25-45			G	$17,000	9/21/2013	WCNY	Oil Pull
25-45			G	$120,000	9/21/2013	WCNY	Model B Oil Pull, project tractor
30-60	1912		G	$200,000	9/21/2013	WCNY	Model E Oil Pull, excellent runner, older restoration, great gearing
30-60			G	$67,500	9/21/2013	WCNY	Model S Oil Pull, SN 68, loose, repainted
40-60			G	$130,000	9/21/2013	WCNY	Model Z Oil Pull, SN 214214, original from factory, many were converted, runs original paint still visible, super rare
DoAll			G	$4,000	9/21/2013	WCNY	
DoAll			G	$8,000	9/21/2013	WCNY	
H			G	$13,000	9/4/2010	NEIN	Oil Pull
L			G	$12,500	9/4/2010	NEIN	Oil Pull

TRACTORS

Sandusky

Model	Year	Hours	Condition	Price	Date	Area	Comments
15-35			E	$210,000	9/21/2013	WCNY	

Sawyer Massey

Model	Year	Hours	Condition	Price	Date	Area	Comments
11-22			G	$13,000	9/21/2013	WCNY	Project
11-22			G	$23,000	9/21/2013	WCNY	Original, SN 5104
20-40			G	$90,000	9/21/2013	WCNY	

Sears

Model	Year	Hours	Condition	Price	Date	Area	Comments
Economy	1938		G	$10,750	10/23/2010	SCPA	

Shephard

Model	Year	Hours	Condition	Price	Date	Area	Comments
SD3	1949		G	$8,750	10/23/2010	SCPA	Diesel
SD3			G	$3,000	9/21/2013	WCNY	Original, diesel, SN 6E15347
SD3			G	$6,750	9/21/2013	ECIL	Running, restored, fenders, PTO, lights, deluxe seat, PPG paint

Silver King

Model	Year	Hours	Condition	Price	Date	Area	Comments
42			G	$1,400	7/10/2010	SEIA	3-wheel, original
N/A	1939		G	$6,250	10/23/2010	SCPA	
N/A	1954		G	$6,750	10/23/2010	SCPA	
N/A			G	$4,200	5/11/2013	NCOH	WF, new tires, electric start, lighting, repainted, runs
N/A			G	$2,000	3/22/2013	NWMN	Single front, repainted, runs
N/A			G	$2,750	10/2/2010	ECMN	Unstyled, NF
N/A			P	$2,100	9/3/2010	NEIN	Dead row, needs work and may not run or drive, as is
N/A			G	$2,900	6/5/2010	WCMO	Single front

Steiger

Model	Year	Hours	Condition	Price	Date	Area	Comments
Bearcat II	1974	987	G	$4,000	8/11/2011	WCMN	Cab, air, heat, Cat 3208 engine, 2 hyd., 3 pt., quick hitch, air ride seat
Bearcat II	1975		F	$5,500	12/12/2013	ECNE	ST 225, Cat 3208 diesel
Bearcat III	1975	2,307	G	$7,800	3/27/2013	Online	ST 225, *BigIron.com,* item in Missouri, standard manual, 6 cyl. engine
Cougar	1973	7,562	G	$7,500	6/27/2012	Online	*BigIron.com,* item in Wyoming, 4WD, 10 speed Hi/Lo, Cat diesel, 3 hyd., PTO, swinging drawbar, repainted
Cougar	1976	2,970	G	$6,500	3/31/2012	SWSK	4WD, 250 hp, Cat 3406 engine, 10 speed, 2 speed transfer case, 18.4x38 duals

TRACTORS

Steiger

Model	Year	Hours	Condition	Price	Date	Area	Comments
Cougar III	1978	6,247	G	$11,000	3/20/2012	WCIL	4WD
Cougar III	1976	1,625	G	$6,050	9/21/2011	Online	ST 250, *BigIron.com,* item in Oklahoma, diesel, 3 hyd., single axle
Cougar III	1977	7,500	G	$12,500	8/15/2013	ECMN	ST 270, 4WD, cab, air, heat, 300 hours on OH
Cougar III	1978		F	$7,000	4/8/2011	SWMN	ST 270, 4WD, 4 hyd.
Panther III	1975	547	G	$4,070	10/31/2012	Online	ST 320, *PurpleWave.com,* item in Missouri, unknown actual hours, Cummins VT 903 8 cyl. diesel, 290 hp, manual
Panther III	1976	6,000	G	$4,500	9/12/2013	SEIA	ST 310, 4WD, Cummins engine, 310 hp, 5F/2R transmission, bareback, 4 hyd., 20.8x38 duals
Panther III	1976	1,300	G	$10,500	12/1/2012	SWMO	ST 325, 4WD, 400 hp, hours given on replaced engine
Panther III	1977		G	$17,200	1/31/2012	NEIN	ST 310, 4WD, bareback
Panther III	1977	5,995	F	$3,800	11/22/2011	WCIL	ST 310, 4WD, Cummins 855 engine, clamp-on duals, 4 hyd.
Panther III	1978	4,200	G	$27,500	3/20/2010	SEIA	ST 325, 4WD, Cat 3406 engine, Firestone radials 95%

Auction prices for one to five-year-old late model four-wheel-drive tractors have been "soft" the past year due to a huge buildup of excess inventory on dealer lots. However, older four-wheel-drive tractors in good condition have held their values much better. This has been shown by some surprisingly strong auction prices reported from around the country.

As case in point, here's a 1979 Steiger PT270 Cougar with 6,900 total hours, but it only has 800 hours on a new engine. It sold for $30,500 in east-central Indiana on Feb. 23, 2013, at a consignment auction.

PETE'S PICK

Tillsoil

Model	Year	Hours	Condition	Price	Date	Area	Comments
18-30	1921		G	$60,000	9/21/2013	WCNY	Really nice original, runs great, very rare, Canadian design, definite Hart Parr influence, SN 158, older restoration

Titan

Model	Year	Hours	Condition	Price	Date	Area	Comments
10-20	1919		G	$9,000	6/22/2013	SEWA	2 cyl., kerosene engine, left side crank start, right side belt drive, 29" right side flywheel
10-20			G	$26,000	9/21/2013	WCNY	Titan, missing fuel tank, good old original, still greasy, good project
10-20			G	$42,500	9/21/2013	WCNY	Rare, mogul, nice, original
10-20			G	$14,000	9/9/2010	NWWI	
10-20			G	$10,000	9/4/2010	NEIN	

Turner-Simplicity

Model	Year	Hours	Condition	Price	Date	Area	Comments
14-25	1919		G	$35,000	9/21/2013	WCNY	

Twin City

Model	Year	Hours	Condition	Price	Date	Area	Comments
FTA	1935		G	$908	8/14/2012	Online	*PurpleWave.com,* item in Kansas, gas, manual, crank start, drawbar, steel seat, 15x32 rear tires

Versatile

Model	Year	Hours	Condition	Price	Date	Area	Comments
300	1974		E	$20,000	10/7/2011	NWSD	4WD, PTO, 3 pt., only 200 made, restored and excellent condition, SN 150 OF 200
700	1972	678	F	$2,640	7/11/2012	Online	*PurpleWave.com,* item in Iowa, Cummins V8 diesel, manual, heat, AM, spring seat, drawbar, 3 hyd., 130" WB, 24.5x32 tires
700	1977		G	$3,900	4/24/2013	Online	*BigIron.com,* item in Kansas, 12F/4R, 3 hyd.
750	1976	8,526	G	$5,000	3/31/2010	ECND	Series 2, cab, air, heat, 855 Cummins, 3 hyd.
750	1977	7,572	G	$8,250	2/12/2013	WCIL	Series 2, 4WD, 24.5x32 duals, 3 hyd., drawbar, 12 speed
800	1974	9,790	G	$5,750	3/13/2010	WCIL	4WD, 855 Cummins, 3 pt., 24.5x32 tires
800	1975	7,017	G	$7,200	6/13/2012	NWMN	4WD, cab, 855 Cummins, 3 hyd., duals
800	1975	4,478	G	$8,910	4/28/2010	Online	*PurpleWave.com,* item in Kansas, Cummins C250 diesel, 3 pt., third link, radio, work lights, heat, 2 hyd., Murphy switch, 72 gal. saddle fuel tanks
800	1976		G	$7,000	7/18/2012	ECND	Series 2, 4WD, cab, 4 hyd., duals
800	1977	8,749	G	$9,250	3/31/2010	ECND	Series 2, 4WD, cab, air, heat, 3 hyd., duals
825	1976		G	$12,650	1/10/2012	Online	*IQBID.com,* 4WD, series 2, cab, air, heat, 855 Cummins, 240 hp, 12 speed, new air and pump, 3,100 hours on OH
825	1977	7,425	G	$11,000	9/23/2011	NWMN	Series 2, 12 speed, 3 hyd., 20.8x38 duals
835	1978	6,125	F	$8,250	12/18/2012	NWMN	4WD, cab, 12 speed, 4 hyd., no PTO or 3 pt., duals

Versatile

Model	Year	Hours	Condition	Price	Date	Area	Comments
835	1978	12,000	G	$6,600	4/13/2011	Online	*BigIron.com,* item in Nebraska, 4WD, Cummins diesel, 230 hp, 4 hyd.
835	1978	6,000	G	$15,000	4/11/2011	Online	*AuctionTime.com*
835	1978	1,200	F	$14,000	11/2/2010	ECOK	4WD, 855 Cummins, duals, cab, air, Bostrom Air Ride seat
835	1978		G	$11,500	9/21/2010	ECND	4WD, cab, air, heat, 4 hyd., radial duals, new paint
850	1974		P	$2,250	6/28/2013	SWIL	4WD, 12 speed, canopy, 1 hyd., ag hitch, 30.5x32, inoperable
850	1976	10,001	G	$13,250	5/8/2013	Online	*IQBID.COM,* series 2, 4WD, cab, air, heat, 12 speed, 3 hyd.
850	1976	4,393	E	$32,500	1/24/2013	WCOH	4WD, series 2, 18.4Rx38 duals, 3 hyd., Cummins motor, 3 pt.
875	1976		G	$8,500	7/31/2013	ECND	Syncro, 3 hyd., 23 gpm hyd. pump
875	1978	6,482	G	$14,000	4/3/2014	NEIN	
875	1978	5,823	G	$26,000	8/13/2011	WCIL	4WD, 20.8x38 tires and duals, good rubber, 4 hyd.
875	1978	8,400	G	$13,500	4/1/2011	ECND	4WD, duals, 4 hyd.
875	1978	7,040	G	$14,000	12/17/2010	WCIL	4WD, 20.8x38 duals, 4 hyd.
895	1977		G	$7,500	2/4/2014	SEAR	Series 3, articulated, 4x4, cab, air, Cummins Big Cam diesel (has updates), 38" tires, 3 pt., quick hitch, drawbar
900	1973	4,323	G	$6,151	3/7/2013	SEIA	12 speed, 903 Cummins turbo, 3 hyd., 20.8x38 tires, needs AC compressor
900	1974	5,289	G	$4,750	3/26/2013	ECND	12 speed, 3 hyd., return flow, 24.5x32 duals
900	1974	13,335	G	$8,000	3/14/2012	ECND	12 speed, 3 hyd., duals
900	1975		F	$3,000	8/20/2011	NEKS	4WD, 38" new rubber, puller only, rubber 20.8x38 (rear 50%/front 75%), 2 hyd., 903 Cummins, SN 900507128
900	1976	2,713	G	$12,100	9/25/2013	Online	*PurpleWave.com,* item in Kansas, series 2, 4WD, 3 pt. Cummins Big Cam 6 cyl. diesel, manual, cab, drawbar

Old four-wheel-drive models in good condition have been attracting some very strong bids across the U.S. and Canada the past few years. Maybe the best example is this beautiful 1976 Versatile 850 Series II. It sold for a whopping $32,500 at a fantastic farm auction January 24, 2013, in west-central Ohio by my friends at Schrader Real Estate & Auction. This auction was so nice that a 1992 John Deere 4960 tractor with 3,045 hours sold for $114,000. That's a new record auction price by a mile, just like on the Versatile 850 four-wheel-drive.

PETE'S PICK

Wallis

Model	Year	Hours	Condition	Price	Date	Area	Comments
1220	1929		G	$2,365	10/10/2012	Online	*PurpleWave.com,* item in Iowa, 4 cyl. gas, manual, spring seat

Wards

Model	Year	Hours	Condition	Price	Date	Area	Comments
N/A	1949		G	$8,000	10/23/2010	SCPA	NF
N/A			G	$9,000	10/23/2010	SCPA	WF

Waterloo Boy

Model	Year	Hours	Condition	Price	Date	Area	Comments
7450			E	$72,000	9/18/2010	ECMO	Chain steer, repainted, very nice
N	1921		G	$64,000	11/9/2013	SWON	Running condition, original fenders included, tag not attached
N			G	$55,000	10/22/2011	NECO	Full steel, automotive steer
N			G	$70,000	7/17/2010	NEMT	
N			G	$95,000	7/17/2010	NEMT	
R	1917		E	$85,000	8/11/2011	WCMN	Single speed slip clutch, chain steering, 1997 restoration, immaculate condition
R			G	$55,000	9/21/2013	WCNY	Loose, needs radiator repair, good original
R			G	$68,000	7/17/2010	NEMT	
T			G	$9,100	7/17/2010	NEMT	Stationary engine

White

Model	Year	Hours	Condition	Price	Date	Area	Comments
2-105	1975	7,421	G	$2,750	3/20/2012	WCIL	
2-105	1975	5,036	G	$3,900	5/18/2011	SEWY	Diesel, WF, 3 pt., cab
2-105	1975		G	$4,400	2/1/2011	NEIN	cab
2-105	1977	4,300	G	$8,000	4/11/2013	NCMI	2WD, diesel, cab, air, heat, 3 pt., PTO, 18.4x39 tires 50%, SN 278927-406
2-105	1977	4,640	G	$9,500	9/29/2010	ECIA	Field Boss, 18.4x38 hub duals, front weights
2-105	1977		F	$5,900	3/6/2010	ECMI	Diesel, cab, 2 hyd., 16.9Rx38 tires and axle duals, 3 pt., 540 PTO
2-135	1977	5,060	G	$4,950	8/4/2012	SWMN	1,000 rpm PTO, 18.4x38 tires, 3 hyd., 3 pt. fast hitch
2-135	1977	8,122	G	$5,500	4/24/2012	SESK	2WD, 138 hp PTO, standard, 1,000 PTO, 2 hyd., 18.4x38 dual tires
2-135	1977	4,003	G	$12,500	4/18/2012	SWSK	138 hp PTO, 6 speed, 1,000 PTO, 3 hyd., 23.1x34 rear, 4 rib front
2-135	1977	3,836	G	$6,000	2/1/2011	NEIN	Front weights, dual hyd., quick hitch, duals
2-135	1977		G	$8,900	2/1/2011	NEIN	cab
2-135	1978	4,925	G	$9,500	8/30/2013	NCIA	2 hyd.

White

Model	Year	Hours	Condition	Price	Date	Area	Comments
2-135	1978		G	$6,750	4/22/2013	SWSK	2WD, Ezee-on front-end loader, PTO, 2 hyd., 18.4x38 rear duals, diesel, 7' bucket, joystick, grapple fork
2-135	1978	5,007	G	$3,900	3/15/2011	WCIL	Duals, 2 hyd., 540 PTO, front weights
2-155	1977	6,300	G	$9,750	9/22/2010	NECO	WF, diesel, duals
2-155	1978	5,220	G	$8,000	1/30/2012	NEIA	162 hp, diesel
2255	1974		G	$21,000	8/7/2010	WCMN	Diesel, engine good
2255		4,007	G	$9,750	6/20/2012	ECIL	V8 Cat, 2 hyd., 1 PTO, Wheatland
4-150	1974		G	$4,000	6/13/2012	NWMN	4WD, 3 pt., 1,000 PTO, 3 hyd., duals
4-150	1976	5,072	G	$2,625	7/16/2013	Online	*IQBID.com,* item in Minnesota, 4WD, 3208 Cat, 1 hyd., 3 pt., PTO, no top link, side rock/chain boxes, duals
4-180	1975	3,914	E	$18,000	3/17/2012	NEIA	4WD, fully equipped cab, 3208 Cat, 3 pt., PTO, fender fuel tanks, second owner
4-180	1975	3,755	F	$5,500	1/10/2012	Online	*IQBID.com,* 4WD, Cat 3208 diesel, 2 hyd., PTO, 3 pt., 20% rubbers
4-180	1976	3,192	G	$7,600	1/10/2012	Online	*IQBID.com,* 4WD, Cat 3208 diesel, 2 hyd., PTO, 30% rubber

At a March 28, 2013, farm auction in New Philadelphia, Ohio, three very nice White tractors all sold for strong prices. Pictured is the one-owner 1979 White 2-135 with 6,457 hours. It sold for $16,000. That's the highest price I've seen on a 2-135 in 12 years. Also sold at this auction was a 1979 White 2-105 with 3,234 hours for $16,500, and that's the third-highest price for that model in the past 18 years. The third tractor was a 1979 White 2-85 with 4,736 hours and a Freeman 4000 loader sold for $10,000.

PETE'S PICK

Yanmar

Model	Year	Hours	Condition	Price	Date	Area	Comments
YM2000	1976		G	$2,300	6/22/2013	SESC	2 wheel, 2 cyl., SN 2TR20A-818863

Corn Pickers

Allis-Chalmers

Model	Year	Condition	Price	Date	Area	Comments
GI		F	$700	12/1/2011	SEMN	1R, stripper, in working condition
WC	1939	F	$605	8/14/2012	Online	*PurpleWave.com*, item in Kansas, 2R, additional corn picker parts

International Harvester Company

Model	Year	Condition	Price	Date	Area	Comments
30		G	$400	8/15/2013	ECMN	Cob/corn elevators, steel cylinder, original, unrestored
N/A		G	$1,400	8/24/2013	SCMI	1R
N/A		G	$2,000	8/24/2013	SCMI	1R, binder, wood, loading chute
N/A		G	$500	3/2/2013	WCIN	2R mounted
N/A		G	$1,350	4/25/2012	Online	*BigIron.com,* item in Nebraska, 2R
N/A		G	$650	8/25/2011	ECND	PT, PTO, binder, 2R, working order

IMPLEMENTS

John Deere

Model	Year	Condition	Price	Date	Area	Comments
7		F	$319	6/24/2013	ECMN	PTO drive, shedded
18		F	$450	8/20/2011	NEMN	1R
227		F	$350	8/24/2013	SEMN	Mounted
300		G	$2,100	2/16/2013	NEIA	PT, 244 head
300		F	$2,000	8/4/2012	WCWI	John Deere 244 head, 2R
300		G	$2,500	8/4/2012	ECMN	Head, walking tandems, 1,000 PTO, electric controls
300		G	$3,600	2/7/2012	SEIA	Husker, John Deere 343 head
300		G	$3,000	1/13/2012	NCIA	PT, John Deere 244 head
300		G	$3,200	8/31/2011	SEMN	244 head
300		G	$1,800	8/24/2011	Online	*BigIron.com,* item in Nebraska, PT, 1,000 PTO, 3R, 30" spacing, 444 head, 12 roll bed, quick release wagon hitch, recently replaced bearings and chains, tin damage, cracks in tires, stored inside
300		G	$700	3/26/2011	NECO	PT, PTO, 343 head, 3R, 30" spacing
300		G	$800	2/19/2011	ECNE	243 head, 2R, 30" spacing, PTO, PT
300		G	$800	2/19/2011	ECNE	PT, PTO, 244 head, 2R, 38" spacing
300		G	$1,150	2/19/2011	ECNE	PT, PTO, 343 head, 3R, 30" spacing
300		G	$1,475	5/5/2011	ECNE	244 head
300		G	$4,750	1/21/2011	NEMO	343 head

McCormick-Deering

Model	Year	Condition	Price	Date	Area	Comments
N/A		G	$400	6/1/2013	NEKS	Hand crank

Minneapolis

Model	Year	Condition	Price	Date	Area	Comments
N/A		G	$2,000	2/22/2014	NEIN	PT, PTO, 50' drag chain

New Holland

Model	Year	Condition	Price	Date	Area	Comments
324		G	$825	9/14/2011	Online	*BigIron.com,* item in South Dakota, 540 PTO, few extra parts in tool box
N/A		G	$1,000	1/27/2012	SEAL	2R, WR

New Idea

Model	Year	Condition	Price	Date	Area	Comments
10		G	$300	1/8/2011	ECMI	
308		G	$1,950	8/4/2012	SWKY	
311		G	$1,300	1/27/2012	SEAL	2R
311		G	$700	4/21/2011	WCMI	2R, 8 roll bed
323		G	$1,600	11/23/2013	SWOH	1R
323		G	$500	2/25/2012	WCMI	1R
323		G	$1,950	1/27/2012	SEAL	1R
323		G	$2,700	1/27/2012	SEAL	1R, 6 roll bed, trash remover
323		G	$1,800	8/20/2011	SWOH	1R, PTO, PT
324		E	$3,000	8/27/2013	NCWI	2R, PT, hyd. swing tongue, 12 roll bed, rubber fingers, very nice, SN 229083
324		G	$1,700	8/20/2013	WCIL	2R, 38" spacing, PT, nice
324		F	$200	8/4/2012	ECMN	2R, 36" spacing, up to 40" spacing, 12 roll husking reel
324		F	$600	3/22/2012	ECMN	2R, 36" spacing, 8 roll bed, shedded, working order
324		G	$1,900	1/27/2012	SEAL	2R, WR, 8 roll bed
324		F	$500	11/12/2011	SCWI	2R
324		G	$300	2/19/2011	ECNE	2R, 38" spacing, PTO, PT
325		G	$1,250	1/27/2012	SEAL	2R, 8 roll bed
325		G	$360	5/11/2011	Online	*BigIron.com,* 540 PTO, 2R, 30" spacing, husking bed
325		G	$1,700	4/23/2011	WCMI	2NR, 8 roll bed, harvest ready

Oliver

Model	Year	Condition	Price	Date	Area	Comments
5		E	$2,000	8/29/2011	WCWI	No. 5, 1R
83		G	$550	4/13/2011	Online	*BigIron.com,* item in Nebraska, PT, WR, 540 PTO, missing cleaning fan belt
83		G	$450	1/8/2011	ECMI	2R, NR

Rosenthal

Model	Year	Condition	Price	Date	Area	Comments
40		F	$500	8/24/2013	SCMI	Shredder

Case

Model	Year	Condition	Price	Date	Area	Comments
10'		F	$462	4/23/2013	Online	*HansenandYoung.com,* located in Wisconsin
11'		F	$950	4/10/2013	Online	*BigIron.com,* item in Nebraska, 6x16 tires, 8" spacing, rear press wheels

International Harvester Company

Model	Year	Condition	Price	Date	Area	Comments
10		G	$6,200	3/22/2014	SWMI	
10		G	$2,700	3/1/2014	SEMN	12', hyd. lift, grass seeder, double disk
10		G	$4,250	12/4/2013	ECIN	24', 6"
10		G	$750	10/3/2013	NCIN	24', 6" spacing
10		G	$2,300	11/24/2012	SEMN	Grass seeder, double disk, hyd. lift
10		G	$950	5/22/2012	WCMN	10' end wheel, grass seeder, hyd. lift
10		G	$921	9/28/2011	Online	*BigIron.com*, item in Nebraska, 8" spacing, 20R, dry fertilizer, markers, hyd. lift, mechanical acre counter, full set of press wheels and disk blades
10		G	$1,450	4/21/2011	WCMI	18 hole, single disk, seeder
10		G	$1,200	4/9/2011	WCNE	12', 7", PT, hyd. lift
10		G	$1,500	4/2/2011	ECMN	
100		F	$650	3/14/2012	ECND	Three 8', grass seeders, hitch
100		F	$600	10/27/2011	NWND	14' press drill Rollin seeder-weeder
100		G	$900	6/29/2011	NEND	12' press drill, dry fertilizer, working unit
105		G	$5,000	8/15/2013	ECMN	Soybean special, open station
150		G	$2,050	9/19/2012	Online	*BigIron.com,* item in Kansas, 40', 2 hyds., three sets of 1610 hoe drills, 48Rx10, crank winch, end transports
150		G	$1,900	8/22/2012	Online	*BigIron.com,* item in Colorado, 36' press drill, 7.6x15 tires, 10" spacing, hard surfaced steel press wheels, MandM transport system, Blumhardt fertilizer system
510		G	$1,900	1/17/2014	SEOK	
510		G	$3,700	12/30/2013	SEMN	12', grass seeder
510		G	$2,500	12/28/2013	NEWI	Grain drill
510		G	$535	12/4/2013	Online	*BigIron.com,* item in Kansas, 20 hole, 7.50x20 tires, drawbar, 7" spacing
510		G	$990	11/13/2013	Online	*PurpleWave.com,* item in Kansas, 10', 7.5" spacing
510		G	$2,035	10/16/2013	Online	*PurpleWave.com,* item in Kansas, 8" spacing drills, fertilizer/grain boxes
510		G	$3,650	9/7/2013	NCOH	18', 7" grain drill, seeder, new style press wheels
510		G	$3,500	8/8/2013	WCMN	12' drill, grass seeder, on rubber, one owner
510		G	$3,320	5/1/2013	Online	*BigIron.com,* item in Nebraska, 12', draw bar, 7" spacing, end wheels, alfalfa seeder, rubber press wheels
510		G	$675	3/23/2013	NCOH	Grain drill
510		G	$1,800	3/5/2013	ECWI	10', 6" spacing, low rear grass, HD hitch, marker tires and very straight
510		G	$3,000	3/2/2013	NCWI	18', 7" spacing, double disk, cylinder
510		G	$3,900	3/2/2013	NCWI	Double disk, 24x6 tires, grass seeder, hyd. cylinder

International Harvester Company

Model	Year	Condition	Price	Date	Area	Comments
510		G	$1,725	10/24/2012	NECO	10', 7" spacing, PT, seeder
510		G	$3,200	10/13/2012	NCCO	14'
510		G	$605	4/25/2012	Online	*PurpleWave.com,* item in Kansas, 20R, 8" spacing, disks, rubber tubes, press wheels
510		G	$1,430	4/25/2012	Online	*PurpleWave.com,* item in Kansas, 20R, 8" spacing, 13.5', fold up marker arm, twin cyl. lift, adj. height pin hitch
510		G	$1,000	3/21/2012	ECMN	12', 6" spacing, concave tires
510		G	$525	2/15/2012	Online	*BigIron.com,* 16Rx10, hyd. Cylinder, press wheels, planted less than 200 acres
510		G	$1,350	1/28/2012	ECMO	15' bean drill
510		G	$2,000	1/27/2012	SEAL	Hydraulic cylinder
510		G	$1,500	12/14/2011	WCMN	12', 6" spacing, grass seeder
510		G	$990	8/31/2011	Online	*PurpleWave.com,* item in Texas, 10" spacing
510		G	$2,900	8/6/2011	SCMN	12', hyd. lift, SN 0390146C004472
510		F	$660	6/29/2011	Online	*PurpleWave.com,* item in Kansas, 13" disks, 7.5", seed and fertilizer
510		G	$900	4/16/2011	ECMI	16 hoe grass seeder, single disk
510		G	$1,000	3/19/2011	SEIA	
510		G	$1,500	1/29/2011	ECMO	Soybean special
620		G	$2,100	3/13/2014	SCID	Press wheels, 6" spacing
620		G	$2,255	12/26/2013	Online	*BigIron.com,* item in South Dakota, grass seed drill, 24'
620		G	$700	11/26/2013	ECND	28' press drill, liquid attachment, on transport
620		G	$1,800	5/5/2013	WCMN	14' press drill, grass seeder, 6" spacing, large rear press wheels
620		G	$1,200	2/6/2013	SESD	28', markers, transport, two 14'
620		G	$725	8/14/2012	Online	*IQBID.com,* item in Minnesota, 14' press drill, track scratcher
620		F	$1,000	6/14/2012	SEND	Two 10' press drills, 6" spacing, dry fertilizer, rubber press, hyd. markers
620		G	$1,500	3/14/2012	ECND	Press drill, three 12s, transport hitch, liquid fertilizer
620		G	$1,000	11/22/2011	NCMN	Press drills, two 8's, dry fertilizer, solid rubber press
620		F	$560	7/28/2011	Online	*IQBID.com,* press drill, two 14s, dry fertilizer, hyd. fold, markers
620		G	$1,000	7/27/2011	ECND	Two 14', transport
620		G	$1,300	7/27/2011	ECND	Press drills, two 14s, 6" spacing, rubber press, transport
9'		G	$975	1/21/2012	SEIL	
11'		G	$650	9/14/2013	SCIL	18 hole
12'		G	$650	2/20/2014	ECAR	PT

John Deere

Model	Year	Condition	Price	Date	Area	Comments
245		G	$650	6/22/2011	Online	*BigIron.com,* item in Nebraska, corn drill, 1R, wooden handles, corn plate
10'		G	$1,750	9/7/2013	SEMN	Grain drill, 10', 6", grass seeder, low rubber, hyd. lift

IMPLEMENTS

John Deere

Model	Year	Condition	Price	Date	Area	Comments
10'		G	$250	8/20/2013	WCIL	Cylinder, grass seeder
8'		G	$550	7/15/2013	Online	*HansenandYoung.com,* item in Wisconsin
8'		G	$1,700	2/20/2012	WCWI	8' grain drill
10'		G	$1,237	2/19/2013	NWWI	Double disk, hyd. lift, cylinder, grass seeder
10'		G	$800	6/16/2012	WCSD	Old 10' disk drill
12'		G	$3,000	4/18/2013	WCMN	Older 12', end wheels, grain drill, hyd. lift, grass seeder
12'		G	$505	8/8/2012	Online	*BigIron.com,* item in Nebraska, 7" spacing, single disk, grain and alfalfa seeder, seed chart
12'		F	$550	3/24/2012	SCMN	12', double disk, grass hoppers, mechanical lift on rubber
12'		G	$950	11/27/2011	ECIA	Galvanized boxes
12'		G	$600	9/19/2011	NCIL	Grass seeder
20'		G	$2,100	8/8/2012	Online	*BigIron.com,* item in Colorado, markers, 3 pt., 10" spacing
24'		G	$625	5/9/2012	Online	*BigIron.com,* item in Kansas, 12" spacing, hitch for follow transport, marker, assorted parts, LG CAP 9300 model
B		G	$1,000	2/22/2014	WCNE	7"x10', PT, single disk, seeder
B		G	$1,400	2/22/2014	WCNE	7"x12', PT, double disk, seeder
B		G	$1,100	1/17/2014	SEOK	
B		F	$700	9/25/2013	NECO	7"x12', PT, ground lift, seeder
B		G	$600	8/20/2013	WCIL	10', grass seeder
B		G	$1,050	1/27/2012	SEAL	
B		F	$650	8/13/2011	WCIL	
B		G	$850	5/25/2011	NECO	7" spacing, 10', PT, ground lift, seeder
B		G	$600	4/27/2011	NECO	7"x10', PT, seeder, ground lift
B		G	$675	4/27/2011	NECO	7" spacing, 14', PT, manual lift, seeder
B		G	$800	4/27/2011	NECO	6" spacing, 14', PT, ground lift, seeder
B		G	$950	3/26/2011	NECO	7" spacing, 14', PT, seeder, hyd. lift
B		G	$1,100	3/26/2011	NECO	7" spacing, 12', PT, seeder, ground lift, double disk
B		G	$850	1/26/2011	NECO	7" spacing, 12', PT, hyd. lift, seeder
DR		G	$651	9/28/2011	Online	*BigIron.com,* item in Nebraska, 7.6x15 tires
FBB		G	$550	11/13/2013	Online	*PurpleWave.com,* item in Kansas, 9', 7.5" spacing
FBB		G	$1,400	4/11/2013	NCMI	
FBB		G	$575	12/15/2012	WCMI	Single disk, seeder
FBB		G	$1,200	2/1/2011	NEIN	15x7, double disk, grass seeder
LL		G	$800	4/25/2012	Online	*BigIron.com,* item in Nebraska, alfalfa seeder in front
LL207A		G	$1,300	3/26/2011	NECO	6"x12', PT, seeder, hyd. lift
LLA		G	$625	9/28/2013	ECNE	Grain drill, 24', 7", small seed attachment, double disk
LLA		G	$1,600	11/15/2011	Online	*IQBID.com,* 24' press drills, grass seeder, ground-drive, liquid fertilizer, three 100 gal. tanks, always shedded

John Deere

Model	Year	Condition	Price	Date	Area	Comments
LZ		F	$1,150	3/23/2012	WCNE	Three LZ247B drills, steel press wheels, set at 14", 42', transport
LZ		F	$1,300	3/23/2012	WCNE	Three LZ 812 shoe drills, Acra-Plant points, big pneumatic press wheels
LZ		F	$1,300	3/23/2012	WCNE	Three LZB drills, rubber press wheels, 14" spacing, 42', transport
LZ10		F	$310	12/18/2013	Online	*BigIron.com,* item in Kansas, hoe drill, 24', 6.70-15 tires, drawbar, 10" spacing, one set of hyd. hoses, 2 tires weather cracked
LZ1010		G	$726	6/5/2013	Online	*BigIron.com,* item in Montana, four 8' section seed drills, 32', 4.0-18 tires, drawbar, 10" spacing
LZ1010		G	$550	3/23/2011	SWNE	Shedded, set of three
LZ1010		F	$600	3/1/2011	SCNE	PT
LZ8		G	$800	10/18/2012	WCNE	36' shoe drill
LZ812		G	$827	4/24/2013	Online	*BigIron.com,* item in Colorado, 32', hoe drill
Van Brunt		F	$800	3/15/2014	WCIL	
Van Brunt		G	$550	4/13/2013	SEMN	11', 7" spacing
Van Brunt		F	$650	8/23/2012	SWMN	12', LR, grass
Van Brunt		F	$700	3/31/2012	NEIA	10', grass seeder
Van Brunt		G	$750	12/3/2011	ECNE	PT

Massey Ferguson

Model	Year	Condition	Price	Date	Area	Comments
33		G	$1,250	1/31/2012	NEIN	10', seeder
33		G	$1,000	1/27/2012	SEAL	
43		G	$578	10/16/2013	Online	*PurpleWave.com,* item in Kansas, 13', 20 seed drops, 8" spacing
43		G	$800	7/27/2012	SWKY	Wheat drill
424		G	$900	4/9/2011	WCNE	7", 16', PT, grass seeder
9'		G	$825	8/21/2012	WCIL	
13'		G	$1,050	8/11/2012	NWIA	13', grass seeder, new bearings in disk wheels

McCormick

Model	Year	Condition	Price	Date	Area	Comments
8'		G	$650	8/15/2013	ECMN	On wood spoke wheels, original, unrestored
8'		G	$650	8/15/2013	ECMN	
10'		G	$1,650	3/2/2013	NCWI	20', 6" spacing, double disk, grass, double clutch lift
10'		G	$800	3/22/2013	WCIL	Double disk, grass seeder
10'		E	$3,000	1/19/2013	NEIA	Hyd. lift, double disk, 7" spacing, grass seeder

Minneapolis Moline

Model	Year	Condition	Price	Date	Area	Comments
12'		G	$500	3/22/2014	SEMN	Double disk, grass seeder

IMPLEMENTS

Drills

Oliver

Model	Year	Condition	Price	Date	Area	Comments
10'		F	$700	2/12/2014	WCIL	Superior, 10', on rubber
10'		G	$700	12/10/2012	ECIL	Clover, grass seeder, fertilizer, one owner
12'		G	$950	4/2/2011	ECMN	6" spacing, grass seeder
12'		G	$950	4/2/2011	ECMN	Tall rubber, 6" spacing
Superior		G	$900	10/12/2013	NEOH	Alfalfa and grass drill
Superior		G	$2,350	1/31/2012	NEIN	

Hay Balers

IMPLEMENTS

Allis-Chalmers

Model	Year	Condition	Price	Date	Area	Comments
303		G	$625	8/21/2012	WCIL	Small square, twine
444		F	$600	6/20/2012	Online	*BigIron.com,* item in Iowa, small square, 540 PTO, used two years ago, 4 twine boxes
444		F	$600	2/7/2012	WCOK	Square, wire
Roto-Baler		G	$1,050	6/15/2013	WCMI	Round, PTO powered
Roto-Baler		G	$525	3/30/2013	NWIL	
Roto-Baler		G	$700	1/28/2012	ECMO	
Roto-Baler		G	$525	7/27/2011	Online	*BigIron.com,* item in Nebraska, shedded, 540 PTO, belts, 5.5x16 tires

Case

Model	Year	Condition	Price	Date	Area	Comments
230	1972	G	$750	2/22/2014	NEIN	Square, twine, original

Ford

Model	Year	Condition	Price	Date	Area	Comments
532		G	$600	2/22/2013	SWKY	Square
532		G	$600	8/4/2012	SWKY	Square
542		G	$825	7/30/2011	ECMO	Square, shaft

International Harvester Company

Model	Year	Condition	Price	Date	Area	Comments
37		G	$750	3/15/2014	WCIL	Twine
37		G	$1,000	3/19/2011	SEIA	Square
46		G	$1,100	10/30/2013	Online	*PurpleWave.com,* item in Kansas, square, twine, 540 PTO, rear hitch
46		G	$625	6/13/2012	Online	*BigIron.com,* item in Nebraska, small square, 15" tires, 540 PTO, twine, pickup wheel, rear hitch and long bale chute, counter
46		G	$600	11/15/2011	ECND	Small square, 540 PTO
47		G	$500	8/27/2013	NWIA	Square, SN 7329
47		G	$800	1/28/2012	ECMO	Square, working counter, shedded, 540 PTO
425		G	$1,300	5/1/2013	Online	*BigIron.com,* item in Nebraska, twine, 1 tire is weather checked and flat
428		G	$2,100	1/27/2012	SEAL	Square
430		G	$750	2/22/2014	NEIN	Twine

International Harvester Company

Model	Year	Condition	Price	Date	Area	Comments
430		G	$1,000	3/30/2013	SCMN	Square
430		F	$650	3/22/2013	WCMI	Square
430		G	$800	2/12/2013	WCIL	Square, wire
430		G	$800	1/28/2012	ECMO	Square, 540 PTO, shaft on machine
430		G	$1,050	9/9/2011	ECND	Small square
435		G	$2,400	8/20/2013	WCIL	Square
435		F	$700	1/31/2012	NEIN	Square
445		G	$1,300	2/26/2011	ECIA	Square, 15 thrower, rollers
2400		G	$550	2/22/2014	ECMI	Round, PTO shaft on front, no monitor, manual tie, 5x6 bales
430W		G	$1,400	3/22/2014	ECKS	Square
430W		G	$1,705	5/8/2013	Online	*BigIron.com,* item in Nebraska, square, 540 PTO, wire, 2 boxes of wire, rear hitch
440T		G	$2,400	4/17/2013	Online	*BigIron.com,* item in Kansas, twine, square, 540 PTO, 56" intake, drawbar attach
440T		G	$1,200	1/27/2012	SEAL	Square
440W		G	$825	9/27/2013	Online	*PurpleWave.com,* item in Oklahoma, square, 60" wide pickup, 540 PTO, 26x12 left tire, 11x15 right tire

John Deere

Model	Year	Condition	Price	Date	Area	Comments
14T		G	$850	3/15/2014	WCIL	Twine
14T		F	$1,300	3/15/2014	ECKS	Twine
14T		F	$1,600	2/9/2013	SWOH	
14T		G	$700	8/21/2012	WCIL	Square
14T		G	$900	2/25/2012	WCMI	
14T		F	$550	8/24/2011	SCMI	
14T		G	$550	6/8/2011	Online	*BigIron.com,* item in Nebraska, square, 15" tires, 540 PTO
14T		G	$550	4/13/2011	Online	*BigIron.com,* item in Nebraska, square, 15" tires, 54 PTO, shedded
14T		G	$600	1/29/2011	ECMO	Square
24T		G	$750	4/3/2014	NEIN	
24T		G	$650	3/22/2014	SEMN	
24T		G	$2,550	3/1/2014	ECMO	
24T		G	$800	2/22/2014	NEIN	Twine
24T		G	$2,750	12/28/2013	SEIA	Small square
24T		G	$935	6/10/2013	NWWI	Square, hyd. kicker
24T		G	$1,700	4/13/2013	SCMI	Square
24T		G	$852	4/9/2013	NWWI	Square, working
24T		G	$2,900	3/2/2013	ECMN	
24T		F	$650	2/23/2013	ECMI	Square
24T		F	$650	9/3/2012	SEMN	
24T		G	$875	8/22/2012	Online	*BigIron.com,* item in Nebraska, square, 540 PTO, twine
24T		G	$600	8/4/2012	ECMN	Square, 540 PTO
24T		G	$975	3/24/2012	SWMI	
24T		F	$1,050	3/24/2012	SCMN	Square, no thrower

IMPLEMENTS

John Deere

Model	Year	Condition	Price	Date	Area	Comments
24T		G	$900	2/25/2012	WCMI	Square
24T		G	$750	1/31/2012	NEIN	Square
24T		F	$850	1/27/2012	SEAL	Square
24T		G	$1,800	12/10/2011	SEIA	Small square
24T		G	$1,100	9/10/2011	ECIA	
24T		G	$2,900	6/29/2011	NEND	PTO, square, hyd. lift package and bale turner, stored inside and reconditioned
24T		G	$650	6/17/2011	SWMN	
24T		G	$750	4/27/2011	NECO	Small square, twine, PTO
24T		G	$950	3/19/2011	SEIA	Square
24T		G	$2,000	3/19/2011	SEIA	
24T		F	$900	2/5/2011	SEMI	
24T		G	$1,500	1/29/2011	ECMO	Square
24T		F	$900	1/17/2011	WCIL	Two sold on this sale
24T		F	$1,300	1/17/2011	WCIL	Two sold on this sale
24T		G	$1,050	1/1/2011	ECKS	Square, twine
216	1968	G	$775	5/8/2013	Online	*BigIron.com,* item in Montana, square, 540 PTO, 16x18 bales
336	1974	G	$1,925	7/11/2012	Online	*PurpleWave.com,* item in Kansas, square, 540 PTO, twine, one flat tire
336	1974	G	$3,000	4/27/2011	Online	*BigIron.com,* item in Nebraska, square, 18"x14" bales, about 4' pickup, twine
336	1979	G	$2,750	1/29/2011	ECMO	
336	1979	G	$3,000	1/29/2011	ECMO	Square, twine, shaft
336		G	$1,000	4/3/2014	NEIN	Twine
336		G	$6,500	1/4/2014	WCNY	Square, ejector
336		G	$2,250	12/19/2013	SCNY	Thrower
336		G	$4,600	9/28/2013	SESD	Small square, newer style knotter
336		G	$2,000	9/21/2013	SWOH	
336		G	$4,800	9/14/2013	SEMI	
336		G	$2,800	8/20/2013	WCIL	Square, twine with kicker
336		G	$2,900	8/20/2013	WCIL	Square, wire
336		G	$2,600	8/15/2013	ECMN	Square, thrower, 540 RPM, PTO
336		G	$2,900	8/15/2013	ECMN	Small square, hitch, 540 PTO, thrower
336		G	$1,000	8/7/2013	Online	*IQBID.com,* square, 540 PTO, thrower
336		G	$3,500	7/25/2013	ECND	Small square, PTO
336		G	$1,705	6/10/2013	NWWI	Square, hyd. kicker
336		G	$3,200	4/24/2013	Online	*BigIron.com,* item in Colorado, small square, 540 PTO
336		G	$3,000	4/13/2013	SEMN	Kicker
336		G	$2,000	4/10/2013	NETX	Square, 540 PTO
336		E	$5,100	4/6/2013	WCMO	Low use, one owner, stored inside
336		E	$5,300	3/16/2013	NEKS	One owner, bought new in 1980, always under cover when not in use
336		G	$3,500	3/2/2013	NETN	Square
336		G	$3,500	2/23/2013	ECMI	
336		G	$3,800	2/12/2013	WCIL	Twine
336		G	$4,900	11/24/2012	SEMN	52 thrower
336		G	$2,800	9/20/2012	ECIN	Square

IMPLEMENTS

John Deere

Model	Year	Condition	Price	Date	Area	Comments
336		G	$2,100	8/30/2012	SEMN	
336		G	$3,600	8/21/2012	WCIL	Square, twine
336		G	$1,850	8/9/2012	NEIL	Square, new knotter
336		G	$2,000	6/2/2012	SEMN	Kicker, 540 PTO, works well
336		G	$2,400	6/2/2012	SEMN	Kicker
336		G	$1,650	5/23/2012	Online	*BigIron.com,* item in South Dakota, square, 1x14 left tire, 26x12 right tire, bent needle, bale tipping shoot
336		G	$2,000	5/22/2012	WCMN	Small square, thrower
336		G	$1,200	3/22/2012	ECMN	Small square, 540 PTO, pan extension, field ready
336		G	$2,900	2/25/2012	WCMI	Square, recent inspection
336		G	$3,900	2/7/2012	SEIA	Square
336		G	$3,100	1/28/2012	ECMO	Square
336		G	$3,200	1/28/2012	ECMO	Square
336		F	$2,150	1/24/2012	NWWI	Working, kicker
336		G	$3,000	7/30/2011	ECMO	Square
336		G	$3,900	7/30/2011	ECMO	Square, twine, shaft, hitch
336		G	$2,350	6/22/2011	NECO	Small square, twine, PTO
336		F	$1,700	5/25/2011	NECO	Small square, twine, PT, PTO
336		G	$2,900	4/27/2011	NECO	Small square, twine, PT, PTO
336		G	$3,500	4/8/2011	WCMI	Square
336		G	$2,100	4/2/2011	ECMN	Square
336		G	$3,150	3/26/2011	NECO	Small square, twine, PTO
336		G	$3,000	3/15/2011	WCIL	Square, twine
336		G	$2,350	3/5/2011	SEMN	John Deere kicker, 540 PTO

Massey Ferguson

Model	Year	Condition	Price	Date	Area	Comments
3		G	$750	1/29/2014	Online	*BigIron.com,* item in Kansas, square, 540 PTO, 14x18 bales
5		G	$3,250	12/14/2011	WCMN	3x3 square, 2nd owner
9		G	$800	7/30/2011	ECMO	Square, twine, shaft
12		G	$2,500	3/30/2013	NWIL	Square
12		G	$688	8/22/2012	Online	*PurpleWave.com,* item in Kansas, square, twine, 540 PTO
124		G	$1,500	1/19/2013	NEMS	
124		G	$1,600	3/24/2012	SWMI	Square
124		F	$900	1/28/2012	ECMO	Square
124		*G*	*$1,500*	*12/28/2011*	*Online*	*BigIron.com*, item in Wyoming, square, 540 PTO, 4.5' manual pickup head, manual tension, 6 roll twine compartment
126		G	$575	6/13/2012	Online	*BigIron.com,* item in Colorado, small square, 540 PTO, wire, shedded
128		G	$1,600	3/5/2013	ECWI	Chute
128		G	$1,600	5/18/2011	SEWY	Small square, twine, PTO
1560		F	$675	3/22/2013	WCMI	Round
1565		G	$1,300	7/30/2011	ECMO	Round, shaft

New Holland

Model	Year	Condition	Price	Date	Area	Comments
68		G	$750	4/1/2014	WCMN	Small square, PTO
68		G	$900	11/3/2012	SWMI	Super Hayliner, square
68		G	$1,700	2/25/2012	WCMI	Square
268		G	$600	1/4/2014	WCNY	Square, thrower
268		G	$1,050	12/15/2012	WCMI	
268		G	$800	3/24/2012	SWMI	Square
268		G	$1,650	1/31/2012	NEIN	500 bales total use
268		F	$650	8/21/2011	WCOH	
268		G	$3,600	8/6/2011	SWMN	
268		G	$700	4/23/2011	WCMI	Square
268		G	$800	3/15/2011	WCIL	Square, twine
268		F	$650	2/27/2011	NWIL	
269		G	$750	8/20/2013	WCIL	Square
269		G	$688	3/27/2013	Online	*PurpleWave.com,* item in Oklahoma, small square, 540 PTO, twine, extra knotter parts, pin hitch
269		G	$1,100	3/2/2013	ECMN	Hayliner, 540 PTO
269		G	$900	5/9/2012	Online	*BigIron.com,* item in Kansas, wire, square, 540 PTO, shedded, not used for several years, works
269		G	$700	3/22/2012	ECMN	Small square, bale ejector
269		G	$700	3/20/2012	WCIL	Square
269		G	$1,650	2/4/2012	ECTX	Square, wire
269		G	$1,750	2/1/2011	NEIN	
271		G	$1,500	3/16/2013	SEMN	
271		G	$1,100	9/14/2011	Online	*BigIron.com,* item in Nebraska, small square, twine, 14x18" bales, 70 strokes/minute, 56" pickup head, twine cutting knives, clam shell gears
273	1971	G	$1,000	7/30/2011	ECMO	Square
273	1971	G	$1,500	7/30/2011	ECMO	Gauge wheels, manual swing tongue, bale chute extension, wagon hitch, shaft
275	1968	G	$1,026	5/8/2013	Online	*IQBID.com,* square, super sweep pickux
286	1973	G	$2,800	7/25/2012	Online	*BigIron.com,* item in Nebraska, square, 14Lx16.1 tires, 540 PTO, counter, hyd. bale tension, hyd. lift on pickup, 2 wire rolls

Oliver

Model	Year	Condition	Price	Date	Area	Comments
62T		G	$600	10/12/2013	NEOH	
62T		G	$2,750	10/12/2013	NEOH	
100		G	$500	12/10/2012	ECIL	Automatic wire, V4 Wisconsin gas, 1 owner
520		F	$1,100	2/18/2012	ECIL	Small square
520		F	$500	1/28/2012	ECMO	Square, 540 PTO, twine, rear tongue, shaft on machine

IMPLEMENTS

Allis-Chalmers

Model	Year	Condition	Price	Date	Area	Comments
333		G	$1,050	2/18/2012	ECIL	11R
N		F	$900	12/1/2011	SEMN	2R, wire check-row

Ford

Model	Year	Condition	Price	Date	Area	Comments
309		G	$600	2/12/2011	SWOH	2R corn planter, 3pt.

International Harvester Company

Model	Year	Condition	Price	Date	Area	Comments
56		G	$700	11/3/2012	SWMI	4R
56		G	$900	3/24/2012	SWMI	4R, 30"
56		G	$1,200	2/1/2011	NEIN	6R, dry fertilizer, oblong, very good
400		G	$775	9/10/2013	Online	Item in North Dakota, 8R
400		F	$750	3/22/2013	NWMN	Cyclo, 4R, 36", dry fertilizer, PTO fan
400		G	$350	6/27/2012	NEND	Cyclo, 8R, 30", PT
400		G	$578	5/9/2012	Online	*PurpleWave.com,* item in Kansas, 6R, 30", 540 PTO
500		F	$975	3/3/2012	SEMN	12R, 30", corn and soybean drums, John Deere monitor, all 800 updates, field ready, many new parts, 3pt.
500		G	$1,100	6/17/2011	SWMN	19R, skip row

John Deere

Model	Year	Condition	Price	Date	Area	Comments
290		G	$825	4/23/2013	Online	*HansenandYoung.com,* restored
290		G	$687	3/27/2013	NWWI	2R, reconditioned
290		G	$577	12/18/2012	ECWI	2R
290		G	$575	2/25/2012	WCMI	2R, trailer type
290		G	$1,000	10/29/2011	ECMN	
494		F	$800	3/24/2012	NEIN	Completely restored
494A		G	$600	3/4/2014	SWMN	4R, 36", hyd. lift, fertilizer, herbicide and insecticide boxes, row cleaners, markers
4494A		F	$600	2/23/2013	ECMI	
494A		G	$853	4/25/2012	Online	*PurpleWave.com,* item in Kansas, 4R, 11'3" width, 30" spacing
1250		G	$1,100	7/31/2013	ECND	PT, 6R, 30", plate

Oliver

Model	Year	Condition	Price	Date	Area	Comments
543		G	$550	12/14/2012	SWKY	4R

Allis-Chalmers

Model	Year	Hours	Condition	Price	Date	Area	Comments
60	1948		G	$908	8/14/2012	Online	*PurpleWave.com,* item in Kansas, all-crop harvester, 5' sickle bar, wood reel, 80"Lx5.5" diameter auger, 5' canvas conveyor, 18 bu. hopper, ground-driven reel
IB	1969		G	$3,400	4/13/2013	SCMI	Gas, 10' rigid head, 18.4x26 tires, SN 1384

Gleaner

Model	Year	Hours	Condition	Price	Date	Area	Comments
C	1967		G	$1,705	5/30/2012	Online	*PurpleWave.com,* item in Kansas
C2	1964		G	$800	8/6/2011	NCOK	18' header
F	1976		G	$2,200	9/28/2013	NEIA	4R corn head and platform
F		3,170	G	$1,250	11/29/2011	WCMN	Diesel, corn and soybean special, chopper, 18.4x26 tires, SN FKS34188
F2	1978	1,000	G	$7,000	12/4/2013	ECIN	Hydro
F2	1978		G	$9,500	10/3/2013	NCIN	Hydro, air, less than 1,000 hours
F2	1978	607	G	$1,800	8/13/2011	WCIL	23.1x26 tires
F2	1978	607	G	$4,000	6/30/2011	ECMO	Corn and soybean special, gas, 23.1x26 tires, SN FKS 39796, 15' grain platform
F2	1978		F	$800	3/5/2011	NWMO	13' platform
K	1969		G	$1,250	2/22/2014	ECMI	Gas, rasp bar cyl., 10' header
K2	1978		G	$2,860	11/30/2011	Online	*PurpleWave.com,* item in Kansas, 292 6 cyl. gas, 3 speed hydro, air, heat, tilt steering, suspension seat, 75 bu. bin capacity, bin ext., work lights
L	1976	3,031	G	$1,900	8/13/2011	WCIL	23.1x30 tires, 1,843 sep. hours
L	1980	2,170	F	$1,850	2/19/2011	ECNE	Diesel, 6R 30" corn head
L2	1973		G	$2,700	6/22/2011	NECO	Diesel, bin ext., 24' wheat header
L2	1977		F	$2,100	8/24/2011	SCMI	Allis-Chalmers 630 15' grain head
L2	1977	1,064	F	$1,950	5/11/2011	Online	*BigIron.com,* 1,164 sep. hours, hydro, 3500 diesel, soybean special, big engine, 11 drive tire weathered
L2	1978		G	$3,500	7/31/2013	ECND	6 cyl. 3500 diesel, hydro, 16' pickup header with Melroe pickup
L2	1978		G	$1,500	7/27/2011	ECND	Hydro
M	1975	1,138	G	$3,000	9/28/2011	Online	*BigIron.com,* item in Colorado, 6 cyl. diesel, normal maintenance, corn sieve, grain loss monitor, straw cutter, air compressor replaced
M		280	G	$6,000	6/13/2012	NEWI	Diesel, corn and soybean special, 2 heads: 630 6R narrow and 15' flex head and header trailer, 23.1x30 tires 85%
M2	1977	2,489	G	$1,800	2/15/2012	Online	*BigIron.com,* 1,288 sep. hours, hydro, 6 cyl. diesel, 20' header

International Harvester Company

Model	Year	Hours	Condition	Price	Date	Area	Comments
82	1960		E	$3,500	3/15/2014	ECMD	PT, "Clean Grain" unit at grain elevator to bin elevator, Hume reel, cut wheat this spring, works and runs well, new correct implement tires, painted and shed kept since new

International Harvester Company

Model	Year	Hours	Condition	Price	Date	Area	Comments
105			E	$5,000	8/15/2013	WCMN	Barn find from New Prague, MInn., five bidders, buyer from Ill.
615	1970		G	$1,302	7/27/2011	Online	*BigIron.com,* item in Nebraska, 14' grain table, 3 speed gear drive with variable speed belt drive, 6 cyl. gas, 80 bu. bin, cab tight
715	1978		G	$1,100	9/28/2011	Online	*BigIron.com,* item in Nebraska, gear drive transmission, German diesel, corn and soybean special, chopper mounted on the side with deflector, extra light package, manual fold auger, air, heat, AM radio
715	1978	613	G	$3,700	8/6/2011	SCMN	Diesel, 613 hours showing, cab, heat, air, 23.1x26 tires, SN 5-D275448
715	1979	2,121	G	$1,800	9/12/2013	SEIA	Diesel, 2WD, 23.1x26 fronts, 12.4x16 rear tires
715		814	G	$1,550	6/13/2012	Online	*BigIron.com,* item in Kansas, hydro, 6 cyl. diesel, air needs charging, 16-17' cut, IHC 819 header
815		2,732	G	$1,300	2/22/2014	NEIN	Hydro, IH 844 corn head
815		1,802	F	$1,300	4/17/2013	Online	*BigIron.com,* item in Nebraska, hour meter does not work, 3 speed hydro
915	1975		F	$2,000	5/24/2012	SCMI	Hydro, IHC 844 4R corn head and grain header
915	1977		G	$4,000	8/24/2010	NEMO	Hydro, Mud Hog, 4WD, turbo, rice tires
915		3,289	G	$2,250	9/26/2013	NWOH	Hydro, turbo 414 diesel, 28Lx26 tires, 11x16 rears, new Smid straw walkers a few years ago, chopper, Ashman rasp bars, one owner, #810 Gen 3 17.5' grain table
915		2,950	G	$3,700	8/20/2013	WCIL	2WD, hydro, corn and soybean special, 67x34x30 tires
1440	1977		G	$3,900	2/8/2014	NECO	Good rubber
1440	1978	4,414	F	$2,600	3/20/2012	WCIL	2WD
1440	1978		G	$5,000	3/10/2012	NCOH	Axial flow
1460	1978	4,978	G	$3,300	12/4/2013	Online	*BigIron.com,* item in Nebraska, corn and soybean, 3 speed hydro, 6 cyl. diesel, discharge auger, bin ext.

COMBINES

Who would be interested in a very old combine for sale at auction? Lots of folks. In fact, bidders from five states were in on the very nice condition International Harvester 105 combine (pictured here) sold at an Aug. 15, 2013, consignment auction in Litchfield, Minn., a sale by my friends at the Steffes Group. The combine was a true "barn find" from a farm estate near New Prague, Minn., just south of the Twin Cities. How much did it go for? $5,000, to a buyer from Illinois.

PETE'S PICK

International Harvester Company

Model	Year	Hours	Condition	Price	Date	Area	Comments
1460	1978		F	$3,000	8/20/2013	WCIL	4WD, hydro, 28Lx26 tires
1460	1978		G	$3,000	8/20/2013	WCIL	4WD, hydro, 28Lx26 tires
1460	1978	4,901	G	$3,900	8/7/2013	SESD	Hydro, 28Lx26 rubber, local machine, field ready, ride-n-drive
1460	1978		F	$1,900	12/8/2011	NEND	Chopper, SN U002106
1480	1978	4,825	F	$2,500	9/25/2013	NECO	Diesel
1480	1978	5,597	G	$2,700	11/29/2012	ECND	Special rotors, no rock traps or chopper, two sets of concave
1480	1978	5,953	G	$2,700	11/29/2012	ECND	Special rotors, no rock traps or chopper, two sets of concave

John Deere

Model	Year	Hours	Condition	Price	Date	Area	Comments
44H	1956		G	$2,700	5/25/2013	NWMO	10' platform, SN 4621, #10 2R corn head
55			G	$950	9/28/2013	SWMN	Square back, soybean header
55			G	$1,700	9/28/2013	SWMN	Square back, 335 corn head
55			G	$2,100	1/21/2012	SEVA	Corn special grain, all original
65	1960		G	$2,850	8/7/2013	Online	*IQBID.com,* PT, all original, 4-belt pickup, 217 cu. in., gas
95	1964		G	$1,010	12/18/2013	Online	*BigIron.com,* item in Colorado, 217 gas, 18.4x26 front tires, 19' reel and pickup attach, square back, power steering, shedded
95	1969		G	$800	4/9/2011	WCNE	Gas, cab, 20' wheat header
105	1966		F	$1,100	8/25/2012	NWIL	Corn special, gas
105	1968	4,836	P	$825	8/8/2012	Online	*IQBID.com,* item in North Dakota, 362 gas, 19' Sund pickup on John Deere 20' header, spike tooth cylinder, chopper
105		4,617	G	$5,500	2/23/2013	ECMI	Diesel, hydro, variable speed cyl., corn special, hydro reel drive kit
3300	1972		G	$5,200	12/11/2012	SEPA	Gas, cab, 10' cutting platform, John Deere 343 3R corn head
4400	1970		F	$1,300	3/26/2011	NECO	Gas, needs work
4400	1972	2,881	G	$1,101	5/8/2013	Online	*BigIron.com,* item in Kansas, belt drive, 4 speed manual, 100 hp diesel
4400	1974	4,463	G	$2,100	8/22/2012	ECMN	18.4x26 tires, cab, air, heat
4400	1974		G	$1,000	4/8/2011	WCMI	2WD, diesel, four parts
4400	1976	2,635	G	$1,800	9/12/2013	SEIA	Diesel, 2WD, 18.4x26 fronts, 11x16 rear tires, wheel weights
4400	1976		F	$2,750	2/28/2011	SCMI	
4400		1,874	G	$1,080	12/18/2013	Online	*BigIron.com,* item in Nebraska, 4 speed manual, 6 cyl., gas, extra drive tire
4400		1,496	G	$2,500	12/5/2013	SCIA	Gas, second owner
4400		3,521	G	$2,500	12/5/2013	SCIA	Diesel
4400		2,971	G	$1,073	10/16/2013	Online	*PurpleWave.com,* item in Kansas, John Deere 6 cyl. diesel, hydro
4400		3,531	G	$1,750	8/15/2013	ECMN	Diesel, 18.4x26 tires, 215 flex header
4400		1,262	E	$3,500	12/1/2012	NCOH	2nd owner, John Deere 213 flex head, 292 gas

John Deere

Model	Year	Hours	Condition	Price	Date	Area	Comments
4400		4,128	G	$2,900	8/16/2012	Online	*IQBID.com,* item in Minnesota, diesel, rear wheel weights, 28.1x26 tires, 11x16 tires, one owner
4400		4,587	G	$1,102	8/14/2012	Online	*IQBID.com,* item in Minnesota, diesel, cab, air, heat, chopper, 18.4x26 tires
4400		2,172	G	$1,050	8/4/2012	ECMN	Gas, spreader, gear shift, 18.4x26 tires, like-new cyl. bars
4400		2,800	G	$5,000	6/2/2012	SEMN	Gear driven, 18.4x26 tires, diesel, chopper, works
4400		2,706	F	$4,400	4/14/2012	NENC	Second owner, chaff spreader
4400		3,600	G	$1,300	3/22/2012	ECMN	
4400		4,980	G	$1,005	9/14/2011	Online	*BigIron.com,* item in Nebraska, 4 speed hydro, 100hp diesel, regular length auger, air, heat, radio
4400		2,768	G	$1,609	7/27/2011	Online	*BigIron.com,* item in Nebraska, 4 speed, 329 diesel, 400 acres on these repairs, shedded
4440	1977	4,100	F	$1,900	7/30/2011	ECMO	Dial-A-Matic, one owner
6600	1972		G	$1,850	4/14/2011	SEND	SP, cab, chopper, 329 gas, one owner
6600	1973	4,443	G	$2,400	2/7/2013	NEIN	
6600	1974	1,903	G	$5,500	11/10/2012	ECIA	John Deere 454 4R corn head, John Deere soybean table, John Deere pickup header
6600	1974		F	$1,800	3/1/2011	SCNE	18.4x26 front tires, 15" rear tires, John Deere 546 corn head, not running, SN 110439H
6600	1974		F	$2,000	2/19/2011	ECNE	Diesel
6600	1975		F	$2,650	8/11/2012	NWIL	Diesel
6600	1976	4,255	G	$1,750	9/6/2013	ECSD	400 hours on OH, variable speed, diesel
6600	1977	3,351	G	$2,950	3/5/2014	Online	*BigIron.com,* item in Kansas, manual, 404 John Deere diesel, single axle, new starter and batteries
6600	1977	4,443	G	$2,400	2/7/2013	NEIN	23.1x26 tires 30%, chopper, 2WD, very clean
6600	1977		G	$2,600	12/1/2012	SEWY	Diesel
6600	1977	2,236	G	$5,600	8/16/2012	NCIA	Diesel, cab, air, hydro, Hiniker ext., chopper
6600	1977	3,996	G	$2,975	10/11/2011	Online	*BidNow.us,* diesel, 4WD, 100 hours on rebuilt engine, air, new batteries, cup elevator, Maust conveyor, Sund pickup, Mud Hog
6600	1977	4,508	G	$1,850	8/13/2011	WCIL	Bearing out on main shaft, runs okay
6600	1977		G	$2,475	6/22/2011	NECO	Diesel, bin ext.
6600	1977		F	$2,100	5/25/2011	NECO	Diesel, bin ext.
6600	1978	3,256	G	$3,000	2/22/2014	NEIN	Chopper
6600	1978	3,936	G	$2,250	12/4/2013	ECIN	23.1x26 tires, chopper
6600	1978	2,127	G	$2,700	5/29/2013	Online	*BigIron.com,* item in Wyoming, hydro
6600	1978	4,054	G	$3,100	9/13/2012	Online	*IQBID.com,* item in Iowa, side hill
6600	1978	4,170	G	$1,355	7/25/2012	Online	*BigIron.com,* item in Iowa, LG 404 diesel, straight transmission, Dial-a-Matic header control, bin ext., chopper, non-adj. sieve
6600	1978	3,200	G	$2,475	10/11/2011	Online	*BidNow.us,* gear shift, rasp bar, paddle elev, longer elevator

John Deere

Model	Year	Hours	Condition	Price	Date	Area	Comments
6600	1978	3,247	G	$4,750	7/30/2011	ECMO	Mud Hog pusher, header control, John Deere 216 flex platform
6600	1978	3,615	F	$1,200	7/20/2011	NCIA	John Deere, tank ext., chopper
6600	1978	2,136	G	$4,500	5/25/2011	NECO	Diesel, bin ext.
6600		3,873	G	$2,500	8/22/2013	SEMN	SN 207167H
6600		4,231	G	$2,200	1/21/2013	NCIA	404 diesel, hydro, chopper, 23.1x26 tires
6600		3,925	G	$2,550	1/9/2013	Online	*BigIron.com,* item in Kansas, hydro, 404 diesel, 1 hyd., single axle, new feederhouse chain, new batteries, chopper
6600		3,647	G	$2,800	12/6/2012	Online	*BidNow.us,* bucket elevator, conveyor, 23.1x26 fronts, one owner
6600			G	$3,000	11/13/2012	NCIA	Diesel
6600		4,600	G	$1,700	9/13/2012	Online	*IQBID.com,* item in Iowa
6600		4,030	G	$2,900	8/21/2012	WCIL	
6600		3,960	G	$2,700	8/13/2012	ECIL	Diesel, chopper, new feederhouse and clean grain chains with 200 acres use
6600		4,511	G	$1,750	8/8/2012	Online	*BigIron.com,* item in Nebraska, Posi torque variable speed transmission, 6 cyl. diesel, rear inside wheel weights
6600		4,596	G	$2,550	8/8/2012	Online	*BigIron.com,* item in Nebraska, hydro, 6 cyl. 329 diesel, Schaf speed monitors, rear chaff spreader, Murphy switches, chopper
6600		3,621	G	$1,850	6/13/2012	Online	*BigIron.com,* item in Nebraska, 6 cyl. turbo diesel, rear chaff spreaders
6600		4,273	G	$1,700	6/2/2012	SEMN	New batteries, gear drive, 23.1x26 tires, runs
6600		4,626	F	$1,850	12/28/2011	Online	*BigIron.com,* item in Nebraska, 4 speed hydro, 6 cyl. diesel, dual straw spreaders
6600		3,647	G	$2,800	12/6/2011	Online	*BidNow.us,* Maust bucket elevator and conveyor, 23.1x26 fronts, one owner
6600		4,464	G	$3,800	9/14/2011	Online	*BigIron.com,* item in Nebraska, sidehill, John Deere 216 16' flex header, 4 speed hydro, John Deere diesel, chopper, bin ext., ground chain, brakes weak, air does not work
6600		3,853	F	$1,900	8/11/2011	WCMN	Diesel, chopper, rock trap, Hiniker hopper top
6600		1,623	G	$1,400	7/27/2011	Online	*BigIron.com,* item in Colorado, belt drive variable speed transmission, Chrysler diesel, front seal on engine leaks, shedded, header liner gone
6600		2,316	G	$2,250	7/27/2011	Online	*BigIron.com,* item in Nebraska, diesel, rear tires LT235/25Rx16, front tires 18.4x26
6600		3,241	G	$3,150	7/27/2011	Online	*BigIron.com,* item in Nebraska, John Deere diesel, 9 rear wheel weights on steering axles, 10"x12' unloading auger

John Deere

Model	Year	Hours	Condition	Price	Date	Area	Comments
6600		3,742	G	$5,300	7/27/2011	Online	*BigIron.com,* item in Nebraska, 4R38 corn head, hydro, diesel, glass in cab
6600		5,473	G	$2,200	3/23/2011	Online	*BigIron.com,* 4F/1R, 329 diesel, 150 bu. bin, 12' unload auger, HD hubs
6620	1972	518	E	$6,270	6/29/2011	Online	*PurpleWave.com,* item in Kansas, 6 cyl. gas, 4 speed, 20' header, extra sickle section, chopper, shedded, recently replaced battery
6620	1972	413	E	$7,260	6/29/2011	Online	*PurpleWave.com,* item in Kansas, 6 cyl. gas, 4 speed, 20' header, extra sickle section, chopper, shedded, recently replaced battery
6620	1978	3,936	G	$2,600	4/3/2014	NEIN	23.1x26 tires, chopper
7700	1972	4,022	F	$900	5/8/2013	Online	*BigIron.com,* item in Kansas, 4 speed manual, 145 hp
7700	1976	2,745	G	$3,400	3/26/2011	NECO	Diesel
7700	1977		G	$2,400	10/18/2012	WCMI	2WD, chopper
7700	1977	5,762	G	$2,900	8/10/2011	Online	*BigIron.com,* item in Nebraska, hydro, 6 cyl. turbo diesel, AM/FM, air, 14' unload auger
7700	1977		G	$4,250	2/17/2011	WCNE	Diesel, no meter, set for corn
7700	1978	3,477	G	$2,850	9/28/2011	Online	*BigIron.com,* item in Nebraska, 4 speed gear drive transmission, 404 turbo diesel, air, self-locking unloading auger, 200 bu. bin
7700	1978	4,113	G	$4,500	3/26/2011	SWIA	Turbo, hydro, chopper, good rubber, clean, shedded
7700	1978		G	$2,900	2/17/2011	WCNE	Diesel, no meter, 224 header, 2-9' Sund pickups
7700		4,133	F	$1,750	12/19/2013	WCMN	Turbo diesel, rock trap, chopper, Hiniker hopper ext., 30.5x32 Firestone fronts, 11.2x24 rears
7700		3,000	G	$2,600	7/25/2013	ECND	Turbo, shedded until last fall
7700		4,238	G	$3,075	6/19/2013	Online	*BigIron.com,* item in Colorado, hydro
7700			G	$6,000	6/1/2013	SEMN	Hydro, rotary screen, chopper
7700		1,780	F	$1,455	5/22/2013	Online	*BigIron.com,* item in Kansas
7700		2,956	G	$1,600	4/24/2013	Online	*BigIron.com,* item in Colorado, grain
7700		4,224	G	$1,600	4/24/2013	Online	*BigIron.com,* item in Kansas, 4 speed hydro
7700		3,633	G	$3,500	4/24/2013	Online	*BigIron.com,* item in Colorado, 224, 24' grain header
7700		4,787	F	$2,600	10/24/2012	WCWI	
7700		3,094	G	$1,500	8/8/2012	Online	*BigIron.com,* item in Kansas, variable speed transmission, 404 diesel, sieves were upgraded, rear weights, yield monitoring system
7700		5,083	G	$2,800	6/20/2012	ECIL	
7700		3,165	G	$1,900	6/2/2012	SEMN	18.4x38 duals, hydro, chopper, air works
7700		3,869	G	$6,160	5/30/2012	Online	*PurpleWave.com,* item in Kansas, 6 cyl. turbo diesel, 4WD, air needs charged
7700		4,390	G	$2,400	12/1/2011	NEIN	28x26 front tires, 4WD

John Deere

Model	Year	Hours	Condition	Price	Date	Area	Comments
7700			F	$1,400	8/24/2011	Online	*BigIron.com,* item in Nebraska, hydro, for parts
7700		6,012	G	$2,600	8/24/2011	Online	*BigIron.com,* item in Nebraska, hydro, extra long unload auger, recently replaced ext., ladder not attached but included
7700		3,900	E	$4,000	4/14/2011	NCND	Chopper, pickup header, Sund pickup
7720	1978	6,192	F	$2,000	11/15/2011	Online	*IQBID.com,* air foil sieves, cup clean elevator, conveyor unload
6600 SH	1976	4,023	G	$5,500	3/24/2012	SCMN	Side hill, diesel, Posi-torque trans., 2nd owner, SN 209395H
6600 SH	1978	4,677	E	$5,500	11/24/2012	SCIA	Side hill, turbo, hydro, chopper, Dial-A-Matic, SN 307533

Massey Ferguson

Model	Year	Hours	Condition	Price	Date	Area	Comments
50	1974		G	$1,125	8/13/2011	WCIL	23.1x26 tires
510			G	$2,100	8/21/2012	WCIL	
750	1973		G	$2,800	12/15/2012	WCMI	Diesel, 2WD, dual chaff spreader, good rice tires, SN 00959, Massey Ferguson 13' grain platform and 6R corn head
750	1975		G	$3,500	9/14/2011	Online	*BigIron.com,* item in Iowa, hydro, 354 Perkins, turbo, shedded, field ready
750	1977	3,400	G	$1,100	7/31/2013	ECND	Red cab, 6 cyl. gear drive, stored inside
760	1976	75	F	$2,000	11/22/2011	NCMN	V8 Perkins

Massey-Harris

Model	Year	Hours	Condition	Price	Date	Area	Comments
201-520	1949		F	$6,380	11/3/2011	Online	*PurpleWave.com,* item in Kansas, last used in 1960s, all components factory original

New Holland

Model	Year	Hours	Condition	Price	Date	Area	Comments
TR 70	1976	4,007	G	$2,300	8/8/2012	Online	*BigIron.com,* item in Iowa, 3208 Cat diesel, hydro, corn and soybeans, chopper installed by seller, 20' platform
TR 70	1978	3,473	G	$1,661	7/16/2013	Online	*IQBID.com,* item in Minnesota, hydro, 3208 Cat diesel, rock trap, owner's manual, hydro works but overheats under load and will need attention
TR 70		2,295	G	$5,500	12/27/2013	NCOH	New Holland 6R-30 corn head
TR 70		4,566	G	$2,600	8/27/2013	NCWI	Twin Rotor diesel, factory cab, air, 23.1x26 rubber, SN 291125, New Holland 960 13.5' grain table
TR 70		3,978	G	$1,100	8/22/2013	SEMN	SN 289439

Oliver

Model	Year	Hours	Condition	Price	Date	Area	Comments
525	1963		F	$1,900	3/22/2014	NWIL	Pretty rough, #531 3NR corn head

Chevy

Model	Year	Miles	Condition	Price	Date	Area	Comments
10	1970		F	$1,800	9/28/2013	NENE	Lambrecht Dealer auction, custom, C8 350, 3 speed on the column, long box, rust and damage
10	1970	28,775	G	$12,650	5/3/2012	Online	*PurpleWave.com,* item in Missouri, 454, V8 gas, aluminum intake, auto
20	1961		G	$1,101	6/26/2013	Online	*BigIron.com,* item in Nebraska, 4 speed, Chevrolet engine
20	1977	100,000	G	$1,200	8/8/2013	WCMN	Scottsdale, 4x4, single cab under automatic, DMI cushion hitch, 5th wheel plate
30	1968	37,603	G	$1,045	9/5/2012	Online	*PurpleWave.com,* item in Kansas, flatbed pickup, 327 cu in. gas, 4 speed manual
40	1967	60,000	G	$1,980	7/25/2012	Online	*PurpleWave.com,* item in Kansas, dump truck, gas, 4 speed manual, 10' bed, single ram, no battery
50	1967		G	$1,400	8/14/2013	WCMN	'74 Chevy 350 engine, roll tarp, tag tandem, 16' wood box, 4x2 transmission, newer hoist, DOTed
50	1967	11,386	G	$1,155	11/14/2012	Online	*PurpleWave.com,* item in Kansas, flatbed spray truck, 4 speed manual, two speed Hi/Lo axle
50	1968	62,000	G	$8,000	9/18/2013	ECMT	2-ton truck, 16' Omaha Std. steel box, 2-way hoist, 366 V8 engine, 5x2 transmission, tarp, good runner
50	1968		F	$1,400	3/8/2012	SEMI	Grain truck, single axle, gas, 5 speed, 16' dump bed
50	1972	122,000	G	$3,000	11/10/2012	NWOH	Cabover grain truck, 350 engine, 4x2 speed, with Kilbros 375 gravity box

The thing about covering auctions for 25 years is you see about everything. Even so, I've never seen a sale quite like the auction on Sept. 28, 2013, in Pierce, Neb. for 95-year-old Ray Lambrect, the retired local Chevrolet dealer. Turns out Ray kept many unsold new Chevy pickups and cars over his years in business. Just kept them outside on the lot and some in an old warehouse in town that eventually was damaged when a roof laden with snow caved in. This auction was basically a time machine back to the 1950s and 1960s.

A 1958 Chevy Cameo pickup truck with only 1.3 actual miles on it (pictured) sold for a staggering $140,000. A 1958 Chevy Apache 31 pickup with 5 miles on it went for $80,000. A 1960 Chevy Apache C10 half-ton pickup with 2 miles on it sold for $46,000. Like I said, not your average auction here, folks.

PETE'S PICK

Cars more your thing? A 1963 Chevy Impala with 11 miles on it and a spare hubcap in the trunk sold for $97,000.

TRUCKS

Chevy

Model	Year	Miles	Condition	Price	Date	Area	Comments
60	1959	38,000	G	$2,750	7/18/2012	ECND	Single axle, 6 cyl., 4x2 speed, 13' wood box and hoist, 8.25x20 rear tires, rear hitch
60	1961	10,000	F	$1,760	5/9/2012	Online	*PurpleWave.com,* item in Kansas grain truck, gas, 4 speed, bench seat, AM/FM, heater, spring suspension, toolboxes
60	1963	66,982	G	$1,950	12/18/2013	Online	*BigIron.com,* V8 engine, 4x2 transmission
60	1963	27,000	G	$1,300	6/27/2012	Online	*BigIron.com,* item in Kansas, 4x2 transmission, 6 cyl. gas, 13.5'Lx7.5'Wx14" sides on dump bed
60	1966		G	$1,500	1/9/2013	Online	*BigIron.com,* item in Nebraska, straight truck, 4x2 transmission, 6 cyl. gas, 8.25x20 tires, 13' box, rollover tarp
60	1966	65,000	G	$1,249	8/22/2012	Online	*BigIron.com,* item in Nebraska, grain truck, 4x2 transmission, 366 2 barrel gas, single axle, 157"WB, Omaha standard box, 4' sides, 310 bu.
60	1973	119,000	F	$2,750	11/10/2012	NWOH	Cabover grain truck, 350 engine, 4x2 speed, Kilbros 375 gravity box
65	1975	209,000	F	$1,600	9/13/2012	SEIA	Cabover grain truck, tag axle
70	1969		G	$12,000	2/27/2014	NWNE	Gas, V6, 4x2 speed, twin screw, Aulick 20' steel box, roll tarp
2500	1973	17,000	G	$4,070	11/6/2012	Online	*PurpleWave.com,* item in Kansas, 350 cu. in. V8 gas, auto, 4WD, heat, MW, ML, front brush guard, front tow hooks, long bed, bed liner, grill melted
3100	1953		G	$7,000	3/26/2014	ECMS	Pickup, 5 window
3500	1949		G	$2,000	6/11/2013	Online	*IQBID.com,* inline 6 cyl., 3 speed on the floor
3600	1949		P	$1,150	9/28/2013	NENE	Lambrecht Dealer auction, glass broken, rust
3600	1949		G	$11,500	4/2/2012	WCIL	Pickup, 6 cyl., 4 speed, older frame of restoration
3600	1950		G	$2,700	7/18/2012	ECND	6 cyl., 4 speed manual
3800	1953		G	$3,000	8/16/2012	NCIA	8' stock and grain box
3800	1954		G	$6,300	2/17/2014	WCNE	Pickup, hyd. dump bed
6400	1955	33,000	G	$1,600	3/23/2012	WCNE	Flat Box and Hoist, 4x2 speed, Sides for Grain Box
6500	1973		G	$1,600	12/30/2013	WCIL	Grain truck, 366 V87 engine, 5x2 transmission
Apache	1958	63,000	F	$7,500	9/28/2013	NENE	Lambrecht Dealer auction, half-ton pickup, 235 6 cyl., 3 speed on the column, short box, no radio, glass cracked
Apache	1958	5	G	$80,000	9/28/2013	NENE	Lambrecht Dealer auction, some paint fade, light rust, wood in box needs replacement
Apache	1960	2	G	$46,000	9/28/2013	NENE	Lambrecht Dealer auction, surface rust, 6 cyl. motor, manual on the floor MW, ML
C10	1964	2	G	$10,500	9/28/2013	NENE	Lambrecht Dealer auction, no wood in box, paint is faded, some surface rust, no radiator, paint faded, vinyl bench seat, rare

Chevy

Model	Year	Miles	Condition	Price	Date	Area	Comments
C10	1964	4	G	$14,500	9/28/2013	NENE	Lambrecht Dealer auction, manual, 4 speed, 6 cyl., long box
C10	1964	26	G	$20,000	9/28/2013	NENE	Lambrecht Dealer auction, 4 speed manual, 6 cyl., long box, paint is faded, no tailgate
C10	1964		G	$24,000	9/28/2013	NENE	Lambrecht Dealer auction, long box, 4 speed, 6 cyl., vinyl bench
C10	1964		G	$7,600	3/16/2013	NEIL	C10 pickup, red, 327 3 speed, wood box, ready to show
C10	1967	75,000	F	$2,100	9/28/2013	NENE	Lambrecht Dealer auction, 4 speed manual, long box, 6 cyl., does not run, rough condition
C10	1967		G	$15,500	4/2/2012	WCIL	Custom, 454 V8 engine, 350 auto on the column, great restoration
C10	1968		F	$2,100	9/28/2013	NENE	Lambrecht Dealer auction, 3 speed, V8 engine, AM radio, vinyl bench seat, no wood in box
C10	1969	78,000	F	$2,100	9/28/2013	NENE	Lambrecht Dealer auction, V8 engine, 4 speed manual, body rust, long box, glass cracked, MW, ML, AM radio, vinyl bench seat, interior needs work
C10	1969		F	$2,750	9/28/2013	NENE	Lambrecht Dealer auction, manual 4 speed, V8 engine, pickup, some rust and damage, vinyl bench seat
C10	1970	76,473	G	$1,350	3/23/2012	WCNE	Half-ton pickup, red with white top, 4 speed, tow hitch, really clean
C10	1972		G	$10,000	4/2/2012	WCIL	Pickup, 2WD, 350 engine, green on white
C10	1976	67,000	G	$7,050	2/1/2013	Online	*IQBid.com,* long box
C10	1977	5	F	$11,500	9/28/2013	NENE	Lambrecht Dealer auction, automatic, trim loose, does not run, vinyl bench
C10	1978	59,000	E	$4,500	7/27/2013	WCIL	Silverado, heavy half-ton C10 2WD 2-tone blue exterior, blue cloth interior, matching topper, factory rally wheels, 350 V8 engine, miles, one owner
C20	1961	69,000	P	$1,700	9/28/2013	NENE	Lambrecht Dealer auction, 4 speed manual, bench seat, rough condition, custom 3/4-ton, Apache
C20	1966		P	$1,700	9/28/2013	NENE	Lambrecht Dealer auction, manual 4 speed on the floor, 283 V8 engine, AM radio, vinyl bench seat, interior rough, no hood, rust, some parts missing
C20	1970	44,000	G	$4,000	9/28/2013	NENE	Lambrecht Dealer auction, 4 speed manual, vinyl bench
C20	1973	25,000	G	$1,400	9/28/2013	NENE	Lambrecht Dealer auction, dash pad cracked, V8 engine, auto
C20	1973	37,000	P	$1,450	9/28/2013	NENE	Lambrecht Dealer auction, manual 4 speed, vinyl bench, 6 cyl., rough
C20	1977		F	$2,100	9/28/2013	NENE	Lambrecht Dealer auction, automatic 350 V8 engine, bench seat, does not run
C30	1976		G	$1,350	11/24/2012	SEMN	1-ton dually, auto 8' steel bed, 454 engine
C30	1977		G	$1,250	7/18/2012	ECND	1-ton dually, 350 V8 engine, 4 speed, steel bed, fuel service unit, Knapheide tool boxes

Chevy

Model	Year	Miles	Condition	Price	Date	Area	Comments
C50	1967	94,000	G	$1,650	3/15/2014	ECKS	2-ton, 15' steel box, hoist, Knapheide, V8 gas
C50	1967	63,578	G	$2,500	9/28/2013	ECNE	16' steel box, scissors hoist, 327 V8 engine, 4x2 speed, dual fuel tanks, good rubber, one owner
C50	1967	44,000	G	$2,700	8/22/2012	Online	*BigIron.com,* item in Oklahoma, grain truck, 4 speed Hi/Lo, 327 cu. in. gas, 6-ply tube type, 16' bed, tarp cover, hyd. pump
C50	1967	99,000	G	$4,950	8/15/2012	Online	*PurpleWave.com,* item in Kansas grain truck, 6 cyl. gas, 8 speed split axle manual, heater, spring suspension, brush auger, 6" diameter
C50	1969		G	$1,500	7/17/2013	NEND	350 V8 engine, single axle, 4x2, Knapaheide 14' box and hoist, runs
C50	1969	81,000	G	$1,250	4/13/2013	SEMN	Grain truck, 350V8 engine, 4x2 speed, 16' box and hoist, single axle
C50	1969		G	$1,750	3/14/2012	WCNE	Grain truck, 5 speed, 16' steel box, tandem tag axle
C50	1970	40,000	F	$2,800	2/4/2014	WCOK	4x2 speed, 16' bed and hoist
C50	1970	93,518	G	$4,400	10/30/2013	Online	*PurpleWave.com,* item in Missouri, grain truck, 350 cu. in. V8 gas, 4 speed manual, 2 speed rear end
C50	1970	38,800	G	$2,700	12/28/2012	WCIL	2-ton grain truck, 350 engine, 13.5' bed, 52" sides, 4x2 transmission, new twin hoist installed recently for $5,000
C50	1970	30,214	G	$2,860	11/15/2012	Online	*PurpleWave.com,* item in Kansas, grain truck, 4 speed manual
C50	1970		G	$2,400	2/14/2012	WCNE	4x2 speed, 16' beet box, side hoist, side board lifters
C50	1970	10,000	G	$1,550	1/25/2012	Online	*BigIron.com,*iteminMinnesota,graintruck, standard, 350 cu. in. V8 gas, 14' grain box, rear grain door, hyd. hoist works
C50	1971		G	$2,200	7/31/2013	ECND	350, 15'x42" side steel box, wet kit
C50	1971		F	$2,500	2/12/2013	WCIL	Grain truck, 4x2 transmission, 13.5' bed
C50	1971		G	$1,700	8/4/2012	ECMN	Grain truck, 14' box and hoist, 4x2 speed, 6 cyl.
C50	1971	40,000	G	$1,700	5/23/2012	Online	*BigIron.com,* item in Kansas, 8 speed, 350 gas, single axle, Knapheide bed, passenger mirror missing
C50	1971		G	$1,600	3/28/2012	ECND	Single axle farm truck, 350 V8 engine, 4 speed, 13' box and hoist
C50	1972	50,000	G	$1,210	8/28/2013	Online	*PurpleWave.com,* item in Missouri, grain truck, 350 V8 gas, 5x2 speed rear end, heat, spring susp. seat, side DSCHG, 12'Lx92"W grain box
C50	1972		G	$1,250	2/23/2013	ECMI	Grain truck, single axle, 350 V8 engine, 4 speed, 2 speed axle, brakes lock up after some use
C60	1960	134,773	F	$2,800	3/14/2012	ECND	Tagtandem,350,5x2speed,39,000GVL
C60	1962		G	$1,600	1/17/2012	SCKS	Tandem axle grain truck, 20' box, 50" sides, wood floor, 2 cyl. hoist, tarp
C60	1963	57,000	G	$1,100	2/7/2012	WCOK	6 cyl., 4x2 speed, 16' steel box and hoist, hoist does not work, 350 bu., jumps out of reverse

TRUCKS

Chevy

Model	Year	Miles	Condition	Price	Date	Area	Comments
C60	1966		G	$3,000	4/11/2013	SEID	Bobtail, new 350 crate motor, 5x2 speed, 16' Williamsen box, rear hoist
C60	1969	36,592	G	$2,800	10/12/2013	NCMN	Single axle, 350, V8 engine, 4x2 speed, 14' steel box, hoist and fitting tarp
C60	1969		G	$1,100	8/14/2013	WCMN	Grain truck, 427, 6 speed, Allison auto, 18' wood grain box
C60	1969	60,000	G	$2,500	9/12/2012	Online	*IQBid.com,* item in North Dakota, tag axle tandem, 2T, 366 gas, 18' French 3-in-1 box, plumbed for drill fill
C60	1970	13,000	G	$1,105	1/22/2014	Online	*BigIron.com,* item in Oklahoma, 2x5 speed, V8 engine, single axle, speedometer not working
C60	1970	59,000	G	$2,000	7/25/2013	ECND	Single axle, pusher, gas, V8 engine, 5x2 transmission, 16' comb box and hoist, welded steel plate for grain
C60	1970		G	$3,800	7/17/2013	NEND	Twin screw tandem 366, 5x4 speed, Knapheide 18' box and hoist, roll tarp, VIN ME630P159398
C60	1970		E	$17,250	12/7/2012	SENE	Tandem twin screw, 5x4 speed, 427 engine, 18' steel box and new hoist, extra heavy frame
C60	1970	44,000	G	$9,500	5/5/2012	NCKS	Grain truck, 16' steel bed, roll over tarp, 366 V8 engine, 4x2 speed, good rubber
C60	1971	97,172	G	$4,750	7/31/2013	ECND	Custom, tag tandem, 366, 5x2 speed, 19' Westgo box, roll tarp
C60	1971		G	$6,250	11/28/2012	ECND	Tag tandem, 366, 5x2 speed, 20' frontier box, hoist, plumbed for drill fill, 9x20 tires
C60	1971	106,154	G	$3,000	3/3/2012	SEMN	Grain truck, 16' wooden box and hoist, Westfield hyd. brush auger, single axle, 4x2 speed
C60	1972		G	$2,750	8/14/2013	WCMN	18' steel box, roll tarp, air brakes, 5x4 transmission, 10x20 tires
C60	1972	110,000	G	$4,500	7/31/2013	ECND	Twin screw, 366 gas, 5x4 speed, 17' box, roll tarp
C60	1972		G	$4,250	4/26/2013	SWKY	2-ton
C60	1972		G	$3,250	11/29/2012	ECND	TAG axle grain truck, 427 engine, 5x2 speed, 19.5' frontier box
C60	1972		G	$15,000	1/19/2012	SCKS	2.5-ton tandem axle grain truck, 366, 4 barrel engine, 5x2 speed, 20' steel box, 52" sides, roll tarp, 50 gal. fuel tanks, hyd. brakes
C60	1973	91,000	G	$3,850	4/3/2013	Online	*BigIron.com,* item in Nebraska, 4x2 speed, 350 gas, 9x20 tires fuel tanker, 1,500 gal. cap, Neptune pump, 5 compartments, manifold, internal leaking
C60	1973		G	$4,500	3/22/2013	NESD	Grain truck, V8 gas, 4x2 speed, 16' box and hoist, single axle
C60	1973		F	$2,300	3/2/2013	ECMN	Cabover grain truck V8 gas, 14' box and hoist, 4x2 speed, new tires
C60	1973	31,000	G	$8,000	12/1/2012	NCMO	Straight truck small block V8 engine, 4x2 speed, 17' bed, scissor hoist, endgate brush auger

Model	Year	Miles	Condition	Price	Date	Area	Comments
C60	1973	36,211	G	$8,000	6/27/2012	NEND	Single axle, 350, V8 engine, 4x2 speed, 15' Westeel box, hoist and roll tarp
C60	1973		G	$2,255	5/30/2012	Online	*PurpleWave.com,* item in Kansas, feed truck, 360 cu. in. V8 gas, 4 speed manual, 2 speed rear end, JD 18' Chuck wagon feed bed, rear and side delivery, live bottom
C60	1973	18,000	G	$5,001	5/9/2012	Online	*BigIron.com,* item in Nebraska, straight truck, 16' steel box, 5x2 transmission, 350 cu. in. gas, 1 hyd., single axle, PTO, sides and floor, Shur-Lok roll over tarp, hoist, PS, heater, radio
C60	1973		G	$1,050	4/25/2012	Online	*BigIron.com,* item in Nebraska, boom truck, 5x2 transmission, V8 gas, single axle, 20' hyd. Prentice boom
C60	1974	23,216	G	$5,500	4/11/2014	ECND	Single axle, 350, 4x2 speed, frontier 14' box, hoist, plumbed for drill fill
C60	1974	81,361	G	$2,700	1/15/2014	ECIL	Grain truck 350 engine, 5x2 speed, 14' bed, tarp
C60	1974	71,332	G	$2,700	1/15/2014	ECIL	Grain truck, 350 engine, 4x2 speed, 12.5' bed, stock rack
C60	1974	59,515	G	$1,300	12/4/2013	ECND	Single axle, 350, 16' box, hoist, roll tarp
C60	1974	50,772	G	$7,000	3/29/2013	SCMT	366 V8 engine, 4x2 speed, 17' Maxey box, twin cyl. hoist, silage sides, cattle rack, silage/grain endgate, auto closer, 9x20, dual fuel tanks, one owner
C60	1974	94,000	G	$1,750	2/12/2013	WCIL	Grain truck, 16' box, good tires
C60	1974	63,000	G	$4,800	1/11/2013	ECIL	350 engine, 4x2 speed, 14' Midwest grain bed, green
C60	1974	72,500	G	$4,500	12/1/2012	NWIL	14' box, good paint, no rust
C60	1974	79,000	G	$1,045	11/27/2012	Online	*PurpleWave.com,* item in Kansas flatbed pickup, custom gas, 4 speed manual, heat, AM/FM, MW, ML, vinyl interior, Chelsea PTO
C60	1974	16,000	G	$2,500	9/13/2012	Online	*IQBid.com,* item in Iowa, grain truck, 4' box hoist
C60	1974	45,382	G	$6,100	6/14/2012	SEND	Single axle, 350 V8 engine, 4x2 speed, 15' Midwest box, hoist
C60	1974	51,000	G	$2,695	5/2/2012	Online	*PurpleWave.com,* item in Kansas grain truck, 350 V8 gas, 5 speed, split axle, heater, AM radio, MW, ML, vinyl bench seat, 20' bed, 40" sides
C60	1974		G	$5,250	3/14/2012	ECND	Single axle, 366, 4x2 speed, box, hoist
C60	1975	65,959	G	$10,850	12/18/2013	Online	*BigIron.com,* 4x2 speed, 350 engine, day cab, 16' diamond tread steel bed
C60	1975		F	$1,100	12/13/2013	NCMO	Truck, 10' flatbed and MY-D Handi 60 bu. cake feeder
C60	1975		G	$4,000	7/31/2013	ECND	350, 4 speed 15' box, hoist
C60	1975		G	$4,000	7/31/2013	ECND	Single axle, 350 engine, 4 speed, 15' box, hoist
C60	1975	44,000	G	$3,000	4/3/2013	NEND	Grain truck, V8 engine, 4x2 speed, 15' steel box, hoist, roll tarp, swinging endgate, tip tops

TRUCKS

Chevy

Model	Year	Miles	Condition	Price	Date	Area	Comments
C60	1975		G	$8,700	8/14/2012	SWMN	Twin screw, 5x4 speed, 19' Crysteel box, poly floor, roll tarp
C60	1975	50,000	G	$2,000	8/8/2012	SEND	Single axle, 350 V8 engine, 4x2 speed, 14' Midwest box, hoist, roll tarp
C60	1975		G	$3,200	3/17/2012	SEMN	Single axle grain truck, Allison auto, 350 V8 engine, engine only 2 years
C60	1976	59,700	G	$5,250	12/3/2013	NWNE	Grain truck, 4x2 speed, 16' box, Westfield drill filler auger
C60	1976	46,196	G	$5,450	11/30/2013	ECIL	Single axle, grain truck, 350 gas, 4x2 speed, metal grain box, 15' long, 4' tall, 1 owner
C60	1976		G	$1,550	9/10/2013	Online	Single axle, 16' box, hoist, roll tarp
C60	1976	16,909	G	$2,900	7/3/2013	Online	*BigIron.com,* item in Nebraska, dump truck, 4 speed manual, 2 speed axle, V8 gas
C60	1976	63,000	G	$4,750	4/3/2013	Online	*BigIron.com,* item in Nebraska, grain truck, 4x2 transmission, V8 gas, 9x20 rear tires, 8.25x20 front tires, Omaha standard lift hoist, pusher axle
C60	1976	37,322	G	$5,750	11/29/2012	ECIL	Grain truck, 14' Midwest bed and hoist, 4x2 speed
C60	1976		G	$1,200	8/21/2012	WCIL	Grain truck, 350 engine, 4x2 speed
C60	1976	34,493	G	$8,500	6/27/2012	NEND	Single axle, 350, V8 engine, 4x2 speed, 16' grain Master box, hoist and roll tarp, Pintle Hitch
C60	1976	71,000	G	$7,500	5/5/2012	NCKS	Grain truck, 16' steel bed, rollover tarp, 366, V8 engine, 4x2 speed, good rubber
C60	1976		G	$11,000	3/20/2012	WCIL	Grain truck, 13.5 Knapheide bed, 350 engine, 4x2 speed
C60	1976		F	$2,500	2/6/2012	ECIL	14' Midwest bed, engine OH in 2008
C60	1977		G	$4,000	3/26/2014	NEMO	350 new Reman engine, 4x2 speed, 16' grain bed w/ good wooden floor
C60	1977	45,719	G	$13,500	12/7/2013	NCOH	13' Knapheide bed, twin cyl. hoist, double gate doors, small unload doors
C60	1977		G	$1,800	7/28/2012	SWTN	Single axle dump, 350 gas, 5x2 transmission, Heil 10' bed
C60	1977	64,000	G	$6,301	5/23/2012	Online	*BigIron.com,* item in Kansas grain truck, 5x2 speed, 350 gas, 1 hyd., single axle, 14' Omaha standard bed, 52" steel sides, wood floor, hoist, power steering
C60	1977	24,000	G	$1,705	5/11/2012	Online	*PurpleWave.com,* item in Kansas utility truck, V8 gas, 4 speed manual, Hi/Lo, heater, cassette player, MW, ML, vinyl bench seat
C60	1978	58,000	G	$1,600	8/20/2013	WCIL	Single axle grain truck, 16' steel grain bed, V8 engine, 4x2 transmission
C60	1978		G	$3,750	8/20/2013	WCIL	16' box
C60	1978	5,126	G	$1,800	9/13/2012	SEIA	350, auto, Pelican II 36' boom/ manlift, Knapheide box
C60	1979		G	$7,000	2/4/2014	NWNE	350, V8 engine, 4x2 speed, single rear axle, 16' beet box, Harsh rear hoist
C60	1979		G	$1,500	3/30/2013	SCMN	16' flatbed, 350 V8 engine, 4 speed, pusher axle
C60	1979		F	$1,500	3/30/2013	NWIL	Flatbed, hoist
C60	1979	34,100	G	$5,000	11/7/2012	SCNE	4x2 speed, Omaha standard 16' box and hoist, one owner

Chevy

Model	Year	Miles	Condition	Price	Date	Area	Comments
C60	1979		G	$2,100	8/4/2012	ECMN	14' wood box and hoist, grain truck, single axle, 366 V8 engine, 4x2 speed
C60	1979	60,000	F	$1,100	7/25/2012	Online	*BigIron.com,* item in Kansas dump truck, 4x2 speed axle, 350 gas, power steering, steel rims
C65	1973	60,000	G	$9,000	2/17/2014	WCNE	18' grain box, R hoist, tag axle, roll tarp, full endgate, grain gate, clean
C65	1973		F	$2,900	10/26/2013	SEKS	Grain truck, all steel Hillsboro grain bed and hoist, 9x20 tires, 5x2 speed
C65	1973	49,020	F	$1,155	10/16/2013	Online	*PurpleWave.com,* item in Kansas, box truck, 8 cylinder gas, 5 speed, 2 speed rear end
C65	1973	10,000	G	$2,700	8/20/2013	WCIL	Single axle grain truck, Rem 366 engine, radial tires, 5x2 transmission, 16' Omaha steel grain bed, tarp
C65	1973		G	$7,250	7/31/2013	ECND	Tag tandem, 366, 5x2 speed, 19' frontier box, Shur-Lok roll tarp
C65	1973		F	$1,126	4/3/2013	Online	*BigIron.com,* item in Colorado, tandem truck, 5x4 transmission, 366 engine, 10x20 tires, 22' bed
C65	1973		F	$2,100	3/9/2013	SWMN	Tandem axle, wood grain box, hoist, V8
C65	1973		G	$6,000	11/28/2012	ECND	Twin screw, 3x5 speed, 20' box, roll tarp
C65	1973	83,000	G	$4,750	8/21/2012	SENE	18' box, 48" sides, Cheater axle, 366 V8 engine, 5x2 transmission, one owner
C65	1973		G	$4,800	1/11/2012	Online	*BigIron.com,* item in Nebraska, grain truck, 5x2 transmission, 427 V8 4-barrel gas, 218" WB, 90"Wx20'L, 52" side height, 550 bu. box, rear tandem is air tag, air brakes
C65	1974		G	$1,950	12/5/2013	SCIA	Tandem grain truck
C65	1974		G	$3,500	4/3/2013	NEND	Tandem farm truck, tag axle, 366 engine, 5x2 transmission, 20' Westgo box, hoist, Shurco roll tarp, pump, hose reel, rear deck
C65	1974		F	$2,200	3/9/2013	SWMN	Tandem axle, 18' Crysteel box, tag axle, V8 engine, 5x2 speed, power steering
C65	1974		F	$2,800	3/9/2013	SWMN	Tandem axle, air tag axle, 18' steel box, hoist, V8 engine, 5x2 speed, power steering
C65	1974	116,000	G	$2,750	12/10/2012	ECIL	366 V8 engine, propane, 4x2 speed, 14' Schien bed, center post hoist
C65	1974	80,000	G	$4,250	11/28/2012	ECND	Lift tag tandem, 366, 5x2 speed, 20' frontier box, hoist, plumbed for drill fill, 9x20 tires
C65	1974		F	$1,250	9/13/2012	SEIA	Grain truck, 16' box
C65	1974	1,646	G	$10,030	9/12/2012	Online	*IQBid.com,* item in Minnesota, twin screw tandem, 427 V8 engine, Allison auto, 20' box, twin cyl. hoist, TRS roll tarp, plumbed for drill fill, spring ride, air brakes, mud scrapers
C65	1974	67,000	G	$3,500	8/8/2012	Online	*BigIron.com,* item in Nebraska, grain truck, 5x2 transmission, 427 cu. in. gas, single axle, 19'wood box, Schwartz hoist, stock racks

Chevy

Model	Year	Miles	Condition	Price	Date	Area	Comments
C65	1974	91,000	G	$1,705	5/9/2012	Online	*PurpleWave.com,* item in Kansas custom deluxe truck, 366 V8 gas, 13 speed manual, heater, AM radio, CB unit, vinyl interior, air brakes
C65	1974	83,487	G	$8,500	4/12/2012	NWMN	Twin screw, 427, fuller 13 speed, air brakes, 20' loadline box, hoist, combo gate
C65	1975	15,000	G	$3,000	12/12/2013	IRON	Grain truck, tandem axle, 366, 5x2, dump bed, /swing doors, roll tarp,
C65	1975		G	$2,000	12/5/2013	SCIA	Tandem grain truck, roll top coverR
C65	1975	15,200	F	$1,100	9/12/2013	SEIA	Tandem axle grain truck, 20' box
C65	1975	40,000	G	$4,700	7/31/2013	ECND	Single axle, 16' box, twin cyl. hoist, one owner
C65	1975	79,800	G	$2,500	7/17/2013	NEND	Twin screw, 427, automatic, Knapheide 19' box/hoist
C65	1975		G	$4,750	7/1/2013	NEND	Tag tandem, 366 V8 engine, 5x2 speed, 20' steel box, hoist, roll tarp
C65	1975	81,021	G	$4,351	4/24/2013	Online	*BigIron.com,* item in Nebraska, 366 gas, straight truck, 2,600 gal. poly tank
C65	1975	67,000	G	$5,750	3/30/2013	SCMN	Twin screw, parkhurst box, 427 V8 engine, 5x4 transmission, tarp, 10x20 rubber
C65	1975	48,000	G	$3,850	7/25/2012	Online	*PurpleWave.com,* item in Kansas grain truck, 8 speed split axle manual, heat, bench seat, spring suspension, 2-stage cyl. hoist, hyd. driven auger
C65	1975	45,115	G	$11,500	6/14/2012	SEND	Lift tag tandem, 366 V8 engine, 5x2 speed, 19.5' frontier box, hoist, roll tarp

It has been the people I've met that has been the most fun in covering machinery for the past 25 years. For example, Nancy Reed of Sidell, Ill., reached out via email looking for help to sell her beloved 1965 Chevy 60 grain truck.

Just as with old tractors, many folks such as Nancy develop emotional connections to farm trucks. Nancy learned to drive this truck standing up as a 10-year-old girl under the watchful eye of her father, Kenneth Hogan. Nancy, now a retired school teacher, wasn't concerned at all with how much the truck sold for; she wanted help in finding the right home with a buyer who would appreciate the truck's history. This truck was so special it even had a name, "Jenny 2." Jenny 1 was a 1947 green dome-nosed Chevy that Kenneth had bought new.

PETE'S PICK

I'm happy to report Nancy did find the right buyer, a man from just a few miles down the road who owns a detailing shop. Jenny 2 would get a nice makeover and spend the coming years just hauling some grain five miles to the local elevator. There's a happy buyer and a happy seller.

TRUCKS

Chevy

Model	Year	Miles	Condition	Price	Date	Area	Comments
C65	1975		G	$4,500	3/22/2012	ECMN	Tag tandem, V8 engine, 5x2 speed, 20' box, tarp
C65	1975	56,000	G	$3,500	2/25/2012	WCMI	Dump truck, gas, 5x2 Eaton manual, 18' midwest grain box, Shur-Lok roll tarp, new floor, twin cyl. hoist, vacuum booster and lines
C65	1976		G	$10,500	2/4/2014	NWNE	Twin screw, 366, V8 engine, 13 speed Eaton, 20' Freeman slip body, 52" sides, hyd. endgate, scissor hoist
C65	1976	24,000	G	$11,500	9/21/2013	SEMN	Grain truck, V8 engine, 5x2 transmission, single axle, 2 way hoist, 16' steel box, wood floor
C65	1976		G	$2,250	8/14/2013	WCMN	Tandem, 19' steel box, telescopic hoist 366 motor, 5x2 transmission
C65	1976		G	$5,500	4/3/2013	NEND	Twin screw, 427 V8 engine, 13 speed, 20' Hart, 3-in-1 combination box, hoist, tarp, 10x20 tires
C65	1976	39,366	G	$3,190	3/27/2013	Online	*PurpleWave.com,* item in Nebraska, grain truck, V8 gas, 5 speed manual, 2 speed rear end
C65	1976		G	$7,000	11/28/2012	ECND	Lift tag, 366, 5 speed, 20' frontier box, roll tarp, 11Rx22.5 radial tires
C65	1976		G	$6,000	11/24/2012	WCIL	Grain truck
C65	1976	85,337	G	$1,800	7/18/2012	ECND	Lift tag, 427 engine
C65	1976		G	$7,250	4/10/2012	NEND	Single axle, 366 engine, 5 speed, 2 speed rear end
C65	1977	47,000	G	$5,300	1/22/2014	Online	*BigIron.com,* item in Nebraska, grain truck, 24' box, 5x2 transmission, gas, tandem axle, wood floor, steel sides, hyd. brakes, power steering
C65	1977	50,000	G	$10,000	7/31/2013	ECND	Twin screw, 477, V8 engine, Allison auto, 19.5' box, roll tarp, beet endgate, drill fill augers
C65	1977	56,268	G	$7,501	5/22/2013	Online	*BigIron.com,* item in Iowa, grain truck, 5 speed split shift, L 366, V8 engine, day cab, 20' bed
C65	1977	71,000	G	$2,175	4/3/2013	Online	*IQBid.com,* single axle, V8 gas, 5x2 speed, flatbed, 10x22.5 tires
C65	1977	89,600	G	$4,500	2/26/2013	ECIL	Grain truck, 15' bed, 5x2 speed
C65	1977	127K	G	$10,750	2/21/2013	ECMI	Live tandem grain truck, Benders 18' metal grain box and single post hoist, 366 V8 engine, 5x3 speed
C65	1977	80,781	G	$20,500	2/19/2013	WCIL	Grain truck, Custom Deluxe twin cyl., twin screw, tandem axle, 13 speed, 427 engine, 20' bed
C65	1977	47,068	F	$3,000	1/17/2013	ECNE	Air brakes, 427 engine, 5 speed, single axle, flatbed, spoke, 10x20 tires
C65	1977		G	$4,250	11/24/2012	WCIL	Grain truck
C65	1977	45,000	E	$7,100	9/1/2012	SWIA	One owner, always shedded, 366 engine, 16' Omaha standard box and hoist
C65	1977	50,000	G	$10,500	8/21/2012	WCIL	Grain truck, 366 engine, 5x2 transmission, tag axle, roll tarp
C65	1977		G	$7,500	2/18/2012	ECIL	Gas grain truck, tandem, air brakes, twin screw, hoist, Eaton 15 speed

TRUCKS

Chevy

Model	Year	Miles	Condition	Price	Date	Area	Comments
C65	1978	57,000	G	$5,750	3/15/2014	ECKS	2-ton, 16' steel box and hoist, 5x2 transmission, V8 gas
C65	1978		G	$3,700	12/18/2013	Online	*BigIron.com,* 5x4 transmission, 427 V8 engine, 20' bed, twin cylinder Harsh hoist, Shur-Loc tarp, double framed twin screw
C65	1978		F	$1,500	11/7/2013	WCMI	Single axle, 16' Dahlman potato box, V8 gas, 5x4 speed, VIN 159370
C65	1978		G	$6,000	8/20/2013	WCIL	Tandem axle grain truck, 9 speed, 18' aluminum bed, cargo doors, roll tarp
C65	1978		G	$8,500	11/29/2012	ECND	Tandem twin screw, 427, 5x4, 20' strong box, head lift hoist, 3 PC combo endgate and roll tarp
C65	1978	35,200	G	$13,500	11/10/2012	NWOH	Grain truck, 427, 5x2 speed, 20' grain bed, scissors, hoist tag axle
C65	1978		G	$8,500	9/7/2012	ECMO	Grain truck, air tag, 427 V8 gas, single drive axle, 5x2 speed, 18' Knapheide, grain bed, hoist, 52" steel sides, 12" steel extensions, 10x20 tires
C65	1978	106,000	G	$5,200	7/27/2012	SWKY	Tandem, 427 13 speed, twin screw, 20' bed and hoist
C65	1978	40,614	G	$8,000	3/23/2012	WCNE	Grain truck, 10x20 front, 11.1x20 rear, good tubber, tandem tag axle, 18' steel box, 52" sides, 5x2 speed, clean
C65	1978	82,000	F	$1,600	2/7/2012	WCOK	Feed truck, 5x2 speed, V8 engine, BJM silage box, needs augers and liners
C70	1975	3,000	G	$5,000	12/13/2012	WCIA	Rebuilt transmission, 3116 Cat, 18' aluminum box, roll tarp, 11x22.5 drivers, 305/65Rx22.5 steering axle
C70	1975	248,000	G	$2,250	3/9/2012	ECMN	Tandem, duals, 10 speed, air brakes, tilt
C70	1976		G	$12,000	10/25/2012	NEND	Tandem twin screw, 427, auto, nearly new custom built steel 20' stake pocket flatbed, 2010 Conveyall BT290 seed tender
C80	1962	9,000	G	$1,900	8/15/2013	ECMN	TAG axle, V8 gas, 5x2 speed, air brakes, 18' steel box, 10x20 tires
C80	1965	39,000	G	$4,575	1/9/2013	Online	*BigIron.com,* item in Nebraska, grain truck, 5 speed, 2 speed axle, Chevy gas, tandem axle, 18' steel box, wood floor, 2-way hoist, air brakes
C95	1975		G	$4,200	8/30/2012	SEMN	Grain truck
C1500	1966	133	G	$1,073	10/2/2013	Online	*PurpleWave.com,* item in Missouri, 327 cu. in. 8 cyl. gas, 3 speed manual
Cameo	1958	1.3	G	$140,000	9/28/2013	NENE	Lambrecht Dealer auction, 6 cyl., half-ton, 2WD, fiberglass box sides
CE6	1973	96,000	G	$3,125	5/9/2012	Online	*BigIron.com,* item in Nebraska, straight truck, 5x2 speed, 366 gas, 16' Obeco steel box, wood floor, 54" sides, twin cyl., lights work, engine OH at 78,000 miles
Cheyenne	1972		G	$18,500	4/2/2012	WCIL	Super K 20 4WD pickup, 454 V8 engine, 4 speed, great build
Cheyenne	1976	4	F	$20,000	9/28/2013	NENE	Lambrecht Dealer auction, V8 engine, half-ton, vinyl bench, carpet, needs work

Chevy

Model	Year	Miles	Condition	Price	Date	Area	Comments
Cheyenne	1977		G	$2,100	4/1/2013	WCIL	Areas of rust
CST 10	1970		G	$7,500	4/1/2013	WCIL	
Fleetside	1963	80,000	G	$6,000	9/28/2013	NENE	Lambrecht Dealer auction, 6 cyl., manual, 3 speed, some rust, AM radio, bench seat, MW, ML
Fleetside	1975	68,750	G	$8,000	4/1/2013	WCIL	Half-ton, 4x4, V6, snowplow, hookups minus the plow
K30	1969	76,000	F	$1,650	12/16/2013	NWWI	Cassette player, CB radio, alum. rims, scratches and dings
Scotsdale	1976	10,000	F	$6,250	9/28/2013	NENE	Lambrecht Dealer auction, automatic, vinyl bench, glass broke, rust
Viking	1959		F	$1,500	3/14/2012	ECND	Single axle, box, hoist, 3 PC endgate

Diamond

Model	Year	Miles	Condition	Price	Date	Area	Comments
921T	1953	44,313	G	$7,040	10/3/2012	Online	*PurpleWave.com,* item in Missouri, deluxe semi truck, Cummins 6 cyl. diesel, 220 hp, 5 speed

Dodge

Model	Year	Miles	Condition	Price	Date	Area	Comments
500	1965		G	$2,900	8/8/2012	Online	*BigIron.com,* item in Colorado, gas, straight truck, 5 speed, single axle PTO, tag, 16' Freeman box
500	1968		G	$1,400	4/10/2012	ECND	Single axle, V8 engine, 4x2 speed, 14' box, hoist, roll tarp
500	1970		G	$4,400	3/8/2014	NEMO	Grain truck, roll tarp, 13' Knapheide, 318 motor, 4x2 transmission
600	1974	53,200	G	$2,300	7/11/2013	SCMN	Tandem tag axle grain truck, 318 gas, tag axle, 4x2 speed, 15.5 box and hoist, 5' high
600	1975		G	$2,500	3/26/2014	Online	*BigIron.com,* item in Nebraska, 4 speed manual, 361 cu. in. engine
600	1975	57,000	G	$3,100	11/13/2012	NCIA	Grain truck, tag axle, miles, 2nd owner
800	1965		G	$1,300	12/15/2012	WCMI	Gas, 5x3 speed, 20' box
D350	1977	39,000	G	$3,760	2/9/2012	Online	*IQBid.com*
D600	1974	44,006	G	$2,001	12/18/2013	Online	*BigIron.com,* 4x2 transmission, 318 V8 engine, 16' box bed, new radiator
D600	1974	24,594	E	$5,750	8/11/2012	SEMN	Single axle grain truck, 360 V8 engine, 5x2 speed, 16' box and hoist, steel sides, wood floor, white, 1 owner
N80	1974		G	$6,300	5/1/2013	Online	*BigIron.com,* item in Kansas, 10 speed, Cummins V8 diesel, 11Rx22.5 tires, tandem axle, 20' steel grain box, Shur-Lok rollover tarp, twin scissor hoist
N80	1974		G	$6,300	5/1/2013	Online	*BigIron.com,* item in Kansas, odometer inoperable, 10 speed, Cummins V8 diesel
T24	1952	18,552	G	$3,520	10/8/2013	Online	*PurpleWave.com,* item in Kansas, 6 cyl. gas, 4 speed, 4WD

TRUCKS

Dodge

Model	Year	Miles	Condition	Price	Date	Area	Comments
W200	1977	51,748	G	$2,365	9/11/2012	Online	*PurpleWave.com,* item in Oklahoma, flatbed pickup, 318 cu. in. gas, auto, 4WD
WP435	1972	75,000	F	$1,025	7/11/2012	Online	*IQBid.com,* item in Wyoming, 16' flatbed, V8 gas, 4 speed with splitter, 4' side rails wood deck, PTO driven end dump

Ford

Model	Year	Miles	Condition	Price	Date	Area	Comments
100	1970	76,000	E	$3,400	3/24/2012	SEOH	Custom, long bed, only 3 speed
600	1963	82,802	G	$1,800	4/10/2012	ECND	Tilt cab tag tandem, 330 V8 engine, 4x2 speed, 16' Knapheide box, hoist, roll tarp
600	1967		G	$1,400	3/8/2014	NEMO	Grain truck, 16' bed, tag axle, Vin 73985
600	1967	46,906	G	$1,400	6/19/2013	Online	*BigIron.com,* item in Nebraska, dump truck, 4x2 transmission, 6 cyl. gas
600	1967		G	$1,200	8/21/2012	WCIL	Dump truck
600	1968	35,000	F	$1,300	2/27/2014	NWNE	Gas, V8 engine, 4x2 speed, 16' beet box, side hoist, 1,400 gal. tank and pump
600	1969	28,000	F	$1,500	2/4/2012	ECSC	Dump truck
600	1971	15,583	G	$3,510	5/1/2013	Online	*BigIron.com,* item in Wyoming, 5 speed, V8 engine
600	1972	80,000	G	$1,700	3/26/2013	ECND	Single axle, V8 engine, 5x2 speed, 14' Westgo box, 9x20 tires
600	1972		G	$2,200	2/21/2013	ECMI	Single axle, Kilbros 350 gravity box extensions, 112 hyd. fertilizer auger, poly flighting, 330 V8 gas, 5x2 speed
600	1974	40,000	G	$2,000	2/12/2013	WCIL	Grain truck, 16' box
600	1975	78,724	G	$2,860	6/27/2012	Online	*PurpleWave.com,* item in Kansas, tow truck, Ford 8 cyl. gas, 5x2 manual
600	1976	100,000	G	$1,400	2/12/2013	WCIL	Grain truck, tag axle, 13.5' bed
600	1981	66,000	G	$3,650	2/15/2012	IRON	4x2 transmission, 370 gas, single axle, 10-ton dry box, roll tarp, hyd. auger raises/lowers, cab and box rust
700	1966		G	$1,100	11/27/2013	ECSD	22' box hoist, scissor lift, lift tag, 330, V8 engine, 5x2 speed
700	1971		G	$7,100	2/17/2014	WCNE	18' Midwest grain box, 50" sides, clean
700	1973		G	$2,000	8/14/2013	WCMN	Tandem, 19' steel box, hoist, V8 361, 5x2 transmission, roll tarp, 3 piece endgate
700	1975		G	$1,500	3/20/2012	WCIL	Grain truck, 16' bed, 5x2 transmission
700	1978		G	$4,250	1/11/2013	NWIN	Cabover grain truck, 460 engine, 5 speed, Knapheide 16' grain bed and hoist, white
750	1974		F	$1,200	2/23/2013	ECMI	Grain ready dump truck, gas, 10 speed, 300 bushel box
750	1974	44,000	G	$6,200	6/20/2012	Online	*BigIron.com,* item in Wyoming, boom truck, miles, 5x2 transmission, 392 V8 gas, tandem axle, Hydra-Lift boom, 37' reach, tool box, snarcs
750	1975	80,792	G	$2,500	7/18/2012	ECND	Louisville, tag tandem, 391 gas, box and hoist, new roll tarp

Ford

Model	Year	Miles	Condition	Price	Date	Area	Comments
750	1976	12,000	F	$1,300	2/15/2012	IRON	5x2 transmission, 361 gas, single axle, PTO, 2 compartments, side dump box, stabilizer jacks, rear hitch
800	1971		G	$18,100	8/1/2012	NWMN	Twin screw, 19' box and hoist, Ford diesel, 10x20 rubber
800	1972		G	$2,200	12/15/2012	WCMI	Live tandem, gas, 5x3 speed, 20' potato box
800	1973	71,000	G	$3,350	4/3/2013	Online	*IQBid.com,* tandem axle dump truck, V8 gas, 5x4 speed, 12' box, 10x20 tires
800	1974		G	$14,500	3/22/2014	ECMI	Live tandem grain truck, late Missouri, 20' metal grain body, twin post hoist, 534 V8 gas, fuller 13 speed, air brakes, 10x20 rubber, VIN S912VT09364
800	1974		G	$5,000	7/31/2013	ECND	Tandem axle, 16' dual manure spreader box
800	1975	88,000	G	$2,800	2/15/2012	IRON	5x2 transmission, diesel, single axle, custom cab, AM radio, fiberglass tank approx. 1,600 gal, adj. rear hitch
800			P	$1,300	3/2/2013	NETN	No engine
880	1974		G	$3,750	12/4/2013	ECND	Twin screw, 477 gas, 5x4 speed, 19' Westgo box, hoist, roll tarp, 10x20 tires
880	1975	36,131	G	$3,600	8/29/2013	NWIA	Tandem twin screw dump truck, small block gas, roll tarp, not actual miles
880	1976		F	$3,000	3/14/2012	ECND	Tag tandem, 475 gas, 5x2 speed, 18' box, hoist
900	1971		G	$13,000	11/7/2013	NEND	Tandem twin screw, 534 gas V8 engine, Allison auto, 20' strong box, hoist, roll tarp, beet equipment
900	1974	79,000	G	$3,750	11/28/2012	ECND	Tandem axle, 534 V8 gas, 5x2 speed, 18' Knapheide box, hoist, roll tarp, 10x20 tires
7000	1973		G	$3,500	7/25/2013	ECND	Tag tandem, Cat diesel, 5x2 speed, 12-ton dry fertilizer tender, rear dischange auger
7000	1977		G	$4,575	6/13/2012	Online	*BigIron.com,* item in Kansas manual 5 speed, 3208 Cat diesel, single axle, 16' grain bed, hoist, new floor, always shedded
8000	1972		G	$2,000	4/5/2012	SCND	Service truck, single axle, 1160 Cat diesel, 6x13 transmission, short wheel base, steel service body, gas, air compressor
8000	1973	46,000	G	$8,000	3/26/2013	ECND	Twin screw, 3208 Cat, 10 speed, spring ride, 18' loadline box, hoist, roll tarp, plumbed for drill fill, 11x22.5 tires on steel
8000	1974		G	$2,700	7/31/2013	ECND	Cab and chassis, 391 gas, 5x2 speed, for 20' box
8000	1974	86,791	G	$2,255	11/13/2012	Online	*PurpleWave.com,* item in Missouri, winch truck, Cat 1160 V8 diesel, 13 speed manual
8000	1975		G	$1,800	12/15/2012	WCMI	Live tandem, 5x2 speed, 3208 Cat diesel, 20' potato box

TRUCKS

Ford

Model	Year	Miles	Condition	Price	Date	Area	Comments
8000	1976	78,000	G	$2,500	9/19/2012	Online	*BigIron.com,* item in Kansas dump truck, 24 speed, 636 Cat diesel, air brakes, twin screw rear differential, 13' Galion box
8000	1976	6,000	G	$2,800	6/8/2012	ECMN	Flatbed dually, 3208 Cat engine, rebuilt turbo, 2 speed rear end, tilt bed, hyd. winch on bed, air brakes, air ride seat
8000	1977	348,583	G	$1,925	6/28/2012	Online	*PurpleWave.com,* item in Missouri, dump truck, Cat 3208 engine, road ranger 13 speed manual, twin screw
8000	1978		G	$2,000	6/13/2012	NWMN	Tandem twin screw dump truck. 3208 Cat engine, 13 speed
8000	1978		G	$5,000	6/13/2012	NWMN	Tandem twin screw dump truck w/ 3208 Cat engine, 13 speed
9000	1973	356,000	F	$1,500	3/24/2012	SWMI	Single axle flatbed, Detroit diesel engine, 10 speed
9000	1974	217,368	G	$8,000	3/4/2014	ECND	Twin screw cab and chassis, super 250 Cummins, 10 speed, Berts 18' flatbed, 3,000 gal. fiberglass tank
9000	1974		G	$6,063	8/22/2012	Online	*BigIron.com,* item in Nebraska, 9 speed, 6 cyl. diesel, spring ride, air brakes, pintle hitch, 22' box, 600 BU
9000	1975	231,000	G	$12,751	1/18/2012	Online	*BigIron.com,* item in Wyoming, 13 speed, diesel, tandem axle, 180" WB, full rear fenders, sliding 5th wheel plate, jake brake
9000	1976	512,000	G	$29,000	11/28/2012	ECND	Twin screw, air, up/down 3rd axle, 855 Cummins, 9 speed, 24' strong box, hoist, roll tarp, plumbed for drill fill, spring ride, dual fuel tanks
9000	1977	180,799	G	$2,290	6/5/2013	Online	*BigIron.com,* item in Nebraska, tandem axle, 3,200 gal. tank, manual, Detroit 6 cyl. diesel
9000	1977	551,000	G	$23,000	11/28/2012	ECND	Twin screw, air, up/down 3rd axle, 855 Cummins, 9 speed, 24' strong box, hoist, roll tarp, plumbed for drill fill, spring ride, dual fuel tanks
9000	1977	234,988	G	$6,710	4/25/2012	Online	*PurpleWave.com,* item in Nebraska, tandem axle grain truck, Cummins NTC290 engine, fuller road Ranger RT1110, 10 speed manual, diff. lock
C600	1954	85,000	G	$2,600	4/10/2013	SWMN	239 V8 engine, 4x2 transmission, 15' box and hoist
C600	1964	99,000	G	$2,450	8/8/2012	Online	*IQBid.com,* item in North Dakota, tilt cab, 330 V8 engine, 4x2 speed, 15' Kapco steel box, 2x20 tires
C600	1977	98,000	G	$1,100	3/14/2013	NENE	Single axle grain truck, LP propane engine, 5x2 speed, Unverferth 275 bu. gravity box, 10x20 tires
C700	1971	145,093	F	$1,275	3/24/2012	SCMN	Grain truck, LP motor, Cabover, 14' Omaha standard grain box, Schwartz hoist
C7000	1969	228,000	G	$7,600	8/22/2012	Online	*BigIron.com,* item in Nebraska, grain truck, 5 speed Hi/Lo, diesel, tandem axle, PTO, custom cab, 22'L, box, 60" sides, 60 gal. fuel tank

Ford

Model	Year	Miles	Condition	Price	Date	Area	Comments
C850	1967	197,000	G	$4,020	8/22/2012	Online	*BigIron.com,* item in Nebraska, super duty grain truck, 5x2 transmission, 539 Ford gas, tandem axle, 161" WB, 500 bu., 3 stage lift mast, roll tarp torn
CL9000	1978	533,000	F	$1,750	3/26/2013	ECND	290 Cummins, 10 speed, spring ride, 16' steel bed, two 125 bu. drill fills, 11x22.5 tires
F6	1948		F	$1,225	6/20/2012	Online	*BigIron.com,* item in Arizona, flatbed, single rear axle, metal grain rack, wood on steel, recent brake work, seat worn
F6	1951		F	$1,150	4/1/2013	WCIL	1.5-ton, 2 speed axle and hoist works, needs refreshed
F100	1954		G	$7,600	4/1/2013	WCIL	Solid, 454 V8
F100	1961		F	$1,540	5/2/2012	Online	*PurpleWave.com,* item in Kansas, 289 V8 gas, 4 speed manual, 4WD, heater, MW, ML, vinyl interior, rust
F100	1962	97,992	F	$3,410	8/22/2012	Online	*PurpleWave.com,* item in Nebraska, Unibody hot rod pickup, Mercury 292 V8 gas, 3 speed manual
F100	1968	89,000	G	$2,300	1/29/2014	Online	*BigIron.com,* item in Nebraska, 4x4, 4 speed, 360 engine, reg. cab, flatbed, 2 toolboxed, flatbed, hinged sides
F100	1970		G	$3,600	4/2/2012	WCIL	2WD, auto
F100	1974	30,000	G	$1,350	3/21/2013	WCNE	Pickup, 2WD, automatic, engine rebuild, CTB tool box,100 gal. diesel tank, runs good, straight
F100	1975	76,000	G	$2,900	9/28/2013	NENE	Lambrecht Dealer auction, 4x4, radio vinyl bench seat torn, AC, rust, damage
F100	1969	97,000	G	$2,450	4/1/2013	WCIL	Areas of some rust
F150	1976	86,000	F	$4,300	4/2/2012	WCIL	2WD, original condition, factory fitted original seat cover
F150	1977	17,000	G	$2,970	10/17/2012	Online	*PurpleWave.com,* item in Kansas, pickup, 400 V8 gas, C6 auto, 4WD, 205 transfer case, AC/heat, CD player
F150	1978		G	$2,100	12/4/2013	Online	*BigIron.com,* item in Nebraska, 3 speed, 15" American tires, reg. cab
F150	1978	33,507	F	$1,100	7/3/2013	Online	*BigIron.com,* item in Nebraska, half-ton, auto, V8 gas, reg. cab
F150	1978		F	$3,200	5/8/2013	Online	*BigIron.com,* item in Nebraska, 400 gas, Ranger Explorer, 4 speed manual
F250	1966		G	$5,300	4/1/2013	WCIL	Custom pickup, twin I-beam 250
F250	1973	55,524	G	$1,925	8/29/2013	Online	*PurpleWave.com,* item in Kansas, camper special gin pole, 360 cu. in. 8 cyl. gas, 4 speed manual
F250	1975	2,126	G	$10,890	9/10/2013	Online	*PurpleWave.com,* item in Kansas, utility truck, 360 V8 gas, 4 speed manual, 4WD, heat, MW, ML, vinyl interior, service body, tire chains
F250	1978		G	$3,700	8/10/2013	NCIA	Ranger, 400 CI V8 engine, 4x4, auto, lock out, nice, VIN F265LBK6838
F250	1978	21,000	G	$4,840	6/5/2012	Online	*PurpleWave.com,* item in Kansas, utility pickup, modified gas, auto, 4WD, heat, MW, ML, vinyl interior, reading utility bed, body rust, cosmetic damage

Ford

Model	Year	Miles	Condition	Price	Date	Area	Comments
F350	1964	72,753	G	$2,970	10/2/2013	Online	*PurpleWave.com,* item in Kansas, flatbed, 292 cu. in. V8 gas, 4 speed manual,
F350	1971		G	$4,000	4/1/2013	WCIL	Dually, flatbed, manual
F350	1972	9,000	G	$5,000	11/10/2012	NCNC	Camper special, AC, PS, PB, 390 CU, C6 automatic, sleeps 6
F350	1974	14,000	G	$1,200	6/13/2012	Online	*BigIron.com,* item in Colorado, dually pickup, service box, manual 4 speed, 360 gas
F350	1975	60,405	G	$4,300	8/24/2013	SEMN	Dually 2WD truck, 390 V8 engine, 4 speed
F350	1975	70,659	G	$5,100	10/25/2012	SCWI	1-ton, custom, 4 speed, 12' grain box hoist
F350	1977		E	$1,700	3/20/2013	NCOK	2WD, automatic, 460 V8 engine, J&I flatbed, 115 gal. aux. gas tank, elec pump, new paint and carb
F350	1977		G	$1,400	8/9/2012	NEIL	Flatbed
F600	1957	46,658	G	$4,990	12/10/2013	Online	*IQBid.com,* single axle, 14' box and hoist
F600	1958		G	$2,500	2/17/2014	WCNE	13.5' steel grain box, hoist
F600	1959		G	$1,700	11/10/2012	NCNC	352 cu. in., 4 speed, flatbed
F600	1959		F	$1,265	10/31/2012	Online	*PurpleWave.com,* item in Kansas truck cab and chassis, gas, 4 speed manual, heat, MW, vinyl interior, after market tachometer, PTO, 7' from cab to center of rear axle
F600	1960	73,000	G	$2,255	10/31/2012	Online	*PurpleWave.com,* item in Kansas custom cab dump bed grain truck, gas, 4 speed manual, 2 speed axle, heat, MW, vinyl intcrior, PTO, 13.5'Lx8'W flatbed, rear pin hitch
F600	1961	67,000	G	$1,250	7/18/2012	ECND	V8 engine, 4x2 speed, 14' strong box, hoist, roll tarp, Westfield Tailgate drill fill
F600	1964	55,000	G	$2,250	11/6/2012	ECOK	16' steel bed, V8 engine, 4x2 speed, new rear tires
F600	1964		G	$1,100	3/17/2012	SEMN	Single axle grain truck, 6 cyl., 4 speed, 15' wood box and hoist, DOT
F600	1967	60,089	G	$1,320	10/30/2013	Online	*PurpleWave.com,* item in Kansas, service truck, Cummins 555 cu. in. V8 diesel, 5 speed manual
F600	1967	30,187	G	$3,500	11/17/2012	NWMO	Custom cab, 13.5' combination I Obeco box and hoist
F600	1968		G	$1,700	3/8/2014	NEMO	Grain truck, 13' Knapheide bed, Westfield seed auger
F600	1968	87,281	G	$1,320	10/10/2012	Online	*PurpleWave.com,* item in Kansas, 361, V8 gas, 4 speed manual, 2 speed axle
F600	1970		G	$3,290	8/7/2013	Online	*IQBid.com,* single axle, 300 6 cyl., gas, 4x2 speed, PS, Knapheide 12' box, hoist and roll tarp, 9x20 tires
F600	1970		G	$1,400	7/31/2013	ECND	391, 5 speed, 16' Buffalo box, hoist, roll tarp
F600	1970	55,660	G	$2,500	7/31/2013	ECND	Tag tandem, 361 V8 engine, 5x2 speed, 17' Knapheide box, hoist, roll tarp
F600	1971		G	$3,700	7/1/2013	NEND	Single axle, V8 engine, 4x2 speed, dual compartment

Ford

Model	Year	Miles	Condition	Price	Date	Area	Comments
F600	1972		G	$3,000	1/24/2013	WCOH	Seed tender truck, 300 bu. gravity bed cap, brush auger
F600	1972	105,200	G	$1,400	4/20/2012	NWIA	Single axle, 4x2 speed, 16' wood box, stock rack and hoist
F600	1973	66,000	G	$1,500	12/26/2013	Online	*BigIron.com,* item in Nebraska, 4 speed/ 2 speed, 330 engine, 9x20 tires, 16' bed, grain door on back, double hoist, wood box
F600	1973		G	$1,800	8/20/2013	WCIL	Single axle grain truck, 390 engine, 14.5' steel grain bed
F600	1973	35,000	G	$9,200	4/10/2013	SWMN	330 V8 engine, 4x2 transmission, 13'6" box and hoist
F600	1973		G	$1,750	11/29/2012	ECND	Tag tandem, twin compartment, 240 bu. seed tender, 360 engine, 5x2 transmission, PTO wet kit and steel top
F600	1973	53,000	G	$4,700	7/25/2012	Online	*BigIron.com,* item in Nebraska, 1500 gal. fuel tank, 5 speed Hi/Lo, 9x20 tires
F600	1973	39,000	F	$1,400	2/4/2012	ECSC	
F600	1974	44,700	F	$3,500	1/25/2014	WCIN	Single axle grain truck, 14' Midwest steel bed (wooden floor - hole in floor) and twin cyl. hoist, 40" sides, 330HD V8 engine, 4x2 speed, lime green
F600	1974		G	$1,100	7/31/2013	ECND	
F600	1974	57,000	G	$4,500	11/28/2012	ECND	Single axle, 360 V8 engine, 15' steel box, hoist, Shur-loc roll tarp, plumbed for drill fill, 10x20 tires
F600	1975		F	$2,200	3/22/2014	SWMI	Single axle grain truck, Ford V8 gas, 5x2 speed, 13' bed, dump, brakes weak
F600	1975		G	$4,500	9/28/2013	NCKS	390 V8 engine, 4x2 speed, 16' bed, power up/down hoist, roll over tarp, plumbed for rear drill fill auger
F600	1975	68,000	G	$6,000	4/4/2013	Online	*IQBid.com,* V8 gas, 4x2 transmission, single axle, 16' steel box, wood floor, hoist, roll tarp, 9x20 tires
F600	1975	45,236	G	$2,700	2/23/2013	SENE	4x2 speed, 330 engine, 16' Knapheide steel box, 9x20 tires
F600	1975	50,000	F	$1,600	2/12/2013	WCIL	Grain truck, 15' bed, 4x2 transmission
F600	1975		G	$3,200	2/14/2012	WCNE	V8 engine, 4x2 speed, Freeman 16' beet box, side hoist, side board lifters
F600	1976	67,225	G	$3,100	5/22/2013	Online	*BigIron.com,* item in Iowa, grain truck 4 speed split shift, 391 HD V8 engine
F600	1976		G	$2,500	2/12/2013	WCIL	Grain truck, V8 engine, 4x2 speed
F600	1976		G	$2,900	9/29/2012	WCNE	16' box and hoist, rebuilt 4 speed
F600	1976	62,000	G	$3,950	8/21/2012	WCIL	Grain truck, 15' bed, 4x2 transmission, 9x20 tires, 361 engine
F600	1977	75,000	G	$1,358	9/19/2012	Online	*BigIron.com,* item in Kansas farm truck, dump bed, 4 speed, 300 CI gas, single axle, PTO, 13'x8' box, no endgate
F600	1978	62,000	P	$2,145	8/6/2013	Online	*PurpleWave.com,* item in Kansas dump truck, 8 cyl. gas, 4 speed manual, 2 speed rear end, 10' dump bed, Pintle hitch, hyd. brakes, 194" WB

TRUCKS

Ford

Model	Year	Miles	Condition	Price	Date	Area	Comments
F600	1979	12,001	G	$6,050	11/14/2012	Online	*PurpleWave.com,* item in Kansas, truck cab and chassis, 8 cyl. gas, 4 speed manual, FWD
F600	1979	66,000	G	$7,150	11/6/2012	Online	*PurpleWave.com,* item in Kansas, 370 2V gas, 4 speed manual, 4WD, heat, MW, ML, vinyl bench seat, 14'L bed, side storage compartments, rear tow hook, spring suspension
F700	1966	42,964	G	$1,375	10/10/2012	Online	*PurpleWave.com,* item in Kansas, grain truck, V8 gas, Holley carburetor, 4 speed manual, 2 speed axle, MW, ML
F700	1971	17,623	G	$4,100	4/10/2012	ECND	Tag tandem, 330HD, V8 5x2 speed, 19' Wil-Rich box, hoist, roll tarp
F700	1971		F	$2,500	2/18/2012	ECIL	Grain truck, good tires on back
F700	1973	69,917	G	$6,500	6/28/2012	NEND	Tag tandem, 361, V8 engine, 5x2 speed, 19' Omaha standard steel box and hoist, 52" sides
F700	1974	28,849	G	$6,270	10/16/2013	Online	*PurpleWave.com,* item in Kansas, dump truck, Detroit diesel 8.2L, Allison auto, 2 speed axle
F700	1974	33,708	G	$6,270	10/16/2013	Online	*PurpleWave.com,* item in Kansas, feed truck, 8 cyl. gas, 5 speed manual, 2 speed rear end
F700	1974		G	$3,500	7/31/2013	ECND	Tandem axle, 361, 4 speed, 19' box, hoist, no roll tarp
F700	1974		G	$1,250	10/25/2012	NEND	Tag tandem, 20' French 3 in 1 combo box and hoist, 390 engine, 5x2 speed
F700	1974		G	$3,300	7/12/2012	Online	*PurpleWave.com,* Item in Kansas dump truck, 8 cyl. gas, 5 speed manual, heat, 15' dump bed, hoist, dual fuel tanks
F700	1974		G	$12,650	5/30/2012	Online	*PurpleWave.com,* item in Kansas
F700	1974		G	$1,400	3/24/2012	SETN	Dump truck
F700	1975	55,581	G	$1,500	12/13/2012	WCIA	Single axle, 361, 4x2 speed, 16' steel box, hoist, 9x20 rubber
F700	1975	39,000	G	$5,600	8/8/2012	Online	*IQBid.com,* item in North Dakota, 360 HD V8 engine, 4x2 speed, 16' Rugby steel box, 9x20 tires, 4 new rear tires, one owner
F700	1975	30,821	G	$10,250	1/19/2012	SCKS	Single axle grain truck, 361 engine, 5x2 speed, 16' steel box, 52" sides, roll tarp
F700	1976		G	$6,600	3/21/2013	WCNE	361 V8 engine, 16' steel box, harsh rear hoist, 5x2 speed, Speed King drill fill auger, roll-over tarp, 10x20 rear rubber, 9x20 front rubber
F700	1977		G	$3,750	12/14/2012	SWKY	Bed, hoist, auger
F700	1977	60,844	G	$4,500	7/18/2012	ECND	Lift tag axle, 360 gas, box and hoist, newer roll tarp
F700	1978	12,000	G	$3,725	5/9/2012	Online	*BigIron.com,* item in Kansas grain truck, 5 speed, 351 gas, wood floor, stock rack extensions, motor OH approx. 5,000 miles ago, 6"x13' hyd. folding auger

TRUCKS

Ford

Model	Year	Miles	Condition	Price	Date	Area	Comments
F7000	1973		F	$1,225	2/20/2014	ECAR	Diesel, 5x2, PS, single axle, spring suspension, 10x20 tires on budds
F750	1960		G	$1,200	11/7/2013	WCMI	Single axle, 14' McConnell potato box, V8 gas, 5x2 speed
F750	1965	72,000	G	$1,200	1/25/2012	Online	*BigIron.com,* item in Nebraska, straight truck, 4 speed, 2 speed rear axle, V8 gas
F750	1966	564,000	G	$1,650	10/31/2012	Online	*PurpleWave.com,* item in Kansas V8 gas, 5 speed manual, 2 speed axle, heat, AM/FM, MW, vinyl interior, saddle fuel tanks
F750	1974	56,059	F	$1,700	3/16/2013	NCIL	Single axle, 390 V8 gas, 5x2 transmission, 14' steel dump bed, wood floor, twin hoist, 10x20 tires
F750	1974		G	$4,750	3/31/2012	NEIA	16' grain truck, V8 engine, 5x2 speed, Knapheide steel box, cargo doors
F750	1976	167,414	G	$2,150	5/1/2013	Online	*BigIron.com,* item in Nebraska, 5 speed Hi/Lo, V8 gas, single dual axle
F750	1976	82,000	G	$1,595	11/6/2012	Online	*PurpleWave.com,* item in Kansas flatbed, Fordd 391 gas, 5 speed manual, heat, MW, ML, vinyl bench seat, light bars, Knapheide flatbed, wood floor, rear work lights, air brakes, dead battery
F750	1977		G	$5,200	8/8/2012	Online	*BigIron.com,* item in Colorado, straight truck, 5 speed, 2 speed, 391 gas, single axle, PTO, 16' Scott grain box
F800	1975	63,464	G	$9,500	3/26/2014	NEMO	391 gas, 16' box, 60" sides, wood floor, single ram hoist, roll tarp, air brakes, air cheater axle (up/down), air ride seat
F800	1978		G	$3,500	8/24/2013	SEMN	Single axle, 5x2 speed, 16' steel box, hoist, roll tarp
F800	1978	47,000	F	$1,705	8/21/2013	Online	*PurpleWave.com,* item in Kansas 8 cyl. propane, 5 speed manual, heat, 22" WB, new tires, cosmetic damage, body damage
F900	1973	28,175	G	$2,601	5/1/2013	Online	*BigIron.com,* item in Kansas, 5 speed, V8 engine, twin screw, 120 gal. propane tank
L900	1978	34,000	G	$4,200	1/25/2012	Online	*BigIron.com,* item in Kansas, winch truck, 4x2 speed axle, V8 gas, stainless steel gin poles, 5th wheel hitch
L8000	1972	26,854	G	$2,035	6/28/2012	Online	*PurpleWave.com,* item in Missouri, dump truck, Cat 3115 engine, 13 speed manual, twin screw
L8000	1978	54,000	G	$3,750	11/28/2012	ECND	Tag axle, 534 V8 engine, steel box, hoist, new Shurco roll tarp, wipers not working
L8000	1978	108,000	G	$4,000	6/8/2012	ECMN	Tandem, Cummins engine, 10 speed, 180" WB, air brakes, AC, AM/FM, 15' steel box, steel BUDS
L8000	1978	84,000	G	$4,400	3/24/2012	SWMI	Tandem axle dump truck, Cat diesel 8 speed, air tarp, air gate
L9000	1976		F	$1,705	1/11/2012	Online	*PurpleWave.com,* item in Kansas, diesel, 10 speed manual, recently rebuilt, 22' bed, dual fuel tanks, twin cyl. hoist, new front tires

Ford

Model	Year	Miles	Condition	Price	Date	Area	Comments
L9000	1978	75,000	G	$6,500	11/6/2012	ECOK	Grain truck, diesel, 10 speed, 16' steel bed
L9000	1978		G	$15,500	1/11/2012	Online	*BigIron.com,* item in South Dakota, silage truck, 9 speed, 855 Cummins big cam diesel, tandem axle, air ride seat, double frame rails, 22' combo silage grain box
LN700	1973		G	$2,700	3/30/2013	SCMN	Grain truck, V8 gas engine, 5x2 transmission, lift tag, 18' frontier steel box and hoist
LN700	1975	789	G	$7,100	7/25/2012	Online	*BigIron.com,* item in Nebraska, grain truck, 5x2 transmission, V8 gas, 166" WB, 92"Wx18'L box, 51" sides, 16" trap
LN700	1977	92,000	G	$1,700	8/8/2012	Online	*BigIron.com,* item in Illinois, cattle truck, 16,000 miles on new motor, 20' bed
LN750	1976		G	$4,000	3/21/2013	WCNE	16' Obeco steel box, wood floor, harsh rear hoist, roll over tarp, 9x20 rubber, runs
LN750	1976		G	$4,500	3/14/2012	WCNE	Gas, 14' feed box, chain discharge
LN800	1976	106,058	G	$13,000	6/28/2012	NEND	Tandem twin screw, 475 engine, V8 engine, Allison auto, 19' Buffalo box, 54" sides, hoist, roll tarp, 3 piece endgate
LN800	1977		G	$3,700	12/6/2012	SEIA	Grain truck, 22' box, gas
LN880	1973	94,000	G	$3,700	8/20/2013	WCIL	Tandem axle grain truck, 477 engine, 9 speed, 20' steel grain bed, cargo doors and tarp
LN880	1975	76,000	G	$17,250	3/20/2013	NCOK	Tandem, double action maybar bed hoist, 24'x54" bed, AC, 5 speed Hi/Lo, 10x100x20 tires, propane
LN7000	1978	19,000	G	$4,056	6/13/2012	Online	*BigIron.com,* item in Kansas straight truck, Allison auto, single axle, all-steel bed, V8 diesel, engine block heater
LN8000	1975		G	$7,700	8/22/2012	Online	*BigIron.com,* item in Nebraska, grain truck, 5x2 transmission, 3208 Cat diesel, all alum box, roll tarp, box is 20'L, recent clutch, flywheel, pressure plate
LN8000	1978	69,000	G	$21,250	8/22/2012	Online	*BigIron.com,* item in Kansas silage truck, 653 Allison transmission, Cat diesel, tandem axle, twin screw, 24' silage bed, air shift PTO, AM/FM, AC, air brakes, cable endgate
LN8000	1978	76,000	G	$6,500	3/9/2012	ECMN	Custom cab, tandem, diesel, 13 speed, air brakes, pintle hitch, 15' steel box, steel FLR
LN8000	1978		F	$1,200	2/15/2012	IRON	5x2 transmission, Ford Cat diesel, single axle, hyd. brakes, 167" from rear of frame to back of cab, runs, drives
LN8000	1978	174,000	G	$6,853	1/25/2012	Online	*BigIron.com,* item in Nebraska, dump truck, 6 speed, 2 speed rear, 8 cyl., diesel, 150 hp, tandem axle, 13 yard box, single seat, heat
LN9000	1973		G	$4,100	10/20/2012	SEWY	Grain truck, 20' box, hoist, Detroit engine, 13 speed road ranger

Ford

Model	Year	Miles	Condition	Price	Date	Area	Comments
LN9000	1976		G	$1,300	3/26/2013	ECND	Cab, chassis, 290 Cummins, 10 speed spring ride, 11x24.5 tires on steel
LNT8000	1978		G	$7,000	4/4/2013	NWWA	3208 Cat, 613 Fuller, T/A, 11x20 rear, 275/70Rx22.5 front
LT880	1973		G	$5,000	7/31/2013	ECND	Twin screw, 477, 5x2 speed, 19' box
LT8000	1977		G	$9,000	4/4/2013	NWWA	3208 Cat, 613 Fuller, T/A, 11x20 rear, 275/70Rx22.5 front
LT8000	1978		G	$10,500	4/4/2013	NWWA	3208 Cat, 613 Fuller, T/A, 11x20 rear, 275/70Rx22.5 front
LT9000	1974		G	$2,700	1/25/2012	Online	*BigIron.com,* item in Nebraska, semi tractor, 13 speed, small cam Cummins diesel, tandem, spring ride, uses oil
LTS700	1972		G	$3,900	3/30/2013	NESD	18' Rugby steel box and hoist, 5x4 speed
Model T	1926		E	$12,000	9/22/2012	NEOR	1-ton truck
Ranchero	1977		G	$4,750	4/1/2013	WCIL	351 modified Windsor engine, good loooking
Ranger	1976		G	$2,910	1/9/2013	Online	*BigIron.com,* item in Nebraska, pickup, auto, 390 gas, 2WD, standard box, no AC, 2 lid fold tool box, grill guard, side rails, aluminum wheels

GMC

Model	Year	Miles	Condition	Price	Date	Area	Comments
1000	1950	75,000	F	$3,250	9/12/2012	Online	*IQBid.com,* item in Minnesota, pickup, bad transmission
1500	1972	208,000	G	$1,900	1/26/2012	SEAL	Pickup
2500	1978	73,000	G	$1,100	3/2/2013	NETN	Flatbed
5500	1968	92,000	G	$1,375	5/2/2012	Online	*PurpleWave.com,* item in Missouri, PTO, dump truck, GM V6 gas, 4 speed manual, 2 speed axle, heater, 14' dump flatbed, manual endgate, stake pockets
5500	1970	57,000	G	$3,500	11/10/2012	NCNC	16' dump bed, V6 diesel, 4 speed, 2 speed rear, air brakes, 2 sets side boards
5500	1971	81,000	G	$2,600	8/7/2013	NWMO	Grain truck, V8 motor, 4x2 speed, 9x20 rubber 75%, 350 motor, frame sprung, 16' steel Knapheide box, wood floors, seed tender auger
5500	1971	64,000	F	$1,200	2/15/2012	IRON	Straight truck, 4x2 speed rear axle, V8 gas, single axle, 16'Lx48"H box, rear grain slide and chute, twin cyl. hoist
5500	1972	90,000	G	$2,750	9/28/2013	ECNE	16' steel box, scissors hoist, V8 engine, 4x2 speed, dual fuel tanks, power steering
5500	1972		G	$2,900	8/30/2012	SEMN	V8
6000	1973		G	$1,925	3/28/2013	NWWI	Dump truck, hyd. brakes, 4 speed, dump box, 5YD box, V8 engine, new floor in box, 10x20, brakes need work
6000	1974		G	$3,750	3/4/2014	SWMN	9x20 tires, tandem twin screw, V8 gas, 5x3 speed, 18' Crysteel box, hoist, 3 PC endgate, roll tarp, spring suspension
6000	1974	62,000	F	$1,025	4/5/2013	WCIL	5x2 transmission, 15' grain bed

GMC

Model	Year	Miles	Condition	Price	Date	Area	Comments
6000	1975		G	$7,260	10/25/2012	Online	*PurpleWave.com,* item in Oklahoma, drilling truck, Chevy 350 gas, 5 speed, 2 speed axle, hyd. brakes
6000	1975	33,073	G	$4,400	2/14/2012	WCNE	V8 engine, 4x2 speed, side/rear hoist, Freeman 16' box, side board lifters
6000	1975	31,810	G	$6,800	2/14/2012	WCNE	V8 engine, 4x2 speed, Freeman 16' box, rear hoist, power up and down
6000	1976	32,472	G	$3,500	10/25/2012	SCWI	15' box, hoist, 5x2 speed
6000	1976		G	$3,300	8/21/2012	WCIL	Grain truck
6000	1977	55,000	G	$3,650	8/20/2013	WCIL	Single axle grain truck, recent OH, 15' Midwest grain bed
6500	1970	94,000	G	$1,705	5/31/2012	Online	*PurpleWave.com,* item in Missouri, asphalt oil distributor truck, 8 cyl. 366 hp diesel engine, 5 speed manual transmission, heat, manual windows and locks, vinyl interior
6500	1974		G	$4,500	11/23/2013	WCIL	Super custom grain truck, V6 engine, 5x2 speed, excellent 14' Knapheide bed
6500	1974		G	$3,250	9/6/2013	ECSD	Grain truck, 427 engine, 5x2 speed, 16' box and hoist, new spark plugs and wires, coils and points, good tires
6500	1974		G	$5,500	8/14/2013	WCMN	Twin screw, 427 gas, Allison automatic, 19'6" steel box and hoist, roll tarp, 11x22R rubber
6500	1974		G	$1,605	5/22/2013	Online	*BigIron.com,* item in Nebraska, tag axle straight truck, 5x2 transmission, 427 engine, 51" sides steel box
6500	1974	103,000	G	$2,100	2/12/2013	WCIL	Winch, tilt bed
6500	1974		G	$3,750	11/28/2012	ECND	Single axle, 366, 5x2 speed, 15' steel box
6500	1974		G	$4,600	11/13/2012	NCIA	Twin screw grain truck
6500	1974	40,281	F	$2,000	4/7/2012	SCOK	Dump bed, V8 gas, 29,000 lb.
6500	1975		G	$1,400	12/5/2013	SCIA	Single axle grain truck
6500	1975		G	$16,000	9/28/2013	NCKS	427 V8 engine, 5 speed, 4 speed aux., 20' bed, tag axle, plumbed for rear drill fill auger
6500	1975	60,485	G	$5,100	5/29/2013	Online	*BigIron.com,* item in Nebraska, odometer not working, 13 speed, 427 V8 gas
6500	1975	96,000	G	$1,700	3/7/2013	SEIA	Grain truck, 20' box, V8 engine, 5 speed
6500	1975	53,000	G	$15,000	10/18/2012	WCNE	Grain truck, single axle w/ hyd. tag axle, 18' box and hoist, 5x2 transmission
6500	1975	97,000	G	$3,400	7/18/2012	ECND	Tag tandem, 427, 5x2 transmission, 20' Knapheide box, hoist, roll tarp
6500	1976	24,000	G	$2,400	2/27/2014	NWNE	Diesel, V8 engine, 4x2 speed, 16' beet box, side/rear hoist
6500	1976	80,000	G	$8,100	2/22/2014	NEIN	Grain truck, 427 motor, Fuller transmission, air brakes, 18' Knapheide bed, hoist, 8,000 miles on OH
6500	1977		P	$1,600	2/20/2014	ECAR	Roll back, 427 gas, twin screw, roll back bed
6500	1977	70,000	F	$1,800	2/15/2014	ECMO	Grain truck, 24' bed and fold down stock racks, 5x2 speed, 427 V8, runs, engine, air tag axle, new factory block

TRUCKS

GMC

Model	Year	Miles	Condition	Price	Date	Area	Comments
6500	1977		G	$2,850	4/3/2013	Online	*IQBid.com,* single axle, 396 V8 gas, 5x2 speed, 18' grain box, box endgate
6500	1977		G	$7,000	8/21/2012	WCIL	Grain truck, 15' box, Shur-Lok roll tarp, 366 engine, 5x2 transmission
6500	1977	55,000	G	$6,000	8/9/2012	NEIL	Grain truck, 5x2 speed, 15.5' box, one owner
6500	1977		G	$3,600	6/13/2012	NWMN	Tandem twin screw farm truck, 427 V8 engine, 13 speed, Omaha STD 24' steel grain box and hoist, air brakes, low miles on new engine
6500	1978		G	$3,100	9/12/2013	SEIA	Grain truck, gas, 5x2 transmission, Scott 15' bed, hoist, triple doors, 10x20 tires
6500	1978	60,000	G	$10,000	7/31/2013	ECND	Lift tag, 366 gas 5x2 speed, 19' strong box, roll tarp, center swing gate
7500	1974	22,000	G	$2,000	12/5/2013	SEMN	18' box, hoist, seed brush auger
9500	1974		G	$3,250	3/22/2014	SWMI	Tandem axle grain truck, Detroit diesel, 5x2 speed, 18' box, dump, removeable sides, air brakes
9500	1974	36,000	E	$23,000	12/14/2013	ECPA	10 wheeler dump truck, Rugby 16' aluminum dump-roll tarp, 238 Detroit, 10 speed RR, nice
9500	1974	487,750	G	$3,400	4/24/2013	Online	*BigIron.com,* item in Colorado, potato truck, 13 speed Fuller, V8 Detroit DSL
9500	1977		F	$1,400	2/4/2012	NEAR	Triple axle, Detroit diesel, 10 speed
Brigadier	1978			$3,650	3/2/2013	NCWI	Grain truck, tandem axle, Detroit 10 speed, 18' metal grain box, manual roll tarp
Brigadier	1978		F	$2,035	6/28/2012	Online	*PurpleWave.com,* item in Kansas barrel dump truck, Detroit diesel, 8 speed manual, 8 speed, 14'x8' bed, block heater
C60	1973	84,900	G	$1,700	1/15/2014	ECIL	Grain truck, 350 engine, 4x2 speed, 13.5' bed
C6500	1972	12,000	G	$2,203	12/18/2013	Online	*BigIron.com,* item in Nebraska, grain truck, Allison auto, 427 Invader gas, 9x20 tires, 16' bed
C6500	1973		G	$2,400	4/17/2013	Online	*BigIron.com,* item in Nebraska, grain truck, unreadable miles, 5 speed, 2 speed rear axle, 366, V8 gas
CE66	1975		G	$1,650	10/16/2013	Online	*PurpleWave.com,* item in Oklahoma, float fertilizer truck, 8 cyl. gas, auto
General	1977	50,000	G	$15,000	12/1/2012	NCMO	V8 Detroit, transmission rebuilt in 2012, engine rebuilt,18' Knapheide steel floor bed, scissor hoist, Shur-Lok tarp, tiptops, very clean older truck, brush style seed auger
S15	1950	19,000	G	$1,930	1/25/2012	Online	*BigIron.com,* item in Nebraska, tanker truck, auto, gas, 1K gal, side dump, Onan tiwn cyl. pump, 2" Gorman Rupp pump
Sierra	1978	92,000	F	$2,400	8/7/2013	Online	*IQBid.com,* classic, crew cab, long box, 454, gas, 4 speed manual
Sierra 15	1977		G	$2,600	8/16/2012	NCIA	Sierra Grande 15 pickup, V8 engine, air, auto, ag hitch, Glasstite topper

TRUCKS

International

Model	Year	Miles	Condition	Price	Date	Area	Comments
100	1963		P	$1,100	9/28/2013	NENE	Lambrecht Dealer auction, V8 engine, manual, half-ton, some rust and dings
110	1961	88444	G	$2,300	3/27/2013	Online	*BigIron.com,* item in Nebraska, crew cab pickup, topper, needs battery and clutch
170	1976		G	$1,400	9/6/2013	ECSD	Dump truck, V8 diesel, single axle, 5x2 speed, 10' box and hoist
180	1974	95,168	G	$5,000	7/25/2013	ECND	Twin screw, 478 engine, auto, tarp, 19' Knapheide box, twin post hoist
200	1957	169,000	G	$1,605	7/11/2012	Online	*BigIron.com,* item in Wyoming, grain truck, 5 speed Hi/Lo, 6 cyl. gas, dual tandem axles, 20' straight box, 4' sides
400	1969		F	$1,100	2/4/2014	SEAR	Transtar grain Ntruck, diesel, 5x2 speed, twin screw on spring suspension, 24' bed, 52" sides, 10x20 tires on Daytons
450	1961	68,000	G	$3,001	1/9/2013	Online	*BigIron.com,* item in Nebraska, dump truck, 3 ranges, 4 speed in each range, 6 cyl. gas, 166 hp, tandem axle, PTO, 8 yd, 12' long box
1500	1969		F	$2,500	3/8/2012	NCTX	Oswalt 280 feeder/mixer
1600	1963	39,000	G	$5,250	1/19/2012	SCKS	Loadstar single axle flatbed truck, 304 cu. in. gas, 4x2 speed, 16' Anthony steel flatbed, steel sides, hoist, 2,000 gal. poly nurse tank, transfer pump, one owner, green/white
1600	1964		G	$2,500	2/9/2013	SENE	Loadstar, 4x2 speed, V8 engine, 18' box, new floor and short block
1600	1964	65,000	G	$1,600	8/8/2012	Online	*BigIron.com,* item in Oklahoma, Loadstar grain truck, 4x2 transmission, V8 gas, single axle, 175" WB, 16' Mabar steel bed, 32" metal sides, 43 gal. saddle tank
1600	1965	36,857	G	$1,400	11/20/2012	NEND	Single axle, 345, V8 engine, 4x2 speed, Knapheide 13.5' steel box, hoist, roll tarp
1600	1967	108,000	G	$1,100	9/13/2012	Online	*IQBid.com,* item in Iowa, grain truck, 14' box, single axle
1600	1967		G	$1,200	3/28/2012	ECND	Single axle, 304, V8 engine, 4x2 speed, 15' steel box, hoist
1600	1969		G	$1,250	6/13/2012	NWMN	Tag tandem farm truck, 18' steel grain box and hoist
1600	1970	43,000	G	$2,325	4/12/2014	SEKS	345 V8 motor, 4 speed, 2 speed axle, 16' wood floor bed, 9x20 tires on cast rims
1600	1971		G	$1,500	7/3/2013	Online	*BigIron.com,* item in Nebraska, single axle straight truck, 16' steel box w/ steel floor, V8 gas, 5 speed manual
1600	1973	189,271	F	$1,400	3/19/2014	Online	*BigIron.com,* item in Nebraska, bulk truck, 5 speed Hi/Lo
1600	1973	80,000	G	$1,100	7/31/2013	ECND	Single axle, 345 gas, 4x2 speed, 8'x13' flatbed, no hoist
1600	1973	38,000	E	$2,900	12/1/2012	SWMO	Loadstar, implement bed and hoist, 4x2 speed
1600	1973		G	$1,500	8/21/2012	WCIL	Grain truck

International

Model	Year	Miles	Condition	Price	Date	Area	Comments
1600	1973	57,744	G	$6,300	7/24/2012	NCKS	8 cyl., 4x2 speed, 16' steel box, roll over tarp
1600	1973	104,000	G	$3,700	5/9/2012	Online	*BigIron.com,* item in Nebraska, boom truck, 9Rx20 tires
1600	1973	144,000	G	$1,600	2/4/2012	ECSC	Grain truck
1600	1974	69,000	G	$9,500	11/20/2013	NWNE	20' Harsh steel grain box and floor, 52" sides, 5 speed, 2 speed, tag axle, super clean
1600	1974	7,328	G	$3,200	9/12/2013	SEIA	V8 engine, 5 speed, single axle, Monroe 12" flatbed
1600	1974	56,000	G	$1,100	7/31/2013	ECND	345, V8 engine, 5x2 speed, 16' box, hoist, roll tarp
1600	1974	56,000	G	$4,500	7/31/2013	ECND	Single axle, 345 V8 engine, 5x2 speed, 16' box, hoist, roll tarp, 9x20 tires
1600	1974		F	$1,200	3/22/2012	ECMD	16' dump, 392 gas, 5x2 speed
1600	1974		F	$2,300	3/22/2012	ECMN	Loadstar single axle, 345 gas, 11' metal box, hoist, 300 bu. cap, 3 piece endgate, newer tires
1600	1975		G	$2,400	3/8/2014	NEMO	Loadstar grain truck, 16' bed
1600	1975	30,183	G	$4,000	3/1/2014	SEMN	Loadstar, single axle, 15' steel box, hoist
1600	1975	74,016	G	$1,375	10/8/2013	Online	*PurpleWave.com,* item in Kansas, Loadstar flatbed truck, V8 GA, 4 speed manual
1600	1975	79,000	G	$2,300	4/10/2013	Online	*BigIron.com,* item in Nebraska, grain truck, 5x2 transmission, V8 gas, 10x20 tires, 7'6"Wx17'L box, 55" side height
1600	1976	58,000	G	$1,450	4/5/2013	WCIL	Loadstar, 5x2 transmission, 15' grain bed
1600	1977		G	$2,100	2/23/2013	ECMI	Hoist, 8 ton Port-A-Box, tarp
1600	1977		G	$1,200	11/29/2012	ECND	345, 4x2 transmission, box and hoist, runs well
1600	1977	175,000	G	$1,700	6/2/2012	SEMN	Grain truck, single axle, 4x2 speed, 14' box and hoist, roll tarp, 392 V8
1600	1978		F	$2,750	3/22/2012	ECMD	17' aluminum dump
1700	1964		F	$1,400	1/25/2014	WCIN	Single axle grain truck, 14' Schien steel bed, not used in years, scissor hoist, 40" sides, roll tarp, V8 engine, 4 speed, lime green
1700	1969	78,000	G	$1,600	7/25/2013	ECND	Tag tandem, gas V8 engine, 5x2 speed, 18' frontierbox, hoist, roll tarp, plumbed for drill fill, 10x20 tires
1700	1970		G	$2,300	8/21/2012	WCIL	Grain truck, 13.5' bed and hoist, newer clutch, 5x2 transmission, 308 BD six engine, PS, Bostrom seat, 9x20 tires
1700	1971		G	$1,700	8/22/2012	ECMN	20' box, double hoist, tag axle
1700	1974	103,000	G	$3,800	3/5/2014	Online	*BigIron.com,* item in Nebraska, Landstar, 5 speed Hi/Lo, V8 gas, single axle, PTO, 18' box, tarp, Cheater axle
1700	1974		G	$2,300	4/2/2013	ECIA	Single axle, 5x2 speed, flatbed
1700	1974		G	$1,500	12/14/2012	SWKY	Spreader, lime and fertilizer bed

TRUCKS

International

Model	Year	Miles	Condition	Price	Date	Area	Comments
1700	1974	67,046	F	$2,250	11/20/2012	NEND	Loadstar, lift tag tandem, V8 engine, 4x2 speed, 19.5' steel box, hoist, roll tarp
1700	1974	64,100	G	$3,100	3/14/2012	ECND	Loadstar single axle, 345 V8 engine, 4x2 speed, 15' box, hoist, roll tarp, one owner
1700	1975	19,714	G	$13,000	6/27/2012	NCND	Loadstar, single axle, automatic, leather seats, berts 16' stake body, roll tarp, new 9x20 tires
1700	1975	1,835	G	$3,740	5/16/2012	Online	*PurpleWave.com,* item in Texas, flatbed truck, IHC 392 cu. in. gas, 5 speed manual, speed transfer case, 4WD
1700	1976	45,000	G	$6,500	4/3/2013	NEND	Tag tandem, 16' strong box, 12" tip tops, roll tarp, 9x20 tires, no rust, one owner
1700	1976	33,000	G	$4,100	12/10/2012	ECIL	One owner 408 V8 engine, propane, 5x2 speed, 16' Schien bed, twin hoist
1700	1976		G	$5,500	3/17/2012	SEMN	Loadstar grain truck, single axle, 404 V8 engine, 5x2 speed, Crysteel 15' box and hoist, SRT roll tarp
1700	1977	48,000	G	$6,000	7/31/2013	ECND	Single axle, 404 V8 engine, 5x2 speed, 16' box, hoist, roll tarp, 9x20 tires
1700	1977	122,900	G	$4,500	7/11/2013	SCMN	Loadstar, tandem tag axle grain truck, 22.5' steel box and hoist, roll tarp, 5 speed
1700	1977		G	$1,400	8/21/2012	WCIL	2-ton
1700	1977	66,000	G	$2,700	8/21/2012	WCIL	2-ton grain truck, 16' bed, 5x2 transmission, 345 engine
1700	1978	62,000	G	$4,300	3/22/2013	NWMN	Loadstar, single axle, 304 V8 engine, 4x2 speed, 16' Knapheide box, hoist, 9x20 tires
1750	1978	79,904	G	$4,100	12/18/2013	Online	*BigIron.com,* 4x2 speed rear axle transmission, 6 cyl., turbo diesel
1800	1965	263,000	F	$1,500	12/18/2013	Online	*BigIron.com,* item in Nebraska, tandem axle grain truck, manual, V8 gas, 9x20 rear, 9x29 front tires, PTO, box and hoist, air brakes
1800	1965		F	$1,900	8/28/2012	WCMN	Loadstar single axle grain truck, nice 15' steel box, hoist, roll tarp, gas, 5x2 speed, engine needs repair
1800	1966		G	$5,000	4/12/2014	SEKS	Tandem axle, twin screw, 345 V8 motor, 5 speed, 2 speed brown lite axle, PS, saddle fuel tank, 60" wood grain sides, 9x20 tires on cast rims
1800	1966	120,000	G	$1,400	1/22/2014	Online	*BigIron.com,* item in Nebraska, dump truck, 5 speed, V8 IHC gas, 9x20 tires, twin screw, rear hitch, spring susp.
1800	1967		G	$1,200	12/15/2012	WCMI	Loadstar live T/A, V8 engine, gas, 5x3 speed, Lockwood 20' potato box
1800	1968		G	$4,200	2/21/2013	ECMI	Loadstar live tandem grain truck, 16' metal grain box and twin post hoist, V8 gas, 5x4 speed, good rubber
1800	1970		G	$1,800	10/18/2012	WCMI	Tandem grain truck, 16' metal box and hoist
1800	1973	53,782	G	$4,000	4/10/2012	ECND	Loadstar, twin screw, V8 engine, 5x3 speed, 18' Westgo box, hoist, roll tarp

International

Model	Year	Miles	Condition	Price	Date	Area	Comments
1800	1974		G	$6,000	11/7/2013	NEND	Twin screw, tandem, 446, V8 engine, Allison auto, 20' Knapheide box, hoist, beet equipment
1800	1974		G	$2,000	9/19/2013	SWIA	Rebuilt ENG., runs
1800	1974	73,600	G	$9,000	7/31/2013	ECND	Twin screw, 5x4 speed, 20' box, hoist, roll tarp
1800	1974		G	$6,000	11/29/2012	ECND	478 engine, auto, 19' Knapheide box and hoist, nice older truck
1800	1974		G	$5,250	7/18/2012	ECND	Twin screw, 20' french 3" 1 box and hoist
1800	1975		G	$3,900	3/8/2014	NEMO	Grain truck, 20' bed, twin screw
1800	1975		G	$4,750	8/20/2013	WCIL	Tandem
1800	1975	95,250	G	$6,600	3/9/2013	NCOH	Loadstar, grain box
1800	1975	50,000	G	$2,055	7/11/2012	Online	*BigIron.com,* item in Wyoming, Loadstar grain truck, 13 speed Fuller Road Runner, V8 gas, grill guard, dual tandem axles, 22', dual cyl. lift, straight box
1800	1975		G	$7,500	3/28/2012	ECND	Tandem twin screw, 466 gas, Allison auto, 20' Buffalo box and hoist
1800	1976	84,000	G	$2,750	1/4/2014	ECOH	Grain truck
1800	1976		G	$3,000	3/28/2012	ECND	Single axle, 445, 5x2 speed, power steering, 15' steel box, hoist
1800	1977	67,887	G	$4,100	2/22/2014	SCNE	5 speed, V8 engine, 20' steel box, hoist, good tarp, tandem axle, clean truck
1800	1977	27,000	G	$7,700	3/9/2013	NCOH	Loadstar, live tandem, Henderson suspension, 18' grain box, 446 gas V8
1850	1977	49,000	G	$3,700	4/10/2013	Online	*BigIron.com,* item in Nebraska, Loadstar grain truck, 5x2 transmission, diesel, 10x20 tires, tandem axle, pusher axle, 8'Wx20'L box, 59" sides, extensions, roll tarp, 12" rear trap or 34" rear door, metal floor, 205" WB
1850	1977	222,000	F	$1,702	8/22/2012	Online	*BigIron.com,* item in Nebraska, semi, 5x2 transmission, diesel, needs windshield
1850B	1978	248,000	F	$2,145	5/30/2012	Online	*PurpleWave.com,* item in Texas, semi truck, IHC 6 cyl. turbo diesel, manual, heat, dual fuel tanks, rear exhaust stack, steel deck plate
1900	1968		G	$4,175	4/25/2012	Online	*BigIron.com,* item in Nebraska, 6 cyl. diesel, tandem axle, PTO, air brakes
1910	1972		G	$1,700	11/9/2012	NEAR	Triple axle grain truck, V8 gas, 2 speed rear end, air brakes, steel bed, twin cyl. dump
1910	1974		G	$8,200	8/20/2013	WCMN	Fleetstar, twin screw grain truck, 5x2 speed, 549 gas, roll tarp, 19.5' steel box and hoist, 2 fuel tanks
2000	1971		G	$1,100	6/13/2012	NWMN	Semi tractor, tandem axle, Detroit 6 cyl. inline, 9 speed
2050	1975	220,353	G	$2,090	6/28/2012	Online	*PurpleWave.com,* item in Missouri, dump truck
2070A	1974		F	$1,600	2/20/2014	ECAR	Detroit 238 engine, 10 speed, twin screw, 11Rx24.5 tires on Budds

TRUCKS

International

Model	Year	Miles	Condition	Price	Date	Area	Comments
2070A	1974		G	$8,500	3/22/2012	ECMN	Tri-axle, air lift, push axle, 671 Detroit, 13 speed, 20' box, hoist, roll tarp
2070A	1976		G	$1,900	8/7/2013	Online	*IQBid.com,* tandem axle, Cummins, 13 speed
2070A	1976		G	$3,000	4/3/2013	NEND	TRI-axle, 671 Detroit, 4x4 transmission, 4:44 ratio, 10x20 rubber, full 3rd tag, Hart 24' live bottom box, PTO, hyd. unloader, hoist, roll tarp
2275	1978	50,000	G	$20,000	11/28/2012	ECND	Twin screw tandem, 855 Cummins, 7 speed, 20' box, headlift hoist, air controls, roll tarp, 11Rx22.5 tires, reman. engine
4070	1965		G	$18,500	8/4/2012	ECMN	Cab kit, 855 Cummins diesel, 10 speed, 19' steel box and hoist, roll tarp, 3-piece endgate
4070B	1976		G	$1,500	11/28/2012	ECND	350 hp, 855 Cummins, 13 speed, spring ride, twin alum fuel tanks, single exhaust, 11x22.5 tires on steel
4070B	1977		G	$1,600	2/20/2014	ECAR	Cummins engine, 9 speed, helper axle, 11x22.5 tires, spring suspension
4200	1973		G	$5,500	3/13/2014	SCID	10 wheel, Detroit 8V92 engine, 5x4 transmission, Logan 20' self-unloading bed, 24" belt, single drive
4200	1974		G	$1,200	6/13/2012	NWMN	Transtar, Detroit 8V71, 13 speed, Odler 20' alum box and hoist
4200	1974	75,082	F	$1,700	2/25/2012	SCIL	Semi W/ 903 Cummins Super diesel, 13 speed, non running
4200	1977		G	$5,500	4/11/2013	SEID	Dump truck, Detroit engine, 13 speed, tandem axle, Fruehauf 14' box, air gate, Pintle hitch
4300	1975		G	$2,530	5/22/2012	Online	*PurpleWave.com,* item in Kansas
4300	1977		G	$2,600	2/18/2012	ECIL	Dump truck, 290 Cummins motor, 13 speed, new clutch
5370	1978		G	$6,500	3/27/2013	Online	*BigIron.com,*item in Nebraska, grain truck, 8 speed road ranger
B120	1959	107,000	E	$10,000	3/15/2014	ECMD	Very solid, appears to be all original and runs, not restored but was repainted
Cargostar	1978	249,000	G	$1,705	8/29/2012	Online	*PurpleWave.com,* item in Nebraska, flatbed, 6 cyl. turbo diesel, 5 speed manual, throttle lock, air suspension
F1800	1978		G	$5,500	7/25/2013	ECND	3.5-ton twin screw, 446 engine, 21' Loadline box and 3 pc endgate, beet equipped
F2070A	1977	343,000	G	$1,850	12/18/2013	Online	*BigIron.com,* item in Nebraska, Fuller road ranger, 8 speed manual, slant 6 cyl. diesel, 10Rx20 rear and front tires twin screw, spring suspension, 2 fuel tanks, 5th wheel plate, Chelsea PTO
F5070	1978	261,000	G	$1,250	9/19/2012	Online	*BigIron.com,* item in South Dakota, semi, manual, Cummins diesel, cab and chassis only
L120	1950	6,000	G	$2,000	7/28/2012	SCNE	Pickup, 6 cyl., 3/4 ton, new paint, new interior
Loadstar	1968		G	$1,550	8/21/2012	WCIL	Grain truck, 14' grain box, hoist, 345 cu. in., 5x2 transmission

TRUCKS

International

Model	Year	Miles	Condition	Price	Date	Area	Comments
Loadstar	1969	210,000	G	$1,925	9/10/2013	Online	Twin screw, V8 engine, gas, 5x2 speed, 18' box and hoist, 9x20 tires
Loadstar	1974		G	$1,900	2/23/2013	ECMI	Tandem axle, 3,000 gal. stainless tank, 345 International gas, 5 over 2 speed, diff. locks
Loadstar	1974		G	$2,600	3/17/2012	SEMN	Graintruck,singleaxle,345,V8engine,5x2 speed, Omaha 16' steel box and hoist, roll tarp
Loadstar	1975		G	$2,700	11/26/2013	ECND	Tag tandem, 404, V8 engine, 5x2 speed, 20' box and hoist
Loadstar	1975	17,688	F	$2,000	12/12/2012	NCIL	Loadstar, 14' body and hoist, fold-up sides, 5x2 speed
Loadstar	1976		G	$1,200	8/4/2012	ECMN	Grain truck, V8 gas, 5x2 speed, 1 6' wood box and hoist, single axle
Loadstar	1977	37,704	G	$4,800	8/24/2013	SEMN	16' steel box hoist, DOT
Paystar 5000	1978		G	$5,000	8/1/2012	NCIA	Tandem dump truck, Detroit motor, 8 speed Fuller, tag axle, 16' box
R120	1955	79,140	G	$1,705	10/16/2013	Online	*PurpleWave.com,* item in Kansas, winch dump bed truck, 6 cyl. gas, 4 speed manual
R190	1962		G	$1,900	8/14/2013	WCMN	Twin screw, 5x3 transmission, straight 6 cyl., 18' steel box and hoist
S120	1956	23,050	G	$7,000	6/22/2013	SEWA	4x4, 6 cyl., gas, 4 speed, Warn hubs, VIN S32203
Transtar	1969	42,923	G	$1,500	6/22/2013	SEWA	400 Missouri DEL 559644, 318 6 cyl., diesel, 13 speed, VIN Y019257
Transtar	1974	660,145	G	$2,365	8/22/2012	Online	*PurpleWave.com,* item in Kansas, Cummins diesel, 320 hp, Ruller Road Ranger 16 speed, manual, Hi/Lo
Transtar	1976		G	$1,400	6/22/2013	SEWA	4200, 6V 92T diesel, turbo charged, air start, 6 PTO, VIN D212FGA11717
Transtar	1976		G	$2,100	2/23/2013	ECMI	350 Cummins diesel engine, 13 speed, 50 gal. wet kit, Cabover semi truck

Kenworth

Model	Year	Miles	Condition	Price	Date	Area	Comments
500	1977	358,000	G	$4,500	6/27/2012	Online	*BigIron.com,* item in Kansas, 6 speed, super low, 3306 diesel, no passenger seat, 10 yd.
925	1974	922,000	G	$9,000	7/30/2012	SCMT	20'x96"x55" box, Cummins 400 hp, 13 speed, new Harsh hoist and pump, twin screw, 275/80Rx22.5 tires, double frame
K100	1965		G	$2,250	3/30/2013	NESD	Tandem twin screw, Scott 18' steel box and hoist
W900	1974	300,000	G	$4,500	3/2/2013	NCWI	Tandem, Cummins big cam 3-400 engine, 13 speed
W900	1975	565,104	G	$5,300	3/19/2014	Online	*BigIron.com,* item in Colorado, semi truck, 13 speed, Cummins engine
W900A	1968	58,000	F	$3,000	6/27/2013	SEMN	T/A, Cummins, diesel, Eaton Fuller 13 speed, Neway A/R susp, 11,500 lb. frt, 38,000 lb. rears, 190 in. WB, aluminum wheels
W928	1971		G	$4,180	5/22/2012	Online	*PurpleWave.com,* item in Kansas

Mack

Model	Year	Miles	Condition	Price	Date	Area	Comments
DM600	1974		G	$2,100	11/24/2012	SEMN	Tandem, 16' box
DM685S	1972	15,398	G	$8,600	3/26/2014	Online	*BigIron.com,* item in Nebraska, 10 speed, 6 cyl. diesel
R600	1970	115,000	G	$1,750	7/18/2012	ECND	NEW clutch, fifth wheel, raised 4"
R600	1973	285,000	G	$2,970	10/25/2012	Online	*PurpleWave.com,* item in Kansas, dump truck, Mack 6 cyl. diesel, 5 speed manual, twin screw, heat, 14.5'L bed, 50 gal. fuel tank, spring suspension, PTO
R600	1974		G	$3,500	7/25/2013	ECND	Tri-axle, Mack engine, 5x2 Mack transmission, full third lift tag, 11Rx22.5 tires, 22' Double L Model 802 live bottom box, PTO, hyd. unloader
R600	1975		G	$3,300	5/30/2012	Online	*PurpleWave.com,* item in Kansas
R685ST	1969	839,000	F	$2,300	6/20/2012	Online	*BigIron.com,* item in Nebraska, dump truck, tandem axle, poly liner
R685ST	1977	14,000	G	$16,000	7/28/2012	SWTN	300 Mack engine, 5 speed, double frame cab/chassis, 38,000 lb. Camelback
R686	1972		G	$6,500	3/26/2014	ECMS	Tandem axle dump truck
R686ST	1976		G	$6,000	7/28/2012	SWTN	Day cab, 283 Mack engine, 5 speed, double frame, 44,000 lb. Camelback

Peterbilt

Model	Year	Miles	Condition	Price	Date	Area	Comments
358A	1971		G	$11,000	8/16/2012	Online	*IQBid.com,* item in Minnesota, day cab, Detroit turbo, 13 speed, spring ride, 216" WB, aluminum rims, recent brake job
359	1974		G	$19,250	8/21/2012	Online	*PurpleWave.com,* item in Kansas, Cummins big cam 400 diesel, 15 speed manual, twin screw
359	1975	700,000	G	$6,000	8/16/2012	Online	*IQBid.com,* item in Minnesota, day cab, 400 Cummins, 13 speed, air ride, jake brake, diff. lock, 192"WB, 22.5 on aluminum

Studebaker

Model	Year	Miles	Condition	Price	Date	Area	Comments
2R15-21	1949	35,578	G	$8,360	10/16/2013	Online	*PurpleWave.com,* item in Kansas, pickup, not actual mileage, 6 cyl. flathead gas, 4 speed
M1528	1946	42,027	G	$5,170	10/30/2013	Online	*PurpleWave.com,* item in Kansas, pickup, 6 cylinder flathead gas, 9'4"Lx87.5'W flatbed

Willys

Model	Year	Miles	Condition	Price	Date	Area	Comments
Jeep	1948	26,140	G	$10,000	6/22/2013	SEWA	Model CJ2, 6x16 tires, 4 cyl., 3 speed, 4x4, 12V, VIN J204974
Jeep	1950		G	$6,000	4/2/2012	WCIL	4 speed, convertible, nice older restoration
Jeep	1950		G	$7,000	4/2/2012	WCIL	
Jeep	1953		P	$3,000	4/1/2013	WCIL	Needs total restoration